Roxy Wilson

SOLUTIONS TO RED EXERCISES

CHEMISTRY

THE CENTRAL SCIENCE

Ninth Edition

Brown   LeMay   Bursten

Prentice
Hall

Upper Saddle River, NJ 07458

Project Manager: Kristen Kaiser
Senior Editor: Nicole Folchetti
Editor in Chief: John Challice
Executive Managing Editor: Kathleen Schiaparelli
Assistant Managing Editor: Dinah Thong
Production Editor: Natasha Wolfe
Supplement Cover Management/Design: Paul Gourhan
Manufacturing Buyer: Ilene Kahn
Cover Image Credit: Ken Eward/Biografx

© 2003 by Pearson Education, Inc.
Pearson Education, Inc.
Upper Saddle River, NJ 07458

Printed in the United States of America

10 9 8 7 6
ISBN 0-13-009799-3

Pearson Education Ltd., *London*
Pearson Education Australia Pty. Ltd., *Sydney*
Pearson Education Singapore, Pte. Ltd.
Pearson Education North Asia Ltd., *Hong Kong*
Pearson Education Canada, Inc., *Toronto*
Pearson Educacíon de Mexico, S.A. de C.V.
Pearson Education—Japan, *Tokyo*
Pearson Education Malaysia, Pte. Ltd.
Pearson Education, *Upper Saddle River, New Jersey*

Contents

Introduction

Chemistry: The Central Science, 9th edition, contains nearly 2400 end-of-chapter exercises. Considerable attention has been given to these exercises because one of the best ways for students to master chemistry is by solving problems. Grouping the exercises according to subject matter is intended to aid the student in selecting and recognizing particular types of problems. Within each subject matter group, similar problems are arranged in pairs. This provides the student with an opportunity to reinforce a particular kind of problem. There are also a substantial number of general exercises in each chapter to supplement those grouped by topic. Integrative exercises, which require students to integrate concepts from several chapters, are a continuing feature of the 9th edition. Answers to the odd numbered topical exercises plus selected general and integrative exercises, about 1100 in all, are provided in the text. These appendix answers help to make the text a useful self-contained vehicle for learning.

This manual, **Solutions to Red Exercises** in **Chemistry: The Central Science, 9th edition**, was written to enhance the end-of-chapter exercises by providing documented solutions for those problems answered in the appendix of the text. The manual assists the instructor by saving time spent generating solutions for assigned problem sets and aids the student by offering a convenient independent source to check their understanding of the material. Most solutions have been worked in the same detail as the in-chapter sample exercises to help guide students in their studies.

To reinforce the '*Analyze, Plan, Solve, Check*' problem-solving method used extensively in the text, this strategy has also been incorporated into the Solution Manual. Solutions to most red topical exercises and selected Additional and Integrative exercises feature this four-step approach. We strongly encourage students to master this powerful and totally general method.

When using this manual, keep in mind that the numerical result of any calculation is influenced by the precision of the numbers used in the calculation. In this manual, for example, atomic masses and physical constants are typically expressed to four significant figures, or at least as precisely as the data given in the problem. If students use slightly different values to solve problems, their answers will differ slightly from those listed in the appendix of the text or this manual. This is a normal and a common occurrence when comparing results from different calculations or experiments.

Rounding methods are another source of differences between calculated values. In this manual, when a solution is given in steps, intermediate results will be rounded to the correct number of significant figures; however, unrounded numbers will be used in subsequent calculations. By following this scheme, calculators need not be cleared to re-enter rounded intermediate results in the middle of a calculation sequence. The final answer will appear with the correct number of significant figures. This may result in a small discrepancy in the last significant digit between student-calculated answers and those given in this manual. Variations due to rounding can occur in any analysis of numerical data.

The first step in checking your solution and resolving differences between your answer and the listed value is to look for similarities and differences in problem-solving methods. Ultimately, resolving the small numerical differences described above is less important than understanding the general method for solving a problem. The goal of this manual is to provide a reference for sound and consistent problem-solving methods in addition to accurate answers to text exercises.

Extraordinary efforts have been made to keep this manual as error-free as possible. All exercises were worked and proof-read by at least three chemists to ensure clarity in methods and accuracy in mathematics. The work and advice of Dr. Mary Ellen Biggin, Augustana College and Dr. Angela Manders Cannon, University of Illinois have been invaluable to this project. However, in a written work as technically challenging as this manual, typos and errors inevitably creep in. Please help us find and eliminate them. We hope that both instructors and students will find this manual accurate, helpful and instructive.

Roxy B. Wilson
University of Illinois
School of Chemical Sciences
601 S. Mathews Ave., Box A-2
Urbana, IL 61801
rbwilson@uiuc.edu

1 Introduction: Matter and Measurement

Classification and Properties of Matter

1.1   (a) heterogeneous mixture (b) homogeneous mixture   (If there are undissolved particles, such as sand or decaying plants, the mixture is heterogeneous.)   (c) pure substance (d) homogeneous mixture

1.3   (a) Al   (b) Na   (c) Br   (d) Cu   (e) Si   (f) N   (g) Mg   (h) He

1.5   (a) hydrogen   (b) magnesium   (c) lead   (d) silicon   (e) fluorine   (f) tin (g) manganese   (h) arsenic

1.7   A(s) $\longrightarrow$ B(s) + C(g)

When carbon(s) is burned in excess oxygen the two elements combine to form a gaseous compound, carbon dioxide. Clearly substance C is this compound.

Since C is produced when A is heated in the absence of oxygen (from air), both the carbon and oxygen in C must have been present in A originally. A is, therefore, a compound composed of two or more elements chemically combined. Without more information on the chemical or physical properties of B, we cannot determine absolutely whether it is an element or a compound. However, few if any elements exist as white solids, so B is probably also a compound.

1.9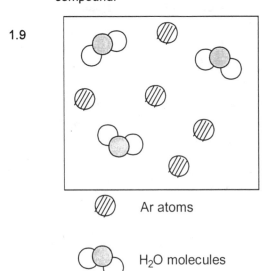

Ar atoms

H_2O molecules

1.11   Physical properties: silvery white (color); lustrous; melting point = 649°C; boiling point = 1105°C; density at 20°C = 1.738 g/cm³; pounded into sheets (malleable); drawn into wires (ductile); good conductor.   Chemical properties: burns in air to give intense white light; reacts with Cl_2 to produce brittle white solid.

1.13   (a) chemical   (b) physical   (c) physical   (d) chemical   (e) chemical

1.15   Take advantage of differences in physical properties to separate the components of a mixture. First heat the liquid to 100°C to evaporate the water. This is conveniently done in a distillation apparatus (Figure 1.13) so that the water can be collected. After the water is completely evaporated and **if** there is a residue, measure the physical properties of the residue such as color, density and melting point. Compare the observed properties of the residue to those of table salt, NaCl. If the properties match, the colorless liquid contained table salt. If the properties don't match, the liquid contained a different dissolved solid. If there is no residue, no dissolved solid is present.

Units and Measurement

1.17   (a) 1×10^{-1} (b) 1×10^{-2} (c) 1×10^{-5} (d) 1×10^{-6} (e) 1×10^{6} (f) 1×10^{3}
        (g) 1×10^{-9} (h) 1×10^{-3} (i) 1×10^{-12}

1.19   (a) $25.5 \text{ mg} \times \dfrac{1 \times 10^{-3} \text{ g}}{1 \text{ mg}} = 0.0255 \text{ g } (2.55 \times 10^{-2} \text{ g})$

        (b) $4.0 \times 10^{-10} \text{ m} \times \dfrac{1 \text{ nm}}{1 \times 10^{-9} \text{ m}} = 0.40 \text{ nm}$

        (c) $0.575 \text{ mm} \times \dfrac{1 \times 10^{-3} \text{ m}}{1 \text{ mm}} \times \dfrac{1 \text{ } \mu\text{m}}{1 \times 10^{-6} \text{ m}} = 575 \text{ } \mu\text{m}$

1.21   (a) time   (b) density   (c) length   (d) area   (e) temperature
        (f) volume   (g) temperature

1.23   (a) $\text{density} = \dfrac{\text{mass}}{\text{volume}} = \dfrac{39.73 \text{ g}}{25.0 \text{ mL}} = 1.59 \text{ g/mL or } 1.59 \text{ g/cm}^3$

        (The units cm³ and mL will be used interchangeably in this manual.)

        Carbon tetrachloride, 1.59 g/mL, is more dense than water, 1.00 g/mL; carbon tetrachloride will sink rather than float on water.

        (b) $75.00 \text{ cm}^3 \times 21.45 \dfrac{\text{g}}{\text{cm}^3} = 1.609 \times 10^3 \text{ g }(1.609 \text{ kg})$

        (c) $87.50 \text{ g} \times \dfrac{1 \text{ cm}^3}{1.738 \text{ g}} = 50.3452 = 50.35 \text{ cm}^3 = 50.35 \text{ mL}$

1.25 (a) density = $\dfrac{38.5 \text{ g}}{45 \text{ mL}}$ = 0.86 g/mL

The substance is probably toluene, density = 0.866 g/mL.

(b) 45.0 g × $\dfrac{1 \text{ mL}}{1.114 \text{ g}}$ = 40.4 mL ethylene glycol

(c) $(5.00)^3 \text{ cm}^3 \times \dfrac{8.90 \text{ g}}{1 \text{ cm}^3}$ = 1.11 × 10^3 g (1.11 kg) nickel

1.27 thickness = volume/area

volume = 200 mg × $\dfrac{1 \times 10^{-3} \text{ g}}{1 \text{ mg}} \times \dfrac{1 \text{ cm}^3}{19.32 \text{ g}}$ = 0.01035 = 0.0104 cm³

area = 2.4 ft × 1.0 ft × $\dfrac{12^2 \text{ in}^2}{1 \text{ ft}^2} \times \dfrac{2.54^2 \text{ cm}^2}{\text{in}^2}$ = 2.23 × 10³ = 2.2 × 10³ cm²

thickness = $\dfrac{0.01035 \text{ cm}^3}{2,230 \text{ cm}^2} \times \dfrac{1 \times 10^{-2} \text{ m}}{1 \text{ cm}}$ = 4.6 × 10^{-8} m

4.6 × 10^{-8} m × $\dfrac{1 \text{ nm}}{1 \times 10^{-9} \text{ m}}$ = 46 nm thick

1.29 (a) °C = 5/9 (°F - 32°); 5/9 (62 - 32) = 17°C

(b) °F = 9/5 (°C) + 32°; 9/5 (216.7) + 32 = 422.1°F

(c) K = °C + 273.15; 233°C + 273.15 = 506 K

(d) 315 K - 273 = 42°C; 9/5 (42°C) + 32 = 108°F

(e) °C = 5/9 (°F - 32°); 5/9 (2500 - 32) = 1371°C; 1371°C + 273 = 1644 K
(assuming 2500 C has 4 sig figs)

Uncertainty In Measurement

1.31 Exact: (c), (d), and (f) (All others depend on measurements and standards that have margins of error, e.g., the length of a week as defined by the earth's rotation.)

1.33 7.5 cm. There are two significant figures in this measurement; the number of cm can be read precisely but there is some estimating (uncertainty) required to read tenths of a centimeter. Two significant figures is consistent with the convention that measured quantities are reported so that there is uncertainty in only the last digit.

1.35 (a) 4 (b) 3 (c) 4 (d) 3 (e) 5

1.37   (a) 3.002×10^2 (b) 4.565×10^5 (c) 6.543×10^{-3}

       (d) 9.578×10^{-4} (e) 5.078×10^4 (f) -3.500×10^{-2}

1.39   (a)   27.04   (b)   -8.0   (c) 1.84×10^{-3} (d) 7.66×10^{-4}

Dimensional Analysis

1.41   In order to cancel units, the conversion factor must have the unit being canceled opposite the starting position. For example, if the unit cm starts in the numerator, then the conversion factor must have cm in its denominator. However, if the unit cm starts in the denominator, the conversion factor must have cm in the numerator. Ideally, this will lead to the desired units in the appropriate location, numerator or denominator. However, the inverse of the answer can be taken when necessary.

1.43   (a) $0.076 \text{ L} \times \dfrac{1000 \text{ mL}}{1 \text{ L}} = 76 \text{ mL}$

       (b) $5.0 \times 10^{-8} \text{ m} \times \dfrac{1 \text{ nm}}{1 \times 10^{-9} \text{ m}} = 50. \text{ nm}$

       (c) $6.88 \times 10^5 \text{ ns} \times \dfrac{1 \times 10^{-9} \text{ s}}{1 \text{ ns}} = 6.88 \times 10^{-4} \text{ s}$

       (d) $\dfrac{1.55 \text{ kg}}{\text{m}^3} \times \dfrac{1000 \text{ g}}{1 \text{ kg}} \times \dfrac{1 \text{ m}^3}{(10)^3 \text{ dm}^3} \times \dfrac{1 \text{ dm}^3}{1 \text{ L}} = 1.55 \text{ g/L}$

       (e) $\dfrac{5.850 \text{ gal}}{\text{hr}} \times \dfrac{3.7854 \text{ L}}{1 \text{ gal}} \times \dfrac{1 \text{ hr}}{60 \text{ min}} \times \dfrac{1 \text{ min}}{60 \text{ s}} = 6.151 \times 10^{-3} \text{ L/s}$

       Estimated answer: $6 \times 4 = 24$; $24/60 = 0.4$; $0.4/60 = 0.0066 = 7 \times 10^{-3}$. This agrees with the calculated answer of 6.151×10^{-3} L/s.

1.45   (a) $5.00 \text{ days} \times \dfrac{24 \text{ hr}}{1 \text{ day}} \times \dfrac{60 \text{ min}}{1 \text{ hr}} \times \dfrac{60 \text{ s}}{1 \text{ min}} = 4.32 \times 10^5 \text{ s}$

       (b) $0.0550 \text{ mi} \times \dfrac{1.6093 \text{ km}}{\text{mi}} \times \dfrac{1000 \text{ m}}{1 \text{ km}} = 88.5 \text{ m}$

       (c) $\dfrac{\$1.89}{\text{gal}} \times \dfrac{1 \text{ gal}}{3.7854 \text{ L}} = \dfrac{\$0.499}{\text{L}}$

       (d) $\dfrac{0.510 \text{ in}}{\text{ms}} \times \dfrac{2.54 \text{ cm}}{1 \text{ in}} \times \dfrac{1 \times 10^{-2} \text{ m}}{1 \text{ cm}} \times \dfrac{1 \text{ km}}{1000 \text{ m}} \times \dfrac{1 \text{ ms}}{1 \times 10^{-3} \text{ s}} \times \dfrac{60 \text{ s}}{1 \text{ min}} \times \dfrac{60 \text{ min}}{1 \text{ hr}}$

                   $= 46.6 \dfrac{\text{km}}{\text{hr}}$

       Estimate: $0.5 \times 2.5 = 1.25$; $1.25 \times 0.01 \approx 0.01$; $0.01 \times 60 \times 60 \approx 36 \text{ km/hr}$

       (e) $\dfrac{22.50 \text{ gal}}{\text{min}} \times \dfrac{3.7854 \text{ L}}{\text{gal}} \times \dfrac{1 \text{ in}}{60 \text{ s}} = 1.41953 = 1.420 \text{ L/s}$

       Estimate: $20 \times 4 = 80$; $80/60 \approx 1.3 \text{ L/s}$

(f) $0.02500 \text{ ft}^3 \times \dfrac{12^3 \text{ in}^3}{1 \text{ ft}^3} \times \dfrac{2.54^3 \text{ cm}^3}{1 \text{ in}^3} = 707.9 \text{ cm}^3$

Estimate: $10^3 = 1000$; $3^3 = 27$; $1000 \times 27 = 27{,}000$; $27{,}000/0.04 \approx 700 \text{ cm}^3$

1.47   (a) $31 \text{ gal} \times \dfrac{4 \text{ qt}}{1 \text{ gal}} \times \dfrac{1 \text{ L}}{1.057 \text{ qt}} = 1.2 \times 10^2 \text{ L}$

Estimate: $(30 \times 4)/1 \approx 120 \text{ L}$

(b) $\dfrac{6 \text{ mg}}{\text{kg (body)}} \times \dfrac{1 \text{ kg}}{2.205 \text{ lb}} \times 150 \text{ lb} = 4 \times 10^2 \text{ mg}$

Estimate: $6/2 = 3$; $3 \times 150 = 450 \text{ mg}$

(c) $\dfrac{254 \text{ mi}}{11.2 \text{ gal}} \times \dfrac{1.609 \text{ km}}{1 \text{ mi}} \times \dfrac{1 \text{ gal}}{4 \text{ qt}} \times \dfrac{1.057 \text{ qt}}{1 \text{ L}} = \dfrac{9.64 \text{ km}}{\text{L}}$

Estimate: $250/10 = 25$; $1.6/4 = 0.4$; $25 \times 0.4 \times 1 \approx 10 \text{ km/L}$

(d) $\dfrac{50 \text{ cups}}{1 \text{ lb}} \times \dfrac{1 \text{ qt}}{4 \text{ cups}} \times \dfrac{1 \text{ L}}{1.057 \text{ qt}} \times \dfrac{1000 \text{ mL}}{1 \text{ L}} \times \dfrac{1 \text{ lb}}{453.6 \text{ g}} = \dfrac{26 \text{ mL}}{\text{g}}$

Estimate: $50/4 = 12$; $1000/500 = 2$; $(12 \times 2)/1 \approx 24 \text{ mL/g}$

1.49 $12.5 \text{ ft} \times 15.5 \text{ ft} \times 8.0 \text{ ft} = 1580 = 1.6 \times 10^3 \text{ ft}^3$ (2 sig figs)

$1550 \text{ ft}^3 \times \dfrac{(1 \text{ yd})^3}{(3 \text{ ft})^3} \times \dfrac{(1 \text{ m})^3}{(1.0936)^3 \text{ yd}^3} \times \dfrac{10^3 \text{ dm}^3}{1 \text{ m}^3} \times \dfrac{1 \text{ L}}{1 \text{ dm}^3} \times \dfrac{1.19 \text{ g}}{\text{L}} \times \dfrac{1 \text{ kg}}{1000 \text{ g}} = 52 \text{ kg air}$

Estimate: $1550/30 = 50$; $(50 \times 1)/1 \approx 50 \text{ kg}$

1.51   A wire is a very long, thin cylinder of volume, $V = \pi r^2 h$, where h is the length of the wire and πr^2 is the cross-sectional area of the wire.

Strategy: 1) Calculate total volume of copper in cm^3 from mass and density

        2) h (length in cm) $= \dfrac{V}{\pi r^2}$

        3) Change cm $\rightarrow$ ft

$150 \text{ lb Cu} \times \dfrac{453.6 \text{ g}}{1 \text{ lb Cu}} \times \dfrac{1 \text{ cm}^3}{8.94 \text{ g}} = 7.61 \times 10^3 \text{ cm}^3$

$r = d/2 = 8.25 \text{ mm} \times \dfrac{1 \text{ cm}}{10 \text{ mm}} \times \dfrac{1}{2} = 0.4125 = 0.413 \text{ cm}$

$h = \dfrac{V}{\pi r^2} = \dfrac{7610.7 \text{ cm}^3}{\pi (0.4125)^2 \text{ cm}^2} = 1.4237 \times 10^4 = 1.42 \times 10^4 \text{ cm}$

$1.4237 \times 10^4 \text{ cm} \times \dfrac{1 \text{ in}}{2.54 \text{ cm}} \times \dfrac{1 \text{ ft}}{12 \text{ in}} = 467 \text{ ft}$

(too difficult to estimate)

1.53   Select a common unit for comparison, in this case the kg.

1 kg > 2 lb, 1 L ≈ 1 qt

5 lb potatoes < 2.5 kg

5 kg sugar = 5 kg

1 gal = 4 qt ≈ 4 L.   1 mL H_2O = 1 g H_2O.   1 L = 1000 g, 4 L = 4000 g = 4 kg

The order of mass from lightest to heaviest is 5 lb potatoes < 1 gal water < 5 kg sugar.

Additional Exercises

1.55   Composition is the contents of a substance, the kinds of elements that are present and their relative amounts. Structure is the arrangement of these contents.

1.58   Any sample of vitamin C has the same relative amount of carbon and oxygen; the ratio of oxygen to carbon in the isolated sample is the same as the ratio in synthesized vitamin C.

$$\frac{2.00 \text{ g O}}{1.50 \text{ g C}} = \frac{x \text{ g O}}{6.35 \text{ g C}}; \quad x = \frac{(2.00 \text{ g O})(6.35 \text{ g C})}{1.50 \text{ g C}} = 8.47 \text{ g O}$$

This calculation assumes the *law of constant composition*.

1.61   K = °C + 273.15;   K = -246.1°C + 273.15 = 27.05 = 27.1 K
°F = 9/5 (°C) + 32;   °F = 9/5 (-246.1) + 32 = -411.0°F

(We consider 32 to be exact, so the result has 4 significant figures, as does the datum.)

1.64   Density is the ratio of mass and volume. For substances with different densities, the greater the density the smaller the volume of substance that will contain a certain mass. Since volume is directly related to diameter (V = 4/3 π r^3 = 1/6 π d^3), the more dense the substance, the smaller the diameter of a ball that contains a certain mass. The order of the sphere diameters is the reverse order of densities: Pb < Ag < Al. Mathematically, assume 10.0 g of material.

Pb: $10.0 \text{ g} \times \frac{1 \text{ cm}^3}{11.3 \text{ g}} = 0.88496 = 0.885 \text{ cm}^3$; d = (6 V/π)$^{1/3}$ = 1.19 cm

Ag: $10.0 \text{ g} \times \frac{1 \text{ cm}^3}{10.5 \text{ g}} = 0.95238 = 0.952 \text{ cm}^3$; d = 1.22 cm

Al: $10.0 \text{ g} \times \frac{1 \text{ cm}^3}{2.70 \text{ g}} = 3.7037 = 3.70 \text{ cm}^3$; d = 1.92 cm

Note that Pb and Ag, with similar densities have similar diameters; Al, with a much smaller density, has a much larger diameter.

1.66   (a) $23.2 \times 10^9 \text{ lb} \times \dfrac{453.6 \text{ g}}{1 \text{ lb}} = 1.05235 \times 10^{13} = 1.05 \times 10^{13} \text{ g NaOH}$

       (b) $1.05235 \times 10^{13} \text{ g} \times \dfrac{1 \text{ cm}^3}{2.130 \text{ g}} \times \dfrac{1 \text{ m}^3}{(100)^3 \text{ cm}^3} \times \dfrac{1 \text{ km}^3}{(1000)^3 \text{ m}^3} = 4.94 \times 10^{-3} \text{ km}^3$

1.69   There are 209.1 degrees between the freezing and boiling points on the Celsius (C) scale and 100 degrees on the glycol (G) scale. Also, -11.5°C = 0°G. By analogy with °F and °C,

     $°G = \dfrac{100}{209.1}(°C + 11.5)$ or $°C = \dfrac{209.1}{100}(°G) - 11.5$

These equations correctly relate the freezing point and boiling point of ethylene glycol on the two scales.

f.p. of H_2O: $°G = \dfrac{100}{209.1}(0°C + 11.5) = 5.50°G$

b.p. of H_2O: $°G = \dfrac{100}{209.1}(100°C + 11.5) = 53.3°G$

1.71   (a) $2.4 \times 10^5 \text{ mi} \times \dfrac{1.609 \text{ km}}{1 \text{ mi}} \times \dfrac{1000 \text{ m}}{1 \text{ km}} = 3.9 \times 10^8 \text{ m}$

       (b) $2.4 \times 10^5 \text{ mi} \times \dfrac{1.609 \text{ km}}{1 \text{ mi}} \times \dfrac{1 \text{ hr}}{2.4 \times 10^3 \text{ km}} \times \dfrac{60 \text{ min}}{1 \text{ hr}} \times \dfrac{60 \text{ s}}{1 \text{ min}} = 5.8 \times 10^5 \text{ s}$

1.74   (a) $\text{volume} = \pi r^2 h = \pi \times (3.55 \text{ cm})^2 \times 75.3 \text{ cm} = 2.98 \times 10^3 \text{ cm}^3$

       (b) $r = d/2 = 12.9 \text{ in}/2 = 6.45 \text{ in}$

            $V = \pi (6.45 \text{ in})^2 \times \dfrac{(2.54 \text{ cm})^2}{1 \text{ in}^2} \times \dfrac{(1 \text{ m})^2}{(100 \text{ cm})^2} \times 22.5 \text{ in} \times \dfrac{2.54 \text{ cm}}{1 \text{ in}} \times \dfrac{1 \text{ m}}{100 \text{ cm}}$

                                                     $= 0.04819 = 0.0482 \text{ m}^3$

       (c) $0.04819 \text{ m}^3 \times \dfrac{(100 \text{ cm})^3}{(1 \text{ m})^3} \times \dfrac{13.6 \text{ g Hg}}{1 \text{ cm}^3} \times \dfrac{1 \text{ kg}}{1000 \text{ g}} = 655 \text{ kg Hg}$

1.76   (a)   Let x = mass of Au in jewelry

            9.85 - x = mass of Ag in jewelry

            The total volume of jewelry = volume of Au + volume of Ag

            $0.675 \text{ cm}^3 = x \text{ g} \times \dfrac{1 \text{ cm}^3}{19.3 \text{ g}} + (9.85-x) \text{ g} \times \dfrac{1 \text{ cm}^3}{10.5 \text{ g}}$

            $0.675 = \dfrac{x}{19.3} + \dfrac{9.85-x}{10.5}$ (To solve, multiply both sides by (19.3)(10.5))

$$0.675 \,(19.3)(10.5) = 10.5 \, x + (9.85 - x)(19.3)$$
$$136.79 = 10.5 \, x + 190.105 - 19.3 \, x$$
$$-53.315 = -8.8 \, x$$
$$x = 6.06 \text{ g Au}; \quad 9.85 \text{ g total} - 6.06 \text{ g Au} = 3.79 \text{ g Ag}$$

$$\text{mass \% Au} = \frac{6.06 \text{ g Au}}{9.85 \text{ g jewelry}} \times 100 = 61.5\% \text{ Au}$$

(b)   24 karats × 0.615 = 15 karat gold

1.79   The densities are:

carbon tetrachloride (methane, tetrachloro) - 1.5940 g/cm^3

hexane - 0.6603 g/cm^3

benzene - 0.87654 g/cm^3

methylene iodide (methane, diiodo) - 3.3254 g/cm^3

Only methylene iodide will separate the two granular solids. The undesirable solid (2.04 g/cm^3) is less dense than methylene iodide and will float; the desired material is more dense than methylene iodide and will sink. The other three liquids are less dense than both solids and will not produce separation.

2 Atoms, Molecules, and Ions

Atomic Theory and Atomic Structure

2.1   Postulate 4 of the atomic theory is the *law of constant composition*. It states that the relative number and kinds of atoms in a compound are constant, regardless of the source. Therefore, 1.0 g of pure water should always contain the same relative amounts of hydrogen and oxygen, no matter where or how the sample is obtained.

2.3   (a) $\dfrac{17.60 \text{ g oxygen}}{30.82 \text{ g nitrogen}} = \dfrac{0.5711 \text{ g O}}{1 \text{ g N}}$; $0.5711/0.5711 = 1.0$

$\dfrac{35.20 \text{ g oxygen}}{30.82 \text{ g nitrogen}} = \dfrac{1.142 \text{ g O}}{1 \text{ g N}}$; $1.142/0.5711 = 2.0$

$\dfrac{70.40 \text{ g oxygen}}{30.82 \text{ g nitrogen}} = \dfrac{2.284 \text{ g O}}{1 \text{ g N}}$; $2.284/0.5711 = 4.0$

$\dfrac{88.00 \text{ g oxygen}}{30.82 \text{ g nitrogen}} = \dfrac{2.855 \text{ g O}}{1 \text{ g N}}$; $2.855/0.5711 = 5.0$

(b)   These masses of oxygen per one gram nitrogen are in the ratio of 1:2:4:5 and thus obey the *law of multiple proportions*. Multiple proportions arise because atoms are the indivisible entities combining, so they must combine in ratios of small whole numbers.

2.5   Evidence that cathode rays were negatively charged particles was (1) that electric and magnetic fields deflected the rays in the same way they would deflect negatively charged particles and (2) that a metal plate exposed to cathode rays acquired a negative charge.

2.7   (a)   In Millikan's oil-drop experiment the X-rays serve as "ionizing radiation". That is, X-rays interact with gaseous atoms or molecules in the chamber in such a way that the particles are ionized. The energy of the X-rays is sufficient to eject electrons from the gaseous particles, forming positive ions and free electrons. The free electrons are then able to recombine with the ions or cling to the oil drops.

(b)   If the positive plate were lower than the negative plate, the oil drops "coated" with negatively charged electrons would be attracted to the positively charged plate and would descend much more quickly.

(c)   The more times a measurement is repeated, the better the chance of detecting and compensating for experimental errors. That is, if a quantity is measured five times and four measurements agree but one does not, the disagreeable measurement is probably the result of an error. Also, the four agreeable measurements can be averaged to compensate for small random fluctuations. Millikan wanted to demonstrate the validity of his result via its reproducibility.

2.9   (a)   Because γ-rays are not deflected by the electric field, they carry no charge. [No conclusion can be made about their mass, or whether they are, in fact, particles or waves.]

(b)   If α and β rays are deflected in opposite directions in an electric field, then they must have opposite electrical charges.

Modern View of Atomic Structure; Atomic Weights

2.11   (a) $1.9 \text{ Å} \times \dfrac{1 \times 10^{-10} \text{ m}}{1 \text{ Å}} \times \dfrac{1 \text{ nm}}{1 \times 10^{-9} \text{ m}} = 0.19 \text{ nm}$

$1.9 \text{ Å} \times \dfrac{1 \times 10^{-10} \text{ m}}{1 \text{ Å}} \times \dfrac{1 \text{ pm}}{1 \times 10^{-12} \text{ m}} = 1.9 \times 10^2 \text{ or } 190 \text{ pm} \ (1 \text{ Å} = 100 \text{ pm})$

(b)   Aligned Kr atoms have **diameters** touching. $d = 2r = 2(1.9 \text{ Å}) = 3.8 \text{ Å}$

$1.0 \text{ mm} \times \dfrac{1 \text{ m}}{1000 \text{ mm}} \times \dfrac{1 \text{ Å}}{1 \times 10^{-10} \text{ m}} \times \dfrac{1 \text{ Kr atom}}{3.8 \text{ Å}} = 2.6 \times 10^6 \text{ Kr atoms}$

(c) $V = 4/3 \, \pi \, r^3.$ $r = 1.9 \text{ Å} \times \dfrac{1 \times 10^{-10} \text{ m}}{1 \text{ Å}} \times \dfrac{100 \text{ cm}}{\text{m}} = 1.9 \times 10^{-8} \text{ cm}$

$V = (4/3)(\pi)(1.9 \times 10^{-8})^3 \text{ cm}^3 = 2.9 \times 10^{-23} \text{ cm}^3$

2.13   (a)   proton, neutron, electron

(b)   proton = +1, neutron = 0, electron = -1

(c)   The neutron is most massive, the electron least massive. (The neutron and proton have very similar masses).

2.15   p = protons, n = neutrons, e = electrons

(a) ^{28}Si has 14 p, 14 n, 14 e   (b) ^{60}Ni has 28 p, 32 n, 28 e

(c) ^{85}Rb has 37 p, 48 n, 37 e   (d) ^{128}Xe has 54 p, 74 n, 54 e

(e) ^{195}Pt has 78 p, 117 n, 78 e   (f) ^{238}U has 92 p, 146 n, 92 e

2.17

Symbol	^{52}Cr	^{75}As	^{40}Ca	^{222}Rn	^{193}Ir
Protons	24	33	20	86	77
Neutrons	28	42	20	136	116
Electrons	24	33	20	86	77
Mass no.	52	75	40	222	193

2.19   (a) $^{179}_{72}$Hf   (b) $^{40}_{18}$Ar   (c) $^{4}_{2}$He   (d) $^{115}_{49}$In   (e) $^{28}_{14}$Si

2.21   (a) $^{12}_{6}$C

(b)   Atomic weights are really average atomic masses, the sum of the mass of each naturally-occurring isotope of an element times its fractional abundance. Each Cl atom will have the mass of one of the naturally-occurring isotopes, while the "atomic weight" is an average value. The naturally-occurring isotopes of Cl, their atomic masses and relative abundances are: ^{35}Cl, 34.968852, 75.77%; ^{37}Cl, 36.965903, 24.23%.

2.23   Average atomic mass (atomic weight) = $\sum$ fractional abundance × mass of isotope
Average atomic mass = 0.014 (203.97302) + 0.241 (205.9744) + 0.221 (206.97587) + 0.524 (207.97663) = 207.22 = 207 amu

(The result has 0 decimal places and 3 sig figs because the fourth term in the sum has 3 sig figs and 0 decimal places.)

2.25   (a)   Compare Figures 2.4 and 2.13, referring to Solution 2.6(c). In Thomson's cathode ray experiments and in mass spectrometry a stream of charged particles is passed through the poles of a magnet. The charged particles are deflected by the magnetic field according to their mass and charge. For a constant magnetic field strength and speed of the particles, the lighter particles experience a greater deflection.

(b)   The x-axis label (independent variable) is atomic weight and the y-axis label (dependent variable) is signal intensity.

(c)   Uncharged particles are not deflected in a magnetic field. The effect of the magnetic field on moving, *charged* particles is the basis of their separation by mass.

2.27   (a)   Average atomic mass = 0.7899(23.98504) + 0.1000(24.98584) + 0.1101(25.98259)
= 24.31 amu

(b)

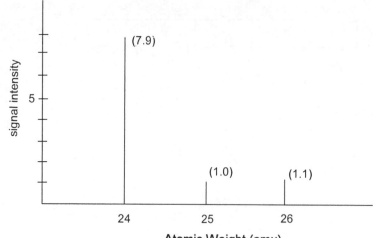

The relative intensities of the peaks in the mass spectrum are the same as the relative abundances of the isotopes. The abundances and peak heights are in the ratio ^{24}Mg: ^{25}Mg: ^{26}Mg as 7.8 : 1.0 : 1.1.

The Periodic Table;   Molecules and Ions

2.29   (a) Ag (metal)   (b) He (nonmetal)   ,(c) P (nonmetal)   (d) Cd (metal)
        (e) Ca (metal)   (f) Br (nonmetal)   (g) As (metalloid)

2.31   (a) K, alkali metals (metal) (b) I, halogens (nonmetal) (c) Mg, alkaline earth metals (metal)

        (d) Ar, noble gases (nonmetal)   (e) S, chalcogens (nonmetal)

2.33   An empirical formula shows the simplest ratio of the different atoms in a molecule. A molecular formula shows the exact number and kinds of atoms in a molecule. A structural formula shows how these atoms are arranged.

2.35   A molecular formula contains all atoms in a molecule. An empirical formula shows the simplest ratio of atoms in a molecule or elements in a compound.

        (a)   molecular formula: C_6H_6; empirical formula: CH
        (b)   molecular formula: $SiCl_4$; empirical formula: $SiCl_4$ (1:4 is the simplest ratio)

2.37   (a) 6   (b) 6   (c) 12

2.39   (a) C_2H_6O H—C—O—C—H   (b) C_2H_6O H—C—C—O—H

        (c) CH_4O H—C—O—H   (d) PF_3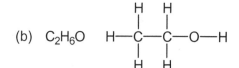

2.41   (a) $AlBr_3$ (b) C_4H_5 (c) C_2H_4O (d) P_2O_5 (e) C_3H_2Cl (f) BNH_2

2.43   (a) Al^{3+} (b) Ca^{2+} (c) S^{2-} (d) I^- (e) Cs^+

2.45   (a) GaF_3, gallium(III) fluoride   (b) LiH, lithium hydride
(c) AlI_3, aluminum iodide   (d) K_2S, potassium sulfide

2.47   (a) $CaBr_2$ (b) NH_4Cl (c) $Al(C_2H_3O_2)_3$ (d) K_2SO_4 (e) $Mg_3(PO_4)_2$

2.49   Molecular (all elements are nonmetals):   (a) B_2H_6 (b) CH_3OH (f) NOCl   (g) NF_3
Ionic (formed by a cation and an anion, usually contains a metal cation):   (c) $LiNO_3$,
(d) Sc_2O_3, (e) CsBr, (h) Ag_2SO_4

Naming Inorganic Compounds; Organic Molecules

2.51   (a) ClO_2^- (b) Cl^- (c) ClO_3^- (d) ClO_4^- (e) ClO^-

2.53   (a) aluminum fluoride   (b) iron(II) hydroxide (ferrous hydroxide)
(c) copper(II) nitrate (cupric nitrate)   (d) barium perchlorate   (e) lithium phosphate
(f) mercury(I) sulfide (mercurous sulfide)   (g) calcium acetate   (h) chromium(III) carbonate
(chromic carbonate)   (i) potassium chromate   (j) ammonium sulfate

2.55   (a) Cu_2O (b) K_2O_2 (c) $Al(OH)_3$ (d) $Zn(NO_3)_2$ (e) Hg_2Br_2 (f) $Fe_2(CO_3)_3$ (g) NaBrO

2.57   (a) bromic acid   (b) hydrobromic acid   (c) phosphoric acid   (d) HClO   (e) HIO_3
(f) H_2SO_3

2.59   (a) sulfur hexafluoride   (b) iodine pentafluoride   (c) xenon trioxide   (d) N_2O_4 (e) HCN
(f) P_4S_6

2.61   (a) $ZnCO_3$, ZnO, CO_2 (b) HF, SiO_2, SiF_4, H_2O (c) SO_2, H_2O, H_2SO_3
(d) H_3P (or PH_3)   (e) $HClO_4$, Cd, $Cd(ClO_4)_2$ (f) VBr_3

2.63   (a)   A hydrocarbon is a compound composed of the elements hydrogen and carbon only.

(b)   All alkanes are hydrocarbons, but compounds other than alkanes can also be
hydrocarbons.

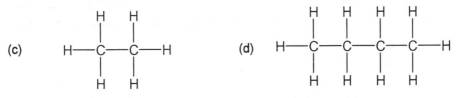

molecular: C_4H_{10}

empirical: C_2H_5

2.65　(a)　*Functional groups* are groups of specific atoms that are constant from one molecule to the next. For example, the alcohol functional group is an –OH. Whenever a molecule is called an alcohol, it contains the –OH group.

(b)　–OH

(c)

Additional Exercises

2.69　Radioactivity is the spontaneous emission of radiation from a substance. Becquerel's discovery showed that atoms could decay, or degrade, *implying* that they are not indivisible. However, it wasn't until Rutherford and others characterized the nature of radioactive emissions, especially the particle nature of α and β rays, that the full significance of the discovery was apparent.

2.72　(a)　^{3}He has 2 protons, 1 neutron and 2 electrons.

(b)　^{3}H has 1 proton, 2 neutrons and 1 electron.

^{3}He: $2(1.6726231 \times 10^{-24}$ g$) + 1.6749286 \times 10^{-24}$ g $+ 2(9.1093897 \times 10^{-28}$ g$)$

$$= 5.021996 \times 10^{-24} \text{ g}$$

^{3}H: $1.6726231 \times 10^{-24}$ g $+ 2(1.6749286 \times 10^{-24}$ g$) + 9.1093897 \times 10^{-28}$ g

$$= 5.023391 \times 10^{-24} \text{ g}$$

Tritium, ^{3}H, is more massive.

(c)　The masses of the two particles differ by 0.0014×10^{-24} g. Each particle loses 1 electron to form the +1 ion, so the difference in the masses of the ions is still 1.4×10^{-27}. A mass spectrometer would need precision to 1×10^{-27} g to differentiate ^{3}He$^+$ and ^{3}H.

2.76　(a)　$^{16}_{8}$O, $^{17}_{8}$O, $^{18}_{8}$O

(b)　All isotopes are atoms of the same element, oxygen, with the same atomic number (Z = 8), 8 protons in the nucleus and 8 electrons. Elements with similar electron arrangements have similar chemical properties (Section 2.5). Since the 3 isotopes all have 8 electrons, we expect their electron arrangements to be the same and their chemical properties to be very similar, perhaps identical. Each has a different number of neutrons (8, 9 or 10), a different mass number (A = 16, 17 or 18) and thus a different atomic mass.

2.78　(a)　The 68.926 amu isotope has a mass number of 69, with 31 protons, 38 neutrons and the symbol $^{69}_{31}$Ga. The 70.926 amu isotope has a mass number of 71, 31 protons, 40 neutrons, and symbol $^{71}_{31}$Ga. (All Ga atoms have 31 protons.)

(b)   The average mass of a Ga atom (given on the inside cover of the text) is 69.72 amu. Let x = abundance of the lighter isotope, 1-x = abundance of the heavier isotope. Then x(68.926) + (1-x)(70.925) = 69.723; x = 0.6013, ^{69}Ga = 60.13%, ^{71}Ga = 39.87%

2.81   (a)   5 significant figures. $^1H^+$ is a bare proton with mass 1.0073 amu. ^1H is a hydrogen atom, with 1 proton and 1 electron. The mass of the electron is 5.486 × 10^{-4} or 0.0005486 amu. Thus the mass of the electron is significant in the fourth decimal place or fifth significant figure in the mass of ^1H.

(b)   Mass of ^1H = 1.0073 amu   (proton)

$\underline{}$ 0.0005486 amu   (electron)

1.0078 amu   (We have not rounded up to 1.0079 since
49 < 50 in the final sum.)

$$\text{Mass \% of electron} = \frac{\text{mass of } e^-}{\text{mass of } ^1H} \times 100 = \frac{5.486 \times 10^{-4} \text{ amu}}{1.0078 \text{ amu}} \times 100 = 0.05444\%$$

2.84   (a) $^{266}_{106}$Sg has 106 protons, 160 neutrons and 106 electrons

(b)   Sg is in Group 6B (or 6) and immediately below tungsten, W. We expect the chemical properties of Sg to most closely resemble those of W.

2.87   (a) nickel(II) oxide, 2+   (b) manganese(IV) oxide, 4+   (c) chromium(III) oxide, 3+
(d) molybdenium(VI) oxide, 6+

2.90   (a) sodium chloride   (b) sodium bicarbonate (or sodium hydrogen carbonate)
(c) sodium hypochlorite   (d) sodium hydroxide   (e) ammonium carbonate
(f) calcium sulfate

2.94   (a)   CH

(b)   No. Benzene is not an alkane because alkanes are hydrocarbons with ALL single bonds.

(c)   In an alcohol, the –OH group replaces an H atom of the hydrocarbon.

The molecular formula is C_6H_6O or C_6H_5OH. (The OH could go on any one of the six carbon atoms.)

3 Stoichiometry: Calculation with Chemical Formulas and Equations

Balancing Chemical Equations

3.1 (a) In balancing chemical equations, the *law of conservation of mass*, that atoms are neither created nor destroyed during the course of a reaction, is observed. This means that the **number** and **kinds** of atoms on both sides of the chemical equation must be the same.

(b) Subscripts in chemical formulas should not be changed when balancing equations because changing the subscript changes the identity of the compound (*law of constant composition*).

(c) gases - (g); liquids - (l); solids - (s); aqueous solutions - (aq)

3.3 Equation (a) best fits the diagram.

Overall, 4 A_2 molecules + 4 B atoms → 4 A_2B molecules

Since 4 is a common factor, this equation reduces to equation (a).

3.5 (a) $2SO_2(g) + O_2(g) → 2SO_3(g)$

(b) $P_2O_5(s) + 3H_2O(l) → 2H_3PO_4(aq)$

(c) $CH_4(g) + 4Cl_2(g) → CCl_4(l) + 4HCl(g)$

(d) $Al_4C_3(s) + 12H_2O(l) → 4Al(OH)_3(s) + 3CH_4(g)$

(e) $C_4H_{10}O(l) + 6O_2(g) → 4CO_2(g) + 5H_2O(l)$

(f) $2Fe(OH)_3(s) + 3H_2SO_4(aq) → Fe_2(SO_4)_3(aq) + 6H_2O(l)$

(g) $Mg_3N_2(s) + 4H_2SO_4(aq) → 3MgSO_4(aq) + (NH_4)_2SO_4(aq)$

3.7 (a) $CaC_2(s) + 2H_2O(l) → Ca(OH)_2(aq) + C_2H_2(g)$

(b) $2KClO_3(s) \overset{\Delta}{→} 2KCl(s) + 3O_2(g)$

(c) $Zn(s) + H_2SO_4(aq) → H_2(g) + ZnSO_4(aq)$

(d) $PCl_3(l) + 3H_2O(l) → H_3PO_3(aq) + 3HCl(aq)$

(e) $3H_2S(g) + 2Fe(OH)_3(s) → Fe_2S_3(s) + 6H_2O(g)$

Patterns of Chemical Reactivity

3.9   (a)   When a metal reacts with a nonmetal, an ionic compound forms. The combining ratio of the atoms is such that the total positive charge on the metal cation(s) is equal to the total negative charge on the nonmetal anion(s). All ionic compounds are solids.
$2 Na(s) + Br_2(l) \rightarrow 2NaBr(s)$

      (b)   The second reactant is oxygen gas from the air, $O_2(g)$. The products are $CO_2(g)$ and $H_2O(l)$. $2C_6H_6(l) + 15O_2(g) \rightarrow 12CO_2(g) + 6H_2O(l)$

3.11   (a) $Mg(s) + Cl_2(g) \rightarrow MgCl_2(s)$

      (b) $Ni(OH)_2(s) \xrightarrow{\Delta} NiO(s) + H_2O(g)$

      (c) $C_3H_8(l) + 10O_2(g) \rightarrow 8CO_2(g) + 4H_2O(l)$

      (d) $2C_5H_{12}O(l) + 15O_2(g) \rightarrow 10CO_2(g) + 12H_2O(l)$

3.13   (a) $2Al(s) + 3Cl_2(g) \rightarrow 2AlCl_3(s)$ combination

      (b) $C_2H_4(g) + 3O_2(g) \rightarrow 2CO_2(g) + 2H_2O(l)$ combustion

      (c) $6Li(s) + N_2(g) \rightarrow 2Li_3N(s)$ combination

      (d) $PbCO_3(s) \rightarrow PbO(s) + CO_2(g)$ decomposition

      (e) $C_7H_8O_2(l) + 8O_2(g) \rightarrow 7CO_2(g) + 4H_2O(l)$ combustion

Formula Weights

3.15   Formula weight (FW) in amu to 1 decimal place (see Sample Exercise 3.5)

      (a) H_2S: $2(1.0) + 1(32.1) = 34.1$ amu

      (b) $NiCO_3$: $1(58.7) + 1(12.0) + 3(16.0) = 118.7$ amu

      (c) $Mg(C_2H_3O_2)_2$: $1(24.3) + 4(12.0) + 6(1.0) + 4(16.0) = 142.3$ amu

      (d) $(NH_4)_3SO_4$: $3(14.0) + 12(1.0) + 1(32.1) + 4(16.0) = 150.1$ amu

      (e) K_3PO_4: $3(39.1) + 1(31.0) + 4(16.0) = 212.3$ amu

      (f) Fe_2O_3: $2(55.8) + 3(16.0) = 159.6$ amu

      (g) P_2S_5: $2(31.0) + 5(32.1) = 222.5$ amu

3.17   *Plan.* Calculate the formula weight (FW), then the mass % oxygen in the compound. *Solve*:

      (a) SO_2: FW = $1(32.1) + 2(16.0) = 64.1$ amu

$$\% \, O = \frac{2(16.0) \, amu}{64.1 \, amu} \times 100 = 49.9\%$$

      (b) Na_2SO_4: FW = $2(23.0) + 1(32.1) + 4(16.0) = 142.1$ amu

$$\% \, O = \frac{4(16.0) \, amu}{142.1 \, amu} \times 100 = 45.0\%$$

      (c) C_2H_5COOH: FW = $3(12.0) + 6(1.0) + 2(16.0) = 74.0$ amu

$$\% \, O = \frac{2(16.0) \, amu}{74.0 \, amu} \times 100 = 43.2\%$$

(d) $Al(NO_3)_3$: FW = 1(27.0) + 3(14.0) + 9(16.0) = 213.0 amu

$$\% \ O = \frac{9(16.0) \ \text{amu}}{213.0 \ \text{amu}} \times 100 = 67.6\%$$

(e) NH_4NO_3: FW = 2(14.0) + 4(1.0) + 3(16.0) = 80.0 amu

$$\% \ O = \frac{3(16.0) \ \text{amu}}{80.0 \ \text{amu}} \times 100 = 60.0\%$$

3.19 *Plan.* Follow the logic for calculating mass % C given in Sample Exercise 3.6. *Solve*:

(a) C_7H_6O: FW = 7(12.0) + 6(1.0) + 1(16.0) = 106.0 amu

$$\%C = \frac{7(12.0) \ \text{amu}}{106.0 \ \text{amu}} \times 100 = 79.2\%$$

(b) $C_8H_8O_3$: FW = 8(12.0) + 8(1.0) + 3(16.0) = 152.0 amu

$$\% \ C = \frac{8(12.0) \ \text{amu}}{152.0 \ \text{amu}} \times 100 = 63.2\%$$

(c) $C_7H_{14}O_2$: FW = 7(12.0) + 14(1.0) + 2(16.0) = 130.0 amu

$$\% \ C = \frac{7(12.0) \ \text{amu}}{130.0 \ \text{amu}} \times 100 = 64.6\%$$

The Mole

3.21 (a) 6.022×10^{23}. This is the number of objects in a mole of anything.

(b) The formula weight of a substance in amu has the same numerical value as the molar mass expressed in grams.

3.23 *Plan.* Since the mole is a counting unit, use it as a basis of comparison; determine the total moles of atoms in each given quantity. *Solve*:

23 g Na contains 1 mol of atoms

0.5 mol H_2O contains (3 atoms × 0.5 mol) = 1.5 mol atoms

6.0×10^{23} N_2 molecules contains (2 atoms × 1 mol) = 2 mol atoms

3.25 *Analyze.* Given: 16 lb/ball; Avogadro's number of balls, 6.022×10^{23} balls. Find: mass in kg of Avogadro's number of balls; compare with mass of Earth.

Plan. balls → mass in lb → mass in kg; mass of balls/mass of Earth

Solve. 6.022×10^{23} balls $\times \dfrac{16 \ \text{lb}}{\text{ball}} \times \dfrac{1 \ \text{kg}}{2.2046 \ \text{lb}} = 4.370 \times 10^{24} = 4.4 \times 10^{24}$ kg

$$\frac{4.370 \times 10^{24} \ \text{kg of balls}}{5.98 \times 10^{24} \ \text{kg Earth}} = 0.73; \ \text{One mole of shotput balls weighs 0.73 times as much as Earth.}$$

Check. This mass of balls is reasonable since Avogadro's number is large.

Estimate: 16 lb ≈ 7 kg; $6 \times 10^{23} \times 7 = 4.2 \times 10^{24}$ kg

3.27   **(a)**   *Analyze.* Given: 1.73 mol CaH_2. Find: mass in g.

             Plan. Use molar mass (g/mol) of CaH_2 to find g CaH_2

             Solve. molar mass = 1(40.08) + 2(1.008) = 42.096 = 42.10 g/mol CaH_2

$$1.73 \text{ mol } CaH_2 \times \frac{42.096 \text{ g}}{1 \text{ mol}} = 72.8 \text{ g } CaH_2$$

             Check. ~2 × 42 = 84 g. The calculated result is reasonable.

      (b)   *Analyze.* Given: mass. Find: moles. *Plan.* Use molar mass of $Mg(NO_3)_2$.

             Solve. molar mass = 1(24.31) + 2(14.01) + 6(16.00) = 148.33 = 148.3

$$3.25 \text{ g } Mg(NO_3)_2 \times \frac{1 \text{ mol}}{148.33 \text{ g}} = 0.0219 \text{ mol } Mg(NO_3)_2$$

             Check. 3/150 ≈ 1/50 = 0.02 mol

      (c)   *Analyze.* Given: moles. Find: molecules. *Plan.* Use Avogadro's number.

$$\text{\textit{Solve.}} \quad 0.245 \text{ mol } CH_3OH \times \frac{6.022 \times 10^{23} \text{ molecules}}{1 \text{ mol}} = 1.47539 \times 10^{23}$$
$$= 1.48 \times 10^{23} \ CH_3OH \text{ molecules}$$

             Check. (0.25 × 6 × 10^{23}) = 1.5 × 10^{23}

      (d)   *Analyze.* Given: mol C_4H_{10}. Find: H atoms.

             Plan. mol C_4H_{10} → mol H atoms → H atoms

$$\text{\textit{Solve.}} \quad 0.585 \text{ mol } C_4H_{10} \times \frac{10 \text{ mol H atoms}}{1 \text{ mol } C_4H_{10}} \times \frac{6.022 \times 10^{23} \text{ atoms}}{1 \text{ mol}}$$
$$= 3.52 \times 10^{24} \text{ H atoms}$$

             Check. (0.6 × 10 × 10^{23}) = 36 × 10^{23} = 3.6 × 10^{24}.

3.29   *Analyze/Plan.* See Solution 3.27 for stepwise problem-solving approach. *Solve*:

      (a)   molar mass = 2(26.98) + 3(32.07) + 12(16.00) = 342.17 = 342.2 g

$$2.50 \times 10^{-3} \text{ mol } Al_2(SO_4)_3 \times \frac{342.2 \text{ g } Al_2(SO_4)_3}{1 \text{ mol}} = 0.856 \text{ g } Al_2(SO_4)_3$$

      (b)   molar mass = 26.982 + 3(35.453) = 133.341 = 133.34 g

$$0.0750 \text{ g } AlCl_3 \times \frac{1 \text{ mol}}{133.34 \text{ g } AlCl_3} \times \frac{3 \text{ mol } Cl^-}{1 \text{ mol } AlCl_3} = 1.69 \times 10^{-3} \text{ mol } Cl^-$$

      (c)   molar mass = 8(12.01) + 10(1.008) + 4(14.01) + 2(16.00) = 194.20 = 194.2 g

$$7.70 \times 10^{20} \text{ molecules} \times \frac{1 \text{ mol}}{6.022 \times 10^{23} \text{ molecules}} \times \frac{194.2 \text{ g } C_8H_{10}N_4O_2}{1 \text{ mol caffeine}}$$
$$= 0.248 \text{ g } C_8H_{10}N_4O_2$$

      (d) $\dfrac{0.406 \text{ g cholesterol}}{0.00105 \text{ mol}} = 387 \text{ g cholesterol/mol}$

3.31 (a) molar mass = 6(12.01) + 10(1.008) + 1(16.00) + 2(32.07) = 162.28 = 162.3 g

(b) *Plan.* mg → g → mol *Solve:*

$$5.00 \text{ mg allicin} \times \frac{1 \times 10^{-3} \text{ g}}{1 \text{ mg}} \times \frac{1 \text{ mol}}{162.3 \text{ g}} = 3.081 \times 10^{-5} = 3.08 \times 10^{-5} \text{ mol allicin}$$

Check. 5.00 mg is a small mass, so the small answer is reasonable.

$$(5 \times 10^{-3})/200 = 2.5 \times 10^{-5}$$

(c) *Plan.* Use mol from part (b) and Avogadro's number to calculate molecules.

Solve. 3.081×10^{-5} mol allicin $\times \dfrac{6.022 \times 10^{23} \text{ molecules}}{\text{mol}} = 1.855 \times 10^{19}$

$$= 1.86 \times 10^{19} \text{ allicin molecules}$$

Check. $(3 \times 10^{-5})(6 \times 10^{23}) = 18 \times 10^{18} = 1.8 \times 10^{19}$

(d) *Plan.* Use molecules from part (c) and molecular formula to calculate S atoms.

Solve. 1.855×10^{19} allicin molecules $\times \dfrac{2 \text{ S atoms}}{1 \text{ allicin molecule}} = 3.71 \times 10^{19}$ S atoms

Check. Obvious.

3.33 (a) *Analyze.* Given: $C_6H_{12}O_6$, 5.77×10^{20} C atoms. Find: H atoms.

Plan. Use molecular formula to determine number of H atoms that are present with 5.77×10^{20} C atoms. *Solve:*

$$\frac{12 \text{ H atoms}}{6 \text{ C atoms}} = \frac{2 \text{ H}}{1 \text{ C}} \times 5.77 \times 10^{20} \text{ C atoms} = 1.15 \times 10^{21} \text{ H atoms}$$

Check. $(2 \times 6 \times 10^{20}) = 12 \times 10^{20} = 1.2 \times 10^{21}$

(b) *Plan.* Use molecular formula to find the number of glucose molecules that contain 5.77×10^{20} C atoms. *Solve:*

$$\frac{1 \text{ } C_6H_{12}O_6 \text{ molecule}}{6 \text{ C atoms}} \times 5.77 \times 10^{20} \text{ C atoms} = 9.617 \times 10^{19}$$

$$= 9.62 \times 10^{19} \text{ } C_6H_{12}O_6 \text{ molecules}$$

Check. $(6 \times 10^{20}/6) = 1 \times 10^{20} = 1 \times 10^{20} = 10 \times 10^{19}$

(c) *Plan.* Use Avogadro's number to change molecules → mol. *Solve:*

$$9.617 \times 10^{19} \text{ } C_6H_{12}O_6 \text{ molecules} \times \frac{1 \text{ mol}}{6.022 \times 10^{23} \text{ molecules}}$$

$$= 1.597 \times 10^{-4} = 1.60 \times 10^{-4} \text{ mol } C_6H_{12}O_6$$

Check. $(9 \times 10^{19})/(6 \times 10^{23}) = 1.5 \times 10^{-4}$

(d) *Plan.* Use molar mass to change mol → g. *Solve:*

1 mole of $C_6H_{12}O_6$ weighs 180.0 g (Sample Exercise 3.9)

$$1.597 \times 10^{-4} \text{ mol } C_6H_{12}O_6 \times \frac{180.0 \text{ g } C_6H_{12}O_6}{1 \text{ mol}} = 0.0287 \text{ g } C_6H_{12}O_6$$

Check. $1.5 \times 180 = 270$; $270 \times 10^{-4} = 0.027$

3.35   *Analyze.* Given: g C_2H_3Cl/L. Find: mol/L, molecules/L.

Plan. The /L is constant throughout the problem, so we can ignore it. Use molar mass for g → mol, Avogadro's number for mol → molecules. *Solve:*

$$\frac{2.05 \times 10^{-6} \text{ g } C_2H_3Cl}{1 \text{ L}} \times \frac{1 \text{ mol } C_2H_3Cl}{62.50 \text{ g } C_2H_3Cl} = 3.280 \times 10^{-8} = 3.28 \times 10^{-8} \text{ mol } C_2H_3Cl/L$$

$$\frac{3.280 \times 10^{-8} \text{ mol } C_2H_3Cl}{1 \text{ L}} \times \frac{6.022 \times 10^{23} \text{ molecules}}{1 \text{ mol}} = 1.97 \times 10^{16} \text{ molecules/L}$$

Check. $(200 \times 10^{-8})/60 = 2.5 \times 10^{-8} \text{ mol}$

$(2.5 \times 10^{-8}) \times (6 \times 10^{23}) = 15 \times 10^{15} = 1.5 \times 10^{16}$

Empirical Formulas

3.37   (a)   There are twice as many O atoms as N atoms, so the empirical formula of the original compound is NO_2.

          (b)   No, because we have no way of knowing whether the empirical and molecular formulas are the same. NO_2 represents the simplest ratio of atoms in a molecule, but not the only possible molecular formula.

3.39   (a)   *Analyze.* Given: moles. Find: empirical formula.
               Plan. Find the **simplest ratio of moles** by dividing by the smallest number of moles present.

               Solve.   0.0130 mol C / 0.0065 = 2
                          0.039 mol H / 0.0065 = 6
                          0.0065 mol O / 0.0065 = 1

               The empirical formula is C_2H_6O.

               Check. The subscripts are simple integers.

          (b)   *Analyze.* Given: grams. Find: empirical formula.

               Plan. Calculate the moles of each element present, then the simplest ratio of moles.

               Solve. 11.66 g Fe $\times \dfrac{1 \text{ mol Fe}}{55.85 \text{ g Fe}} = 0.2088$ mol Fe; 0.2088 / 0.2088 = 1

               5.01 g O $\times \dfrac{1 \text{ mol O}}{16.00 \text{ g O}} = 0.3131$ mol O; 0.3131 / 0.2088 ≈ 1.5

               Multiplying by two, the integer ratio is 2 Fe : 3 O; the empirical formula is Fe_2O_3.

               Check. The subscripts are simple integers.

(c) *Analyze.* Given: mass %.   Find: empirical formulas.

Plan. Assume 100 g sample, calculate moles of each element, find the simplest ratio of moles.

Solve. $40.0 \text{ g C} \times \dfrac{1 \text{ mol C}}{12.01 \text{ g C}} = 3.33 \text{ mol C}$; $3.33 / 3.33 = 1$

$6.7 \text{ g H} \times \dfrac{1 \text{ mol H}}{1.008 \text{ mol H}} = 6.65 \text{ mol H}$; $6.65 / 3.33 \approx 2$

$53.3 \text{ g O} \times \dfrac{1 \text{ mol O}}{16.00 \text{ mol O}} = 3.33 \text{ mol O}$; $3.33 / 3.33 = 1$

The empirical formula is CH_2O.

Check. The subscripts are simple integers.

3.41 *Analyze/Plan.* The procedure in all these cases is to assume 100 g of sample, calculate the number of moles of each element present in that 100 g, then obtain the ratio of moles as smallest whole numbers. *Solve*:

(a) $10.4 \text{ g C} \times \dfrac{1 \text{ mol C}}{12.01 \text{ g C}} = 0.866 \text{ mol C}$; $0.866 / 0.866 = 1$

$27.8 \text{ g S} \times \dfrac{1 \text{ mol S}}{32.07 \text{ g S}} = 0.867 \text{ mol S}$; $0.867 / 0.866 \approx 1$

$61.7 \text{ g Cl} \times \dfrac{1 \text{ mol Cl}}{35.45 \text{ g Cl}} = 1.74 \text{ mol Cl}$; $1.74 / 0.866 \approx 2$

The empirical formula is $CSCl_2$.

(b) $21.7 \text{ g C} \times \dfrac{1 \text{ mol C}}{12.01 \text{ g C}} = 1.81 \text{ mol C}$; $1.81 / 0.600 \approx 3$

$9.6 \text{ g O} \times \dfrac{1 \text{ mol O}}{16.00 \text{ g O}} = 0.600 \text{ mol O}$; $0.600 / 0.600 = 1$

$68.7 \text{ g F} \times \dfrac{1 \text{ mol F}}{19.00 \text{ g F}} = 3.62 \text{ mol F}$; $3.62 / 0.600 \approx 6$

The empirical formula is C_3OF_6.

(c) $32.79 \text{ g Na} \times \dfrac{1 \text{ mol Na}}{22.99 \text{ g Na}} = 1.426 \text{ mol Na}$; $1.426 / 0.4826 \approx 3$

$13.02 \text{ g Al} \times \dfrac{1 \text{ mol Al}}{26.98 \text{ g Al}} = 0.4826 \text{ mol Al}$; $0.4826 / 0.4826 = 1$

$54.19 \text{ g F} \times \dfrac{1 \text{ mol F}}{19.00 \text{ g F}} = 2.852 \text{ mol F}$; $2.852 / 0.4826 \approx 6$

The empirical formula is Na_3AlF_6.

3.43   *Analyze.* Given: empirical formula, molar mass. Find: molecular formula.

Plan. Calculate the empirical formula weight (FW); divide FW by molar mass ($\mathcal{M}$) to calculate the integer that relates the empirical and molecular formulas. Check. If FW/$\mathcal{M}$ is an integer, the result is reasonable. *Solve*:

(a)   FW CH_2 = 12 + 2(1) = 14. $\dfrac{\mathcal{M}}{FW} = \dfrac{84}{14} = 6$

The subscripts in the empirical formula are multiplied by 6. The molecular formula is C_6H_{12}.

(b)   FW NH_2Cl = 14.01 + 2(1.008) + 35.45 = 51.48. $\dfrac{\mathcal{M}}{FW} = \dfrac{51.5}{51.5} = 1$

The empirical and molecular formulas are NH_2Cl.

3.45.   *Analyze.* Given: mass %, molar mass.   Find: molecular formula.   *Plan.* Use the plan detailed in Solution 3.41 to find an empirical formula from mass % data. Then use the plan detailed in 3.43 to find the molecular formula. Note that some indication of molar mass must be given, or the molecular formula cannot be determined. *Check.* If there is an integer ratio of moles and $\mathcal{M}$ / FW is an integer, the result is reasonable. *Solve:*

(a)   49.5 g C $\times \dfrac{1\ mol\ C}{12.01\ g\ C}$ = 4.12 mol C;   4.12 / 1.03 ≈ 4

5.15 g H $\times \dfrac{1\ mol\ H}{1.008\ g\ H}$ = 5.11 mol H;   5.11 / 1.03 ≈ 5

28.9 g N $\times \dfrac{1\ mol\ N}{14.01\ g\ N}$ = 2.06 mol N;   2.06 / 1.03 ≈ 2

16.5 g O $\times \dfrac{1\ mol\ O}{16.00\ g\ O}$ = 1.03 mol O;   1.03 / 1.03 = 1

Thus, $C_4H_5N_2O$, FW = 97. If the molar mass is about 195, a factor of 2 gives the molecular formula $C_8H_{10}N_4O_2$.

(b)   35.51 g C $\times \dfrac{1\ mol\ C}{12.01\ g\ C}$ = 2.96 mol C; 2.96/0.592 = 5

4.77 g H $\times \dfrac{1\ mol\ H}{1.008\ g\ H}$ = 4.73 mol H; 4.73/0.592 = 7.99 ≈ 8

37.85 g O $\times \dfrac{1\ mol\ O}{16.00\ g\ O}$ = 2.37 mol O; 2.37/0.592 = 4

8.29 g N $\times \dfrac{1\ mol\ N}{14.01\ g\ N}$ = 0.592 mol N; 0.592/0.592 = 1

13.60 g Na $\times \dfrac{1\ mol\ Na}{22.99\ g\ Na}$ = 0.592 mol Na; 0.592/0.592 = 1

The empirical formula is $C_5H_8O_4NNa$, FW = 169 g. Since the empirical formula weight and molar mass are approximately equal, the empirical and molecular formulas are both $NaC_5H_8O_4N$.

3.47 (a) *Analyze.* Given: mg CO_2, mg H_2O Find: empirical formula of hydrocarbon, C_xH_y

Plan. Upon combustion, all C → CO_2, all H → H_2O.

mg CO_2 → g CO_2 → mol C; mg H_2O → g H_2O, mol H

Find simplest ratio of moles and empirical formula. *Solve*:

$$5.86 \times 10^{-3} \text{ g CO}_2 \times \frac{1 \text{ mol CO}_2}{44.01 \text{ g CO}_2} \times \frac{1 \text{ mol C}}{1 \text{ mol CO}_2} = 1.33 \times 10^{-4} \text{ mol C.}$$

$$1.37 \times 10^{-3} \text{ g H}_2O \times \frac{1 \text{ mol H}_2O}{18.02 \text{ g H}_2O} \times \frac{2 \text{ mol H}}{1 \text{ mol H}_2O} = 1.52 \times 10^{-4} \text{ mol H.}$$

Dividing both values by 1.33×10^{-4} gives C:H of 1:1.14. This is not "close enough" to be considered 1:1. No obvious multipliers (2, 3, 4) produce an integer ratio. Testing other multipliers (trial and error!), the correct factor seems to be 7. The empirical formula is C_7H_8.

Check. See discussion of C:H ratio above.

(b) *Analyze.* Given: g of menthol, g CO_2, g H_2O, molar mass. Find: molecular formula.

Plan/Solve. Calculate mol C and mol H in the sample.

$$0.2829 \text{ g CO}_2 \times \frac{1 \text{ mol CO}_2}{44.01 \text{ g CO}_2} \times \frac{1 \text{ mol C}}{1 \text{ mol CO}_2} = 0.0064281 = 0.006428 \text{ mol C}$$

$$0.1159 \text{ g H}_2O \times \frac{1 \text{ mol H}_2O}{18.02 \text{ g H}_2O} \times \frac{2 \text{ mol H}}{1 \text{ mol H}_2O} = 0.012863 = 0.01286 \text{ mol H}$$

Calculate g C, g H and get g O by subtraction.

$$0.064281 \text{ mol C} \times \frac{12.01 \text{ g C}}{1 \text{ mol C}} = 0.07720 \text{ g C}$$

$$0.012863 \text{ mol H} \times \frac{1.008 \text{ g H}}{1 \text{ mol H}} = 0.01297 \text{ g H}$$

mass O = 0.1005 g sample - (0.07720 g C + 0.01297 g H) = 0.01033 g O

Calculate mol O and find integer ratio of mol C: mol H: mol O.

$$0.01033 \text{ g O} \times \frac{1 \text{ mol O}}{16.00 \text{ g O}} = 6.456 \times 10^{-4} \text{ mol O}$$

Divide moles by 6.456×10^{-4}.

C: $\frac{0.006428}{6.456 \times 10^{-4}} \approx 10$; H: $\frac{0.01286}{6.456 \times 10^{-4}} \approx 20$; O: $\frac{6.456 \times 10^{-4}}{6.456 \times 10^{-4}} = 1$

The empirical formula is $C_{10}H_{20}O$.

$$FW = 10(12) + 20(1) + 16 = 156; \quad \frac{\mathcal{M}}{FW} = \frac{156}{156} = 1$$

The molecular formula is the same as the empirical formula, $C_{10}H_{20}O$.

Check. The mass of O wasn't negative or greater than the sample mass; empirical and molecular formulas are reasonable.

3.49   *Analyze.* Given 2.558 g $Na_2CO_3 \cdot xH_2O$, 0.948 g Na_2CO_3. Find: x.

         Plan. The reaction involved is $Na_2CO_3 \cdot xH_2O(s) \rightarrow Na_2CO_3(s) + xH_2O(g)$.
         Calculate the mass of H_2O lost and then the mole ratio of Na_2CO_3 and H_2O.   *Solve*:

         g H_2O lost = 2.558 g sample - 0.948 g Na_2CO_3 = 1.610 g H_2O

$$0.948 \text{ g } Na_2CO_3 \times \frac{1 \text{ mol } Na_2CO_3}{106.0 \text{ g } Na_2CO_3} = 0.00894 \text{ mol } Na_2CO_3$$

$$1.610 \text{ g } H_2O \times \frac{1 \text{ mol } H_2O}{18.02 \text{ g } H_2O} = 0.08935 \text{ mol } H_2O$$

$$\frac{\text{mol } H_2O}{\text{mol } Na_2CO_3} = \frac{0.08935}{0.00894} = 9.99; \quad x = 10.$$

         The formula is $Na_2CO_3 \cdot \underline{\mathbf{10}} \ H_2O$.

         Check. x is an integer.

Calculations Based on Chemical Equations

3.51   The mole ratios implicit in the coefficients of a balanced chemical equation express the fundamental relationship between amounts of reactants and products. If the equation is not balanced, the mole ratios will be incorrect and lead to erroneous calculated amounts of products.

3.53   *Analyze. Given: 4.0 mol CH_4. Find: mol CO and mol H_2.*
         Plan. Examine the boxes to determine the CH_4:CO mol ratio and CH_4:H_2O mole ratio.
         Solve. There are 2CH_4 molecules in the reactant box and 2CO molecules in the product box. The mole ratio is 2:2 or 1:1. Therefore, 4.0 mol CH_4 can produce 4.0 mol CO. There are 2CH_4 molecules in the reactant box and 6H_2 molecules in the product box. The mole ratio is 2:6 or 1:3. So, 4.0 mol CH_4 can produce 12:0 mol H_2.

         Check. Use proportions. 2 mol CH_4/2 mol CO = 4 mol CH_4/4 mol CO;
         2 mol CH_4/6 mol H_2 = 4 mol CH_4/12 mol H_2.

3.55 $Na_2SiO_3(s) + 8HF(aq) \rightarrow H_2SiF_6(aq) + 2NaF(aq) + 3H_2O(l)$

(a)   *Analyze.* Given: mol Na_2SiO_3. Find: mol HF. *Plan.* Use the mole ratio 8HF:1Na_2SiO_3 from the balanced equation to relate moles of the two reactants. *Solve*:

$$0.300 \text{ mol } Na_2SiO_3 \times \frac{8 \text{ mol HF}}{1 \text{ mol } Na_2SiO_3} = 2.4 \text{ mol HF}$$

Check. Mol HF should be greater than mol Na_2SiO_3.

(b)   *Analyze.* Given: mol HF. Find: g NaF. *Plan.* Use the mole ratio 2NaF:8HF to change mol HF to mol NaF, then molar mass to get NaF. *Solve:*

$$0.500 \text{ mol HF} \times \frac{2 \text{ mol NaF}}{8 \text{ mol HF}} \times \frac{41.99 \text{ g NaF}}{1 \text{ mol NaF}} = 5.25 \text{ g NaF}$$

Check. (0.5/4) = 0.125; 0.13 × 42 > 4 g NaF

(c)   *Analyze.* Given: g HF Find: g Na_2SiO_3.

Plan. g HF $\rightarrow$ mol HF $\left(\dfrac{\text{mol}}{\text{ratio}}\right)$ $\rightarrow$ mol Na_2SiO_3 $\rightarrow$ g Na_2SiO_3

The mole ratio is at the heart of every stoichiometry problem. Molar mass is used to change to and from grams. *Solve:*

$$0.800 \text{ g HF} \times \frac{1 \text{ mol HF}}{20.01 \text{ g HF}} \times \frac{1 \text{ mol } Na_2SiO_3}{8 \text{ mol HF}} \times \frac{122.1 \text{ g } Na_2SiO_3}{1 \text{ mol } Na_2SiO_3} = 0.610 \text{ g } Na_2SiO_3$$

Check. 0.8 (120/160) < 0.75 mol

3.57   (a) $Al_2S_3(s) + 6H_2O(l) \rightarrow 2Al(OH)_3(s) + 3H_2S(g)$

(b)   *Plan.* g A $\rightarrow$ mol A $\rightarrow$ mol B $\rightarrow$ g B. See Solution 3.55 (c). *Solve:*

$$10.5 \text{ g } Al_2S_3 \times \frac{1 \text{ mol } Al_2S_3}{150.2 \text{ g } Al_2S_3} \times \frac{2 \text{ mol } Al(OH)_3}{1 \text{ mol } Al_2S_3} \times \frac{78.00 \text{ g } Al(OH)_3}{1 \text{ mol } Al(OH)_3}$$

$$= 10.9 \text{ g } Al(OH)_3$$

Check. $10 \left(\dfrac{2 \times 78}{150}\right) \approx 10(1) \approx 10 \text{ g } Al(OH)_3$

3.59   (a)   *Analyze.* Given: mol NaN_3. Find: mol N_2. *Plan.* Use mole ratio from balanced equation. *Solve*:

$$2.50 \text{ mol } NaN_3 \times \frac{3 \text{ mol } N_2}{2 \text{ mol } NaN_3} = 3.75 \text{ mol } N_2$$

Check. The resulting mol N_2 should be greater than mol NaN_3, (the N_2:NaN_3 ratio is > 1), and it is.

(b)   *Analyze.* Given: g N_2 Find: g NaN_3. *Plan.* Use molar masses to get from and to grams, mol ratio to relate moles of the two substances. *Solve:*

$$6.00 \text{ g N}_2 \times \frac{1 \text{ mol N}_2}{28.01 \text{ g N}_2} \times \frac{2 \text{ mol NaN}_3}{3 \text{ mol N}_2} \times \frac{65.01 \text{ g NaN}_3}{1 \text{ mol NaN}_3} = 9.28 \text{ g NaN}_3$$

Check. Mass relations are less intuitive than mole relations. Estimating the ratio of molar masses is sometimes useful. In this case, 65 g NaN_3/28 g $N_2 \approx 2.25$ Then, $(6 \times 2/3 \times 2.25) \approx 9$ g NaN_3. The calculated result looks reasonable.

(c)   *Analyze.* Given: vol N_2 in ft^3, density N_2 in g/L. Find: g NaN_3. *Plan.* First determine how many g N_2 are in 10.0 ft^3, using the density of N_2. *Solve:*

$$\frac{1.25 \text{ g}}{1 \text{ L}} \times \frac{1 \text{ L}}{1000 \text{ cm}^3} \times \frac{(2.54)^3 \text{ cm}^3}{1 \text{ in}^3} \times \frac{(12)^3 \text{ in}^3}{1 \text{ ft}^3} \times 10.0 \text{ ft}^3 = 354.0 = 354 \text{ g N}_2$$

$$354.0 \text{ g N}_2 \times \frac{1 \text{ mol N}_2}{28.01 \text{ g N}_2} \times \frac{2 \text{ mol NaN}_3}{3 \text{ mol N}_2} \times \frac{65.01 \text{ g NaN}_3}{1 \text{ mol NaN}_3} = 548 \text{ g NaN}_3$$

Check. 1 $ft^3 \sim 28$ L; 10 $ft^3 \sim 280$ L; 280 L $\times 1.25 \sim 350$ g N_2

Using the ratio of molar masses from part (b), $(350 \times 2/3 \times 2.25) \approx 525$ g NaN_3

3.61   (a)   *Analyze.* Given: dimensions of Al foil. Find: mol Al.

Plan. Dimensions $\longrightarrow$ vol $\xrightarrow{\text{density}}$ mass $\xrightarrow{\frac{\text{molar}}{\text{mass}}}$ mol Al

Solve. 1.00 cm $\times$ 1.00 cm $\times$ 0.550 mm $\times \dfrac{1 \text{ cm}}{10 \text{ mm}} = 0.0550 \text{ cm}^3$ Al

$$0.0550 \text{ cm}^3 \text{ Al} \times \frac{2.699 \text{ g Al}}{1 \text{ cm}^3} \times \frac{1 \text{ mol Al}}{26.98 \text{ g Al}} = 5.502 \times 10^{-3} = 5.50 \times 10^{-3} \text{ mol Al}$$

Check. $2.699/26.98 \approx 0.1$; $(0.055 \text{ cm}^3 \times 0.1) = 5.5 \times 10^{-3}$ mol Al

(b)   *Plan.* Write the balanced equation to get a mole ratio; change mol Al $\rightarrow$ mol $AlBr_3 \rightarrow$ g $AlBr_3$.

Solve. $2Al(s) + 3Br_2(l) \rightarrow 2AlBr_3(s)$

$$5.502 \times 10^{-3} \text{ mol Al} \times \frac{2 \text{ mol AlBr}_3}{2 \text{ mol Al}} \times \frac{266.69 \text{ g AlBr}_3}{1 \text{ mol AlBr}_3} = 1.467 = 1.47 \text{ g AlBr}_3$$

Check. $(0.006 \times 1 \times 270) \approx 1.6$ g $AlBr_3$

Limiting Reactants, Theoretical Yields

3.63   (a)   The *limiting reactant* determines the maximum number of product moles resulting from a chemical reaction; any other reactant is an *excess reactant*.

(b)   The limiting reactant regulates the amount of products because it is completely used up during the reaction; no more product can be made when one of the reactants is unavailable.

3.65 $N_2 + 3H_2 \rightarrow 2NH_3$. N_2 = ⬭⬭, NH_3 = ◖◗

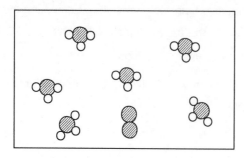

Each N atom (1/2 of an N_2 molecule), reacts with 3 H atoms (1.5 H_2 molecules) to form an NH_3 molecule. Eight N atoms (4 N_2 molecules) require 24 H atoms (12 H_2 molecules) for complete reaction. Only 9 H_2 molecules are available, so H_2 is the limiting reactant. Nine H_2 molecules (18 H atoms) determine that 6 NH_3 molecules are produced. One N_2 molecule is in excess.

3.67   (a)   Each bicycle needs 2 wheels, 1 frame and 1 set of handlebars. A total of 4250 wheels corresponds to 2125 pairs of wheels. This is fewer than the number of frames or handlebars. The 4250 wheels determine that 2125 bicycles can be produced.

         (b)   2755 frames - 2125 bicycles = 630 frames left over

               (2255 handlebars - 2125 bicycles) = 130 handlebars left over

         (c)   The wheels are the "limiting reactant" in that they determine the number of bicycles that can be produced.

3.69   *Analyze.* Given: 1.70 mol NaOH, 1.00 mol CO_2. Find: mol Na_2CO_3.

Plan. Amounts of more than one reactant are given, so we must determine which reactant regulates (limits) product. Then apply the appropriate mole ratio from the balanced equation.

Solve. The mole ratio is 2NaOH:1CO_2, so 1.00 mol CO_2 requires 2.00 mol NaOH for complete reaction. Less than 2.00 mol NaOH are present, so NaOH is the limiting reactant.

$$1.70 \text{ mol NaOH} \times \frac{1 \text{ mol } Na_2CO_3}{2 \text{ mol NaOH}} = 0.850 \text{ mol } Na_2CO_3 \text{ can be produced}$$

The Na_2CO_3:CO_2 ratio is 1:1, so 0.850 mol Na_2CO_3 produced requires 0.850 mol CO_2 consumed. (Alternately, 1.70 mol NaOH × 1 mol CO_2/2 mol NaOH = 0.850 mol CO_2 reacted). 1.00 mol CO_2 initial - 0.850 mol CO_2 reacted = 0.15 mol CO_2 remain.

Check.

	$2NaOH(s)$	$+$	$CO_2(g)$	$\rightarrow$	$Na_2CO_3(s)$	$+$	$H_2O(l)$
initial	1.70 mol		1.00 mol		0 mol		
change (reaction)	-1.70 mol		-0.85 mol		+0.850 mol		
final	0 mol		0.15 mol		0.850 mol		

Note that the "change" line (but not necessarily the "final" line) reflects the mole ratios from the balanced equation.

3.71 $3NaHCO_3(aq) + H_3C_6H_5O_7(aq) \rightarrow 3CO_2(g) + 3H_2O(l) + Na_3C_6H_5O_7(aq)$

(a)   *Analyze/Plan.* Abbreviate citric acid as H_3Cit. Follow the approach in Sample Exercise 3.19. *Solve:*

$$1.00 \text{ g NaHCO}_3 \times \frac{1 \text{ mol NaHCO}_3}{84.01 \text{ g NaHCO}_3} = 1.190 \times 10^{-2} = 1.19 \times 10^{-2} \text{ mol NaHCO}_3$$

$$1.00 \text{g H}_3\text{C}_6\text{H}_5\text{O}_7 \times \frac{1 \text{ mol H}_3\text{Cit}}{192.1 \text{ g H}_3\text{Cit}} = 5.206 \times 10^{-3} = 5.21 \times 10^{-3} \text{ mol H}_3\text{Cit}$$

But $NaHCO_3$ and H_3Cit react in a 3:1 ratio, so 5.21×10^{-3} mol H_3Cit require $3(5.21 \times 10^{-3}) = 1.56 \times 10^{-2}$ mol $NaHCO_3$. We have only 1.19×10^{-2} mol $NaHCO_3$, so $NaHCO_3$ is the limiting reactant.

(b) $$1.190 \times 10^{-2} \text{ mol NaHCO}_3 \times \frac{3 \text{ mol CO}_2}{3 \text{ mol NaHCO}_3} \times \frac{44.01 \text{ g CO}_2}{1 \text{ mol CO}_2} = 0.524 \text{ g CO}_2$$

(c) $$1.190 \times 10^{-2} \text{ mol NaHCO}_3 \times \frac{1 \text{ mol H}_3\text{Cit}}{3 \text{ mol NaHCO}_3} = 3.968 \times 10^{-3}$$
$$= 3.97 \times 10^{-3} \text{ mol H}_3\text{Cit react}$$

5.206×10^{-3} mol H_3Cit - 3.968×10^{-3} mol react = 1.238×10^{-3}

$$= 1.24 \times 10^{-3} \text{ mol H}_3\text{Cit remain}$$

$$1.238 \times 10^{-3} \text{ mol H}_3\text{Cit} \times \frac{192.1 \text{ g H}_3\text{Cit}}{\text{mol H}_3\text{Cit}} = 0.238 \text{ g H}_3\text{Cit remain}$$

3.73   *Analyze.* Given: initial g Na_2CO_3, g $AgNO_3$. Find: final g Na_2CO_3, $AgNO_3$, Ag_2CO_3, $NaNO_3$

Plan. Write balanced equation; determine limiting reactant; calculate amounts of excess reactant remaining and products, based on limiting reactant.

Solve. $2AgNO_3(aq) + Na_2CO_3(aq) \rightarrow Ag_2CO_3(s) + 2NaNO_3(aq)$

$$6.50 \text{ g Na}_2\text{CO}_3 \times \frac{1 \text{ mol Na}_2\text{CO}_3}{106.0 \text{ g Na}_2\text{CO}_3} = 0.06132 \text{ g} = 0.0613 \text{ mol Na}_2\text{CO}_3$$

$$7.00 \text{ g AgNO}_3 \times \frac{1 \text{ mol AgNO}_3}{169.9 \text{ g AgNO}_3} = 0.04120 = 0.0412 \text{ mol AgNO}_3$$

$$0.04120 \text{ mol AgNO}_3 \times \frac{1 \text{ mol Na}_2\text{CO}_3}{2 \text{ mol AgNO}_3} = 0.02060 = 0.0206 \text{ mol Na}_2\text{CO}_3 \text{ required}$$

$AgNO_3$ is the limiting reactant and Na_2CO_3 is present in excess.

	$2AgNO_3(aq)$	$+ Na_2CO_3(aq)$	$\rightarrow$	$Ag_2CO_3(s)$	$+ 2NaNO_3(aq)$
initial	0.0412 mol	0.0613 mol		0 mol	0 mol
reaction	-0.0412 mol	-0.0206 mol		+0.0206 mol	+0.0412 mol
final	0 mol	0.0407 mol		0.0206 mol	0.0412 mol

0.04072 mol $Na_2CO_3 \times 106.0$ g/mol $= 4.316 = 4.32$ g Na_2CO_3

0.02060 mol $Ag_2CO_3 \times 275.8$ g/mol $= 5.681 = 5.68$ g Ag_2CO_3

0.04120 mol $NaNO_3 \times 85.00$ g/mol $= 3.502 = 3.50$ g $NaNO_3$

Check. The initial mass of reactants was 13.50 g, and the final mass of excess reactant and products is 13.50 g; mass is conserved.

3.75   *Analyze.* Given: amounts of two reactants. Find: theoretical yield.

Plan. Determine the limiting reactant and the maximum amount of product it could produce. Then calculate % yield. *Solve:*

(a) 30.0 g $C_6H_6 \times \dfrac{1 \text{ mol } C_6H_6}{78.11 \text{ g } C_6H_6} = 0.3841 = 0.384$ mol C_6H_6

65.0 g $Br_2 \times \dfrac{1 \text{ mol } Br_2}{159.8 \text{ g } Br_2} = 0.4068 = 0.407$ mol Br_2

Since C_6H_6 and Br_2 react in a 1:1 mole ratio, C_6H_6 is the limiting reactant and determines the theoretical yield.

0.3841 mol $C_6H_6 \times \dfrac{1 \text{ mol } C_6H_5Br}{1 \text{ mol } C_6H_6} \times 157.0$ g $C_6H_5Br = 60.30 = 60.3$ g C_6H_5Br

Check. 30/78 ~ 3/8 mol C_6H_6. 65/160 ~ 3/8 mol Br_2. Since moles of the two reactants are similar, a precise calculation is needed to determine the limiting reactant. $3/8 \times 160 \approx 60$ g product

(b)   % yield $= \dfrac{56.7 \text{ g } C_6H_5Br \text{ actual}}{60.3 \text{ g } C_6H_5Br \text{ theoretical}} \times 100 = 94.0\%$

3.77   *Analyze.* Given: g of two reactants, % yield. Find: g Li_3N.

Plan. Determine limiting reactant and theoretical yield. Use definition of % yield to calculate actual yield. *Solve:*

(a) 5.00 g $Li \times \dfrac{1 \text{ mol } Li}{6.941 \text{ g } Li} = 0.7204 = 0.720$ mol Li

5.00 g $N_2 \times \dfrac{1 \text{ mol } N_2}{28.01 \text{ g } N_2} = 0.1785 = 0.179$ mol N_2

0.1785 mol $N_2 \times \dfrac{6 \text{ mol } Li}{1 \text{ mol } N_2} = 1.071 = 1.07$ mol Li required

Since there is less than enough Li to react exactly with 0.179 mol N_2, Li is the limiting reactant.

$$0.7204 \text{ mol Li} \times \frac{2 \text{ mol Li}_3\text{N}}{6 \text{ mol Li}} \times \frac{34.83 \text{ g Li}_3\text{N}}{1 \text{ mol Li}_3\text{N}} = 8.363 = 8.36 \text{ g Li}_3\text{N theoretical yield}$$

Check. $5/7 \approx$ mol Li; $5/(4 \times 7) \approx$ mol N_2. There are 1/4 as many mol N_2 as moles Li, but only 1/6 as many moles N_2 are required for exact reaction. N_2 is in excess and Li limits. $0.7 \times (36/3) \approx 8.4$ g Li_3N theoretical

(b) $$\% \text{ yield} = \frac{\text{actual}}{\text{theoretical}} \times 100; \quad \frac{\% \text{ yield} \times \text{theoretical}}{100} = \text{actual yield}$$

$$\frac{80.5 \%}{100} \times 8.363 \text{ g Li}_3\text{N} = 6.7325 = 6.73 \text{ g Li}_3\text{N actual}$$

Additional Exercises

3.79   (a) $C_4H_8O_2(l) + 5O_2(g) \rightarrow 4CO_2(g) + 4H_2O(l)$

(b) $Cu(OH)_2(s) \rightarrow CuO(s) + H_2O(g)$

(c) $Zn(s) + Cl_2(g) \rightarrow ZnCl_2(s)$

3.81   (a) $$1.25 \text{ carat} \times \frac{0.200 \text{ g}}{1 \text{ carat}} \times \frac{1 \text{ mol C}}{12.01 \text{ g C}} = 0.020816 = 0.0208 \text{ mol C}$$

$$0.020816 \text{ mol C} \times \frac{6.022 \times 10^{23} \text{ C atoms}}{1 \text{ mol C}} = 1.25 \times 10^{22} \text{ C atoms}$$

(b) $$0.500 \text{ g C}_9\text{H}_8\text{O}_4 \times \frac{1 \text{ mol C}_9\text{H}_8\text{O}_4}{180.2 \text{ g C}_9\text{H}_8\text{O}_4} = 2.7747 \times 10^{-3} = 2.77 \times 10^{-3} \text{ mol C}_9\text{H}_8\text{O}_4$$

$$0.0027747 \text{ mol C}_9\text{H}_8\text{O}_4 \times \frac{6.022 \times 10^{23} \text{ molecules}}{1 \text{ mol}} = 1.67 \times 10^{21} \text{ C}_9\text{H}_8\text{O}_4 \text{ molecules}$$

3.83   (a) $$1.0000 \times 10^4 \text{ Si atoms} \times \frac{1 \text{ mol}}{6.022 \times 10^{23} \text{ atoms}} \times \frac{28.0855 \text{ g SI}}{1 \text{ mol Si}} = 4.6638 \times 10^{-19} \text{ g Si}$$

(b) $$4.6638 \times 10^{-19} \text{ g Si} \times \frac{1 \text{ cm}^3 \text{ Si}}{2.3 \text{ g Si}} = 2.03 \times 10^{-19} = 2.0 \times 10^{-19} \text{ cm}^3$$

(c) $V = l^3; \; l = (V)^{1/3} = (2.03 \times 10^{-19} \text{ cm}^3)^{1/3} = 5.9 \times 10^{-7} \text{ cm } (= 5.9 \text{ nm})$

3.85   *Plan.* Assume 1.000 g and get mass O by subtraction. *Solve*:

(a) $$0.7787 \text{ g C} \times \frac{1 \text{ mol C}}{12.01 \text{ g C}} = 0.06484 \text{ mol C}$$

$$0.1176 \text{ g H} \times \frac{1 \text{ mol H}}{1.008 \text{ g H}} = 0.1167 \text{ mol H}$$

$$0.1037 \text{ g O} \times \frac{1 \text{ mol C}}{16.00 \text{ g O}} = 0.006481 \text{ mol O}$$

Dividing through by the smallest of these values we obtain $C_{10}H_{18}O$.

(b)   The formula weight of $C_{10}H_{18}O$ is 154. Thus, the empirical formula is also the molecular formula.

3.87   *Plan.* Because different sample sizes were used to analyze the different elements, calculate mass % of each element in the sample.

i.   Calculate mass % C from g CO_2.

ii.   Calculate mass % Cl from AgCl.

iii.   Get mass % H by subtraction.

iv.   Calculate mole ratios and the empirical formulas.

Solve:

i. $3.52 \text{ g } CO_2 \times \dfrac{1 \text{ mol } CO_2}{44.01 \text{ g } CO_2} \times \dfrac{1 \text{ mol C}}{1 \text{ mol } CO_2} \times \dfrac{12.01 \text{ g C}}{1 \text{ mol C}} = 0.9606 = 0.961 \text{ g C}$

$\dfrac{0.9606 \text{ g C}}{1.50 \text{ g sample}} \times 100 = 64.04 = 64.0\% \text{ C}$

ii. $1.27 \text{ g AgCl} \times \dfrac{1 \text{ mol AgCl}}{143.3 \text{ g AgCl}} \times \dfrac{1 \text{ mol Cl}}{1 \text{ mol AgCl}} \times \dfrac{35.45 \text{ g Cl}}{1 \text{ mol Cl}} = 0.3142 = 0.314 \text{ g Cl}$

$\dfrac{0.3142 \text{ g Cl}}{1.00 \text{ g sample}} \times 100 = 31.42 = 31.4\% \text{ Cl}$

iii.   % H = 100.0 - (64.04% C + 31.42% Cl) = 4.54 = 4.5% H

iv.   Assume 100 g sample.

$64.04 \text{ g C} \times \dfrac{1 \text{ mol C}}{12.01 \text{ g C}} = 5.33 \text{ mol C}; \ 5.33 / 0.886 = 6.02$

$31.42 \text{ g Cl} \times \dfrac{1 \text{ mol Cl}}{35.45 \text{ g Cl}} = 0.886 \text{ mol Cl}; \ 0.886 / 0.886 = 1.00$

$4.54 \text{ g H} \times \dfrac{1 \text{ mol H}}{1.008 \text{ g H}} = 4.50 \text{ mol H}; \ 4.50 / 0.886 = 5.08$

The empirical formula is probably C_6H_5Cl.

The subscript for H, 5.08, is relatively far from 5.00, but C_6H_5Cl makes chemical sense. More significant figures in the mass data are required for a more accurate mole ratio.

3.90 $O_3(g) + 2NaI(aq) + H_2O(l) \rightarrow O_2(g) + I_2(s) + 2NaOH(aq)$

(a) $3.8 \times 10^{-5} \text{ mol } O_3 \times \dfrac{2 \text{ mol NaI}}{1 \text{ mol } O_3} = 7.6 \times 10^{-5} \text{ mol NaI}$

(b) $0.550 \text{ mg } O_3 \times \dfrac{1 \times 10^{-3} \text{g}}{1 \text{ mg}} \times \dfrac{1 \text{ mol } O_3}{48.00 \text{ g } O_3} \times \dfrac{2 \text{ mol NaI}}{1 \text{ mol } O_3} \times \dfrac{149.9 \text{ g NaI}}{1 \text{ mol NaI}}$

$= 3.4352 \times 10^{-3} = 3.44 \times 10^{-3} \text{ g NaI} = 3.44 \text{ mg NaI}$

3.92 $2C_{57}H_{110}O_6 + 163O_2 \rightarrow 114CO_2 + 110H_2O$

molar mass of fat = 57(12.01) + 110(1.008) + 6(16.00) = 891.5

$$1.0 \text{ kg fat} \times \frac{1000 \text{ g}}{1 \text{ kg}} \times \frac{1 \text{ mol fat}}{891.5 \text{ g fat}} \times \frac{110 \text{ mol H}_2\text{O}}{2 \text{ mol fat}} \times \frac{18.02 \text{ g H}_2\text{O}}{1 \text{ mol H}_2\text{O}} \times \frac{1 \text{ kg}}{1000 \text{ g}} = 1.1 \text{ kg H}_2\text{O}$$

3.95   All of the O_2 is produced from $KClO_3$; get g $KClO_3$ from g O_2. All of the H_2O is produced from $KHCO_3$; get g $KHCO_3$ from g H_2O. The g H_2O produced also reveals the g CO_2 from the decomposition of $NaHCO_3$. The remaining CO_2 (13.2 g CO_2 - g CO_2 from $NaHCO_3$) is due to K_2CO_3 and g K_2CO_3 can be derived from it.

$$4.00 \text{ g O}_2 \times \frac{1 \text{ mol O}_2}{32.00 \text{ g O}_2} \times \frac{2 \text{ mol KClO}_3}{3 \text{ mol O}_2} \times \frac{122.6 \text{ g KClO}_3}{1 \text{ mol KClO}_3} = 10.22 = 10.2 \text{ g KClO}_3$$

$$1.80 \text{ H}_2\text{O} \times \frac{1 \text{ mol H}_2\text{O}}{18.02 \text{ g H}_2\text{O}} \times \frac{2 \text{ mol KHCO}_3}{1 \text{ mol H}_2\text{O}} \times \frac{100.1 \text{ g KHCO}_3}{1 \text{ mol KHCO}_3} = 20.00 = 20.0 \text{ g KHCO}_3$$

$$1.80 \text{ g H}_2\text{O} \times \frac{1 \text{ mol H}_2\text{O}}{18.02 \text{ g H}_2\text{O}} \times \frac{2 \text{ mol CO}_2}{1 \text{ mol H}_2\text{O}} \times \frac{44.01 \text{ g CO}_2}{1 \text{ mol CO}_2} = 8.792 = 8.79 \text{ g CO}_2 \text{ from KHCO}_3$$

13.20 g CO_2 total - 8.792 CO_2 from $KHCO_3$ = 4.408 = 4.41 g CO_2 from K_2CO_3

$$4.408 \text{ g CO}_2 \times \frac{1 \text{ mol CO}_2}{44.01 \text{ g CO}_2} \times \frac{1 \text{ mol K}_2\text{CO}_3}{1 \text{ mol CO}_2} \times \frac{138.2 \text{ g K}_2\text{CO}_3}{1 \text{ mol K}_2\text{CO}_3} = 13.84 = 13.8 \text{ g K}_2\text{CO}_3$$

100.0 g mixture - 10.22 g $KClO_3$ - 20.00 g $KHCO_3$ - 13.84 g K_2CO_3 = 56.0 g KCl

Integrative Exercises

3.98   *Plan.* Volume cube $\xrightarrow{\text{density}}$ mass $CaCO_3$ $\rightarrow$ moles $CaCO_3$ $\rightarrow$ moles O $\rightarrow$ O atoms

$$\textit{Solve.} \quad (1.25)^3 \text{ in}^3 \times \frac{(2.54)^3 \text{ cm}^3}{1 \text{ in}^3} \times \frac{2.71 \text{ g CaCO}_3}{1 \text{ cm}^3} \times \frac{1 \text{ mol CaCO}_3}{100.1 \text{ g CaCO}_3} \times \frac{3 \text{ mol O}}{1 \text{ mol CaCO}_3}$$

$$\times \frac{6.022 \times 10^{23} \text{ O atoms}}{1 \text{ mol O}} = 1.57 \times 10^{24} \text{ O atoms}$$

3.100   *Analyze.* Given: gasoline = C_8H_{18}, density = 0.69 g/mL, 19.5 mi/gal, 125 mi. Find: kg CO_2. *Plan.* Write and balance the equation for the combustion of octane. Change mi $\rightarrow$ gal octane $\rightarrow$ mL $\rightarrow$ g octane. Use stoichiometry to calculate g and kg CO_2 from g octane.

Solve. $2C_8H_{18}(l) + 25O_2(g) \rightarrow 16CO_2(g) + 18H_2O(l)$

$$125 \text{ mi} \times \frac{1 \text{ gal}}{19.5 \text{ mi}} \times \frac{3.7854 \text{ L}}{1 \text{ gal}} \times \frac{1 \text{ mL}}{1 \times 10^{-3} \text{ L}} \times \frac{0.69 \text{ g octane}}{1 \text{ mL}} = 1.6743 \times 10^4 \text{ g}$$
$$= 17 \text{ kg octane}$$

$$1.6743 \times 10^4 \text{ g } C_8H_{18} \times \frac{1 \text{ mol } C_8H_{18}}{114.2 \text{ g } C_8H_{18}} \times \frac{16 \text{ mol } CO_2}{2 \text{ mol } C_8H_{18}} \times \frac{44.01 \text{ g } CO_2}{1 \text{ mol } CO_2} = 5.1619 \times 10^4 \text{ g}$$
$$= 52 \text{ kg } CO_2$$

Check. $\left(\dfrac{125 \times 4 \times 0.7}{20} \right) \times 10^3 = (25 \times 0.7) \times 10^3 = 17.5 \times 10^3 \text{ g} = 17.5 \text{ kg octane}$

$\dfrac{44}{114} \approx \dfrac{1}{3}; \ \dfrac{17 \text{ kg} \times 8}{3} \approx 48 \text{ kg } CO_2$

3.102   (a) $S(s) + O_2(g) \rightarrow SO_2(g); \ SO_2(g) + CaO(s) \rightarrow CaSO_3(s)$

       (b) $\dfrac{2000 \text{ tons coal}}{\text{day}} \times \dfrac{2000 \text{ lb}}{1 \text{ ton}} \times \dfrac{1 \text{ kg}}{2.20 \text{ lb}} \times \dfrac{1000 \text{ g}}{1 \text{ kg}} \times \dfrac{0.025 \text{ g S}}{1 \text{ g coal}} \times \dfrac{1 \text{ mol S}}{32.1 \text{ g S}}$

$$\times \frac{1 \text{ mol } SO_2}{1 \text{ mol S}} \times \frac{1 \text{ mol } CaSO_3}{1 \text{ mol } SO_2} \times \frac{120 \text{ g } CaSO_3}{1 \text{ mol } CaSO_3} \times \frac{1 \text{ kg } CaSO_3}{1000 \text{ g } CaSO_3}$$

$$= 1.7 \times 10^5 \text{ kg } CaSO_3/\text{day}$$

This corresponds to about 190 tons of $CaSO_3$ per day as a waste product.

4 Aqueous Reactions and Solution Stoichiometry

Electrolytes

4.1 Tap water contains enough dissolved electrolytes to conduct a significant amount of electricity. Thus, water can complete a circuit between an electrical appliance and our body, producing a shock.

4.3 When CH_3OH dissolves, neutral CH_3OH molecules are dispersed throughout the solution. These electrically neutral particles do not carry charge and the solution is nonconducting. When $HC_2H_3O_2$ dissolves, mostly neutral molecules are dispersed throughout the solution. A few of the dissolved molecules ionize to form $H^+(aq)$ and $C_2H_3O_2^-(aq)$. These few ions carry some charge and the solution is weakly conducting.

4.5 (a) $ZnCl_2(aq) \rightarrow Zn^{2+}(aq) + 2Cl^-(aq)$ (b) $HNO_3(aq) \rightarrow H^+(aq) + NO_3^-(aq)$
     (c) $K_2SO_4(aq) \rightarrow 2K^+(aq) + SO_4^{2-}(aq)$ (d) $Ca(OH)_2(aq) \rightarrow Ca^{2+}(aq) + 2OH^-(aq)$

4.7 (a) AX is a nonelectrolyte, because no ions form when the molecules dissolve.

(b) AY is a weak electrolyte because a few molecules ionize when they dissolve, but most do not.

(c) AZ is a strong electrolyte because all molecules break-up into ions when they dissolve.

4.9 When $HCHO_2$ dissolves in water, neutral $HCHO_2$ molecules, H^+ ions and CHO_2^- ions are all present in the solution. $HCHO_2(aq) \rightleftharpoons H^+(aq) + CHO_2^-(aq)$

Precipitation Reactions and Net Ionic Equations

4.11 *Analyze.* Given: formula of compound. Find: solubility.

Plan. Follow the guidelines in Table 4.1, in light of the anion present in the compound and notable exceptions to the "rules". *Solve*:

(a) $NiCl_2$: soluble   (b) Ag_2S: insoluble

(c) Cs_3PO_4: soluble (Cs^+ is an alkali metal cation)

(d) $SrCO_3$: insoluble   (e) $(NH_4)_2SO_4$: soluble

4.13   *Analyze.* Given: formulas of reactants. Find: balanced equation including precipitates.

      Plan. Follow the logic in Sample Exercise 4.3.

      Solve. In each reaction, the precipitate is in bold type.

      (a) $Na_2CO_3(aq) + 2AgNO_3(aq) \rightarrow \mathbf{Ag_2CO_3(s)} + 2NaNO_3(aq)$

      (b)   No precipitate (all nitrates and most sulfates are soluble).

      (c) $FeSO_4(aq) + Pb(NO_3)_2(aq) \rightarrow \mathbf{PbSO_4(s)} + Fe(NO_3)_2(aq)$

4.15   *Analyze/Plan.* Follow the logic in Sample Exercise 4.4.   *Solve:*

      (a) $2Na^+(aq) + CO_3^{2-}(aq) + Mg^{2+}(aq) + SO_4^{2-}(aq) \rightarrow MgCO_3(s) + 2Na^+(aq) + SO_4^{2-}(aq)$

                $Mg^{2+}(aq) + CO_3^{2-}(aq) \rightarrow MgCO_3(s)$

      (b) $Pb^{2+}(aq) + 2NO_3^-(aq) + 2Na^+(aq) + S^{2-}(aq) \rightarrow PbS(s) + 2Na^+(aq) + 2NO_3^-(aq)$

                $Pb^{2+}(aq) + S^{2-}(aq) \rightarrow PbS(s)$

      (c) $6NH_4^+(aq) + 2PO_4^{3-}(aq) + 3Ca^{2+}(aq) + 6Cl^-(aq) \rightarrow Ca_3(PO_4)_2(s) + 6NH_4^+(aq) + 6Cl^-(aq)$

                $3Ca^{2+}(aq) + 2PO_4^{3-}(aq) \rightarrow Ca_3(PO_4)_2(s)$

4.17   *Analyze.* Given: reactions of unknown with HBr, H_2SO_4, NaOH. Find: The unknown contains a single salt. Is K^+ or Pb^{2+} or Ba^{2+} present?

      Plan. Analyze solubility guidelines for Br^-, SO_4^{2-} and OH^- and select the cation that produces the observed solubility pattern.

      Solve. Pb^{2+} is not present or an insoluble hydroxide would have formed. $BaSO_4$ is insoluble and $Ba(OH)_2$ is soluble, so the solution must contain Ba^{2+}. It could also contain K^+, but since we are dealing with a single salt, we will assume that only Ba^{2+} is present.

4.19   *Analyze.* Given: $Mg(NO_3)_2(aq)$, $Pb(NO_3)_2(aq)$, $H_2SO_4(aq)$. Find: identify $Mg^{2+}(aq)$ and $Pb^{2+}(aq)$ solutions. *Plan.* Use difference in reactivities with SO_4^{2-} to identify $Pb^{2+}(aq)$ and $Mg^{2+}(aq)$.

      Solve. Test a portion of each solution with $H_2SO_4(aq)$. $Pb^{2+}(aq)$ is an exception to the soluble sulfates rule, so $Pb(NO_3)_2(aq)$ will form a precipitate, while $Mg(NO_3)_2(aq)$ will not.

Acid-Base Reactions

4.21   (a)   A *monoprotic acid* has one ionizable (acidic) H and a *diprotic acid* has two.

      (b)   A *strong acid* is completely ionized in aqueous solution whereas only a fraction of *weak acid* molecules are ionized.

      (c)   An *acid* is an H^+ donor, a substance that increases the concentration of H^+ in aqueous solution. A *base* is an H^+ acceptor and thus increases the concentration of OH^- in aqueous solution.

4.23   *Analyze.* Given: chemical formulas. Find: acid-base properties.

Plan. Use Table 4.2 to identify common strong acids and bases. If a compound doesn't appear in the table, it is either a weak acid or base, or a nonelectrolyte.

Solve. (a) strong acid   (b) weak acid   (c) weak base   (d) strong base

4.25   *Analyze.* Given: chemical formulas. Find: classify as acid, base, salt; strong, weak or nonelectrolyte. *Plan.* Examine formula for: H-first, acid; OH^- anion, base; NH_3, weak base; ionic compound, salt and strong electrolyte; strong acid or base, Table 4.2. *Solve*:

     (a)   HF: acid, mixture of ions and molecules (weak electrolyte)

     (b) CH_3CN: none of the above, entirely molecules (nonelectrolyte)

     (c) $NaClO_4$: salt, entirely ions (strong electrolyte)

     (d) $Ba(OH)_2$: base, entirely ions (strong electrolyte)

4.27   *Analyze.* Given: chemical formulas. Find: electrolyte properties.

Plan. In order to classify as electrolytes, formulas must be identified as acids, bases or salts as in Solution 4.25. *Solve*:

     (a) H_2SO_3: H first, so acid; not in Table 4.2, so weak acid; therefore, weak electrolyte

     (b) C_2H_5OH: not acid, not ionic (no metal cation), contains OH group, but not as anion so not a base; therefore, nonelectrolyte

     (c) NH_3: common weak base; therefore, weak electrolyte

     (d) $KClO_3$: ionic compound, so strong electrolyte

     (e) $Cu(NO_3)_2$: ionic compound, so strong electrolyte

4.29   *Plan.* Follow Sample Exercise 4.7. *Solve*:

     (a) $2HBr(aq) + Ca(OH)_2(aq) \rightarrow CaBr_2(aq) + 2H_2O(l)$

             $H^+(aq) + OH^-(aq) \rightarrow H_2O(l)$

     (b) $Cu(OH)_2(s) + 2HClO_4(aq) \rightarrow Cu(ClO_4)_2(aq) + 2H_2O(l)$

             $Cu(OH)_2(s) + 2H^+(aq) \rightarrow 2H_2O(l) + Cu^{2+}(aq)$

     (c) $Al(OH)_3(s) + 3HNO_3(aq) \rightarrow Al(NO_3)_3(aq) + 3H_2O(l)$

             $Al(OH)_3(s) + 3H^+(aq) \rightarrow 3H_2O(l) + Al^{3+}(aq)$

4.31   *Analyze.* Given: names of reactants. Find: gaseous products.

Plan. Write correct chemical formulas for the reactants, complete and balance the metathesis reaction, and identify either H_2S or CO_2 products as gases. *Solve*:

     (a) $CdS(s) + H_2SO_4(aq) \rightarrow CdSO_4(aq) + H_2S(g)$

             $CdS(s) + 2H^+(aq) \rightarrow H_2S(g) + Cd^{2+}(aq)$

     (b) $MgCO_3(s) + 2HClO_4(aq) \rightarrow Mg(ClO_4)_2(aq) + H_2O(l) + CO_2(g)$

             $MgCO_3(s) + 2H^+(aq) \rightarrow H_2O(l) + CO_2(g) + Mg^{2+}(aq)$

4.33   *Analyze/Plan.* Given the balanced complete molecular equation, determine the spectator ion(s) and write the net ionic equation. In each case, $HClO_4$ and the metal perchlorate are strong electrolytes, so ClO_4^- (aq) is the only spectator. All other species change form upon reaction. *Solve*:

(a) $FeO(s) + 2H^+(aq) \rightarrow H_2O(l) + Fe^{2+}(aq)$

(b) $NiO(s) + 2H^+(aq) \rightarrow H_2O(l) + Ni^{2+}(aq)$

Oxidation-Reduction Reactions

4.35   (a)   In terms of electron transfer, *oxidation* is the loss of electrons by a substance, and *reduction* is the gain of electrons (LEO says GER).

      (b)   Relative to oxidation numbers, when a substance is oxidized, its oxidation number increases. When a substance is reduced, its oxidation number decreases.

4.37   The most easily oxidized metals are near the bottom of groups on the left side of the chart, especially groups 1A and 2A. The least easily oxidized metals are on the lower right of the transition metals, particularly those near the bottom of groups 8B and 1B.

4.39   (a) +6   (b) +4   (c) +7   (d) +1   (e) 0   (f) -1 (O_2^{2-} is peroxide ion)

4.41   *Analyze.* Given: chemical reaction. Find: element oxidized or reduced. *Plan.* Assign oxidation numbers to all species. The element whose oxidation number becomes more positive is oxidized; the one whose oxidation number decreases is reduced. *Solve*:

(a) $Ni \rightarrow Ni^{2+}$, Ni is oxidized; $Cl_2 \rightarrow 2Cl^-$, Cl is reduced

(b) $Fe^{2+} \rightarrow Fe$, Fe is reduced; $Al \rightarrow Al^{3+}$, Al is oxidized

(c) $Cl_2 \rightarrow 2Cl$, Cl is reduced; $2I^- \rightarrow I_2$, I is oxidized

(d) $S^{2-} \rightarrow SO_4^{2-}$ (S, +6), S is oxidized; H_2O_2 (O, -1) $\rightarrow H_2O$ (O, -2); O is reduced

4.43   *Analyze.* Given: reactants. Find: balanced molecular and net ionic equations.

Plan. Metals oxidized by H^+ form cations. Predict products by exchanging cations and balance. The anions are the spectator ions and do not appear in the net ionic equations. *Solve*:

(a) $Mn(s) + H_2SO_4(aq) \rightarrow MnSO_4(aq) + H_2(g)$; $Mn(s) + 2H^+(aq) \rightarrow Mn^{2+}(aq) + H_2(g)$

(b) $2Cr(s) + 6HBr(aq) \rightarrow 2CrBr_3(aq) + 3H_2(g)$; $2Cr(s) + 6H^+(aq) \rightarrow 2Cr^{3+}(aq) + 3H_2(g)$

(c) $Sn(s) + 2HCl(aq) \rightarrow SnCl_2(aq) + H_2(g)$; $Sn(s) + 2H^+(aq) \rightarrow Sn^{2+}(aq) + H_2(g)$

(d) $2Al(s) + 6HCHO_2(aq) \rightarrow 2Al(CHO_2)_3(aq) + 3H_2(g)$;

        $2Al(s) + 6HCHO_2(aq) \rightarrow 2Al^{3+}(aq) + 6CHO_2^-(aq) + 3H_2(g)$

4.45   *Analyze.* Given: a metal and an aqueous solution. Find: balanced equation.

     Plan. Use Table 4.5. If the metal is above the aqueous solution, reaction will occur; if the aqueous solution is higher, NR. If reaction occurs, predict products by exchanging cations (a metal ion or H^+), then balance the equation. *Solve:*

     (a) $2Al(s) + 3NiCl_2(aq) \rightarrow 2AlCl_3(aq) + 3Ni(s)$

     (b) $Ag(s) + Pb(NO_3)_2(aq) \rightarrow NR$

     (c) $2Cr(s) + 3NiSO_4(aq) \rightarrow Cr_2(SO_4)_3(aq) + 3Ni(s)$

     (d) $Mn(s) + 2HBr(aq) \rightarrow MnBr_2(aq) + H_2(g)$

     (e) $H_2(g) + CuCl_2(aq) \rightarrow Cu(s) + 2HCl(aq)$

4.47   (a)   i. $Zn(s) + Cd^{2+}(aq) \rightarrow Cd(s) + Zn^{2+}(aq)$

              ii. $Cd(s) + Ni^{2+}(aq) \rightarrow Ni(s) + Cd^{2+}(aq)$

     (b)   According to Table 4.5, the most active metals are most easily oxidized, and Zn is more active than Ni. Observation (i) indicates that Cd is less active than Zn; observation (ii) indicates that Cd is more active than Ni. Cd is between Zn and Ni on the activity series.

     (c)   Place an iron strip in $CdCl_2(aq)$. If Cd(s) is deposited, Cd is less active than Fe; if there is no reaction, Cd is more active than Fe. Do the same test with Co if Cd is less active than Fe or with Cr if Cd is more active than Fe.

Solution Composition; Molarity

4.49   (a)   Concentration is an intensive property; it is **ratio** of the amount of solute present in a certain quantity of solvent or solution. This ratio remains constant regardless of how much solution is present.

     (b)   The term *0.50 mol HCl* defines an amount (~18 g) of the pure substance HCl. The term 0.50 *M* HCl is a ratio; it indicates that there are 0.50 mol of HCl solute in 1.0 liter of solution. This same ratio of moles solute to solution volume is present regardless of the volume of solution under consideration.

4.51   *Analyze/Plan.* Follow the logic in Sample Exercise 4.11. *Solve:*

     (a) $M = \dfrac{\text{mol solute}}{\text{L solution}}; \; \dfrac{0.0345 \text{ mol } NH_4Cl}{400 \text{ mL}} \times \dfrac{1000 \text{ mL}}{1 \text{ L}} = 0.0863 \; M \; NH_4Cl$

          Check. Check. $(0.035 \times 0.4) \approx 0.09 \; M$

     (b) $\text{mol} = M \times L; \; \dfrac{2.20 \text{ mol } HNO_3}{1 \text{ L}} \times 0.0350 \text{ L} = 0.0770 \text{ mol } HNO_3$

          Check. $(2 \times 0.035) \approx 0.07 \; M$

(c) $\quad L = \dfrac{mol}{M}; \quad \dfrac{0.125 \text{ mol KOH}}{1.50 \text{ mol KOH/L}} = 0.0833$ L or 83.3 mL of 1.50 M KOH

Check. (0.125/1.5) is greater than 0.06 and less than 0.12, ≈ 0.08 M.

4.53 Plan. Proceed as in Sample Exercise 4.11.

$M = \dfrac{mol}{L}; \quad mol = \dfrac{g}{\mathcal{M}} \qquad$ (*$\mathcal{M}$ is the symbol for molar mass in this manual.*)

(a) $\quad \dfrac{0.150 \, M \text{ KBr}}{1 \text{ L}} \times 0.250 \text{ L} \times \dfrac{119.0 \text{ g KBr}}{1 \text{ mol KBr}} = 4.46$ g KBr

Check. $(0.15 \times 120) \approx 18$; $18 \times 0.25 = 18/4 \approx 4.5$ g KBr

(b) $\quad 4.75 \text{ g Ca(NO}_3)_2 \times \dfrac{1 \text{ mol Ca(NO}_3)_2}{164.1 \text{ g Ca(NO}_3)_2} \times \dfrac{1}{0.200 \text{ L}} = 0.145 \, M \text{ Ca(NO}_3)_2$

Check. $(4.8/0.2) \approx 24$; $24/160 = 3/20 \approx 0.15 \, M \text{ Ca(NO}_3)_2$

(c) $\quad 5.00 \text{ g Na}_3\text{PO}_4 \times \dfrac{1 \text{ mol Na}_3\text{PO}_4}{163.9 \text{ g Na}_3\text{PO}_4} \times \dfrac{1 \text{ L}}{1.50 \text{ mol Na}_3\text{PO}_4} \times \dfrac{1000 \text{ mL}}{1 \text{ L}}$

$$= 20.3 \text{ mL solution}$$

Check. $[5/(160 \times 1.5)] \approx 5/240 \approx 1/50 \approx 0.02$ L $= 20$ mL

4.55 *Analyze.* Given: formula and concentration of each solute. Find: concentration of K^+ in each solution. *Plan.* Note mol K^+/mol solute and compare concentrations or total moles. *Solve*:

(a) $\quad$ KCl $\rightarrow$ K^+ + Cl$^-$; 0.20 M KCl = 0.20 M K^+

$K_2CrO_4 \rightarrow$ **2** K^+ + CrO_4^{2-}; 0.15 M K_2CrO_4 = 0.30 M K^+

$K_3PO_4 \rightarrow$ **3** K^+ + PO_4^{3-}; 0.080 M K_3PO_4 = 0.24 M K^+

0.15 M K_2CrO_4 has the highest K^+ concentration.

(b) $\quad$ K_2CrO_4: 0.30 M K^+ $\times$ 0.0300 L = 0.0090 mol K^+

K_3PO_4: 0.24 M K^+ $\times$ 0.0250 L = 0.0060 mol K^+

30.0 mL of 0.15 M K_2CrO_4 has more K^+ ions.

4.57 *Analyze.* Given: formula and concentration of each solute. Find: concentration of each species in solution. *Plan.* Decide whether the solute is a strong, weak or nonelectrolyte, which species are in solution, and concentrations. *Solve*:

(a) $\quad$ 0.14 M Na$^+$, 0.14 M OH$^-$

(b) $\quad$ 0.25 M Ca^{2+}, 0.50 M Br$^-$

(c) $\quad$ 0.25 M (CH$_3$OH is a molecular solute)

(d) $\quad$ Mixing two solutions is, in effect, a dilution, Equation 4.35.

$M_2 = M_1V_1/V_2$, where V_2 is the total solution volume.

K^+: $\dfrac{0.10 \, M \times 0.050 \text{ L}}{0.075 \text{ L}} = 0.00667 = 0.067 \, M$

ClO_3^-: concentration ClO_3^- = concentration K^+ = 0.067 M

SO_4^{2-}: $\dfrac{0.20\ M \times 0.0250\ L}{0.075\ L}$ = 0.0667 = 0.067 M SO_4^{2-}

Na^+: concentration Na^+ = 2 × concentration SO_4^{2-} = 0.13 M

4.59   *Analyze/Plan.* Follow the logic of Sample Exercise 4.14.   *Solve:*

(a) $V_1 = M_2V_2/M_1$; $\dfrac{0.250\ M\ NH_3 \times 100.0\ mL}{14.8\ M\ NH_3}$ = 1.689 = 1.69 mL 14.8 M NH_3

Check. 250/15 ≈ 1.5 mL

(b) $M_2 = M_1V_1/V_2$; $\dfrac{14.8\ M\ NH_3 \times 10.0\ mL}{250\ mL}$ = 0.592 M NH_3

Check. 150/250 ≈ 0.60 M

4.61   (a)   *Plan/Solve.* Follow the logic in Sample Exercise 4.13.   The number of moles of sucrose needed is $\dfrac{0.150\ mol}{1\ L}$ × 0.125 L = 0.01875 = 0.0188 mol

Weigh out 0.01875 mol $C_{12}H_{22}O_{11}$ × $\dfrac{342.3\ g\ C_{12}H_{22}O_{11}}{1\ mol\ C_{12}H_{22}O_{11}}$ = 6.42 g $C_{12}H_{22}O_{11}$

Add this amount of solid to a 125 mL volumetric flask, dissolve in a small volume of water, and add water to the mark on the neck of the flask. Agitate thoroughly to ensure total mixing.

(b)   *Plan/Solve.* Follow the logic in Sample Exercise 4.14. Calculate the moles of solute present in the final 400.0 mL of 0.100 M $C_{12}H_{22}O_{11}$ solution:

moles $C_{12}H_{22}O_{11}$ = M × L = $\dfrac{0.100\ mol\ C_{12}H_{22}O_{11}}{1\ L}$ × 0.4000 L = 0.0400 mol $C_{12}H_{22}O_{11}$

Calculate the volume of 1.50 M glucose solution that would contain 0.04000 mol $C_{12}H_{22}O_{11}$:

L = moles/M; 0.04000 mol $C_{12}H_{22}O_{11}$ × $\dfrac{1\ L}{1.50\ mol\ C_{12}H_{22}O_{11}}$ = 0.02667 = 0.0267 L

0.02667 L × $\dfrac{1000\ mL}{1\ L}$ = 26.7 mL

Thoroughly rinse, clean and fill a 50 mL buret with the 1.50 M $C_{12}H_{22}O_{11}$. Dispense 26.7 mL of this solution into a 400 mL volumetric container, add water to the mark and mix thoroughly. (26.7 mL is a difficult volume to measure with a pipette.)

4.63   *Analyze.* Given: density of pure acetic acid, volume pure acetic acid, volume new solution. Find: molarity of new solution.   *Plan.* Calculate the mass of acetic acid, $HC_2H_3O_2$, present in 20.0 mL of the pure liquid.   *Solve:*

$$20.00 \text{ mL acetic acid} \times \frac{1.049 \text{ g acetic acid}}{1 \text{ mL acetic acid}} = 20.98 \text{ g acetic acid}$$

$$20.98 \text{ g HC}_2\text{H}_3\text{O}_2 \times \frac{1 \text{ mol HC}_2\text{H}_3\text{O}_2}{60.05 \text{ g HC}_2\text{H}_3\text{O}_2} = 0.349375 = 0.3494 \text{ mol HC}_2\text{H}_3\text{O}_2$$

$$M = \text{mol/L} = \frac{0.349375 \text{ mol HC}_2\text{H}_3\text{O}_2}{0.2500 \text{ L solution}} = 1.39750 = 1.398 \text{ } M \text{ HC}_2\text{H}_3\text{O}_2$$

Check. $(20 \times 1) \approx 20$ g acid; $(20/60) \approx 0.33$ mol acid; $(0.33/0.25 = 0.33 \times 4) \approx 1.33 \text{ } M$

Solution Stoichiometry; Titrations

4.65   *Analyze.* Given: volume and molarity $AgNO_3$. Find: mass NaCl.

Plan. $M \times L = \text{mol AgNO}_3 = \text{mol Ag}^+$; balanced equation gives ratio mol NaCl/mol $AgNO_3$; mol NaCl → g NaCl. *Solve*:

$$\frac{0.100 \text{ mol AgNO}_3}{1 \text{ L}} \times 0.0200 \text{ L} = 2.00 \times 10^{-3} \text{ mol AgNO}_3(aq)$$

$$\text{AgNO}_3(aq) + \text{NaCl}(aq) \rightarrow \text{AgCl}(s) + \text{NaNO}_3(aq)$$

$$\text{mol NaCl} = \text{mol AgNO}_3 = 2.00 \times 10^{-3} \text{ mol NaCl}$$

$$2.00 \times 10^{-3} \text{ mol NaCl} \times \frac{58.44 \text{ g NaCl}}{1 \text{ mol NaCl}} = 0.117 \text{ g NaCl}$$

Check. $(0.1 \times 0.02) = 0.002$ mol; $(0.002 \times 60) \approx 0.12$ g NaCl

4.67   (a)   *Analyze.* Given: M and vol base, M acid. Find: vol acid

Plan/Solve. Write the balanced equation for the reaction in question:
$$\text{HClO}_4(aq) + \text{NaOH}(aq) \rightarrow \text{NaClO}_4(aq) + \text{H}_2\text{O}(l)$$

Calculate the moles of the known substance, in this case NaOH.

$$\text{moles NaOH} = M \times L = \frac{0.0875 \text{ mol NaOH}}{1 \text{ L}} \times 0.0500 \text{ L} = 0.004375$$
$$= 0.00438 \text{ mol NaOH}$$

Apply the mole ratio (mol unknown/mol known) from the chemical equation.

$$0.004375 \text{ mol NaOH} \times \frac{1 \text{ mol HClO}_4}{1 \text{ mol NaOH}} = 0.004375 \text{ mol HClO}_4$$

Calculate the desired quantity of unknown, in this case the volume of 0.115 M $HClO_4$ solution.

$$L = \text{mol}/M; \quad L = 0.004375 \text{ mol HClO}_4 \times \frac{1 \text{ L}}{0.115 \text{ mol HClO}_4} = 0.0380 \text{ L} = 38.0 \text{ mL}$$

Check. $(0.09 \times 0.045) = 0.0045$ mol; $(0.0045/0.11) \approx 0.040$ L ≈ 40 mL

(b)   Following the logic outlined in part (a):

$$2HCl(aq) + Mg(OH)_2(s) \rightarrow MgCl_2(aq) + 2H_2O(l)$$

$$2.87 \text{ g Mg(OH)}_2 \times \frac{1 \text{ mol Mg(OH)}_2}{58.32 \text{ g Mg(OH)}_2} = 0.049211 = 0.0492 \text{ mol Mg(OH)}_2$$

$$0.0492 \text{ mol Mg(OH)}_2 \times \frac{2 \text{ mol HCl}}{1 \text{ mol Mg(OH)}_2} = 0.0984 \text{ mol HCl}$$

$$L = \text{mol}/M = 0.09840 \text{ mol HCl} \times \frac{1 \text{ L HCl}}{0.128 \text{ mol HCl}} = 0.769 \text{ L} = 769 \text{ mL}$$

(c) $AgNO_3(aq) + KCl(aq) \rightarrow AgCl(s) + KNO_3(aq)$

$$785 \text{ mg KCl} \times \frac{1 \times 10^{-3} \text{ g}}{1 \text{ mg}} \times \frac{1 \text{ mol KCl}}{74.55 \text{ g KCl}} \times \frac{1 \text{ mol AgNO}_3}{1 \text{ mol KCl}} = 0.01053$$

$$= 0.0105 \text{ mol AgNO}_3$$

$$M = \text{mol}/L = \frac{0.01053 \text{ mol AgNO}_3}{0.0258 \text{ L}} = 0.408 \, M \text{ AgNO}_3$$

(d) $HCl(aq) + KOH(aq) \rightarrow KCl(aq) + H_2O(l)$

$$\frac{0.108 \text{ mol HCl}}{1 \text{ L}} \times 0.0453 \text{ L} \times \frac{1 \text{ mol KOH}}{1 \text{ mol HCl}} \times \frac{56.11 \text{ g KOH}}{1 \text{ mol KOH}} = 0.275 \text{ g KOH}$$

4.69   *Analyze/Plan.* See Exercise 4.67(a) for a more detailed approach. *Solve*:

$$\frac{6.0 \text{ mol H}_2SO_4}{1 \text{ L}} \times 0.027 \text{ L} \times \frac{2 \text{ mol NaHCO}_3}{1 \text{ mol H}_2SO_4} \times \frac{84.01 \text{ g NaHCO}_3}{1 \text{ mol NaHCO}_3} = 27 \text{ g NaHCO}_3$$

4.70   See Exercise 4.67 (a) for a more detailed approach.

$$\frac{0.102 \text{ mol NaOH}}{1 \text{ L}} \times 0.0355 \text{ L} \times \frac{1 \text{ mol HC}_2H_3O_2}{1 \text{ mol NaOH}} \times \frac{60.05 \text{ g HC}_2H_3O_2}{1 \text{ mol HC}_2H_3O_2}$$

$$= 0.21744 = 0.217 \text{ g HC}_2H_3O_2 \text{ in 2.50 mL}$$

$$1.00 \text{ qt vinegar} \times \frac{1 \text{ L}}{1.057 \text{ qt}} \times \frac{1000 \text{ mL}}{1 \text{ L}} \times \frac{0.21744 \text{ g HC}_2H_3O_2}{2.50 \text{ mL vinegar}} = 82.3 \text{ g HC}_2H_3O_2/\text{qt}$$

4.71   *Analyze.* Given: M and vol HBr, vol $Ca(OH)_2$. Find: M $Ca(OH)_2$, g $Ca(OH)_2$/100 mL soln

Plan. Write balanced equation;

$$\text{mol HBr} \xrightarrow{\overset{\text{mol}}{\text{ratio}}} \text{mol Ca(OH)}_2 \rightarrow M \text{ Ca(OH)}_2; \rightarrow \text{g Ca(OH)}_2/100 \text{ mL}$$

Solve. The neutralization reaction here is:

$$2HBr(aq) + Ca(OH)_2(aq) \rightarrow CaBr_2(aq) + 2H_2O(l)$$

$$0.0488 \text{ L HBr soln} \times \frac{5.00 \times 10^{-2} \text{ mol HBr}}{1 \text{ L soln}} \times \frac{1 \text{ mol Ca(OH)}_2}{2 \text{ mol HBr}} \times \frac{1}{0.100 \text{ L of Ca(OH)}_2}$$

$$= 1.220 \times 10^{-2} = 1.22 \times 10^{-2} \ M \ Ca(OH)_2$$

From the molarity of the saturated solution, we can calculate the gram solubility of $Ca(OH)_2$ in 100 mL of H_2O.

$$0.100 \text{ L soln} \times \frac{1.220 \times 10^{-2} \text{ mol Ca(OH)}_2}{1 \text{ L soln}} \times \frac{74.10 \text{ g Ca(OH)}_2}{1 \text{ mol Ca(OH)}_2}$$

$$= 0.0904 \text{ g Ca(OH)}_2 \text{ in 100 mL soln}$$

Check. $(0.05 \times 0.05/0.2) = 0.0125 \ M; (0.1 \times 0.0125 \times 64) \approx 0.085 \text{ g/100 mL}$

4.73   (a) $NiSO_4(aq) + 2KOH(aq) \rightarrow Ni(OH)_2(s) + K_2SO_4(aq)$

       (b)   The precipitate is $Ni(OH)_2$.

       (c)   *Plan.* Compare mol of each reactant; mol = $M \times L$

            Solve. 0.200 M KOH × 0.1000 L   KOH = 0.0200 mol KOH

            0.150 M $NiSO_4$ × 0.2000 L KOH = 0.0300 mol $NiSO_4$

            1 mol $NiSO_4$ requires 2 mol KOH, so 0.0300 mol $NiSO_4$ requires 0.0600 mol KOH. Since only 0.0200 mol KOH is available, KOH is the limiting reactant.

       (d)   *Plan.* The amount of the limiting reactant (KOH) determines amount of product, in this case $Ni(OH)_2$.

$$\textit{Solve.} \ 0.0200 \text{ mol KOH} \times \frac{1 \text{ mol Ni(OH)}_2}{2 \text{ mol KOH}} \times \frac{92.71 \text{ g Ni(OH)}_2}{1 \text{ mol Ni(OH)}_2} = 0.927 \text{ g Ni(OH)}_2$$

       (e)   *Plan/Solve.* Limiting reactant: OH^-: no excess OH^- remains in solution.

            Excess reactant: Ni^{2+}: $M \ Ni^{2+}$ remaining = mol Ni^{2+} remaining/L solution

            0.0300 mol Ni^{2+} initial - 0.0100 mol Ni^{2+} reacted = 0.0200 mol Ni^{2+} remaining

            0.0200 mol Ni^{2+}/0.3000 L = 0.0667 $M \ Ni^{2+}(aq)$

            Spectators: SO_4^{2-}, K^+. These ions do not react, so the only change in their concentration is dilution. The final volume of the solution is 0.3000 L.

            $M_2 = M_1V_1/V_2$: 0.200 $M \ K^+$ × 0.1000 L / 0.3000 L = 0.0667 $M \ K^+(aq)$

            0.150 $M \ SO_4^{2-}$ × 0.2000 L/0.3000 L = 0.100 $M \ SO_4^{2-}(aq)$

4.75   *Analyze.* Given: mass impure $Mg(OH)_2$; M and vol **excess** HCl; M and vol NaOH. Find: mass % $Mg(OH)_2$ in sample. *Plan/Solve.* Write balanced equations.

       $Mg(OH)_2(s) + 2HCl(aq) \rightarrow MgCl_2(aq) + 2H_2O(l)$

       $HCl(aq) + NaOH(aq) \rightarrow NaCl(aq) + 2H_2O(l)$

Calculate total moles HCl = M HCl × L HCl

$$\frac{0.2050 \text{ mol HCl}}{1 \text{ L soln}} \times 0.1000 \text{ L} = 0.02050 \text{ mol HCl total}$$

mol excess HCl = mol NaOH used = M NaOH × L NaOH

$$\frac{0.1020 \text{ mol NaOH}}{1 \text{ L soln}} \times 0.01985 \text{ L} = 0.0020247 = 0.002025 \text{ mol NaOH}$$

mol HCl reacted with $Mg(OH)_2$ = total mol HCl - excess mol HCl

0.02050 mol total - 0.0020247 mol excess = 0.0184753 = 0.01848 mol HCl reacted

(The result has 5 decimal places and 4 sig. figs.)

Use mol ratio to get mol $Mg(OH)_2$ in sample, then molar mass of $Mg(OH)_2$ to get g pure $Mg(OH)_2$.

$$0.0184753 \text{ mol HCl} \times \frac{1 \text{ mol } Mg(OH)_2}{2 \text{ mol HCl}} \times \frac{58.32 \text{ g } Mg(OH)_2}{1 \text{ mol } Mg(OH)_2} = 0.5387 \; Mg(OH)_2$$

$$\text{mass \% } Mg(OH)_2 = \frac{\text{g } Mg(OH)_2}{\text{g sample}} \times 100 = \frac{0.5388 \text{ g } Mg(OH)_2}{0.5895 \text{ g sample}} \times 100 = 91.40\% \; Mg(OH)_2$$

Additional Exercises

4.77   The precipitate is CdS(s). $Na^+(aq)$ and $NO_3^-(aq)$ are spectator ions and remain in solution. Any excess reactant ions also remain in solution. The net ionic equation is:

$Cd^{2+}(aq) + S^{2-}(aq) \rightarrow CdS(s)$.

4.80   (a) $Al(OH)_3(s) + 3H^+(aq) \rightarrow Al^{3+}(aq) + 3H_2O(l)$

       (b) $Mg(OH)_2(s) + 2H^+(aq) \rightarrow Mg^{2+}(aq) + 2H_2O(l)$

       (c) $MgCO_3(s) + 2H^+(aq) \rightarrow Mg^{2+}(aq) + H_2O(l) + CO_2(g)$

       (d) $NaAl(CO_3)(OH)_2(s) + 4H^+(aq) \rightarrow Na^+(aq) + Al^{3+}(aq) + 3H_2O(l) + CO_2(g)$

       (e) $CaCO_3(s) + 2H^+(aq) \rightarrow Ca^{2+}(aq) + H_2O(l) + CO_2(g)$

[In (c), (d) and (e), one could also write the equation for formation of bicarbonate, e.g., $MgCO_3(s) + H^+(aq) \rightarrow Mg^{2+} + HCO_3^-(aq)$.]

4.83   A metal on Table 4.5 is able to displace the metal cations below it from their compounds. That is, zinc will reduce the cations below it to their metals.

       (a) $Zn(s) + Na^+(aq) \rightarrow$ no reaction

       (b) $Zn(s) + Pb^{2+}(aq) \rightarrow Zn^{2+}(aq) + Pb(s)$

       (c) $Zn(s) + Mg^{2+}(aq) \rightarrow$ no reaction

       (d) $Zn(s) + Fe^{2+}(aq) \rightarrow Zn^{2+}(aq) + Fe(s)$

       (e) $Zn(s) + Cu^{2+}(aq) \rightarrow Zn^{2+}(aq) + Cu(s)$

       (f) $Zn(s) + Al^{3+}(aq) \rightarrow$ no reaction

4.86 *Plan.* Calculate moles KBr from the two quantities of solution (mol = $M \times$ L), then new molarity (M = mol/L). KBr is nonvolatile, so no solute is lost when the solution is evaporated to reduce the total volume. *Solve:*

1.00 M KBr × 0.0250 L = 0.0250 mol KBr; 0.800 M KBr × 0.0750 L = 0.0600 mol KBr

0.0250 mol KBr + 0.0600 mol KBr = 0850 mol KBr total

$$\frac{0.0850 \text{ mol KBr}}{0.0500 \text{ L soln}} = 1.70 \ M \text{ KBr}$$

4.89 Na^+ must replace the total positive (+) charge due to Ca^{2+} and Mg^{2+}. Think of this as moles of charge rather than moles of particles.

$$\frac{0.010 \text{ mol Ca}^{2+}}{1 \text{ L water}} \times 1.0 \times 10^3 \text{ L} \times \frac{2 \text{ mol + charge}}{1 \text{ mol Ca}^{2+}} = 20 \text{ mol of + charge}$$

$$\frac{0.0050 \text{ mol Mg}^{2+}}{1 \text{ L water}} \times 1.0 \times 10^3 \text{ L} \times \frac{2 \text{ mol + charge}}{1 \text{ mol Mg}^{2+}} = 10 \text{ mol of + charge}$$

30 moles of + charge must be replaced; 30 mol Na^+ are needed.

4.91 *Plan.* mol MnO_4^- = $M \times$ L → mol ratio → mol H_2O_2 → M H_2O_2. *Solve:*

$$2MnO_4^-(aq) + 5H_2O_2(aq) + 6H^+ \rightarrow 2Mn^{2+}(aq) + 5O_2(aq) + 8H_2O(l)$$

$$\frac{0.109 \text{ mol MnO}_4^-}{L} \times 0.0135 \text{ L MnO}_4^- \times \frac{5 \text{ mol H}_2O_2}{2 \text{ mol MnO}_4^-} \times \frac{1}{0.0100 \text{ L H}_2O_2}$$

$$= 0.3679 \text{ mol H}_2O_2 / L = 0.368 \ M \text{ H}_2O_2$$

Integrative Exercises

4.93 *Plan.* $M \times$ L = mol Na_3PO_4 → mol Na^+ → Na^+ ions.   *Solve:*

$$\frac{0.0100 \text{ mol Na}_3PO_4}{1 \text{ L solution}} \times 1.00 \text{ mL} \times \frac{1 \text{ L}}{1000 \text{ mL}} \times \frac{3 \text{ mol Na}^+}{1 \text{ mol Na}_3PO_4}$$

$$\frac{6.022 \times 10^{23} \text{ Na}^+ \text{ ions}}{1 \text{ mol Na}^+} = 1.81 \times 10^{19} \text{ Na}^+ \text{ ions}$$

4.96 *Plan.* Write balanced equation.

mass H_2SO_4 soln $\xrightarrow{\text{mass \%}}$ mass H_2SO_4 → mol H_2SO_4 → mol Na_2CO_3 → mass Na_2CO_3

Solve. $H_2SO_4(aq) + Na_2CO_3(s) \rightarrow Na_2SO_4(aq) + H_2O(l) + CO_2(g)$

$$5.0 \times 10^3 \text{ kg conc. H}_2SO_4 \times \frac{0.950 \text{ kg H}_2SO_4}{1.00 \text{ kg conc. H}_2SO_4} = 4.75 \times 10^3 = 4.8 \times 10^3 \text{ kg H}_2SO_4$$

$$4.75 \times 10^3 \text{ kg H}_2\text{SO}_4 \times \frac{1 \times 10^3 \text{ g}}{1 \text{ kg}} \times \frac{1 \text{ mol H}_2\text{SO}_4}{98.08 \text{ g H}_2\text{SO}_4} \times \frac{1 \text{ mol Na}_2\text{CO}_3}{1 \text{ mol H}_2\text{SO}_4}$$

$$\times \frac{105.99 \text{ g NaHCO}_3}{1 \text{ mol NaHCO}_3} \times \frac{1 \text{ kg}}{1 \times 10^3 \text{ g}} = 5.133 \times 10^3 = 5.1 \times 10^3 \text{ kg Na}_2\text{CO}_3$$

4.99   *Plan.* Cl^- is present in NaCl and $MgCl_2$; using mass %, calculate mass NaCl and $MgCl_2$ in mixture, mol Cl^- in each, then molarity of Cl^- in 0.500 L solution.   *Solve*:

$$7.50 \text{ mixture} \times \frac{0.890 \text{ g NaCl}}{1.00 \text{ g mixture}} \times \frac{1 \text{ mol NaCl}}{58.44 \text{ g NaCl}} \times \frac{1 \text{ mol Cl}^-}{1 \text{ mol NaCl}} = 0.1142 = 0.114 \text{ mol Cl}^-$$

$$7.50 \text{ mixture} \times \frac{0.015 \text{ g MgCl}_2}{1.00 \text{ g mixture}} \times \frac{1 \text{ mol MgCl}_2}{95.21 \text{ g MgCl}_2} \times \frac{2 \text{ mol Cl}^-}{1 \text{ mol MgCl}_2} = 0.00236 = 0.0024 \text{ mol Cl}^-$$

$$\text{mol Cl}^- = 0.1142 + 0.00236 = 0.11656 = 0.117 \text{ mol Cl}^-; \quad M = \frac{0.11656 \text{ mol Cl}^-}{0.5000 \text{ L}} = 0.233 \text{ M Cl}^-$$

4.102   (a) AsO_4^{3-}; +5

(b) Ag_3PO_4 is silver phosphate; Ag_3AsO_4 is silver arsenate

(c) $$0.0250 \text{ L soln} \times \frac{0.102 \text{ mol Ag}^+}{1 \text{ L soln}} \times \frac{1 \text{ mol Ag}_3\text{AsO}_4}{3 \text{ mol Ag}^+} \times \frac{1 \text{ mol As}}{1 \text{ mol Ag}_3\text{AsO}_4} \times \frac{74.92 \text{ g As}}{1 \text{ mol As}}$$

$$= 0.06368 = 0.0637 \text{ g As}$$

$$\text{mass percent} = \frac{0.06368 \text{ g As}}{1.22 \text{ g sample}} \times 100 = 5.22\% \text{ As}$$

5 Thermochemistry

Nature of Energy

5.1 An object can possess energy by virtue of its motion or position. Kinetic energy, the energy of motion, depends on the mass of the object and its velocity. Potential energy, stored energy, depends on the position of the object relative to the body with which it interacts.

5.3 (a) *Analyze.* Given: mass and speed of ball. Find: kinetic energy.
Plan. Since $1\ J = 1\ kg \cdot m^2/s^2$, convert $g \to kg$ to obtain E_k in joules.

Solve. $E_k = 1/2\ mv^2 = 1/2 \times 45\ g \times \dfrac{1\ kg}{1000\ g} \times \left(\dfrac{61\ m}{1\ s}\right)^2 = \dfrac{84\ kg \cdot m^2}{1\ s^2} = 84\ J$

Check. $1/2(45 \times 3600/1000) \approx 1/2(40 \times 4) \approx 80\ J$

(b) $83.72\ J \times \dfrac{1\ cal}{4.184\ J} = 20\ cal$

(c) As the ball hits the sand, its speed (and hence its kinetic energy) drops to zero. Most of the kinetic energy is transferred to the sand, which deforms when the ball lands. Some energy is released as heat through friction between the ball and the sand.

5.5 *Analyze.* Given: heat capacity of water = 1 Btu/lb•°F Find: J/Btu

Plan. heat capacity of water = 4.184 J/g•°C; $\dfrac{J}{g \cdot °C} \to \dfrac{J}{lb \cdot °F} \to \dfrac{J}{Btu}$

This strategy requires changing °F to °C. Since this involves the magnitude of a degree on each scale, rather than a specific temperature, the 32 in the temperature relationship is not needed.

100 °C = 180 °F; 5 °C = 9 °F

Solve. $\dfrac{4.184\ J}{g \cdot °C} \times \dfrac{453.6\ g}{lb} \times \dfrac{5\ °C}{9\ °F} \times \dfrac{1\ lb \cdot °F}{1\ Btu} = 1054\ J/Btu$

5.7 *Analyze.* Given: 100 watt bulb. Find: heat in kcal radiated by bulb or person in 24 hr.

Plan. 1 watt = 1 J/s; 1 kcal = 4.184×10^3 J; watt $\to$ J/s $\to$ J $\to$ kcal. *Solve:*

$$100 \text{ watt} = \frac{100 \text{ J}}{1 \text{ s}} \times \frac{60 \text{ sec}}{\text{min}} \times \frac{60 \text{ min}}{\text{hr}} \times 24 \text{ hr} \times \frac{1 \text{ kcal}}{4.184 \times 10^3 \text{ J}} = 2065 = 2.1 \times 10^3 \text{ kcal}$$

24 hr has 2 sig figs, but 100 watt is ambiguous. The answer to 1 sig fig would be 2×10^3 kcal.

Check. $(1 \times 10^2 \times 6 \times 10^1 \times 6/10^3) \approx 6^3 \times 10 \approx 2000$ kcal

5.9   The air gun imparts a certain amount of kinetic energy to the pellet. As the pellet rises against the force of gravity, kinetic energy is changed to potential energy. When all kinetic energy has been transferred to potential energy (or lost as heat through friction) the pellet stops rising and falls to earth. In principle, if enough kinetic energy could be imparted to the pellet, it could escape the force of gravity and move into space. For an air gun and a pellet, this is 'practically' impossible.

5.11   (a)   In thermodynamics, the *system* is the well-defined part of the universe whose energy changes are being studied.

       (b)   A closed system can exchange heat but not mass with its surroundings.

5.13   (a)   *Work* is a force applied over a distance.

       (b)   The amount of work done is the magnitude of the force times the distance over which it is applied. $w = F \times d.$

5.15   (a)   Gravity; work is done because the force of gravity is opposed and the pencil is lifted.

       (b)   Mechanical force; work is done because the force of the coiled spring is opposed as the spring is compressed over a distance.

The First Law of Thermodynamics

5.17   (a)   In any chemical or physical change, energy can be neither created nor destroyed, but it can be changed in form.

       (b)   The total *internal energy* (E) of a system is the sum of all the kinetic and potential energies of the system components.

       (c)   The internal energy of a system increases when work is done on the system by the surroundings and/or when heat is transferred to the system from the surroundings (the system is heated).

5.19   *Analyze.* Given: heat and work. Find: magnitude and sign of ΔE.

       Plan. In each case, evaluate q and w in the expression ΔE = q + w. For an exothermic process, q is negative; for an endothermic process, q is positive. *Solve:*

       (a)   q is negative because the system loses heat and w is negative because the system does work. ΔE = -113 kJ - 39 kJ = -152 kJ. The process is exothermic.

(b)　　　$\Delta E = +1.62$ kJ - 847 J $= +1.62$ kJ - 0.847 kJ $= +0.746 = +0.75$ kJ. The process is endothermic.

(c)　　　q is positive because the system gains heat and w is negative because the system does work. $\Delta E = +77.5$ kJ - 63.5 kJ $= +14.0$ kJ. The process is endothermic.

5.21　(a)　　　For an endothermic process, the sign of q is positive; the system gains heat. This is true only for system (iii).

(b)　　　In order for ΔE to be less than 0, there is a net transfer of heat or work from the system to the surroundings. The magnitude of the quantity leaving the system is greater than the magnitude of the quantity entering the system. In system (i), the magnitude of the heat leaving the system is less than the magnitude of the work done on the system. In system (iii), the magnitude of the work done by the system is greater than the magnitude of the heat entering the system. $\Delta E < 0$ for system (iii) only.

(c)　　　In order for ΔE to be greater than 0, there is a net transfer of work or heat to the system from the surroundings. In system (i), the magnitude of the work done on the system is greater than the magnitude of the heat leaving the system. In system (ii), work is done on the system with no change in heat. $\Delta E > 0$ for systems (i) and (ii).

5.23　　*Analyze.* How do the different physical situations (cases) affect the changes to heat and work of the system upon addition of 100 J of energy? *Plan.* Use the definitions of heat and work and the First Law to answer the questions. *Solve:*

If the piston is allowed to move, case (1), the heated gas will expand and push the piston up, doing work on the surroundings. If the piston is fixed, case (2), most of the electrical energy will be manifested as an increase in heat of the system.

(a)　　　Since little or no work is done by the system in case (2), the gas will absorb most of the energy as heat; the case (2) gas will have the higher temperature.

(b)　　　In case (2), w ≈ 0 and q ≈ 100 J. In case (1), a significant amount of energy will be used to do work on the surroundings (-w), but some will be absorbed as heat (+q). [The transfer of electrical energy into work is never completely efficient!]

(c)　　　ΔE is greater for case (2), because the entire 100 J increases the internal energy of the system, rather than a part of the energy doing work on the surroundings.

5.25　(a)　　　A *state function* is a property of a system that depends only on the physical state (pressure, temperature, etc.) of the system, not on the route used by the system to get to the current state.

(b)　　　Internal energy and enthalpy <u>are</u> state functions; work <u>is not</u> a state function.

(c)　　　Temperature is a state function; regardless of how hot or cold the sample has been, the temperature depends only on its present condition.

Enthalpy

5.27   (a)   For the many laboratory and real world processes that occur at constant atmospheric pressure, the enthalpy change is a meaningful measure of the energy change associated with the process. At constant pressure, most of the energy change is transferred as heat ($\Delta H = q_p$), even if gases are involved in the process.

        (b)   Only under conditions of constant pressure is ΔH for a process equal to the heat transferred during the process.

        (c)   If ΔH is negative, the enthalpy of the system decreases and the process is exothermic.

5.29   (a) $HC_2H_3O_2(l) + 2O_2(g) \rightarrow 2H_2O(l) + 2CO_2(g)$

              $\Delta H = -871.7$ kJ

        (b)   *Analyze.* How are reactants and products arranged on an enthalpy diagram?

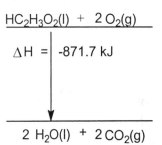

              Plan. The substances (reactants or products, collectively) with higher enthalpy are shown on the upper level, and those with lower enthalpy are shown on the lower level.

              Solve. For this reaction, ΔH is negative, so the products have lower enthalpy and are shown on the lower level; reactants are on the upper level. The arrow points in the direction of reactants to products and is labeled with the value of ΔH.

5.31   *Plan.* Consider the sign of ΔH.   *Solve:*

        Since ΔH is negative, the reactants, $2Cl(g)$ have the higher enthalpy.

5.33   *Analyze/Plan.* Follow the strategy in Sample Exercise 5.5.   *Solve:*

        (a)   Exothermic (ΔH is negative)

        (b) $2.4 \text{ g Mg} \times \dfrac{1 \text{ mol Mg}}{24.305 \text{ g Mg}} \times \dfrac{-1204 \text{ kJ}}{2 \text{ mol Mg}} = -59$ kJ heat transferred

              Check. The units of kJ are correct for heat. The negative sign indicates heat is evolved.

        (c) $-96.0 \text{ kJ} \times \dfrac{2 \text{ mol MgO}}{-1204 \text{ kJ}} \times \dfrac{40.30 \text{ g MgO}}{1 \text{ mol Mg}} = 6.43$ g MgO produced

              Check. Units are correct for mass. $(100 \times 2 \times 40/1200) \approx (8000/1200) \approx 6.5$ g

(d) $2MgO(s) \rightarrow 2Mg(s) + O_2(g)$ $\Delta H = +1204$ kJ

This is the reverse of the reaction given above, so the sign of ΔH is reversed.

$$7.50 \text{ g MgO} \times \frac{1 \text{ mol MgO}}{40.30 \text{ g MgO}} \times \frac{1204 \text{ kJ}}{2 \text{ mol MgO}} = +112 \text{ kJ heat absorbed}$$

Check. The units are correct for energy. (~9000/80) $\approx$ 110 kJ)

5.35   *Analyze.* Given: balanced thermochemical equation, various quantities of substances and/or enthalpy. *Plan.* Enthalpy is an extensive property; it is "stoichiometric". Use the mole ratios implicit in the balanced thermochemical equation to solve for the desired quantity. Use molar masses to change mass to moles and vice versa where appropriate. *Solve:*

(a) $0.540 \text{ mol AgCl} \times \dfrac{-65.5 \text{ kJ}}{1 \text{ mol AgCl}} = -35.4$ kJ

Check. Units are correct; sign indicates heat evolved.

(b) $1.66 \text{ g AgCl} \times \dfrac{1 \text{ mol AgCl}}{143.3 \text{ g AgCl}} \times \dfrac{-65.5 \text{ kJ}}{1 \text{ mol AgCl}} = -0.759$ kJ

Check. Units correct; sign indicates heat evolved.

(c) $0.188 \text{ mmol AgCl} \times \dfrac{1 \times 10^{-3} \text{ mol}}{1 \text{ mmol}} \times \dfrac{+65.5 \text{ kJ}}{1 \text{ mol AgCl}} = + 0.0123 \text{ kJ} = +12.3$ J

Check. Units correct; sign of ΔH reversed; sign indicates heat is absorbed during the reverse reaction.

5.37   At constant pressure, $\Delta E = \Delta H - P\Delta V$. In order to calculate ΔE, more information about the conditions of the reaction must be known. For an ideal gas at constant pressure and temperature, $P\Delta V = RT\Delta n$. The values of either P and ΔV or T and Δn must be known to calculate ΔE from ΔH.

5.39   *Analyze/Plan.* q = -89 kJ (heat is given off by the system), w = -36 kJ (work is done by the system). *Solve:*

$\Delta E = q + w = -89 \text{ kJ} - 36 \text{ kJ} = -125 \text{ kJ}$. $\Delta H = q = -89$ kJ (at constant pressure).

Check. The reaction is exothermic.

5.41   *Analyze.* Given: balanced thermochemical equation. *Plan.* Follow the guidelines given in Section 5.4 for evaluating thermochemical equations. *Solve:*

(a)   When a chemical equation is reversed, the sign of ΔH is reversed.
         $CO_2(g) + 2H_2O(l) \rightarrow CH_3OH(l) + 3/2 \, O_2(g)$ $\Delta H = +726.5$ kJ

(b)   Enthalpy is extensive. If the coefficients in the chemical equation are multiplied by 2 to obtain all integer coefficients, the enthalpy change is also multiplied by 2.
         $2CH_3OH(l) + 3O_2(g) \rightarrow 2CO_2(g) + 4H_2O(l)$ $\Delta H = 2(-726.5) \text{ kJ} = -1453$ kJ

(c)   The exothermic forward reaction is more likely to be thermodynamically favored.

(d)   Vaporization (liquid → gas) is endothermic. If the product were $H_2O(g)$, the reaction would be more endothermic and would have a smaller negative ΔH. (Depending on temperature, the enthalpy of vaporization for 2 mol H_2O is about +88 kJ, not large enough to cause the overall reaction to be endothermic.)

Calorimetry

The specific heat of water to four significant figures, 4.184 J/g • K, will be used in many of the following exercises; temperature units of K and °C will be used interchangeably.

5.43   (a)   J/°C or J/K. Heat capacity is the amount of heat in J required to raise the temperature of an object or a certain amount of a substance 1°C or 1 K. Since the amount is defined, units of amount are not included.

      (b) $\dfrac{J}{g \bullet °C}$ or $\dfrac{J}{g \bullet °K}$ Specific heat is a particular kind of heat capacity where the amount of substance is 1 g.

5.45   *Plan*. Manipulate the definition of specific heat to solve for the desired quantity, paying close attention to units. specific heat = q/(m × Δt).   *Solve*:

      (a) $\dfrac{4.184 \, J}{1 \, g \bullet K}$ or $\dfrac{4.184 \, J}{1 \, g \bullet °C}$ (b) $\dfrac{185 \, g \, H_2O \times 4.184 \, J}{1 \, g \bullet °C} = 774 \, J/°C$

      (c) $10.00 \, kg \, H_2O \times \dfrac{1000 \, g}{1 \, kg} \times \dfrac{4.184 \, J}{1 \, g \bullet °C} \times \dfrac{1 \, kJ}{1000 \, J} \times (46.2°C - 24.6°C) = 904 \, kJ$

            Check. (10 × 4 × 20) ≈ 800 kJ; the units are correct. Note that the conversion factors for kg → g and J → kJ cancel. An equally correct form of specific heat would be kJ/kg • C°.

5.47   *Analyze/Plan*. Follow the logic in Sample Exercise 5.6.   *Solve*:

      $1.42 \, kg \, Cu \times \dfrac{1000 \, g}{1 \, kg} \times \dfrac{0.385 \, J}{g \bullet K} \times (88.5°C - 25.0°C) = 3.47 \times 10^4 \, J$ (or 34.7 kJ)

5.49   *Analyze*. Since the temperature of the water increases, the dissolving process is exothermic and the sign of ΔH is negative. The heat lost by the NaOH(s) dissolving equals the heat gained by the solution.

      Plan/Solve. Calculate the heat gained by the solution. The temperature change is 47.4 - 23.6 = 23.8°C. The total mass of solution is (100.0 g H_2O + 9.55 g NaOH) = 109.55 = 109.6 g.

      $109.55 \, g \, solution \times \dfrac{4.184 \, J}{1 \, g \bullet °C} \times 23.8°C \times \dfrac{1 \, kJ}{1000 \, J} = 10.909 = 10.9 \, kJ$

This is the amount of heat lost when 9.55 g of NaOH dissolves.

The heat loss per mole NaOH is

$$\frac{-10.909 \text{ kJ}}{9.55 \text{ g NaOH}} \times \frac{40.00 \text{ g NaOH}}{1 \text{ mol NaOH}} = -45.7 \text{ kJ/mol} \quad \Delta H = q_p = -45.7 \text{ kJ/mol NaOH}$$

Check. $(-11/9 \times 40) \approx -45$ kJ; the units and sign are correct.

5.51   *Analyze/Plan.* Follow the logic in Sample Exercise 5.8. *Solve:*

$q_{bomb} = -q_{rxn}$; $\Delta T = 30.57°C - 23.44°C = 7.13°C$

$$q_{bomb} = \frac{7.854 \text{ kJ}}{1°C} \times 7.13°C = 56.00 = 56.0 \text{ kJ}$$

At constant volume, $q_V = \Delta E$. ΔE and ΔH are very similar.

$$\Delta H_{rxn} \approx \Delta E_{rxn} = q_{rxn} = -q_{bomb} = \frac{-56.0 \text{ kJ}}{2.20 \text{ g } C_6H_4O_2} = -25.454 = -25.5 \text{ kJ/g } C_6H_4O_2$$

$$\Delta H_{rxn} = \frac{-25.454 \text{ kJ}}{1 \text{ g } C_6H_4O_2} \times \frac{108.1 \text{ g } C_6H_4O_2}{1 \text{ mol } C_6H_4O_2} = -2.75 \times 10^3 \text{ kJ/mol } C_6H_4O_2$$

5.53   *Analyze.* Given: specific heat and mass of glucose, ΔT for calorimeter. Find: heat capacity, C, of calorimeter. *Plan.* All heat from the combustion raises the temperature of the calorimeter. Calculate heat from combustion of glucose, divide by ΔT for calorimeter to get kJ/°C. *Solve:*

(a) $C_{total} = 2.500 \text{ g glucose} \times \dfrac{15.57 \text{ kJ}}{1 \text{ g glucose}} \times \dfrac{1}{2.70°C} = 14.42 = 14.4 \text{ kJ/°C}$

(b)   Qualitatively, assuming the same exact initial conditions in the calorimeter, twice as much glucose produces twice as much heat, which raises the calorimeter temperature by twice as many °C. Quantitatively,

$$5.000 \text{ g glucose} \times \frac{15.57 \text{ kJ}}{1 \text{ g glucose}} \times \frac{1 \text{ °C}}{14.42 \text{ kJ}} = 5.40°C$$

Check. Units are correct. ΔT is twice as large as in part (a). The result has 3 sig figs, because the heat capacity of the calorimeter is known to 3 sig figs.

Hess's Law

5.55   If a reaction can be described as a series of steps, ΔH for the reaction is the sum of the enthalpy changes for each step. As long as we can describe a route where ΔH for each step is known, ΔH for any process can be calculated.

5.57 (a) *Analyze/Plan.* Arrange the reactions so that in the overall sum, B appears in both reactants and products and can be canceled. This is a general technique for using Hess's Law. *Solve*:

$$A \rightarrow B \qquad \Delta H = +30 \text{ kJ}$$
$$\underline{B \rightarrow C} \qquad \underline{\Delta H = +60 \text{ kJ}}$$
$$A \rightarrow C \qquad \Delta H = +90 \text{ kJ}$$

(b)
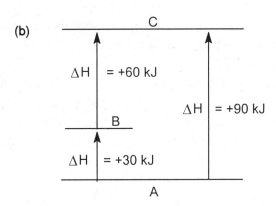

Check. The process of A forming C can be described as A forming B and B forming C.

5.59 *Analyze/Plan.* Follow the logic in Sample Exercise 5.9. Manipulate the equations so that "unwanted" substances can be canceled from reactants and products. Adjust the corresponding sign and magnitude of ΔH. *Solve*:

$$P_4O_6(s) \rightarrow P_4(s) + 3O_2(g) \qquad \Delta H = 1640.1 \text{ kJ}$$
$$P_4(s) + 5O_2(g) \rightarrow P_4O_{10}(s) \qquad \Delta H = -2940.1 \text{ kJ}$$
$$\overline{P_4O_6(s) + 2O_2(g) \rightarrow P_4O_{10}(s)} \qquad \Delta H = -1300.0 \text{ kJ}$$

Check. We have obtained the desired reaction.

5.61 *Analyze/Plan.* Follow the logic in Sample Exercise 5.9. Manipulate the equations so that "unwanted" substances can be canceled from reactants and products. Adjust the corresponding sign and magnitude of ΔH. *Solve*:

$$C_2H_4(g) \rightarrow 2 H_2(g) + 2C(s) \qquad \Delta H = -52.3 \text{ kJ}$$
$$2C(s) + 4F_2(g) \rightarrow 2CF_4(g) \qquad \Delta H = 2(-680 \text{ kJ})$$
$$2H_2(g) + 2F_2(g) \rightarrow 4HF(g) \qquad \Delta H = 2(-537 \text{ kJ})$$
$$\overline{C_2H_4(g) + 6F_2(g) \rightarrow 2CF_4(g) + 4HF(g)} \qquad \Delta H = -2.49 \times 10^3 \text{ kJ}$$

Check. We have obtained the desired reaction.

Enthalpies of Formation

5.63   (a)   *Standard conditions* for enthalpy changes are usually P = 1 atm and T = 298 K. For the purpose of comparison, standard enthalpy changes, ΔH°, are tabulated for reactions at these conditions.

       (b)   *Enthalpy of formation*, ΔH_f, is the enthalpy change that occurs when a compound is formed from its component elements.

       (c)   Standard enthalpy of formation, ΔH_f° is the enthalpy change that accompanies formation of one mole of a substance from elements in their standard states.

5.65   Yes, it would still be possible to have tables of standard enthalpies of formation like Table 5.3. Standard enthalpies of formation are the overall **enthalpy difference** between a compound and its component elements in their standard states. Regardless of the value of the enthalpy of formation of the elements, the magnitude of the difference in enthalpies should be the same (assuming the same reaction stoichiometry).

5.67   (a) $1/2\ N_2(g) + 3/2\ H_2(g) \rightarrow NH_3(g)$ $\Delta H_f^{\circ} = -80.29\ kJ$

       (b) $1/8\ S_8(s) + O_2(g) \rightarrow SO_2(g)$ $\Delta H_f^{\circ} = -269.9\ kJ$

       (c) $Rb(s) + 1/2\ Cl_2(g) + 3/2\ O_2(g) \rightarrow RbClO_3(s)$ $\Delta H_f^{\circ} = -392.4\ kJ$

       (d) $N_2(g) + 2H_2(g) + 3/2\ O_2(g) \rightarrow NH_4NO_3(s)$ $\Delta H_f^{\circ} = -365.6\ kJ$

5.69   *Plan.* $\Delta H_{rxn}^{\circ} = \Sigma n \Delta H_f^{\circ}$ (products) $- \Sigma n \Delta H_f^{\circ}$ (reactants). Be careful with coefficients, states and signs. *Solve:*

$\Delta H_{rxn}^{\circ} = \Delta H_f^{\circ}\ Al_2O_3(s) + 2\Delta H_f^{\circ}\ Fe(s) - \Delta H_f^{\circ}\ Fe_2O_3 - 2\Delta H_f^{\circ}\ Al(s)$

$\Delta H_{rxn}^{\circ} = (-1669.8\ kJ) + 2(0) - (-822.16\ kJ) - 2(0) = -847.6\ kJ$

5.71   *Plan.* $\Delta H_{rxn}^{\circ} = \Sigma n \Delta H_f^{\circ}$ (products) $- \Sigma n \Delta H_f^{\circ}$ (reactants). Be careful with coefficients, states and signs. *Solve:*

       (a) $\Delta H_{rxn}^{\circ} = 2\Delta H_f^{\circ}\ SO_3(g) - 2\Delta H_f^{\circ}\ SO_2(g) - \Delta H_f^{\circ}\ O_2(g)$

                 $= 2(-395.2\ kJ) - 2(-296.9\ kJ) - 0 = -196.6\ kJ$

       (b) $\Delta H_{rxn}^{\circ} = \Delta H_f^{\circ}\ MgO(s) + \Delta H_f^{\circ}\ H_2O(l) - \Delta H_f^{\circ}\ Mg(OH)_2(s)$

                 $= -601.8\ kJ + (-285.83\ kJ) - (-924.7\ kJ) = 37.1\ kJ$

       (c) $\Delta H_{rxn}^{\circ} = 2\Delta H_f^{\circ}\ Fe_2O_3(s) - 4\Delta H_f^{\circ}\ FeO(s) - \Delta H_f^{\circ}\ O_2(g)$

                 $= 2(-822.16\ kJ) - 4(-271.9\ kJ) - 0 = -556.7\ kJ$

       (d) $\Delta H_{rxn}^{\circ} = \Delta H_f^{\circ}\ SiO_2(s) + 4\Delta H_f^{\circ}\ HCl(g) - \Delta H_f^{\circ}\ SiCl_4(l) - 2\ \Delta H_f^{\circ}\ H_2O(l)$

                 $= -910.9\ kJ + 4(-92.30\ kJ) - (-640.1\ kJ) - 2(-285.83\ kJ) = -68.3\ kJ$

5.73   *Analyze.* Given: combustion reaction, enthalpy of combustion, enthalpies of formation for most reactants and products. Find: enthalpy of formation for acetone. *Plan.* Rearrange the expression for enthalpy of reaction to calculate the desired enthalpy of formation. *Solve*:

$$\Delta H^{\circ}_{rxn} = 3\Delta H^{\circ}_f \ CO_2(g) + 3\Delta H^{\circ}_f \ H_2O(l) - \Delta H^{\circ}_f \ C_3H_6O(l)$$

$$-1790 \ kJ = 3(-393.5 \ kJ) + 3(-285.83 \ kJ) - \Delta H^{\circ}_f \ C_3H_6O(l)$$

$$\Delta H^{\circ}_f \ C_3H_6O(l) = -248 \ kJ$$

5.75   *Plan.* Use Hess's Law to arrange the given reactions so the overall sum is the formation reaction for $Mg(OH)_2(s)$. Adjust the corresponding ΔH values and calculate ΔH°_f for $Mg(OH)_2(s)$. *Solve*:

$Mg(s) + 1/2 \ O_2(g) \rightarrow MgO(s)$	$\Delta H^{\circ} = 1/2(-1203.6 \ kJ)$
$MgO(s) + H_2O(l) \rightarrow Mg(OH)_2(s)$	$\Delta H^{\circ} = -(37.1 \ kJ)$
$H_2(g) + 1/2 \ O_2(g) \rightarrow H_2O(l)$	$\Delta H^{\circ} = 1/2(-571.7 \ kJ)$

$$Mg(s) + O_2(g) + H_2(g) \rightarrow Mg(OH)_2(s) \qquad \Delta H^{\circ}_f = -924.8 \ kJ$$

Check. The overall reaction is correct.

5.77   (a) $C_8H_{18}(l) + 25/2 \ O_2(g) \rightarrow 8CO_2(g) + 9H_2O(g) \qquad \Delta H^{\circ} = -5069 \ kJ$

   (b) $8C(s, gr) + 9H_2(g) \rightarrow C_8H_{18}(l) \qquad \Delta H^{\circ}_f = ?$

   (a)   *Plan.* Follow the logic in Solution 5.73. *Solve*:

$$\Delta H^{\circ}_{rxn} = 8\Delta H^{\circ}_f \ CO_2(g) + 9\Delta H^{\circ}_f \ H_2O(g) - \Delta H^{\circ}_f \ C_8H_{18}(l) - 25/2 \ \Delta H^{\circ}_f \ O_2(g)$$

$$-5069 \ kJ = 8(-393.5 \ kJ) + 9(-241.82 \ kJ) - \Delta H^{\circ}_f \ C_8H_{18}(l) - 25/2(0)$$

$$\Delta H^{\circ}_f \ C_8H_{18}(l) = 8(-393.5 \ kJ) + 9(-241.82 \ kJ) + 5069 \ kJ = -255 \ kJ$$

Foods and Fuels

5.79   (a)   *Fuel value* is the amount of heat produced when 1 gram of a substance (fuel) is combusted.

   (b)   Glucose, $C_6H_{12}O_6$, is referred to as *blood sugar*. It is important because glucose is the fuel that is carried by blood to cells and combusted to produce energy in the body.

   (c)   The fuel value of fats is 9 kcal/g and of carbohydrates is 4 kcal/g. Therefore, 5 g of fat produce 45 kcal, while 9 g of carbohydrates produce 36 kcal; 5 g of fat are a greater energy source.

5.81   *Plan.* Calculate the Cal (kcal) due to each nutritional component of the Campbell's® soup, then sum. *Solve.*

$$9 \ g \ carbohydrates \times \frac{17 \ kJ}{1 \ g \ carbohydrate} = 153 \ or \ 2 \times 10^2 \ kJ$$

$$1 \text{ g protein} \times \frac{17 \text{ kJ}}{1 \text{ g protein}} = 17 \text{ or } 0.2 \times 10^2 \text{ kJ}$$

$$7 \text{ g fat} \times \frac{38 \text{ kJ}}{1 \text{ g fat}} = 266 \text{ or } 3 \times 10^2 \text{ kJ}$$

total energy = 153 kJ + 17 kJ + 266 kJ = 436 or 4×10^2 kJ

$$436 \text{ kJ} \times \frac{1 \text{ kcal}}{4.184 \text{ kJ}} \times \frac{1 \text{ Cal}}{1 \text{ kcal}} = 104 \text{ or } 1 \times 10^2 \text{ Cal/serving}$$

Check. 100 Cal/serving is a reasonable result; units are correct. The data and the result have 1 sig fig.

5.83 *Plan.* g → mol → kJ → Cal *Solve*:

$$16.0 \text{ g C}_6\text{H}_{12}\text{O}_6 \times \frac{1 \text{ mol C}_6\text{H}_{15}\text{O}_6}{180.2 \text{ g C}_6\text{H}_{12}\text{O}_6} \times \frac{2812 \text{ kJ}}{\text{mol C}_6\text{H}_{12}\text{O}_6} \times \frac{1 \text{ Cal}}{4.184 \text{ kJ}} = 59.7 \text{ Cal}$$

Check. 60 Cal is a reasonable result for most of the food value in an apple.

5.85 *Plan.* Use enthalpies of formation to calculate molar heat (enthalpy) of combustion using Hess's Law. Use molar mass to calculate heat of combustion per kg of hydrocarbon. *Solve*:

Propyne: $C_3H_4(g) + 4O_2(g) \rightarrow 3CO_2(g) + 2H_2O(g)$

(a) $\Delta H = 3(-393.5 \text{ kJ}) + 2(-241.82 \text{ kJ}) - (185.4 \text{ kJ}) - 4(0) = -1849.5 = -1850 \text{ kJ/mol C}_3\text{H}_4$

(b) $\dfrac{-1849.5 \text{ kJ}}{1 \text{ mol C}_3\text{H}_4} \times \dfrac{1 \text{ mol C}_3\text{H}_4}{40.065 \text{ g C}_3\text{H}_4} \times \dfrac{1000 \text{ g C}_3\text{H}_4}{1 \text{ kg C}_3\text{H}_4} = -4.616 \times 10^4 \text{ kJ/kg C}_3\text{H}_4$

Propylene: $C_3H_6(g) + 9/2 \, O_2(g) \rightarrow 3CO_2(g) + 3H_2O(g)$

(a) $\Delta H = 3(-393.5 \text{ kJ}) + 3(-241.82 \text{ kJ}) - (20.4 \text{ kJ}) - 9/2(0) = -1926.4 = -1926 \text{ kJ/mol C}_3\text{H}_6$

(b) $\dfrac{-1926.4 \text{ kJ}}{1 \text{ mol C}_3\text{H}_6} \times \dfrac{1 \text{ mol C}_3\text{H}_6}{42.080 \text{ g C}_3\text{H}_6} \times \dfrac{1000 \text{ g C}_3\text{H}_6}{1 \text{ kg C}_3\text{H}_6} = -4.578 \times 10^4 \text{ kJ/kg C}_3\text{H}_6$

Propane: $C_3H_8(g) + 5O_2(g) \rightarrow 3CO_2(g) + 4H_2O(g)$

(a) $\Delta H = 3(-393.5 \text{ kJ}) + 4(-241.82 \text{ kJ}) - (-103.8 \text{ kJ}) - 5(0) = -2044.0 = -2044 \text{ kJ/mol C}_3\text{H}_8$

(b) $\dfrac{-2044.0 \text{ kJ}}{1 \text{ mol C}_3\text{H}_8} \times \dfrac{1 \text{ mol C}_3\text{H}_8}{44.096 \text{ g C}_3\text{H}_8} \times \dfrac{1000 \text{ g C}_3\text{H}_8}{1 \text{ kg C}_3\text{H}_8} = -4.635 \times 10^4 \text{ kJ/kg C}_3\text{H}_8$

(c) These three substances yield nearly identical quantities of heat per unit mass, but propane is marginally higher than the other two.

Additional Exercises

5.87 (a) mi/hr → m/s

$$1050 \frac{\text{mi}}{\text{hr}} \times \frac{1.6093 \text{ km}}{1 \text{ mi}} \times \frac{1000 \text{ m}}{1 \text{ km}} \times \frac{1 \text{ hr}}{3600 \text{ s}} = 469.38 = 469.4 \text{ m/s}$$

(b)   Find the mass of one N_2 molecule in kg.

$$\frac{28.0134 \text{ g } N_2}{1 \text{ mol}} \times \frac{1 \text{ mol}}{6.022 \times 10^{23} \text{ molecules}} \times \frac{1 \text{ kg}}{1000 \text{ g}} = 4.6518 \times 10^{-26}$$

$$= 4.652 \times 10^{-26} \text{ kg}$$

$$E_k = 1/2 \, mv^2 = 1/2 \times 4.6518 \times 10^{-26} \text{ kg} \times (469.38 \text{ m/s})^2$$

$$= 5.1244 \times 10^{-21} \frac{\text{kg} \cdot \text{m}^2}{\text{s}^2} = 5.124 \times 10^{-21} \text{ J}$$

(c) $\dfrac{5.1244 \times 10^{21} \text{ J}}{\text{molecule}} \times \dfrac{6.022 \times 10^{23} \text{ molecules}}{1 \text{ mol}} = 3086 \text{ J/mol} = 3.086 \text{ kJ/mol}$

5.90   Like the combustion of $H_2(g)$ and $O_2(g)$ described in Section 5.4, the reaction that inflates airbags is spontaneous after initiation. Spontaneous reactions are usually exothermic, $-\Delta H$. The airbag reaction occurs at constant atmospheric pressure, $\Delta H = q_p$; both are likely to be large and negative. When the bag inflates, work is done by the system on the surroundings so the sign of w is negative.

5.93   (a) $q = 0$, $w > 0$ (work done to system), $\Delta E > 0$

       (b)   Since the system (the gas) is losing heat, the sign of q is negative. The changes in state described in cases (a) and (b) are identical and ΔE is the same in both cases. The distribution of energy transferred as either work or heat is different in the two scenarios. In case (b), more work is required to compress the gas because some heat is lost to the surroundings. [The moral of this story is that the more energy lost by the system as heat, the greater the work on the system required to accomplish the desired change.]

5.96   Find the heat capacity of 1.7×10^3 gal H_2O.

$$C_{H_2O} = 1.7 \times 10^3 \text{ gal } H_2O \times \frac{4 \text{ qt}}{1 \text{ gal}} \times \frac{1 \text{ L}}{1.057 \text{ qt}} \times \frac{1 \times 10^3 \text{ cm}^3}{1 \text{ L}} \times \frac{1 \text{ g}}{1 \text{ cm}^3} \times \frac{4.184 \text{ J}}{1 \text{ g} \cdot {}^\circ C}$$

$$= 2.692 \times 10^7 \text{ J/}^\circ C = 2.7 \times 10^4 \text{ kJ/}^\circ C; \text{ then,}$$

$$\frac{2.692 \times 10^7 \text{ J}}{1 \, {}^\circ C} \times \frac{1 \, {}^\circ C \cdot g}{0.85 \text{ J}} \times \frac{1 \text{ kg}}{1 \times 10^3 \text{ g}} \times \frac{1 \text{ brick}}{1.8 \text{ kg}} = 1.8 \times 10^4 \text{ or } 18{,}000 \text{ bricks}$$

Check. $(1.7 \times {\sim}16 \times 10^6) / ({\sim}1.6 \times 10^3) \approx 17 \times 10^3$ bricks; the units are correct.

5.100   (a)   For comparison, balance the equations so that 1 mole of CH_4 is burned in each.

          $CH_4(g) + O_2(g) \rightarrow C(s) + 2H_2O(l)$ $\Delta H^\circ = -496.9 \text{ kJ}$

          $CH_4(g) + 3/2 \, O_2(g) \rightarrow CO(g) + 2H_2O(l)$ $\Delta H^\circ = -607.4 \text{ kJ}$

          $CH_4(g) + 2O_2(g) \rightarrow CO_2(g) + 2H_2O(l)$ $\Delta H^\circ = -890.4 \text{ kJ}$

       (b) $\Delta H^\circ_{rxn} = \Delta H^\circ_f \, C(s) + 2\Delta H^\circ_f \, H_2O(l) - \Delta H^\circ_f \, CH_4(g) - \Delta H^\circ_f \, O_2(g)$

            $= 0 + 2(-285.83 \text{ kJ}) - (-74.8) - 0 = -496.9 \text{ kJ}$

            $\Delta H^\circ_{rxn} = \Delta H^\circ_f \, CO(g) + 2\Delta H^\circ_f \, H_2O(l) - \Delta H^\circ_f \, CH_4(g) - 3/2 \, \Delta H^\circ_f \, O_2(g)$

              $= (-110.5 \text{ kJ}) + 2(-285.83 \text{ kJ}) - (-74.8 \text{ kJ}) - 3/2(0) = -607.4 \text{ kJ}$

$$\Delta H_{rxn}^{\circ} = \Delta H_f^{\circ}\ CO_2(g) + 2\Delta H_f^{\circ}\ H_2O(l) - \Delta H_f^{\circ}\ CH_4(g) - 2\Delta H_f^{\circ}\ O_2(g)$$
$$= -393.5\ kJ + 2(-285.83\ kJ) - (-74.8\ kJ) - 2(0) = -890.4\ kJ$$

(c)   Assuming that $O_2(g)$ is present in excess, the reaction that produces $CO_2(g)$ represents the most negative ΔH per mole of CH_4 burned. More of the potential energy of the reactants is released as heat during the reaction to give products of lower potential energy. The reaction that produces $CO_2(g)$ is the most "downhill" in enthalpy.

5.103   **1,3-butadiene**, C_4H_6, $\mathcal{M}$ = 54.092 g/mol

     (a) $C_4H_6(g) + 11/2\ O_2(g) \rightarrow 4CO_2(g) + 3H_2O(l)$

$$\Delta H_{rxn}^{\circ} = 4\Delta H_f^{\circ}\ CO_2(g) + 3\Delta H_f^{\circ}\ H_2O(l) - \Delta H_f^{\circ}\ C_4H_6(g) - 11/2\ \Delta H_f^{\circ}\ O_2(g)$$

$$= 4(-393.5\ kJ) + 3(-285.83\ kJ) - 111.9\ kJ + 11/2\ (0) = -2543.4\ kJ/mol\ C_4H_6$$

     (b) $\dfrac{-2543.4\ kJ}{1\ mol\ C_4H_6} \times \dfrac{1\ mol\ C_4H_6}{54.092\ g} = 47.020 \rightarrow 47\ kJ/g$

     (c)   % H $= \dfrac{6(1.008)}{54.092} \times 100 = 11.18\%$ H

1-butene, C_4H_8, $\mathcal{M}$ = 56.108 g/mol

     (a) $C_4H_8(g) + 6O_2(g) \rightarrow 4CO_2(g) + 4H_2O(l)$

$$\Delta H_{rxn}^{\circ} = 4\Delta H_f^{\circ}\ CO_2(g) + 4\Delta H_f^{\circ}\ H_2O(l) - \Delta H_f^{\circ}\ C_4H_8(g) - 6\Delta H_f^{\circ}\ O_2(g)$$

$$= 4(-393.5\ kJ) + 4(-285.83\ kJ) - 1.2\ kJ - 6(0) = -2718.5\ kJ/mol\ C_4H_8$$

     (b) $\dfrac{-2718.5\ kJ}{1\ mol\ C_4H_8} \times \dfrac{1\ mol\ C_4H_8}{56.108\ g\ C_4H_8} = 48.451 \rightarrow 48\ kJ/g$

     (c)   % H $= \dfrac{8(1.008)}{56.108} \times 100 = 14.37\%$ H

n-butane, $C_4H_{10}(g)$, $\mathcal{M}$ = 58.124 g/mol

     (a) $C_4H_{10}(g) + 13/2\ O_2(g) \rightarrow 4CO_2(g) + 5H_2O(l)$

$$\Delta H_{rxn}^{\circ} = 4\Delta H_f^{\circ}\ CO_2(g) + 5\Delta H_f^{\circ}\ H_2O(l) - \Delta H_f^{\circ}\ C_4H_{10}(g) - 13/2\ \Delta H_f^{\circ}\ O_2(g)$$

$$= 4(-393.5\ kJ) + 5(-285.83\ kJ) - (-124.7\ kJ) - 13/2(0) = -2878.5\ kJ/mol\ C_4H_{10}$$

     (b) $\dfrac{-2878.5\ kJ}{1\ mol\ C_4H_{10}} \times \dfrac{1\ mol\ C_4H_{10}}{58.124\ g\ C_4H_{10}} = 49.523 \rightarrow 50\ kJ/g$

     (c)   % H $= \dfrac{10(1.008)}{58.124} \times 100 = 17.34\%$ H

     (d)   It is certainly true that as the mass % H increases, the fuel value (kJ/g) of the hydrocarbon increases, given the same number of C atoms. A graph of the data in parts (b) and (c) (see below) suggests that mass % H and fuel value are directly proportional when the number of C atoms is constant.

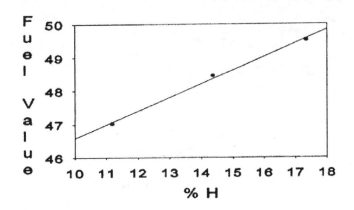

Integrative Exercises

5.107 (a) $CH_4(g) + 2O_2(g) \rightarrow CO_2(g) + 2H_2O(l)$

$\Delta H° = \Delta H_f° \ CO_2(g) + 2\Delta H_f° \ H_2O(l) - \Delta H_f° \ CH_4(g) - 2\Delta H_f° \ O_2(g)$

$= -393.5 \ kJ + 2(-285.83 \ kJ) - (-74.8 \ kJ) - 2(0) = -890.36 = -890.4 \ kJ/mol \ CH_4$

$$\frac{-890.36 \ kJ}{mol \ CH_4} \times \frac{1000 \ J}{1 \ kJ} \times \frac{1 \ mol}{6.022 \times 10^{23} \ molecules \ CH_4} = 1.4785 \times 10^{-18}$$

$$= 1.479 \times 10^{-18} \ J/molecule$$

(b) $1eV = 96.485 \ kJ/mol$

$$8 \ keV \times \frac{1000 \ eV}{1 \ keV} \times \frac{96.485 \ kJ}{eV \cdot mol} \times \frac{1 \ mol}{6.022 \times 10^{23}} \times \frac{1000 \ J}{kJ} = 1.282 \times 10^{-15}$$

$$= 1 \times 10^{-15} \ J/X\text{-ray}$$

The X-ray has approximately 1000 times more energy than is produced by the combustion of 1 molecule of $CH_4(g)$.

5.111 (a)   mol Cu = M × L = 1.00 M × 0.0500 L = 0.0500 mol

g = mol × $\mathcal{M}$ = 0.0500 × 63.546 = 3.1773 = 3.18 g Cu

(b)   The precipitate is copper(II) hydroxide, $Cu(OH)_2$.

(c) $CuSO_4(aq) + 2KOH(aq) \rightarrow Cu(OH)_2(s) + K_2SO_4(aq)$, complete

$Cu^{2+}(aq) + 2OH^-(aq) \rightarrow Cu(OH)_2(s)$, net ionic

(d)   The temperature of the calorimeter rises, so the reaction is exothermic and the sign of q is negative.

$$q = -6.2°C \times 100 \ g \times \frac{4.184 \ J}{1 \ g \cdot °C} = -2.6 \times 10^3 \ J = -2.6 \ kJ$$

The reaction as carried out involves only 0.050 mol of $CuSO_4$ and the stoichiometrically equivalent amount of KOH. On a molar basis,

$$\Delta H = \frac{-2.6 \ kJ}{0.050 \ mol} = -52 \ kJ \ \text{for the reaction as written in part (c)}$$

6 Electronic Structure of Atoms

Radiant Energy

6.1   (a) meters (m)   (b) 1/seconds (s^{-1})   (c) meters/second ($m \cdot s^{-1}$ or m/s)

6.3   (a)   True.

   (b)   False. The frequency of radiation decreases as the wavelength increases.

   (c)   False. Ultraviolet light has shorter wavelengths than visible light. [See Solution 6.2(b)]

   (d)   False. Electromagnetic radiation and sound waves travel at different speeds.

6.5   *Analyze/Plan*. Use the electromagnetic spectrum in Figure 6.4 to determine the wavelength of each type of radiation; put them in order from shortest to longest wavelength.

   Solve. Wavelength of X-rays < ultraviolet < green light < red light < infrared < radio waves

   Check. These types of radiation should read from left to right on Figure 6.4

6.7   *Analyze/Plan*. These questions involve relationships between wavelength, frequency and the speed of light. Manipulate the equation $\nu = c/\lambda$ to obtain the desired quantities, paying attention to units. *Solve*:

   (a) $\nu = c/\lambda$; $\dfrac{2.998 \times 10^8 \text{ m}}{s} \times \dfrac{1}{0.452 \text{ pm}} \times \dfrac{1 \text{ pm}}{1 \times 10^{-12} \text{ m}} = 6.63 \times 10^{20} \text{ s}^{-1}$

   (b) $\lambda = c/\nu$; $\dfrac{2.998 \times 10^8 \text{ m}}{s} \times \dfrac{1 \text{ s}}{2.55 \times 10^{16}} = 1.18 \times 10^{-8} \text{ m}$ (11.8 nm)

   (c)   No. The radiation in (a) is gamma rays and in (b) is ultraviolet. Neither is visible to humans.

   (d) $7.50 \text{ ms} \times \dfrac{1 \text{ s}}{1 \times 10^3 \text{ ms}} \times \dfrac{2.998 \times 10^8 \text{ m}}{s} = 2.25 \times 10^6 \text{ m}$

   Check. Confirm that powers of 10 make sense and units are correct.

6.9   *Analyze/Plan*. $\nu = c/\lambda$; change nm → m.

   Solve: $\nu = c/\lambda$; $\dfrac{2.998 \times 10^8 \text{ m}}{1 \text{ s}} \times \dfrac{1}{436 \text{ nm}} \times \dfrac{1 \text{ nm}}{1 \times 10^{-9} \text{ m}} = 6.88 \times 10^{14} \text{ s}^{-1}$

   The color is blue.

   Check. $(3000 \times 10^5/500 \times 10^{-9}) = 6 \times 10^{14} \text{ s}^{-1}$; units are correct.

Quantized Energy and Photons

6.11 (a) *Quantization* means that energy can only be absorbed or emitted in specific amounts or multiples of these amounts. This minimum amount of energy is called a quantum and is equal to a constant times the frequency of the radiation absorbed or emitted. **E = hν**.

  (b) In everyday activities, we deal with macroscopic objects such as our bodies or our cars, which gain and lose total amounts of energy much larger than a single quantum, hν. The gain or loss of the relatively minuscule quantum of energy is unnoticed.

6.13 *Analyze/Plan.* These questions deal with the relationships between energy, wavelength and frequency. Use the relationships $E = h\nu = hc/\lambda$ to calculate the desired quantities. Pay attention to units. *Solve:*

  (a) $E = h\nu = hc/\lambda = 6.626 \times 10^{-34} \, \text{J} \cdot \text{s} \times \dfrac{2.998 \times 10^8 \, \text{m}}{1 \, \text{s}} \times \dfrac{1}{812 \, \text{nm}} \times \dfrac{1 \, \text{nm}}{1 \times 10^{-9} \, \text{m}}$

$$= 2.45 \times 10^{-19} \, \text{J}$$

  (b) $E = h\nu = 6.626 \times 10^{-34} \, \text{J} \cdot \text{s} \times \dfrac{2.72 \times 10^{13}}{1 \, \text{s}} = 1.80 \times 10^{-20} \, \text{J}$

  (c) $\lambda = hc/E = 6.626 \times 10^{-34} \, \text{J} \cdot \text{s} \times \dfrac{2.998 \times 10^8 \, \text{m}}{1 \, \text{s}} \times \dfrac{1}{7.84 \times 10^{-18} \, \text{J}} = 2.53 \times 10^{-8} \, \text{m}$

$$= 25.3 \, \text{nm}$$

  This radiation is in the ultraviolet region.

  Check. Units are correct and powers of 10 are reasonable.

6.15 *Analyze/Plan.* Use $E = hc/\lambda$; pay close attention to units. *Solve:*

  (a) $E = hc/\lambda = 6.626 \times 10^{-34} \, \text{J} \cdot \text{s} \times \dfrac{2.998 \times 10^8 \, \text{m}}{1 \, \text{s}} \times \dfrac{1}{3.3 \, \mu\text{m}} \times \dfrac{1 \, \mu\text{m}}{1 \times 10^{-6} \, \text{m}}$

$$= 6.0 \times 10^{-20} \, \text{J}$$

  $E = hc/\lambda = 6.626 \times 10^{-34} \, \text{J} \cdot \text{s} \times \dfrac{2.998 \times 10^8 \, \text{m}}{1 \, \text{s}} \times \dfrac{1}{0.154 \, \text{nm}} \times \dfrac{1 \, \text{nm}}{1 \times 10^{-9} \, \text{m}}$

$$= 1.29 \times 10^{-15} \, \text{J}$$

  Check. $(6.6 \times 3/3.3) \times (10^{-34} \times 10^8/10^{-6}) \approx 6 \times 10^{-20} \, \text{J}$

  $(6.6 \times 3/0.15) \times (10^{-34} \times 10^8/10^{-9}) \approx 120 \times 10^{-17} \approx 1.2 \times 10^{-15} \, \text{J}$

  The results are reasonable. We expect the longer wavelength 3.3 μm radiation to have the lower energy.

  (b) The 3.3 μm photon is in the infrared and the 0.154 nm (1.54×10^{-10} m) photon is in the X-ray region; the X-ray photon has the greater energy.

6.17   *Analyze/Plan.* Use $E = hc/\lambda$ to calculate J/photon; Avogadro's number to calculate J/mol; photon/J (the result from part (a)) to calculate photons in 1.00 mJ. Pay attention to units. *Solve*:

(a) $E_{photon} = hc/\lambda = \dfrac{6.626 \times 10^{-34} \text{ J} \cdot \text{s}}{325 \times 10^{-9} \text{ m}} \times \dfrac{2.998 \times 10^8 \text{ m}}{\text{s}} = 6.1122 \times 10^{-19}$

$= 6.11 \times 10^{-19}$ J/photon

(b) $\dfrac{6.1122 \times 10^{-19} \text{ J}}{1 \text{ photon}} \times \dfrac{6.022 \times 10^{23} \text{ photons}}{1 \text{ mol}} = 3.68 \times 10^5$ J/mol = 368 kJ/mol

(c) $\dfrac{1 \text{ photon}}{6.1122 \times 10^{-19} \text{ J}} \times 1.00 \text{ mJ} \times \dfrac{1 \times 10^{-3}}{1 \text{ mJ}} = 1.64 \times 10^{15}$ photons

Check. Powers of 10 (orders of magnitude) and units are correct.

6.19   *Analyze/Plan.* $E = hc/\lambda$ gives J/photon. Use this result with J/s (given) to calculate photons/s. *Solve*:

$E_{photon} = hc/\lambda = \dfrac{6.626 \times 10^{-34} \text{ J} \cdot \text{s}}{987 \times 10^{-9} \text{ m}} \times \dfrac{2.998 \times 10^8 \text{ m}}{1 \text{ s}} = 2.0126 \times 10^{-19} = 2.01 \times 10^{-19}$ J/photon

$\dfrac{0.52 \text{ J}}{32 \text{ s}} \times \dfrac{1 \text{ photon}}{2.0126 \times 10^{-19} \text{ J}} = 8.1 \times 10^{16}$ photons/s

Check. $(7 \times 3/1000) \times (10^{-34} \times 10^8/10^{-9}) \approx 21 \times 10^{-20} \approx 2.1 \times 10^{-19}$ J/photon

$(0.5/30/2) \times (1/10^{-19}) = 0.008 \times 10^{19} = 8 \times 10^{16}$ photons/s

Units are correct; powers of 10 are reasonable.

6.21   *Analyze/Plan.* Use $E = h\nu$ and $\nu = c/\lambda$. Calculate the desired characteristics of the photons. Compare E_{min} and E_{120} to calculate maximum kinetic energy of the emitted electron. *Solve*:

(a) $E = h\nu = 6.626 \times 10^{-34}$ J•s $\times 1.09 \times 10^{15}$ s^{-1} $= 7.22 \times 10^{-19}$ J

(b) $\lambda = c/\nu = \dfrac{2.998 \times 10^8 \text{ m}}{1 \text{ s}} \times \dfrac{1 \text{ s}}{1.09 \times 10^{15}} = 2.75 \times 10^{-7}$ m = 275 nm

(c) $E_{120} = hc/\lambda = 6.626 \times 10^{-34}$ J•s $\times \dfrac{2.998 \times 10^8 \text{ m}}{1 \text{ s}} \times \dfrac{1}{120 \text{ nm}} \times \dfrac{1 \text{ nm}}{1 \times 10^{-9} \text{ m}}$

$= 1.655 \times 10^{-18} = 1.66 \times 10^{-18}$ J

The excess energy of the 120 nm photon is converted into the kinetic energy of the emitted electron.

$E_k = E_{120} - E_{min} = 16.55 \times 10^{-19}$ J $- 7.22 \times 10^{-19}$ J $= 9.3 \times 10^{-19}$ J/electron

Check. E_{120} must be greater than E_{min} in order for the photon to impart kinetic energy to the emitted electron. Our calculations are consistent with this requirement.

Bohr's Model; Matter Waves

6.23   When applied to atoms, the notion of quantized energies means that only certain energies can be gained or lost, only certain values of ΔE are allowed. The allowed values of ΔE are represented by the lines in the emission spectra of excited atoms.

6.25   *Analyze/Plan.* An isolated electron is assigned an energy of zero; the closer the electron comes to the nucleus, the more negative its energy. Thus, as an electron moves closer to the nucleus, the energy of the electron decreases and the excess energy is emitted. Conversely, as an electron moves further from the nucleus, the energy of the electron increases and energy must be absorbed. *Solve:*

(a)   As the principle quantum number decreases, the electron moves toward the nucleus and energy is **emitted**.

(b)   An increase in the radius of the orbit means the electron moves away from the nucleus; energy is **absorbed**.

(c)   An isolated electron is assigned an energy of zero. As the electron moves to the n = 3 state closer to the H^+ nucleus, its energy becomes more negative (decreases) and energy is **emitted**.

6.27   *Analyze/Plan.* Equation 6.5: $E = (-2.18 \times 10^{-18} \text{ J})(1/n^2)$. *Solve:*

$E_2 = -2.18 \times 10^{-18} \text{ J}/(2)^2 = -5.45 \times 10^{-19} \text{ J}$

$E_6 = -2.18 \times 10^{-18} \text{ J}/(6)^2 = -6.0556 \times 10^{-20} = -0.606 \times 10^{-19} \text{ J}$

$\Delta E = E_6 - E_2 = (-0.606 \times 10^{-19} \text{ J}) - (-5.45 \times 10^{-19} \text{ J}) = 4.844 \times 10^{-19} \text{ J} = 4.84 \times 10^{-19} \text{ J}$

$$\lambda = hc/\Delta E = \frac{6.626 \times 10^{-34} \text{ J} \cdot \text{s}}{4.844 \times 10^{-19} \text{ J}} \times \frac{2.998 \times 10^8 \text{ m}}{\text{s}} = 4.10 \times 10^{-7} \text{ m} = 410 \text{ nm}$$

The visible range is 400 - 700 nm, so this line is visible; the observed color is violet.

Check. We expect E_6 to be a more positive (or less negative) than E_2, and it is. ΔE is positive, which indicates emission. The orders of magnitude make sense and units are correct.

6.29   (a)   Only lines with $n_f = 2$ represent ΔE values and wavelengths that lie in the visible portion of the spectrum. Lines with $n_f = 1$ have larger ΔE values and shorter wavelengths that lie in the ultraviolet. Lines with $n_f > 2$ have smaller ΔE values and lie in the lower energy longer wavelength regions of the electromagnetic spectrum.

(b)   *Analyze/Plan.* Use Equation 6.7 to calculate ΔE, then $\lambda = hc/\Delta E$. *Solve:*

$$n_i = 3, n_f = 2; \quad \Delta E = -2.18 \times 10^{-18} \text{ J} \left[\frac{1}{n_f^2} - \frac{1}{n_i^2} \right] = -2.18 \times 10^{-18} \text{ J} (1/4 - 1/9)$$

$$\lambda = hc/E = \frac{6.626 \times 10^{-34} \text{ J} \cdot \text{s} \times 2.998 \times 10^8 \text{ m/s}}{-2.18 \times 10^{-18} \text{ J} (1/4 - 1/9)} = 6.56 \times 10^{-7} \text{ m}$$

This is the red line at 656 nm.

$n_i = 4$, $n_f = 2$; $\lambda = hc/E = \dfrac{6.626 \times 10^{-34} \text{ J} \bullet \text{s} \times 2.998 \times 10^8 \text{ m/s}}{-2.18 \times 10^{-18} \text{ J} (1/4 - 1/16)} = 4.86 \times 10^{-7} \text{ m}$

This is the blue line at 486 nm.

$n_i = 5$, $n_f = 2$; $\lambda = hc/E = \dfrac{6.626 \times 10^{-34} \text{ J} \bullet \text{s} \times 2.998 \times 10^8 \text{ m/s}}{-2.18 \times 10^{-18} \text{ J} (1/4 - 1/25)} = 4.34 \times 10^{-7} \text{ m}$

This is the violet line at 434 nm.

Check. The calculated wavelengths correspond well to 3 lines in the H emission spectrum in Figure 6.12, so the results are sensible.

6.31   (a)   93.8 nm × $\dfrac{1 \times 10^{-9} \text{ m}}{1 \text{ nm}}$ = 9.38×10^{-8} m; this line is in the ultraviolet region.

(b)   *Analyze/Plan.* Only lines with $n_f = 1$ have a large enough ΔE to lie in the ultraviolet region (see Solution 6.29 and 6.30). Solve Equation 6.7 for n_i, recalling that ΔE is negative for emission.   *Solve:*

$$\frac{-hc}{\lambda} = -2.18 \times 10^{-18} \text{ J} \left[\frac{1}{n_f^2} - \frac{1}{n_i^2} \right]; \quad \frac{hc}{\lambda(2.18 \times 10^{-18} \text{ J})} = \left[1 - \frac{1}{n_i^2} \right]$$

$$-\frac{1}{n_i^2} = \left[\frac{hc}{\lambda(2.18 \times 10^{-18} \text{ J})} - 1 \right]; \quad \frac{1}{n_i^2} = \left[1 - \frac{hc}{\lambda(2.18 \times 10^{-18} \text{ J})} \right]$$

$$n_i^2 = \left[1 - \frac{hc}{\lambda(2.18 \times 10^{-18} \text{ J})} \right]^{-1}; \quad n_i = \left[1 - \frac{hc}{\lambda(2.18 \times 10^{-18} \text{ J})} \right]^{-1/2}$$

$$n_i = \left(1 - \frac{6.626 \times 10^{-34} \text{ J} \bullet \text{s} \times 2.998 \times 10^8 \text{ m/s}}{9.38 \times 10^{-8} \text{ m} \times 2.18 \times 10^{-18} \text{ J}} \right)^{-1/2} = 6 \text{ (} n \text{ values must be integers)}$$

$n_i = 6$, $n_f = 1$

Check. From Solution 6.30, we know that $n_i > 4$ for $\lambda = 93.8$ nm. The calculated result is close to 6, so the answer is reasonable.

6.33   *Analyze/Plan.* $\lambda = \dfrac{h}{mv}$; $1 \text{ J} = \dfrac{1 \text{ kg} \bullet \text{m}^2}{\text{s}^2}$;   Change mass to kg and velocity to m/s in each case.   *Solve:*

(a) $\dfrac{50 \text{ km}}{1 \text{ hr}} \times \dfrac{1000 \text{ m}}{1 \text{ km}} \times \dfrac{1 \text{ hr}}{60 \text{ min}} \times \dfrac{1 \text{ min}}{60 \text{ s}} = 13.89 = 14 \text{ m/s}$

$\lambda = \dfrac{6.626 \times 10^{-34} \text{ kg} \bullet \text{m}^2 \bullet \text{s}}{1 \text{ s}^2} \times \dfrac{1}{85 \text{ kg}} \times \dfrac{1 \text{ s}}{13.89 \text{ m}} = 5.6 \times 10^{-37} \text{ m}$

(b) $10.0 \text{ g} \times \dfrac{1 \text{ kg}}{1000 \text{ g}} = 0.0100 \text{ kg}$

$$\lambda = \frac{6.626 \times 10^{-34} \text{ kg} \cdot \text{m}^2 \cdot \text{s}}{1 \text{ s}^2} \times \frac{1}{0.0100 \text{ kg}} \times \frac{1 \text{ s}}{250 \text{ m}} = 2.65 \times 10^{-34} \text{ m}$$

(c)   We need to calculate the mass of a single Li atom in kg.

$$\frac{6.94 \text{ g Li}}{1 \text{ mol Li}} \times \frac{1 \text{ kg}}{1000 \text{ g}} \times \frac{1 \text{ mol}}{6.022 \times 10^{23} \text{ Li atoms}} = 1.152 \times 10^{-26} = 1.15 \times 10^{-26} \text{ kg}$$

$$\lambda = \frac{6.626 \times 10^{-34} \text{ kg} \cdot \text{m}^2 \cdot \text{s}}{1 \text{ s}^2} \times \frac{1}{1.152 \times 10^{-26} \text{ kg}} \times \frac{1 \text{ s}}{2.5 \times 10^5 \text{ m}} = 2.3 \times 10^{-13} \text{ m}$$

6.35   *Analyze/Plan.* Use $v = h/m\lambda$; change wavelength to meters and mass of neutron (back-inside cover) to kg. *Solve:*

$$\lambda = 0.955 \text{ Å} \times \frac{1 \times 10^{-10} \text{ m}}{1 \text{ Å}} = 0.955 \times 10^{-10} \text{ m}; \quad m = 1.6749 \times 10^{-27} \text{ kg}$$

$$v = \frac{6.626 \times 10^{-34} \text{ kg} \cdot \text{m}^2 \cdot \text{s}}{1 \text{ s}^2} \times \frac{1}{1.6749 \times 10^{-27} \text{ kg}} \times \frac{1}{0.955 \times 10^{-10} \text{ m}} = 4.14 \times 10^3 \text{ m/s}$$

Check. $(6.6/1.6/1) \times (10^{-34}/10^{-27}/10^{-10}) \approx 4 \times 10^3 \text{ m/s}$

6.37   *Analyze/Plan.* Use $\Delta x \geq h/4\pi \, m \, \Delta v$, paying attention to appropriate units. Note that the uncertainty in speed of the particle (Δv) is important, rather than the speed itself. *Solve:*

(a) $m = 1.50 \text{ mg} \times \dfrac{1 \text{ g}}{1000 \text{ mg}} \times \dfrac{1 \text{ kg}}{1000 \text{ g}} = 1.50 \times 10^{-6} \text{ kg}; \quad \Delta v = 0.01 \text{ m/s}$

$$\Delta x \geq = \frac{6.626 \times 10^{-34} \text{ J} \cdot \text{s}}{4\pi (1.50 \times 10^{-6} \text{ kg})(0.01 \times 10^4 \text{ m/s})} \geq 3.52 \times 10^{-27} = 4 \times 10^{-27} \text{ m}$$

(b) $m = 1.673 \times 10^{-24} \text{ g} = 1.673 \times 10^{-27} \text{ kg}; \quad \Delta v = 0.01 \times 10^4 \text{ m/s}$

$$\Delta x \geq = \frac{6.626 \times 10^{-34} \text{ J} \cdot \text{s}}{4\pi (1.673 \times 10^{-27} \text{ kg})(0.01 \times 10^4 \text{ m/s})} \geq 3 \times 10^{-10} \text{ m}$$

Check. The more massive particle in (a) has a much smaller uncertainty in position.

Quantum Mechanics and Atomic Orbitals

6.39   The Bohr model states with 100% certainty that the electron in hydrogen can be found 0.53 Å from the nucleus. The quantum mechanical model, taking the wave nature of the electron and the uncertainty principle into account, is a statistical model that states the probability of finding the electron in certain regions around the nucleus. While 0.53 Å might be the radius with highest probability, that probability would always be less than 100%.

6.41   (a)   The possible values of l are (n-1) to 0. $n = 4$, $l = 3, 2, 1, 0$

        (b)   The possible values of m_l are $-l$ to $+l$. $l = 2$, $m_l = -2, -1, 0, 1, 2$

6.43   (a)   3p: $n = 3$, $l = 1$ (b)   2s: $n = 2$, $l = 0$ (c)   4f: $n = 4$, $l = 3$ (d)   5d: $n = 5$, $l = 2$

6.45   impossible: (a) 1p, only $l = 0$ is possible for $n = 1$;   (d)   2d, for $n = 2$, $l = 1$ or 0, but not 2

6.47   a) 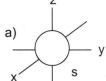   b)   c)

6.49   (a)   The 1s and 2s orbitals of a hydrogen atom have the same overall spherical shape. The 2s orbital has a larger radial extension and one node, while the 1s orbital has continuous electron density. Since the 2s orbital is "larger", there is greater probability of finding an electron further from the nucleus in the 2s orbital.

        (b)   A single 2p orbital is directional in that its electron density is concentrated along one of the three cartesian axes of the atom. The $d_{x^2-y^2}$ orbital has electron density along both the x- and y-axes, while the p_x orbital has density only along the x-axis.

        (c)   The average distance of an electron from the nucleus in a 3s orbital is greater than for an electron in a 2s orbital. In general, for the same kind of orbital, the larger the n value, the greater the average distance of an electron from the nucleus of the atom.

        (d)   1s < 2p < 3d < 4f < 6s. In the hydrogen atom, orbitals with the same n value are degenerate and energy increases with increasing n value. Thus, the order of increasing energy is given above.

Many-Electron Atoms and Electron Configurations

6.51   (a)   In the hydrogen atom, orbitals with the same principle quantum number, n, have the same energy; they are degenerate.

        (b)   In a many-electron atom, for a given n-value, orbital energy increases with increasing l-value: s < p < d < f

6.53   (a)   +1/2, - 1/2

        (b)   Electrons with opposite spins are affected differently by a strong inhomogeneous magnetic field. An apparatus similar to that in Figure 6.24 can be used to distinguish electrons with opposite spins.

        (c)   The Pauli exclusion principle states that no two electrons can have the same four quantum numbers. Two electrons in a 1s orbital have the same, n, l and m_l values. They must have different m_s values.

6.55 Each subshell has an *l*-value associated with it. For a particular *l*-value, permissible m_l-values are -*l* to +*l*. Each m_l-value represents an orbital, which can hold two electrons.

    (a) 10   (b) 2   (c) 6   (d) 14

6.57 (a)   Each box represents an orbital.

       (b)   Electron spin is represented by the direction of the half-arrows.

       (c)   No. The electron configuration of Be is $1s^2 2s^2$. There are no electrons in subshells that have degenerate orbitals, so Hund's rule is not used.

6.59 (a)   Cs: $[Xe]6s^1$ (b) Ni: $[Ar]4s^2 3d^8$ (c) Se: $[Ar]4s^2 3d^{10} 4p^4$

       (d)   Cd: $[Kr]5s^2 4d^{10}$ (e) Ac: $[Rn]7s^2 6d^1$ (f) Pb: $[Xe]6s^2 4f^{14} 5d^{10} 6p^2$

6.61 (a)   S: [Ne]   [↑↓]   [↑↓][↑][↑]   2 unpaired electrons
                        3s   3p

       (b)   Sr: [Kr]   [↑↓]   0 unpaired electrons
                     5s

       (c)   Fe: [Ar]   [↑↓]   [↑↓][↑][↑][↑][↑]   4 unpaired electrons
                       4s   3d

       (d)   Zr: [Kr]   [↑↓]   [↑][↑][ ][ ][ ]   2 unpaired electrons
                     5s   4d

       (e)   Sb: [Kr]   [↑↓]   [↑↓][↑↓][↑↓][↑↓][↑↓]   [↑][↑][↑]   3 unpaired electrons
                     5s   4d   5p

       (f)   U: [Rn]   [↑↓]   [↑][↑][↑][ ][ ][ ][ ]   [↑][ ][ ][ ][ ]
                     7s   5f   6d

                                                           4 unpaired electrons

6.63 (a)   Mg   (b) Al   (c) Cr   (d) Te

6.65 (a)   The fifth electron would fill the 2p subshell (same *n*-value as 2s) before the 3s.

       (b)   The Ne core has filled 2s and 2p subshells. Either the core is [He] or the outer electron configuration should be $3s^2 3p^3$.

       (c)   The 3p subshell would fill before the 3d because it has the lower *l*-value and the same *n*-value.

Additional Exercises

6.67 (a) $\lambda_A = 1.6 \times 10^{-7}$ m / 4.5 = 3.56×10^{-8} = 3.6×10^{-8} m

             $\lambda_B = 1.6 \times 10^{-7}$ m / 2 = 8.0×10^{-8} m

(b) $\nu = c/\lambda$; $\nu_A = \dfrac{2.998 \times 10^8 \text{ m}}{1 \text{ s}} \times \dfrac{1}{3.56 \times 10^{-8} \text{ m}} = 8.4 \times 10^{15} \text{ s}^{-1}$

$\nu_B = \dfrac{2.998 \times 10^8 \text{ m}}{1 \text{ s}} \times \dfrac{1}{8.0 \times 10^{-8} \text{ m}} = 3.7 \times 10^{15} \text{ s}^{-1}$

(c)   A: ultraviolet,   B: ultraviolet

6.69   All electromagnetic radiation travels at the same speed, 2.998×10^8 m/s. Change miles to meters and seconds to some appropriate unit of time.

$522 \times 10^6 \text{ mi} \times \dfrac{1.6093 \text{ km}}{1 \text{ mi}} \times \dfrac{1000 \text{ m}}{1 \text{ km}} \times \dfrac{1 \text{ s}}{2.998 \times 10^8 \text{ m}} \times \dfrac{1 \text{ min}}{60 \text{ s}} = 46.7 \text{ min}$

6.71 $E = hc/\lambda \rightarrow$ J/photon; total energy = power × time; photons = total energy / J / photon

$E = \dfrac{6.626 \times 10^{-34} \text{ J}\bullet\text{s} \times 2.998 \times 10^8 \text{ m/s}}{780 \times 10^{-9} \text{ m}} = 2.5468 \times 10^{-19} = 2.55 \times 10^{-19} \text{ J/photon}$

$0.10 \text{ mW} = \dfrac{0.10 \times 10^{-3} \text{ J}}{1 \text{ s}} \times 69 \text{ min} \times \dfrac{60 \text{ s}}{1 \text{ min}} = 0.4140 = 0.41 \text{ J}$

$0.4140 \text{ J} \times \dfrac{1 \text{ photon}}{2.5468 \times 10^{-19} \text{ J}} = 1.626 \times 10^{18} = 1.6 \times 10^{18} \text{ photons}$

6.73 $\dfrac{5.8 \times 10^{-13} \text{ C}}{1 \text{ s}} \times \dfrac{1 e^-}{1.602 \times 10^{-19} \text{ C}} \times \dfrac{1 \text{ photon}}{1 e^-} = 3.620 \times 10^6 = 3.6 \times 10^6 \text{ photons/s}$

$\dfrac{E}{\text{photon}} = hc/\lambda = \dfrac{6.626 \times 10^{-34} \text{ J}\bullet\text{s}}{550 \text{ nm}} \times \dfrac{2.998 \times 10^8 \text{ m}}{1 \text{ s}} \times \dfrac{1 \text{ nm}}{1 \times 10^{-9} \text{ m}} \times \dfrac{3.620 \times 10^6 \text{ photon}}{\text{s}}$

$= 1.3 \times 10^{-12} \text{ J/s}$

6.75   (a)   Gaseous atoms of various elements in the sun's atmosphere typically have ground state electron configurations. When these atoms are exposed to radiation from the sun, the electrons change from the ground state to one of several allowed excited states. Atoms absorb the wavelengths of light which correspond to these allowed energy changes. All other wavelengths of solar radiation pass through the atmosphere unchanged. Thus, the dark lines are the wavelengths that correspond to allowed energy changes in atoms of the solar atmosphere. The continuous background is all other wavelengths of solar radiation.

       (b)   The scientist should record the absorption spectrum of pure neon or other elements of interest. The black lines should appear at the same wavelengths regardless of the source of neon.

6.77 $\lambda = h/mv$; $v = h/m\lambda$. $\lambda = 0.711 \text{ Å} \times \dfrac{1 \times 10^{-10} \text{ m}}{1 \text{ Å}} = 7.11 \times 10^{-11} \text{ m}$; $m_e = 9.1094 \times 10^{-31} \text{ kg}$

$v = \dfrac{6.626 \times 10^{-34} \text{ J}\bullet\text{s}}{9.1094 \times 10^{-31} \text{ kg} \times 7.11 \times 10^{-11} \text{ m}} \times \dfrac{1 \text{ kg}\bullet\text{m}^2/\text{s}^2}{1 \text{ J}} = 1.02 \times 10^7 \text{ m/s}$

6.79   (a) l (b) n and l (c) m_s (d) m_l

6.81   (a) 1   (b) 3   (c) 5   (d) 9

6.83   (a)   The p_z orbital has a nodal plane where z = 0. This is the xy plane.

        (b)   The d_{xy} orbital has 4 lobes and 2 nodal planes, the two planes where x = 0 and
               y = 0. These are the yz and xz planes.

        (c)   The $d_{x^2-y^2}$ has 4 lobes and 2 nodal planes, the planes where $x^2 - y^2 = 0$. These are
               the planes that bisect the x and y axes and contain the z axis.

6.85   Mt: [Rn] $7s^2 5f^{14} 6d^7$

Integrative Exercises

6.87   We know the wavelength of microwave radiation, the volume of coffee to be heated and the
        desired temperature change. Assume the density and heat capacity of coffee are the same
        as pure water. We need to calculate: (i) the total energy required to heat the coffee and (ii)
        the energy of a single photon in order to find (iii) the number of photons required.

        (i)   From Chapter 5, the heat capacity of liquid water is 4.184 J/g°C.

               To find the mass of 200 mL of coffee at 23°C, use the density of water given in
               Appendix B.

               $$200 \text{ mL} \times \frac{0.997 \text{ g}}{1 \text{ mL}} = 199.4 = 199 \text{ g coffee}$$

               $$\frac{4.184 \text{ J}}{1 \text{ g °C}} \times 199.4 \text{ g} \times (60°C - 23°C) = 3.087 \times 10^4 \text{ J} = 31 \text{ kJ}$$

        (ii) $$E = hc/\lambda = 6.626 \times 10^{-34} \text{ J} \cdot \text{s} \times \frac{2.998 \times 10^8 \text{ m}}{1 \text{ s}} \times \frac{1}{0.112 \text{ m}} = \frac{1.77 \times 10^{-24} \text{ J}}{1 \text{ photon}}$$

        (iii) $$3.087 \times 10^4 \text{ J} \times \frac{1 \text{ photon}}{1.774 \times 10^{-24} \text{ J}} = 1.7 \times 10^{28} \text{ photons}$$

        (The answer has 2 sig figs because the temperature change, 43°C, has 2 sig figs)

7 Periodic Properties of the Elements

Periodic Table; Effective Nuclear Charge

7.1   Mendeleev insisted that elements with similar chemical and physical properties be placed within a family or column of the table. Since many elements were as yet undiscovered, Mendeleev left blanks. He predicted properties for the "blanks" based on properties of other elements in the family.

7.3   (a)   Effective nuclear charge, Z_{eff}, is a representation of the average electrical field experienced by a single electron. It is the average environment created by the nucleus and the other electrons in the molecule, expressed as a **net** positive charge at the nucleus. It is approximately the nuclear charge, Z, minus the number of core electrons.

       (b)   Going from left to right across a period, nuclear charge increases while the number of electrons in the core is constant. This results in an increase in Z_{eff}.

7.5   *Analyze/Plan*. The problem states that shielding, S, is exactly equal to the number of electrons in the core. Z_{eff} = Z - # of core electrons. *Solve*:

       (a)   K: 19 - 18 = +1   (b)   Br: 35 - 28 = +7

7.7   Krypton has a larger nuclear charge (Z = 36) than argon (Z = 18). The shielding of electrons in the n = 3 shell by the 1s and 2s core electrons in the two atoms is approximately equal, so the n = 3 electrons in Kr experience a greater effective nuclear charge and are thus situated closer to the nucleus.

Atomic and Ionic Radii

7.9   Atomic radii are determined by distances between atoms (interatomic distances) in various situations. **Bonding radii** are calculated from the internuclear separation of two atoms joined by a chemical bond. **Nonbonding radii** are calculated from the internuclear separation between two gaseous atoms that collide and move apart, but do not bond.

7.11   The atomic radius of Au is the interatomic Au-Au distance divided by 2, 2.88 Å/2 = 1.44 Å.

7.13   From atomic radii, As-I = 1.19 Å + 1.33 Å = 2.52 Å. This is very close to the experimental value of 2.55 Å.

7.15   (a)   Atomic radii **decrease** moving from left to right across a row and (b) **increase** from top to bottom within a group.

(c)   F < S < P <As. The order is unambiguous according to the trends of increasing atomic radius moving down a column and to the left in a row of the table.

7.17   *Plan.* Locate each element on the periodic charge and use trends in radii to predict their order. *Solve*:

(a) Be < Mg < Ca   (b) Br < Ge < Ga   (c) Si < Al < Tl

7.19   (a)   Electrostatic repulsions are reduced by removing an electron from a neutral atom, Z_{eff} increases, and the cation is smaller.

(b)   The additional electrostatic repulsion produced by adding an electron to a neutral atom causes the electron cloud to expand, so that the radius of the anion is larger than the radius of the neutral atom.

(c)   Going down a column, the *n* value of the valence electrons increases and they are further from the nucleus. Thus, the size of particles with like charge increases.

7.21   The size of the blue sphere decreases on reaction, so it loses one or more electrons and becomes a cation. Metals lose electrons when reacting with nonmetals, so the blue sphere represents a metal. The size of the red sphere increases on reaction, so it gains one or more electrons and becomes an anion. Nonmetals gain electrons when reacting with metals, so the red sphere represents a nonmetal.

7.23   (a)   An isoelectronic series is a group of atoms or ions that have the same number of electrons, and thus the same electron configuration.

(b)   (i) Cl^- : **Ar**   (ii) Se^{2-} : **Kr**   (iii) Mg^{2+} : **Ne**

7.25   (a)   Since the electron configurations of the ions in an isoelectronic series are the same, shielding effects do not vary for the different particles. As Z increases, Z_{eff} increases, the valence electrons are more strongly attracted to the nucleus and the size of the particle decreases.

(b)   Because F^-, Ne and Na^+ have the same electron configuration, the 2p electron in the particle with the largest Z experiences the largest effective nuclear charge. A 2p electron in Na^+ experiences the greatest effective nuclear charge.

7.27   *Plan.* Use relative location on periodic chart and trends in ionic radii to establish the order.
  Solve: (a) Se < Se^{2-}< Te^{2-} (b) Co^{3+} < Fe^{3+} < Fe^{2+} (c) Ti^{4+} < Sc^{3+} < Ca   (d) Be^{2+} < Na^+ < Ne

Ionization Energies; Electron Affinities

7.29 $Te(g) \rightarrow Te^+(g) + 1e^-$; $Te^+(g) \rightarrow Te^{2+}(g) + 1e^-$; $Te^{2+}(g) \rightarrow Te^{3+}(g) + 1e^-$

7.31   (a)   According to Coulomb's law, the energy of an electron in an atom is negative, because of the electrostatic attraction of the electron for the nucleus. In order to overcome this attraction, remove the electron and increase it's energy; energy must be added to the atom. Ionization energy, ΔE for this process, is positive, regardless of the magnitude of Z or the quantum numbers of the electron.

         (b)   F has a greater first ionization energy than O, because F has a greater Z_{eff} and the outer electrons in both elements are approximately the same distance from the nucleus.

         (c)   The second ionization energy of an element is greater than the first because Z_{eff} is larger for the +1 cation than the neutral atom; more energy is required to overcome the larger Z_{eff}.

7.33   (a)   In general, the smaller the atom, the larger its first ionization energy.

         (b)   According to Figure 7.10, He has the largest and Cs the smallest first ionization energy of the nonradioactive elements.

7.35   *Plan*. Use periodic trends in first ionization energy. *Solve*:

         (a) Ne   (b) Mg   (c) Cr   (d) Br   (e) Ge

7.37   *Plan*. Follow the logic of Sample Exercise 7.7. *Solve:*

         (a) Sb^{3+}: $[Kr]5s^24d^{10}$ (b) Ga^+: $[Ar]4s^23d^{10}$ (c) P^{3-}: $[Ne]3s^23p^6$ or $[Ar]$

         (d) Cr^{3+}: $[Ar]3d^3$ (e) Zn^{2+}: $[Ar]3d^{10}$ (f) Ag^+: $[Kr]4d^{10}$

7.39   *Plan*. Follow the logic in Sample Exercise 7.7. Construct a mental box diagram for the outer electrons to determine how many are unpaired.

         (a) Co^{2+}: $[Ar]3d^7$, 3 unpaired electrons

         (b) In^+: $[Kr]5s^24d^{10}$, 0 unpaired electrons

7.41   Ionization energy: $Se(g)$ $\rightarrow$ $Se^+(g) + 1e^-$

                           $[Ar]4s^23e^{10}4p^4$ $[Ar]4s^23d^{10}4p^3$

         Electron affinity: $Se(g)$ + $1e^-$ $\rightarrow$ $Se^-(g)$

                           $[Ar]4s^23d^{10}4p^4$ $[Ar]4s^23d^{10}4p^5$

7.43   Li   + 1e⁻   →   Li⁻   ;   Be   + 1e⁻   →   Be⁻

Li $+ 1e^- \rightarrow$ Li⁻ ; Be $+ 1e^- \rightarrow$ Be⁻
[He]$2s^1$ [He]$2s^2$ [He]$2s^2$ [He]$2s^2 2p^1$

Adding an electron to Li completes the 2s subshell. The added electron experiences essentially the same effective nuclear charge as the other valence electron, except for the repulsion of pairing electrons in a orbital. There is an overall stabilization; ΔE is negative.

An extra electron in Be would occupy the higher energy 2p subshell. This electron is shielded from the full nuclear charge by the 2s electrons and does not experience a stabilization in energy; ΔE is positive.

Properties of Metals and Nonmetals

7.45   The smaller the first ionization energy of an element, the greater the metallic character of that element.

7.47   *Analyze/Plan.* Metallic character increases moving down a family and to the left in a period. Use these trends to select the element with greater metallic character. *Solve*:

     (a) Li   (b) Na   (c) Sn   (d) Al

7.49   Analyze/Plan. Ionic compounds are formed by combining a metal and a nonmetal; molecular compounds are formed by two or more nonmetals. *Solve*:

     Ionic: MgO, Li_2O, Y_2O_3; molecular: SO_2, P_2O_5, N_2O, XeO_3

7.51   (a)   When dissolved in water, an "acidic oxide" produces an acidic (pH < 7) solution. A "basic oxide" dissolved in water produces a basic (pH > 7) solution.

       (b)   Oxides of nonmetals are acidic. Example: $SO_3(g) + H_2O(l) \rightarrow H_2SO_4(aq)$. Oxides of metals are basic. Example: CaO (quick lime). $CaO(s) + H_2O(l) \rightarrow Ca(OH)_2(aq)$

7.53   (a) $BaO(s) + H_2O(l) \rightarrow Ba(OH)_2(aq)$

       (b) $FeO(s) + 2HClO_4(aq) \rightarrow Fe(ClO_4)_2(aq) + H_2O(l)$

       (c) $SO_3(g) + H_2O(l) \rightarrow H_2SO_4(aq)$

       (d) $CO_2(g) + 2NaOH(aq) \rightarrow Na_2CO_3(aq) + H_2O(l)$

Group Trends in Metals and Nonmetals

7.55

	Na	**Mg**
(a)	[Ne] $3s^1$	[Ne] $3s^2$
(b)	+1	+2
(c)	+496 kJ/mol	+738 kJ/mol
(d)	very reactive	reacts with steam, but not $H_2O(l)$
(e)	1.54 Å	1.30 Å

(b)   When forming ions, both adopt the stable configuration of Ne, but Na loses one electron and Mg two electrons to achieve this configuration.

(c),(e)   The nuclear charge of Mg (Z = 12) is greater than that of Na, so it requires more energy to remove a valence electron with the same n value from Mg than Na. It also means that the 2s electrons of Mg are held closer to the nucleus, so the atomic radius (e) is smaller than that of Na.

(d)   Mg is less reactive because it has a filled subshell and it has a higher ionization energy.

7.57   (a)   Ca and Mg are both metals; they tend to lose electrons and form cations when they react. Ca is more reactive because it has a lower ionization energy than Mg. The Ca valence electrons in the 4s orbital are less tightly held because they are farther from the nucleus than the 3s valence electrons of Mg.

(b)   K and Ca are both metals; they tend to lose electrons and form cations when they react. K is more reactive because it has a lower ionization energy. The 4s valence electron in K is less tightly held because it experiences a smaller nuclear charge (Z = 19 for K versus Z = 20 for Ca) with similar shielding effects than the 4s valence electrons of Ca.

7.59   (a) $2K(s) + Cl_2(g) \rightarrow 2KCl(s)$

(b) $SrO(s) + H_2O(l) \rightarrow Sr(OH)_2(aq)$

(c) $4Li(s) + O_2(g) \rightarrow 2Li_2O(s)$

(d) $2Na(s) + S(l) \rightarrow Na_2S(s)$

7.61   H: $1s^1$; Li: [He] $2s^1$; F: [He] $2s^2 2p^5$. Like Li, H has only one valence electron, and its most common oxidation number is +1, which both H and Li adopt after losing the single valence electron. Like F, H needs only one electron to adopt the stable electron configuration of the nearest noble gas. Both H and F can exist in the -1 oxidation state, when they have gained an electron to complete their valence shells.

7.63

	F	**Cl**
(a)	[He] $2s^2 2p^5$	[Ne] $3s^2 3p^5$
(b)	-1	-1
(c)	1681 kJ/mol	1251 kJ/mol
(d)	reacts exothermically to form HF	reacts slowly to form HCl
(e)	-328 kJ/mol	-349 kJ/mol
(f)	0.71 Å	0.99 Å

(b)   F and Cl are in the same group, have the same valence electron configuration and common ionic charge.

(c),(f)   The $n = 2$ valence electrons in F are closer to the nucleus and more tightly held than the $n = 3$ valence electrons in Cl. Therefore, the ionization energy of F is greater, and the atomic radius is smaller.

(d)   In its reaction with H_2O, F is reduced; it gains an electron. Although the electron affinity, a gas phase single atom property, of F is less negative than that of Cl, the tendency of F to hold its own electrons (high ionization energy) coupled with a relatively large exothermic electron affinity makes it extremely susceptible to reduction and chemical bond formation. Cl is unreactive to water because it is less susceptible to reduction.

(e)   While F has approximately the same Z_{eff} as Cl, its small atomic radius gives rise to large repulsions when an extra electron is added, so the overall electron affinity of F is smaller (less exothermic) than that of Cl.

(f)   The $n = 2$ valence electrons in F are closer to the nucleus so the atomic radius is smaller than that of Cl.

7.65   Under ambient conditions, the Group 8A elements are all gases that are extremely unreactive, owing to their stable core electron configurations. Thus, the name "inert gases" seemed appropriate.

In the 1960s, scientists discovered that Xe, which has the lowest ionization energy of the nonradioactive Noble gases, would react with substances having a strong tendency to remove electrons, such as PtF_6 or F_2. Thus, the term "inert" no longer described all the Group 8A elements. (Kr also reacts with F_2, but reactions of Ar, Ne and He are as yet unknown.)

7.67   (a) $2O_3(g) \rightarrow 3O_2(g)$

        (b) $Xe(g) + F_2(g) \rightarrow XeF_2(g)$

              $Xe(g) + 2F_2(g) \rightarrow XeF_4(s)$

              $Xe(g) + 3F_2(g) \rightarrow XeF_6(s)$

        (c) $S(s) + H_2(g) \rightarrow H_2S(g)$

        (d) $2F_2(g) + 2H_2O(l) \rightarrow 4HF(aq) + O_2(g)$

7.69   (a)   Te has more metallic character and is a better electrical conductor.

        (b)   At room temperature, oxygen molecules are diatomic and exist in the gas phase. Sulfur molecules are 8-membered rings and exist in the solid state.

        (c)   Chlorine is generally more reactive than bromine because Cl atoms have a greater (more exothermic) electron affinity than Br atoms.

Additional Exercises

7.71   Up to $Z = 83$, there are three instances where atomic weights are reversed relative to atomic numbers: Ar and K; Co and Ni; Te and I.

In each case, the most abundant isotope of the element with the larger atomic number (Z) has one more proton, but fewer neutrons than the element with the smaller atomic number. The smaller number of neutrons causes the element with the larger Z to have a smaller than expected atomic weight.

7.73 (a) Na. In an isoelectronic series, all electronic effects (shielding and repulsion) are the same, so the particle with the smallest Z will have the smallest effective nuclear charge.

(b) Si^{3+}. Si has the largest Z and effective nuclear charge.

(c) The greater the effective nuclear charge experienced by a valence electron, the larger the ionization energy for that electron. According to Table 7.2, I_1 for Na is 496 kJ/mol. I_4 for Si is 4360 kJ/mol.

7.76 (a) Mo – F distance = $r_{Mo} + r_F$ = 1.45 + 0.71 = 2.16 Å
(b) S – F distance = $r_S + r_F$ = 1.02 + 0.71 = 1.73 Å
(c) Cl – F distance = $r_{Cl} + r_F$ = 0.99 + 0.71 = 1.70 Å

7.79 Y: $[Kr]5s^2 4d^1$, Z = 39; La: $[Xe]6s^2 5d^1$, Z = 57; Zr: $[Kr] 5s^2 4d^2$, Z = 40; Hf: $[Xe] 6s^2 4f^{14} 5d^2$, Z = 72. The completed 4f subshell in Hf leads to a much larger change in Z going from Zr to Hf (72 - 40 = 32) than in going from Y to La (57 - 39 = 18). The 4f electrons in Hf do not completely shield the 5d valence electrons, so there is also a larger increase in Z_{eff}. This larger increase in Z_{eff} going from Zr to Hf leads to a smaller increase in atomic radius than in going from Y to La.

7.82 Ionization energy of F^-: $F^-(g) \rightarrow F(g) + 1e^-$

Electron affinity of F: $F(g) + 1e^- \rightarrow F^-(g)$

The two processes are the reverse of each other. The energies are equal in magnitude but opposite in sign. $I_1 (F^-) = -E (F)$

7.84 O: $[He]2s^2 2p^4$

O^{2-}: $[He]2s^2 2p^6 = [Ne]$

O^{3-}: $[Ne]3s^1$ The third electron would be added to the 3s orbital, which is further from the nucleus and more strongly shielded by the [Ne] core. The overall attraction of this 3s electron for the O nucleus is not large enough for O^{3-} to be a stable particle.

7.86 (a) The group 2B metals have complete $(n-1)$d subshells. An additional electron would occupy an np subshell and be substantially shielded by both ns and $(n-1)$d electrons. Overall this is not a lower energy state than the neutral atom and a free electron.

(b) Valence electrons in Group 1B elements experience a relatively large effective nuclear charge due to the build-up in Z with the filling of the $(n-1)$d subshell. Thus, the electron affinities are large and negative. Group 1B elements are exceptions to the usual electron filling order and have the generic electron configuration ns$^1(n-1)$d^{10}. The additional electron would complete the ns subshell and experience repulsion with the other ns electron. Going down the group, size of the ns subshell increases and repulsion effects decrease. That is, effective nuclear charge is greater going down the group because it is less diminished by repulsion, and electron affinities become more negative.

7.89 $O_2 < Br_2 < K < Mg$. O_2 and Br_2 are (nonpolar) nonmetals. We expect O_2, with the much lower molar mass, to have the lower melting point. This is confirmed by data in Tables 7.6 and 7.7. K and Mg are metallic solids (all metals are solids), with higher melting points than the two nonmetals. Since alkaline earth metals (Mg) are typically harder, more dense and higher melting than alkali metals (K), we expect Mg to have the highest melting point of the group. This is confirmed by data in Tables 7.4 and 7.5.

7.91 Moving one place to the right in a horizontal row of the table, for example, from Li to Be, there is an increase in ionization energy. Moving downward in a given family, for example from Be to Mg, there is usually a decrease in ionization energy. Similarly, atomic size decreases in moving one place to the right and increases in moving downward. Thus, two elements such as Li and Mg that are diagonally related tend to have similar ionization energies and atomic sizes. This in turn gives rise to some similarities in chemical behavior. Note, however, that the valences expected for the elements are not the same. That is, lithium still appears as Li^+, magnesium as Mg^{2+}.

7.94 Ionic "inorganic" halogen compounds are formed when a metal with low ionization energy and small negative electron affinity combines with a halogen with large ionization energy and large negative electron affinity. That is, it is relatively easy to remove an electron from a metal, and there is only a small energy payback if a metal gains an electron. The opposite is true of a halogen; it is hard to remove an electron and there is a large energy advantage if a halogen gains an electron. Thus, the metal "gives up" an electron to the halogen and an ionic compound is formed. Carbon, on the other hand, is much closer in ionization energy and electron affinity to the halogens. Carbon has a much greater tendency than a metal to keep its own electrons and at least some attraction for the electrons of other elements. Thus, compounds of carbon and the halogens are molecular, rather than ionic.

Integrative Exercises

7.96 (a) Li: $[He]2s^1$. Assume that the [He] core is 100% effective at shielding the 2s valence electron $Z_{eff} = Z - S \approx 3 - 2 = +1$.

(b) The first ionization energy represents loss of the 2s electron.

ΔE = energy of free electron (n = ∞) - energy of electron in ground state (n = 2)

$\Delta E = I_1 = [-2.18 \times 10^{-18} \text{ J } (Z^2 / \infty 2)] - [-2/18 \times 10^{-18} \text{ J}(Z^2/2^2]$

$\Delta E = I_1 = 0 + 2.18 \times 10^{-18} \text{ J } (Z^2/2^2)$

For Li, which is not a one-electron particle, let $Z = Z_{eff}$.

$\Delta E \approx 2.18 \times 10^{-18} \text{ J } (+1^2 / 4) \approx 5.45 \times 10^{-19} \text{ J/atom}$

(c) Change the result from part (b) to kJ/mol so it can be compared to the value in

Table 7.4. $5.45 \times 10^{-19} \dfrac{J}{atom} \times \dfrac{6.022 \times 10^{23} \text{ atom}}{mol} \times \dfrac{1 \text{ kJ}}{1000 \text{ J}} = 328 \text{ kJ/mol}$

The value in Table 7.4 is 520 kJ/mol. This means that our estimate for Z_{eff} was a lower limit; that the [He] core electrons do not perfectly shield the 2s electron from the nuclear charge.

(d) From Table 7.4, I_1 = 520 kJ/mol.

$\dfrac{520 \text{ kJ}}{mol} \times \dfrac{1000 \text{ J}}{kJ} \times \dfrac{1 \text{ mol}}{6.022 \times 10^{23} \text{ atoms}} = 8.6350 \times 10^{-19} \text{ J/atom}$

Use the relationship for I_1 and Z_{eff} developed in part (b).

$Z_{eff}^2 = \dfrac{4(8.6350 \times 10^{-19} \text{ J})}{2.18 \times 10^{-18} \text{ J}} = 1.5844 = 1.58; Z_{eff} = 1.26$

This value, Z_{eff} = 1.26, based on the experimental ionization energy, is greater than our estimate from part (a), which is consistent with the explanation in part (c).

7.99 (a) Mg_3N_2

(b) $Mg_3N_2(s) + 3H_2O(l) \rightarrow 3MgO(s) + 2NH_3(g)$
The driving force is the production of $NH_3(g)$.

(c) After the second heating, all the Mg is converted to MgO.
Calculate the initial mass Mg.

$0.486 \text{ g MgO} \times \dfrac{24.305 \text{ g Mg}}{40.305 \text{ g MgO}} = 0.293 \text{ g Mg}$

x = g Mg converted to MgO; y = g Mg converted to Mg_3N_2; x = 0.293 - y

$\text{g MgO} = x \left(\dfrac{40.305 \text{ g MgO}}{24.305 \text{ g Mg}} \right)$; $\text{g Mg}_3N_2 = y \left(\dfrac{100.929 \text{ g Mg}_3N_2}{72.915 \text{ g Mg}} \right)$

g MgO + g Mg_3N_2 = 0.470

$$(0.293 - y)\left(\frac{40.305}{24.305}\right) + y\left(\frac{100.929}{72.915}\right) = 0.470$$

(0.293 - y)(1.6583) + y(1.3842) = 0.470

-1.6583 y + 1.3842 y = 0.470 - 0.48588

-0.2741 y = -0.016

y = 0.05794 = 0.058 g Mg in Mg_3N_2

$$g\ Mg_3N_2 = 0.05794\ g\ Mg \times \frac{100.929\ g\ Mg_3N_2}{72.915\ g\ Mg} = 0.0802 = 0.080\ g\ Mg_3N_2$$

$$mass\ \%\ Mg_3N_2 = \frac{0.0802\ g\ Mg_3N_2}{0.470\ g\ (MgO + Mg_3N_2)} \times 100 = 17\%$$

(The final mass % has 2 sig figs because the mass of Mg obtained from solving simultaneous equations has 2 sig figs.)

(d) $3Mg(s) + 2NH_3(g) \rightarrow Mg_3N_2(s) + 3H_2(g)$

$$6.3\ g\ Mg \times \frac{1\ mol\ Mg}{24.305\ g\ Mg} = 0.2592 = 0.26\ mol\ Mg$$

$$2.57\ g\ NH_3 \times \frac{1\ mol\ NH_3}{17.031\ g\ NH_3} = 0.1509 = 0.16\ mol\ NH_3$$

$$0.2592\ mol\ Mg \times \frac{2\ mol\ NH_3}{3\ mol\ Mg} = 0.1728 = 0.17\ mol\ NH_3$$

0.26 mol Mg requires more than the available NH_3 so NH_3 is the limiting reactant.

$$0.1509\ mol\ NH_3 \times \frac{3\ mol\ H_2}{2\ mol\ NH_3} \times \frac{2.016\ g\ H_2}{mol\ H_2} = 0.4563 = 0.46\ g\ H_2$$

(e) $\Delta H^{\circ}_{rxn} = \Delta H^{\circ}_f\ Mg_3N_2(s) + 3\Delta H^{\circ}_f\ H_2(g) - 3\Delta H^{\circ}_f\ Mg(s) - 2\Delta H^{\circ}_f\ NH_3(g)$

= -461.08 kJ + 0 - 3(0) - 2(-46.19) = -368.70 kJ

8 Basic Concepts of Chemical Bonding

Lewis Symbols and Ionic Bonding

8.1   (a)   Valence electrons are those that take part in chemical bonding, those in the outermost electron shell of the atom. This usually means the electrons beyond the core noble-gas configuration of the atom, although it is sometimes only the outer shell electrons.

(b)   N: [He] $2s^2 2p^3$ A nitrogen atom has 5 valence electrons.
     |____|
     valence electrons

(c) $1s^2 2s^2 2p^6$ $3s^2 3p^2$ The atom (Si) has 4 valence electrons.
     |_____| |_____|
        [Ne]   valence electrons

8.3   P: $1s^2 2s^2 2p^6 3s^2 3p^3$. A 3s electron is a valence electron; a 2s (or 1s) electron is a non-valence electron. The 3s valence electron is involved in chemical bonding, while the 2s or 1s non-valence electron is not.

8.5   (a) $\overset{\cdot}{C}\overset{\cdot}{a}\cdot$ (b) $\cdot\overset{\cdot}{\underset{\cdot}{P}}\cdot$ (c) $:\overset{\cdot\cdot}{Ne}:$ (d) $\cdot\overset{\cdot}{B}\cdot$

8.7 $\overset{\cdot}{Mg}\cdot$ + $\cdot\overset{\cdot\cdot}{\underset{\cdot\cdot}{O}}:$ $\longrightarrow$ Mg^{2+} + $\left[:\overset{\cdot\cdot}{\underset{\cdot\cdot}{O}}:\right]^{2-}$

8.9   Potassium has a single valence electron, which it tends to lose to achieve a completed octet. Calcium has two valence electrons, which it tends to lose to achieve a completed octet. Thus, K loses a single electron while Ca loses two electrons when reacting with Cl. Removing one electron from the core of either K^+ or Ca^{2+} would be energetically unfavorable, because the core electrons are stabilized by a strong electrostatic attraction for the nucleus. Even a large lattice energy is not enough to promote removal of a core electron.

8.11 (a) AlF_3 (b) K_2S (c) Y_2O_3 (d) Mg_3N_2

8.13 (a) Sr^{2+}: [Kr], noble-gas configuration   (b) Ti^{2+}: $[Ar]3d^2$

(b) Se^{2-}: $[Ar]4s^2 3d^{10}4p^6$ = [Kr], noble-gas configuration   (d) Ni^{2+}: $[Ar]3d^8$

(c) Br^-: $[Ar]4s^2 3d^{10}4p^6$ = [Kr], noble-gas configuration   (f) Mn^{3+}: $[Ar]3d^4$

8.15 (a) *Lattice energy* is the energy required to totally separate one mole of solid ionic compound into its gaseous ions.

(b) The magnitude of the lattice energy depends on the magnitudes of the charges of the two ions, their radii and the arrangement of ions in the lattice. The main factor is the charges, because the radii of ions do not vary over a wide range.

8.17 KF, 808 kJ/mol; CaO, 3414 kJ/mol; ScN, 7547 kJ/mol

The sizes of the ions vary as follows: $Sc^{3+} < Ca^{2+} < K^+$ and $F^- < O^{2-} < N^{3-}$. Therefore, the interionic distances are similar. According to Coulomb's law for compounds with similar ionic separations, the lattice energies should be related as the product of the charges of the ions. The lattice energies above are approximately related as (1)(1): (2)(2): (3)(3) or 1 : 4 : 9. Slight variations are due to the small differences in ionic separations.

8.19 Since the ionic charges are the same in the two compounds, the K–Br and Cs–Cl separations must be approximately equal. Since the radii are related as $Cs^+ > K^+$ and $Br^- > Cl^-$, the difference between Cs^+ and K^+ must be approximately equal to the difference between Br^- and Cl^-. This is somewhat surprising, since K^+ and Cs^+ are two rows apart and Cl^- and Br^- are only one row apart.

8.21. Equation 8.4 predicts that as the oppositely charged ions approach each other, the energy of interaction will be large and negative. This more than compensates for the energy required to form Ca^{2+} and O^{2-} from the neutral atoms (see Figure 8.4 for the formation of NaCl).

8.23 $RbCl(s) \rightarrow Rb^+(g) + Cl^-(g)$ ΔH (lattice energy) = ?

By analogy to NaCl, Figure 8.4, the lattice energy is

$\Delta H_{latt} = -\Delta H_f^{\circ}\ RbCl(s) + \Delta H_f^{\circ}\ Rb(g) + \Delta H_f^{\circ}\ Cl(g) + I_1\ (Rb) + E\ (Cl)$

   $= -(-430.5\ kJ) + 85.8\ kJ + 121.7\ kJ + 403\ kJ + (-349\ kJ) = +692\ kJ$

This value is smaller than that for NaCl (+788 kJ) because Rb^+ has a larger ionic radius than Na^+. This means that the value of d in the denominator of Equation 8.4 is larger for RbCl, and the potential energy of the electrostatic attraction is smaller.

Covalent Bonding, Electronegativity and Bond Polarity

8.25 (a) A *covalent bond* is the bond formed when two atoms share one or more pairs of electrons.

(b) The ionic bonding in NaCl is due to strong electrostatic attraction between oppositely charged Na^+ and Cl^- ions. The covalent bonding in Cl_2 is due to sharing of a pair of electrons by two neutral chlorine atoms.

8.27. *Analyze/Plan.* Follow the logic in Sample Exercise 8.3. *Solve:*

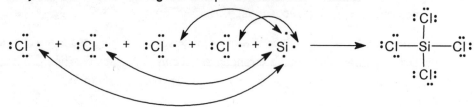

Check. Each pair of shared electrons in $SiCl_4$ is shown as a line; each atom is surrounded by an octet of electrons.

8.29 (a)   :Ö══O:

(b) A double bond is required because there are not enough electrons to satisfy the octet rule with single bonds and unshared pairs.

(c) The greater the number of shared electron pairs between two atoms, the shorter the distance between the atoms. If O_2 has a double bond, the O–O distance will be shorter than the O–O single bond distance.

8.31 (a) *Electronegativity* is the ability of an atom in a molecule (a bonded atom) to attract electrons to itself.

(b) The range of electronegativities on the Pauling scale is 0.7–4.0.

(c) Fluorine, F, is the most electronegative element.

(d) Cesium, Cs, is the least electronegative element that is not radioactive.

8.33 *Plan.* Electronegativity increases going up and to the right in the periodic table. *Solve:*

(a) S   (b) C   (c) As   (d) Mg

Check. The electronegativity values in Figure (8.9) confirm these selections.

8.35 The bonds in (a), (b) and (d) are polar because the atoms involved differ in electronegativity. The more electronegative element in each polar bond is: (a) O   (b) F   (d) O

8.37 (a) A polar molecule has a measurable dipole moment; its centers of positive and negative charge do not coincide. A nonpolar molecule has a zero net dipole moment; its centers of positive and negative charge do coincide.

(b) Yes. If X and Y have different electronegativities, they have different attractions for the electrons in the molecule. The electron density around the more electronegative atom will be greater, producing a charge separation or dipole in the molecule.

(c) $\mu = Qr$. The dipole moment, μ, is the product of the magnitude of the separated charges, Q, and the distance between them, r.

8.39   *Analyze/Plan.* Q is the charge at either end of the dipole. $Q = \mu/r$. From Table 8.3, the values for HF are $\mu = 1.82$ D and $r = 0.92$ Å. Change Å to m and use the definition of the Debye and the charge of an electron to calculate the charge in units of *e*.   *Solve:*

$$Q = \frac{\mu}{r} = \frac{1.82\,D}{0.92\,\text{Å}} \times \frac{1\,\text{Å}}{1 \times 10^{-10}\,m} \times \frac{3.34 \times 10^{-30}\,C \bullet m}{1\,D} \times \frac{1\,e}{1.60 \times 10^{-19}\,C} = 0.41\,e$$

Check. The calculated charge on H and F is 0.41 *e*. This can be thought of as the amount of charge "transferred" from H to F. This value is consistent with our idea that HF is a polar covalent molecule; the bonding electron pair is unequally shared, but not totally transferred from H to F.

8.41   *Analyze/Plan.* Generally, compounds formed by a metal and a nonmetal are described as ionic, while compounds formed from two or more nonmetals are covalent.   *Solve:*

(a) MnO_2, ionic

(b) Ga_2S_3, ionic   (Although their electronegativities are similar, Ga is a metal and S is a nonmetal. Use of a roman numeral usually presumes an ionic compound.)

(c)   CoO, ionic   (d) copper(I) sulfide, ionic   (e) chlorine trifluoride, covalent

(f)   vanadium(V) fluoride, ionic

Lewis Structures; Resonance Structures

8.43   *Analyze.* Counting the **correct number of valence electrons** is the foundation of every Lewis structure. *Plan/Solve:*

(a)   Count valence electrons: $4 + (4 \times 1) = 8$ e⁻, 4 e⁻ pairs. Follow the procedure in Sample Exercise 8.6.

$$H—\underset{\underset{H}{|}}{\overset{\overset{H}{|}}{Si}}—H$$

(b)   Valence electrons: $4 + 6 = 10$ e⁻, 5 e⁻ pairs

$$:C \equiv O:$$

(c)   Valence electrons: $[6 + (2 \times 7)] = 20$ e⁻, 10 e⁻ pairs.

$$:\overset{..}{\underset{..}{F}}—\overset{..}{\underset{..}{S}}—\overset{..}{\underset{..}{F}}:$$

     i.   Place the S atom in the middle and connect each F atom with a single bond; this requires 2 e⁻ pairs.

     ii.   Complete the octets of the F atoms with nonbonded pairs of electrons; this requires an additional 6 e⁻ pairs.

     iii.   The remaining 2 e⁻ pairs complete the octet of the central S atom.

(d)   32 valence e⁻, 16 e⁻ pairs

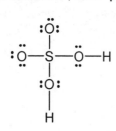

(Choose the Lewis structure that
obeys the octet rule, Section 8.7.)

(e)   Follow Sample Exercise 8.8.
20 valence e⁻, 10 e⁻ pairs

$$\left[\; :\ddot{O}\!-\!\ddot{C}l\!-\!\ddot{O}: \;\right]^{-}$$

(f)   14 valence e⁻, 7 e⁻ pairs

$$H\!-\!\overset{\cdot\cdot}{\underset{\underset{H}{|}}{N}}\!-\!\overset{\cdot\cdot}{\underset{\cdot\cdot}{O}}\!-\!H$$

Check. In each molecule, bonding e⁻ pairs are shown as lines, and each atom is surrounded by an octet of electrons (duet for H).

8.45   *Analyze/Plan.* Draw the correct Lewis structure: count valence electrons in each atom, sum, determine electron pairs in the molecule; connect bonded atoms with a line, place the remaining e⁻ pairs as needed, in nonbonded pairs or multiple bonds, so that each atom is surrounded by an octet (or duet for H). Assign formal charges: assign electrons to individual atoms [nonbonding e⁻ + 1/2 (bonding e⁻)]; formal charge = valence electrons - assigned electrons. *Solve:*

(a)   10 e⁻, 5 e⁻ pairs

$$\left[\; :N\!\equiv\!O: \;\right]^{+}$$
$$\;\;\;\;0\;\;\;+1$$

(b)   32 valence e⁻, 16 e⁻ pairs

$$0\;\; :\ddot{C}l\!-\!\underset{\underset{\underset{0}{:\ddot{C}l:}}{|+1}}{\overset{\overset{-1}{:\ddot{O}:}}{P}}\!-\!\ddot{C}l:\;\; 0$$

(c)   32 valence e⁻, 16 e⁻ pairs

$$\left[\; -1\; :\ddot{O}\!-\!\underset{\underset{\underset{-1}{:\ddot{O}:}}{|+3}}{\overset{\overset{-1}{:\ddot{O}:}}{C}l}\!-\!\ddot{O}:\; -1 \;\right]^{-}$$

(d)   26 valence e⁻, 13 e⁻ pairs

$$-1\; :\ddot{O}\!-\!\underset{\underset{\underset{-1}{:\ddot{O}:}}{}}{\overset{\overset{+2}{\ddot{C}l}}{}}\!-\!\overset{\cdot\cdot}{\underset{\cdot\cdot}{O}}\!-\!H$$
$$\;0\;\;\;0$$

Check. Each atom is surrounded by an octet (or duet) and the sum of the formal charges in particle is the charge on the particle.

8.47 (a) *Plan.* Count valence electrons, draw all possible correct Lewis structures, taking note of alternate placements for multiple bonds. *Solve*:

18 e⁻, 9 e⁻ pairs

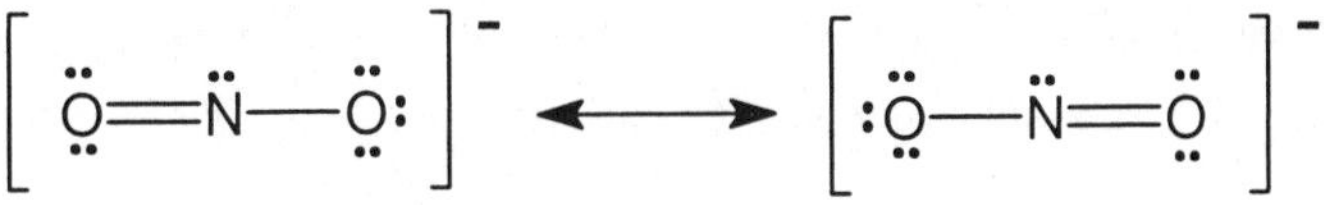

$$\left[\ddot{O}=\ddot{N}-\ddot{O}:\right]^{-} \longleftrightarrow \left[:\ddot{O}-\ddot{N}=\ddot{O}\right]^{-}$$

Check. The octet rule is satisfied.

(b) *Plan.* Isoelectronic species have the same number of valence electrons and the same electron configuration. *Solve*:

A single O atom has 6 valence electrons, so the neutral ozone molecule O_3 is isoelectronic with NO_2^-.

$$\ddot{O}=\ddot{O}-\ddot{O}: \longleftrightarrow :\ddot{O}-\ddot{O}=\ddot{O}$$

Check. The octet rule is satisfied.

(c) Since each N–O bond has partial double bond character, the N–O bond length in NO_2^- should be shorter than in species with formal N–O single bonds.

8.49 *Plan/Solve.* The Lewis structures are as follows:

5 e⁻ pairs   8 e⁻ pairs

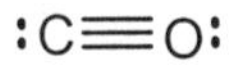

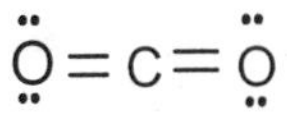

$$:C\equiv O:\qquad\qquad \ddot{O}=C=\ddot{O}$$

12 e⁻ pairs

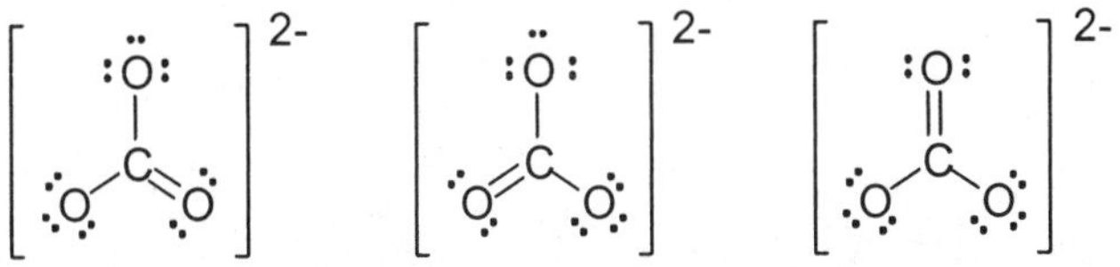

The more pairs of electrons shared by two atoms, the shorter the bond between the atoms. The average number of electron pairs shared by C and O in the three species is 3 for CO, 2 for CO_2 and 1.33 for CO_3^{2-}. This is also the order of increasing bond length: CO < CO_2 < CO_3^{2-}.

8.51 (a) Two equally valid Lewis structures can be drawn for benzene.

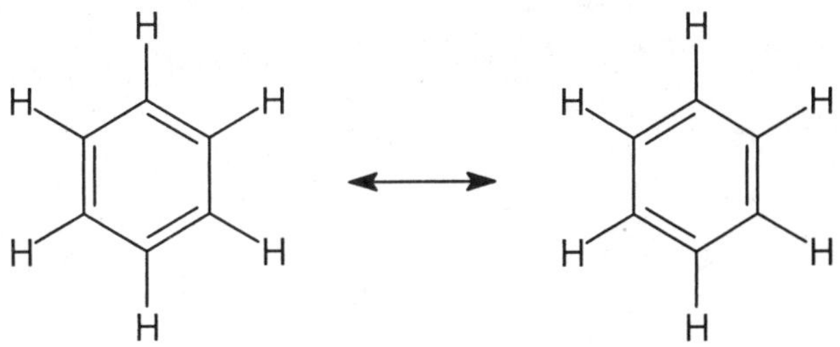

Each structure consists of alternating single and double C–C bonds; a particular bond is single in one structure and double in the other. The concept of resonance dictates that the true description of bonding is some hybrid or blend of the two Lewis structures. The most obvious blend of these two resonance structures is a molecule with six equivalent C–C bonds, each with some but not total double-bond character. If the molecule has six equivalent C–C bonds, the lengths of these bonds should be equal.

(b)   The resonance model described in (a) has 6 equivalent C–C bonds, each with some double bond character. That is, more than 1 pair but less than 2 pairs of electrons is involved in each C–C bond. This model predicts a uniform C–C bond length that is shorter than a single bond but longer than a double bond.

Exceptions to the Octet Rule

8.53   (a)   The *octet rule* states that atoms will gain, lose or share electrons until they are surrounded by eight valence electrons.

          (b)   The octet rule applies to the individual ions in an ionic compound. That is, the cation has lost electrons to achieve an octet and the anion has gained electrons to achieve an octet. For example, in $MgCl_2$, Mg loses 2 e^- to become Mg^{2+} with the electron configuration of Ne. Each Cl atom gains one electron to form Cl^- with the electron configuration of Ar.

8.55   The most common exceptions to the octet rule are molecules with more than eight electrons around one or more atoms, usually the central atom. Examples: SF_6, PF_5

8.57   (a)   24 e^-, 12 e^- pairs

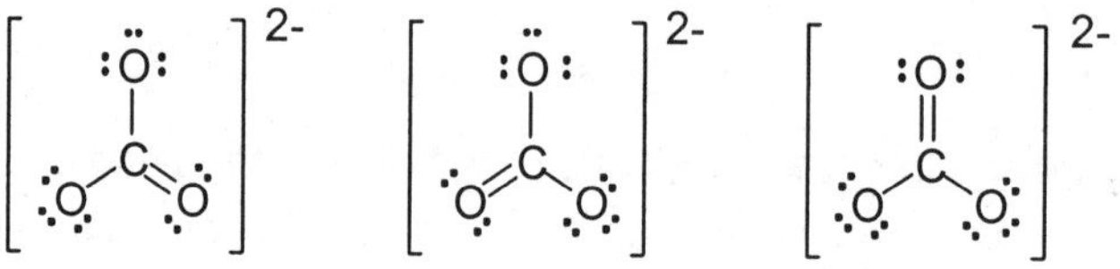

         CO_3^{2-} has three resonance structures, but all obey the octet rule.

         (b)   6 e^-, 3 e^- pairs, impossible to satisfy   (c)   22 e^-, 11 e^- pairs
                 octet rule with only 6 valence electrons

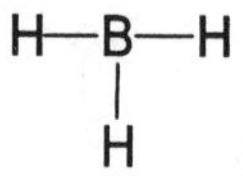

            6 electrons around B   10 e^- around central I

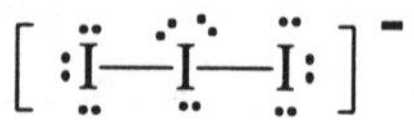

(d)   32 e⁻, 16 e⁻ pairs

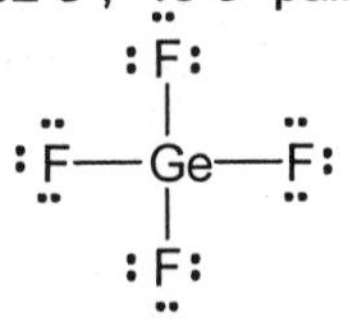

$$
\begin{array}{c}
\text{:F:} \\
| \\
\text{:F—Ge—F:} \\
| \\
\text{:F:}
\end{array}
$$

obeys the octet rule

(e)   48 e⁻, 24 e⁻ pairs

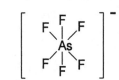

12 e⁻ around As; three
nonbonded pairs on each
F have been omitted

8.59   (a)   16 e⁻, 8 e⁻ pairs

This structure violates the octet rule; Be has only 4 e⁻ around it.

(b) 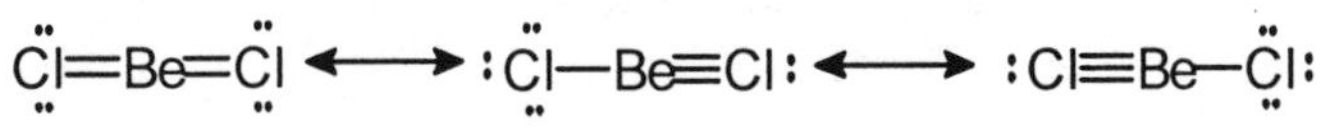   Cl̈=Be=C̈l ⟷ :C̈l—Be≡Cl: ⟷ :Cl≡Be—C̈l:

(c)   The formal charges on each of the atoms in the four resonance structures are:

:C̈l—Be—C̈l: C̈l=Be=C̈l   :C̈l—Be≡Cl: :Cl≡Be—C̈l:

   0   0   0   +1   -2   +1   0   -2   +2   +2   -2   0

Since formal charges are minimized on the structure that violates the octet rule, this
form is probably most important.

Bond Enthalpies

8.61   *Analyze.* Given: structural formulas. Find: enthalpy of reaction.

Plan. Count the number and kinds of bonds that are broken and formed by the reaction. Use
bond enthalpies from Table 8.4 and Equation 8.12 to calculate the overall enthalpy of reaction,
ΔH. *Solve*:

(a)   ΔH = 2D(O-H) + D(O-O) + 4D(C-H) + D(C=C)
              - 2D(O-H) - 2D(O-C) - 4D(C-H) - D(C-C)

     ΔH = D(O-O) + D(C=C) - 2D(O-C) - D(C-C)

         = 146 + 614 - 2(358) - 348 = -304 kJ

(b)   ΔH = 5D(C-H) + D(C ≡ N) + D(C=C) - 5D(C-H) - D(C ≡ N) - 2D(C-C)

         = D(C=C) - 2D(C-C) = 614 - 2(348) = -82 kJ

(c)   ΔH = 6D(N-Cl) - 3D(Cl-Cl) - D(N ≡ N)

         = 6(200) - 3(242) - 941 = -467 kJ

8.63   *Plan.* Draw structural formulas so bonds can be visualized. Then use Table 8.4 and Equation
       8.11.   *Solve*:

(a) 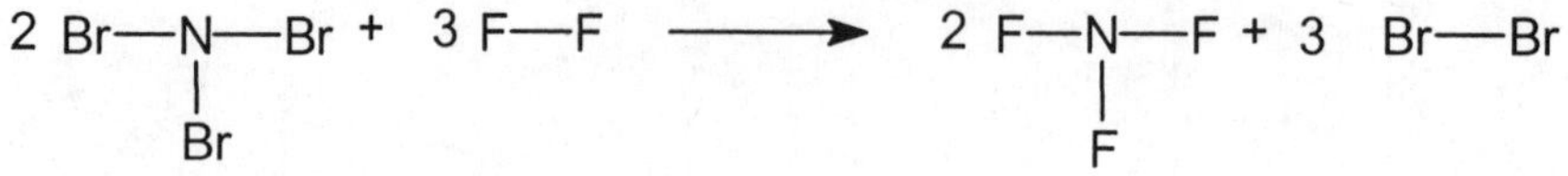 2 Br—N—Br $+$ 3 F—F $\longrightarrow$ 2 F—N—F $+$ 3 Br—Br
           | |
           Br   F

$\Delta H = 6D(\text{N-Br}) + 3D(\text{F-F}) - 6D(\text{N-F}) - 3D(\text{Br-Br})$
$\quad = 6(243) + 3(155) - 6(272) - 3(193) = -288 \text{ kJ}$

(b) 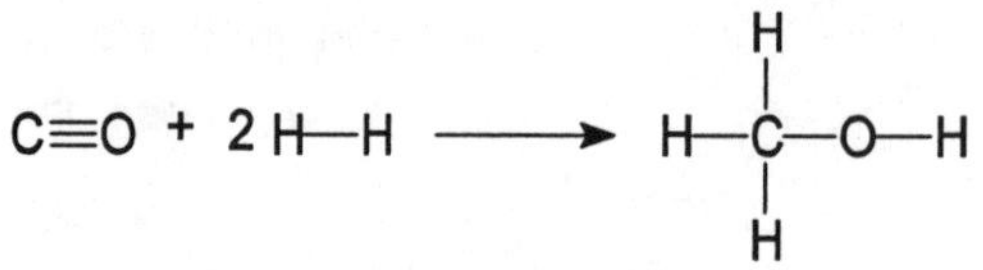   C≡O $+$ 2 H—H $\longrightarrow$ H—C—O—H

with H above and below the C

$\Delta H = D(\text{C} \equiv \text{O}) + 2D(\text{H-H}) - 3D(\text{C-H}) - D(\text{C-O}) - D(\text{O-H})$
$\quad = 1072 + 2(436) - 3(413) - 358 - 463 = -116 \text{ kJ}$

(c) 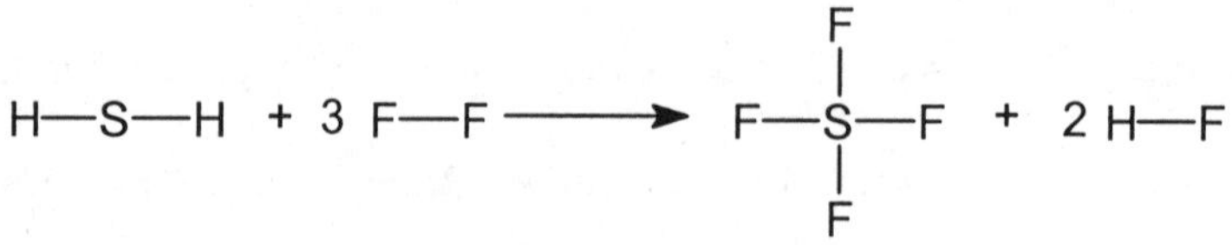   H—S—H $+$ 3 F—F $\longrightarrow$ F—S—F $+$ 2 H—F

with F above and below the S

$\Delta H = 2D(\text{S-H}) + 3D(\text{F-F}) - 4D(\text{S-F}) - 2D(\text{H-F})$
$\quad = 2(339) + 3(155) - 4(327) - 2(567) = -1299 \text{ kJ}$

8.65   *Plan.* Draw structural formulas so bonds can be visualized. Then use Table 8.4 and Equation 8.12. *Solve*:

(a) 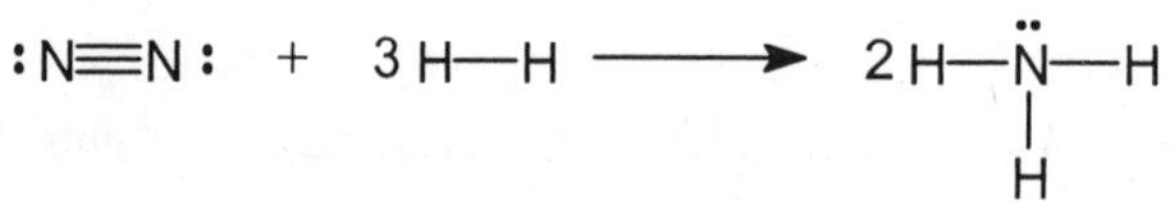   :N≡N: $+$ 3 H—H $\longrightarrow$ 2 H—N̈—H
                                              |
                                              H

$\Delta H = D(\text{N} \equiv \text{N}) + 3D(\text{H-H}) - 6(\text{N-H}) = 941 \text{ kJ} + 3(436 \text{ kJ}) - 6(391 \text{ kJ})$

$\quad = -97 \text{ kJ} / 2 \text{ mol NH}_3 ; \quad \textbf{exothermic}$

(b)   Plan. Use Eq. 5.31 to calculate ΔH_{rxn} from ΔH_f° values.

$\Delta H_{rxn}^{\circ} = \Sigma n \, \Delta H_f^{\circ} \text{ (products)} - \Sigma n \, \Delta H_f^{\circ} \text{ (reactants)}. \quad \Delta H_f^{\circ} \text{ NH}_3(g) = -46.19 \text{ kJ}. \quad Solve:$

$\Delta H_{rxn}^{\circ} = 2 \, \Delta H_f^{\circ} \text{ NH}_3(g) - 3 \, \Delta H_f^{\circ} \text{ H}_2(g) - \Delta H_f^{\circ} \text{ N}_2(g)$

$\Delta H_{rxn}^{\circ} = 2(-46.19) - 3(0) - 0 = -92.38 \text{ kJ}/2 \text{ mol NH}_3$

The ΔH calculated from bond enthalpies is slightly more exothermic (more negative) than that obtained using ΔH_f° values.

8.67   The average Ti–Cl bond enthalpy is just the average of the four values listed, 430 kJ/mol.

Additional Exercises

8.69 (a) Group 14 or 4A   (b) Group 2 or 2A   (c) Group 15 or 5A

(These are the appropriate groups in the s and p blocks, where Lewis symbols are most useful.)

8.71 $E = \dfrac{-8.99 \times 10^9 \text{ J} \cdot \text{m}}{C^2} \times \dfrac{(1.60 \times 10^{-19} \text{ C})^2}{(1.33 + 1.33) \times 10^{-10} \text{ m}} = -8.652 \times 10^{-19} = -8.65 \times 10^{-19} \text{ J}$

On a molar basis: $(-8.652 \times 10^{-19} \text{ J})(6.022 \times 10^{23}) = -5.21 \times 10^5 \text{ J} = -521 \text{ kJ}$

Note that its absolute value is less than the lattice energy, 808 kJ/mol. The difference represents the added energy of putting all the K^+F^- ion pairs together in a three-dimensional array, similar to the one in Figure 8.3.

8.73 (a)

Compound	Lattice Energy (kJ)		Compound	Lattice Energy (kJ)	
NaCl	788		LiCl	834	
NaBr	732	56 kJ	LiBr	779	55 kJ
Na I	682		Li I	730	

106 kJ (NaCl–NaI); 104 kJ (LiCl–LiI)

The difference in lattice energy between LiCl and LiI is 104 kJ. The difference between NaCl and NaI is 106 kJ; the difference between NaCl and NaBr is 56 kJ, or 53% of the difference between NaCl and NaI. Applying this relationship to the Li salts, 0.53(104 kJ) = 55 kJ difference between LiCl and LiBr. The approximate lattice energy of LiBr is (834 - 55) kJ = 779 kJ.

(b)

Compound	Lattice Energy (kJ)		Compound	Lattice Energy (kJ)	
NaCl	788		CsCl	657	
NaBr	732	56 kJ	CsBr	627	30 kJ
Na I	682		Cs I	600	

106 kJ (NaCl–NaI); 57 kJ (CsCl–CsI)

By analogy to the Na salts, the difference between lattice energies of CsCl and CsBr should be approximately 53% of the difference between CsCl and CsI. The lattice energy of CsBr is approximately 627 kJ.

(c)

Compound	Lattice Energy (kJ)		Compound	Lattice Energy (kJ)	
MgO	3795		$MgCl_2$	2326	
CaO	3414	381 kJ	$CaCl_2$	2195	131 kJ
SrO	3217		$SrCl_2$	2127	

578 kJ (MgO–SrO); 199 kJ ($MgCl_2$–$SrCl_2$)

By analogy to the oxides, the difference between the lattice energies of $MgCl_2$ and $CaCl_2$ should be approximately 66% of the difference between $MgCl_2$ and $SrCl_2$. That is, 0.66(199 kJ) = 131 kJ. The lattice energy of $CaCl_2$ is approximately (2326 - 131) kJ = 2195 kJ.

8.76 Molecule (b) H_2S and ion (c) NO_2^- contain polar bonds. The atoms that form the bonds (H–S) and N–O) have different electronegativity values.

8.79   Formal charge (FC) = # valence e⁻ - (# nonbonding e⁻ + 1/2 # bonding e⁻)

(a)   18 e⁻, 9 e⁻ pairs

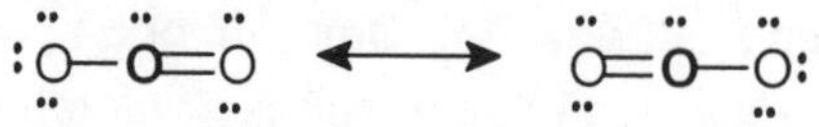

$$:\ddot{O}-\ddot{O}=\ddot{O} \longleftrightarrow \ddot{O}=\ddot{O}-\ddot{O}:$$

FC for the central O = 6 - [2 + 1/2 (6)] = +1

(b)   48 e⁻, 24 e⁻ pairs

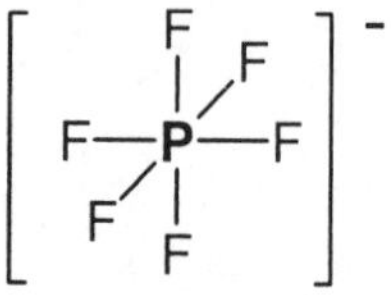

FC for P = 5 - [0 + 1/2 (12)] = -1

The three nonbonded pairs on each F have been omitted.

(c)   17 e⁻; 8 e⁻ pairs, 1 odd e⁻

$$\ddot{O}=N-\ddot{O}: \longleftrightarrow :\ddot{O}-N=\ddot{O}$$

The odd electron is probably on N because it is less electronegative than O.
Assuming the odd electron is on N, FC for N = 5 - [1+ 1/2 (6)] = +1.
If the odd electron is on O, FC for N = 5 - [2 + 1/2 (6)] = 0.

(d)   28 e⁻, 14 e⁻ pairs

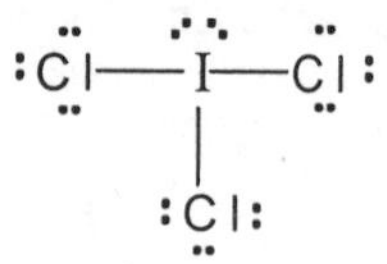

FC for I = 7 - [4 + 1/2 (6)] = 0

(e)   32 e⁻, 16 e⁻ pairs

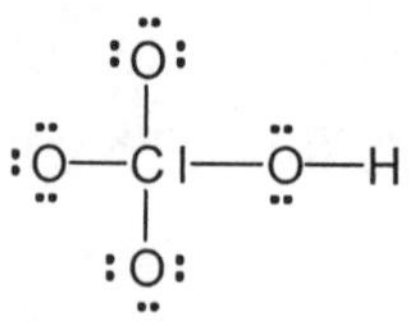

FC for Cl = 7 - [0 + 1/2 (8)] = +3

8.81   (a)

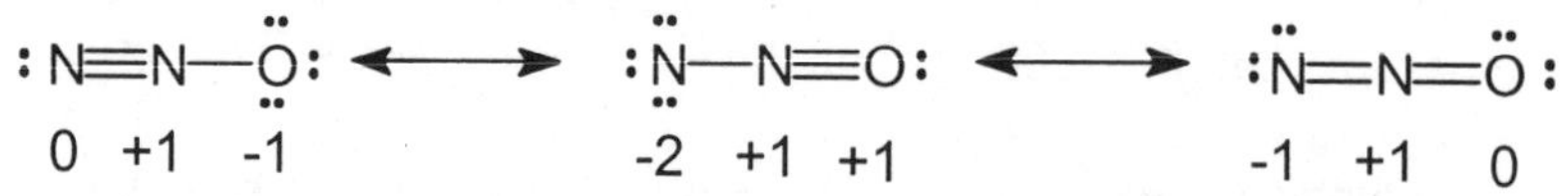

$$:N\equiv N-\ddot{O}: \longleftrightarrow :\ddot{N}-N\equiv O: \longleftrightarrow :\ddot{N}=N=\ddot{O}:$$

    0 +1 -1   -2 +1 +1   -1 +1   0

In the leftmost structure, the more electronegative O atom has the negative formal charge, so this structure is likely to be most important.

(b)   In general, the more shared pairs of electrons between two atoms, the shorter the bond, and vice versa. That the N–N bond length in N_2O is slightly longer than the typical N≡N indicates that the middle and right resonance structures where the N atoms share less than 3 electron pairs are contributors to the true structure. That the N-O bond length is slightly shorter than a typical N=O indicates that the middle structure, where N and O share more than 2 electron pairs, does contribute to the true structure. This physical data indicates that while formal charge can be used to predict which resonance form will be more important to the observed structure, the influence of minor contributors on the true structure cannot be ignored.

8.83 $\Delta H = 8D(C-H) - D(C-C) - 6D(C-H) - D(H-H)$

        $= 2D(C-H) - D(C-C) - D(H-H)$

        $= 2(413) - 348 - 436 = +42 \text{ kJ}$

  $\Delta H = 8D(C-H) + 1/2\, D(O=O) - D(C-C) - 6D(C-H) - 2D(O-H)$

        $= 2D(C-H) + 1/2\, D(O=O) - D(C-C) - 2D(O-H)$

        $= 2(413) + 1/2\,(495) - 348 - 2(463) = -200 \text{ kJ}$

The fundamental difference in the two reactions is the formation of 1 mol of H–H bonds versus the formation of 2 mol of O–H bonds. The latter is much more exothermic, so the reaction involving oxygen is more exothermic.

8.85   (a)

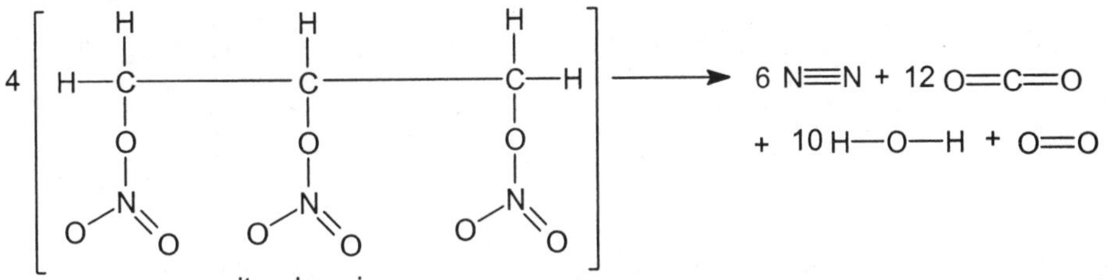

nitroglycerine

$\Delta H = 20D(C-H) + 8D(C-C) + 12D(C-O) + 24D(O-N) + 12D(N=O)$

      $- [6D(N\equiv N) + 24D(C=O) + 20D(H-O) + D(O=O)]$

$\Delta H = 20(413) + 8(348) + 12(358) + 24(201) + 12(607)$

      $- [6(941) + 24(799) + 20(463) + 495]$

   $= -7129 \text{ kJ}$

$$1.00 \text{ g } C_3H_5N_3O_9 \times \frac{1 \text{ mol } C_3H_5N_3O_9}{227.1 \text{ g } C_3H_5N_3O_9} \times \frac{-7129 \text{ kJ}}{4 \text{ mol } C_3H_5N_3O_9} = 7.85 \text{ kJ/g } C_3H_5N_3O_9$$

(b) $4C_7H_5N_3O_6(s) \rightarrow 6N_2(g) + 7CO_2(g) + 10H_2O(g) + 21C(s)$

Integrative Exercises

8.88   (a) Ti^{2+} : $[Ar]3d^2$;   Ca : $[Ar]4s^2$. Yes.   The 2 valence electrons in Ti^{2+} and Ca are in different principle quantum levels and different subshells.

(b)   According to the Aufbau Principle, valence electrons will occupy the lowest energy empty orbital. Thus, in Ca the 4s is lower in energy than the 3d, while in Ti^{2+}, the 3d is lower in energy than the 4s.

(c)   Since there is only one 4s orbital, the 2 valence electrons in Ca are paired. There are 5 degenerate 3d orbitals, so the 2 valence electrons in Ti^{2+} are unpaired. Ca has no unpaired electrons, Ti^{2+} has 2.

8.90   The pathway to the formation of K_2O can be written:

$2K(s) \rightarrow 2K(g)$ $2\Delta H_f^\circ \ K(g)$

$2K(g) \rightarrow 2K^+(g) + 2 \ e^-$ $2 \ I_1(K)$

$1/2 \ O_2(g) \rightarrow O(g)$ $\Delta H_f^\circ \ O(g)$

$O(g) + 1 \ e^- \rightarrow O^-(g)$ $E_1(O)$

$O^-(g) + 1 \ e^- \rightarrow O^{2-}(g)$ $E_2(O)$

$2K^+(g) + O^{2-}(g) \rightarrow K_2O(s)$ $-\Delta H_{latt} \ K_2O(s)$

$2K(s) + 1/2 \ O_2(g) \rightarrow K_2O(s)$ $\Delta H_f^\circ \ K_2O(s)$

$\Delta H_f^\circ \ K_2O(s) = 2\Delta H_f^\circ \ K(g) + 2 \ I_1(K) + \Delta H_f^\circ \ O(g) + E_1(O) + E_2(O) - \Delta H_{latt} \ K_2O(s)$

$E_2(O) = \Delta H_f^\circ \ K_2O(s) + \Delta H_{latt} \ K_2O(s) - 2\Delta H_f^\circ \ K(g) - 2 \ I_1(K) - \Delta H_f^\circ \ O(g) - E_1(O)$

$E_2(O) = -363.2 \ kJ + 2238 \ kJ - 2(89.99) \ kJ - 2(419) \ kJ - 247.5 \ kJ - (-141) \ kJ$

$\qquad = +750 \ kJ$

8.95   (a)

$HF(g) \rightarrow H(g) + F(g)$ $D \ (H\text{-}F)$ $567 \ kJ$

$H(g) \rightarrow H^+(g) + 1 \ e^-$ $I \ (H)$ $1312 \ kJ$

$F(g) + 1 \ e^- \rightarrow F^-(g)$ $E \ (F)$ $-328 \ kJ$

$HF(g) \rightarrow H^+(g) + F^-(g)$ ΔH $1551 \ kJ$

(b) $\Delta H = D(H\text{-}Cl) + I(H) + E(Cl)$

$\Delta H = 431 \ kJ + 1312 \ kJ + (-349) \ kJ = 1394 \ kJ$

(c) $\Delta H = D(H\text{-}Br) + I(H) + E(Br)$

$\Delta H = 366 \ kJ + 1312 \ kJ + (-325) \ kJ = 1353 \ kJ$

8.97   (a) $Br_2(l) \rightarrow 2Br(g)$ $\Delta H^\circ = 2\Delta H_f^\circ \ Br(g) = 2(111.8) \ kJ = 223.6 \ kJ$

(b) $CCl_4(l) \rightarrow C(g) + 4Cl(g)$

$\Delta H^\circ = \Delta H_f^\circ \ C(g) + 4\Delta H_f^\circ \ Cl(g) - \Delta H_f^\circ \ CCl_4(l)$

$\qquad = 718.4 \ kJ + 4(121.7) \ kJ - (-139.3) \ kJ = 1344.5$

$\dfrac{1344.5 \ kJ}{4 \ C\text{-}Cl \ bonds} = 336.1 \ kJ$

(c) $H_2O_2(l) \rightarrow 2H(g) + 2O(g)$

$2H(g) + 2O(g) \rightarrow 2OH(g)$

$H_2O_2(l) \rightarrow 2OH(g)$

$D(O\text{-}O)(l) = 2\Delta H_f^\circ \ H(g) + 2\Delta H_f^\circ \ O(g) - \Delta H_f^\circ \ H_2O_2(l) - 2D(O\text{-}H)(g)$

$\qquad\qquad = 2(217.94) \ kJ + 2(247.5) \ kJ - (-187.8) \ kJ - 2(463) \ kJ$

$\qquad\qquad = 193 \ kJ$

(d)   The data are listed below.

bond	D gas kJ/mol	D liquid kJ/mol
Br–Br	193	223.6
C–Cl	328	336.1
O–O	146	192.7

Breaking bonds in the liquid requires more energy than breaking bonds in the gas phase. For simple molecules, bond dissociation from the liquid phase can be thought of in two steps:

           molecule (l) → molecule (g)

           molecule (g) → atoms (g)

The first step is evaporation or vaporization of the liquid and the second is bond dissociation in the gas phase. Average bond enthalpy in the liquid phase is then the sum of the enthalpy of vaporization for the molecule and the gas phase bond dissociation enthalpies, divided by the number of bonds dissociated. This is greater than the gas phase bond dissociation enthalpy owing to the contribution from the enthalpy of vaporization.

9 Molecular Geometry and Bonding Theories

Molecular Shapes; the VSEPR Model

9.1   Yes. This description means that the three terminal atoms point toward the corners of an equilateral triangle and the central atom is in the plane of this triangle. Only 120° bond angles are possible in this arrangement.

9.3   (a)   An *electron domain* is a region in a molecule where electrons are most likely to be found.

        (b)   Each balloon in Figure 9.5 occupies a volume of space. The best arrangement is one where each balloon has its "own" space, where they are as far apart as possible and repulsions are minimized. Electron domains are negatively charged regions, so they also adopt an arrangement where repulsions are minimized.

9.5   *Analyze/Plan.* See Table 9.1.   *Solve*:

        (a)   trigonal planar   (b) tetrahedral   (c) trigonal bipyramidal   (d) octahedral

9.7   The electron-domain geometry indicated by VSEPR describes the arrangement of all bonding and nonbonding electron domains. The molecular geometry describes just the atomic positions. NH_3 has the Lewis structure given below; there are four electron domains around nitrogen so the electron-domain geometry is tetrahedral, but the molecular geometry of the four atoms is trigonal pyramidal.

            Lewis   electron-domain   molecular
          structure   geometry   geometry

9.9   *Analyze/Plan.* See Table 9.3. *Solve:*

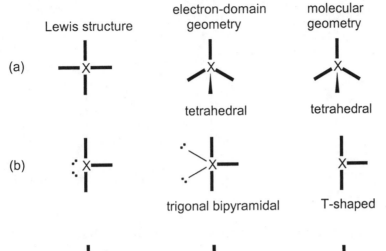

	Lewis structure	electron-domain geometry	molecular geometry
(a)		tetrahedral	tetrahedral
(b)		trigonal bipyramidal	T-shaped
(c)		octahedral	square pyramidal

9.11   *Analyze/Plan.* Follow the logic in Sample Exercise 9.1. *Solve:*

bent (b), linear (l), octahedral (oh), **seesaw (ss) square pyramidal (sp)**, **square planar (spl)**, tetrahedral (td), trigonal bipyramidal (tbp), trigonal planar (tr), trigonal pyramidal (tp), T-shaped (T)

	Molecule or ion	Valence electrons	Lewis structure		Electron-domain geometry	Molecul geomet
(a)	H_3O^+	8	$\left[H-\overset{\cdot\cdot}{O}-H \atop \quad\ H \right]^+$		td	tp
(b)	SCN^-	16	$*\left[:\overset{\cdot\cdot}{\underset{\cdot\cdot}{S}}-C\equiv N: \right]^-$	$\left[S-C\equiv N \right]^-$	l	l
(c)	CS_2	16	$* \ \overset{\cdot\cdot}{\underset{\cdot\cdot}{S}}=C=\overset{\cdot\cdot}{\underset{\cdot\cdot}{S}}$	$S=C=S$	l	l
(d)	BrO_3^-	26	$\left[:\overset{\cdot\cdot}{\underset{\cdot\cdot}{O}}-Br-\overset{\cdot\cdot}{\underset{\cdot\cdot}{O}}: \atop :\overset{\cdot\cdot}{O}: \right]^-$		td	tp
(e)	SeF_4	34	$:\overset{\cdot\cdot}{F}: \atop :\overset{\cdot\cdot}{F}-\overset{\cdot\cdot}{Se}-\overset{\cdot\cdot}{F}: \atop F$		tbp	ss

Molecule or ion	Valence electrons	Lewis structure	Electron-domain geometry	Molecular geometry
(f) ICl_4^-	36	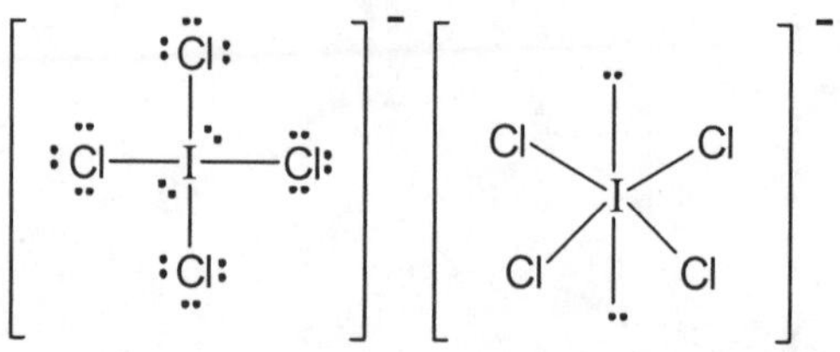	oh	spl

* More than 1 resonance structure is possible. All equivalent resonance structures predict the same molecular geometry.

9.13   *Analyze/Plan*. Work backwards from molecular geometry, using Tables 9.2 and 9.3. *Solve*:

(a)   electron-domain geometries: i, trigonal planar; ii, tetrahedral; iii, trigonal bipyramidal

(b)   nonbonding electron domains: i, 0;   ii, 1;   iii, 2

(c)   N and P. Shape ii has 3 bonding and 1 nonbonding electron domains. Li and Al would form ionic compounds with F, so there would be no nonbonding electron domains. Assuming that F always has 3 nonbonding domains, BF_3 and ClF_3 would have the wrong number of nonbonding domains to produce shape ii.

(d)   Cl (also Br and I, since they have 7 valence electrons). This T-shaped molecular geometry arises from a trigonal bipyramidal electron-domain geometry with 2 nonbonding domains (Table 9.3). Assuming each F atom has 3 nonbonding domains and forms only single bonds with A, A must have 7 valence electrons to produce these electron-domain and molecular geometries. It must be in or below the third row of the periodic table, so that it can accommodate more than 4 electron domains.

9.15   *Analyze/Plan*. Follow the logic in Sample Exercise 9.3.   *Solve*:

(a)   1 – 109°, 2 – 109°   (b) 3 – 109°, 4 – 109°
(c)   5 – 180°   (d) 6 – 120°, 7 – 109°, 8 – 109°

9.17   *Analyze*. Given: molecular formulas. Find: explain features of molecular geometries.

Plan. Draw the correct Lewis structures for the molecules and use VSEPR to predict and explain observed molecular geometry.   *Solve*:

(a) BrF_4^- 36 e⁻, 18 e⁻ pr BF_4^- 32 e⁻, 16 e⁻ pr

6 e⁻ pairs around Br   4 e⁻ pairs around B
octahedral e⁻ domain geometry   tetrahedral e⁻ domain geometry
square planar molecular geometry   tetrahedral molecular geometry

The fundamental feature that determines molecular geometry is the number of electron domains around the central atom, and the number of these that are bonding domains. Although BrF_4^- and BF_4^- are both of the form AX_4^-, the central atoms and thus the number of valence electrons in the two ions are different. This leads to different numbers of e⁻ domains about the two central atoms. Even though both ions have four bonding electron domains, the six total domains around Br require octahedral domain geometry and square planar molecular geometry, while the four total domains about B lead to tetrahedral domain and molecular geometry.

(b) CF_4 32 e⁻, 16 e⁻ pr SF_4 34 e⁻, 17 e⁻ pr

4 e⁻ domains around C   5 e⁻ domains around S
tetrahedral e⁻ domain geometry   trigonal bipyramidal e⁻ domain geometry
tetrahedral molecular geometry   see-saw molecular geometry

CF_4 will have bond angles closest to the value predicted by VSEPR, because there are no nonbonding e⁻ domains around C. The four bonding domains in CF_4 are equivalent and lead to the balance of repulsions implicit in VSEPR theory. In SF_4, one of the e⁻ domains is nonbonding. A nonbonding domain is surely not equivalent to a bonding domain; we expect it to be more diffuse. That is, nonbonding domains will occupy more space, "push back" the bonding domains, and lead to bond angles that are nonideal.

9.19   *Analyze/Plan.* Given the formula of each molecule or ion, draw the correct Lewis structure and use principles of VSEPR to answer the question.   *Solve:*

$$\left[H-\overset{\cdot\cdot}{\underset{\cdot\cdot}{N}}-H \right]^{-} \qquad H-\overset{\cdot\cdot}{\underset{|}{N}}-H \qquad \left[\overset{\textstyle H}{\underset{\textstyle H}{H-\overset{|}{\underset{|}{N}}-H}} \right]^{+}$$

Each species has 4 electron domains around the N atom, but the number of nonbonding domains decreases from 2 to 0, going from NH_2^- to NH_4^+. Since nonbonding domains occupy more space than bonding domains, the bond angles expand as the number of nonbonding domains decreases.

Polarity of Polyatomic Molecules

9.21   See Sample Exercise 9.4(b) for the correct resonance structures and analysis of S–O bond dipoles. According to the electron density model, the net dipole moment vector points along the O–S–O angle bisector with the negative end pointing away from S. the magnitude of this vector is 1.63 D.

9.23   (a)   In Exercise 9.13, molecules ii and iii will have nonzero dipole moments. Molecule i has no nonbonding electron pairs on A, and the 3 A-F dipoles are oriented so that the sum of their vectors is zero (the bond dipoles cancel). Molecules ii and iii have nonbonding electron pairs on A and their bond dipoles do not cancel. A nonbonding electron pair (or pairs) on a central atom guarantees at least a small molecular dipole moment, because no bond dipole exactly cancels a nonbonding pair.

       (b) AF_4 molecules will have a zero dipole moment if there are no nonbonding electron pairs on the central atom and the 4 A-F bond dipoles are arranged (symmetrically) so that they cancel. Therefore, in Exercise 9.14, molecules i and ii have zero dipole moments and are nonpolar.

9.25   *Analyze/Plan.* Given molecular formulas, draw correct Lewis structures, determine molecular structure and polarity.   *Solve:*

Nonpolar, in a symmetrical trigonal planar molecule, the bond dipoles cancel.

Polar, $\Delta EN > 0$

$$C\equiv O$$

$$\underset{F\quad\ \ F}{\overset{F}{\underset{|}{B}}}$$

Nonpolar, in a symmetrical tetrahedral structure (Figure 9.1) the bond dipoles cancel.

Polar, there is an unequal charge distribution due to the nonbonded electron pair on N.

Polar, there is an unequal charge distribution because of the nonbonded electron pairs on S, and the S-F bond dipoles do not cancel.

9.27

polar   nonpolar   polar

All three isomers are planar. The molecules on the left and right are polar because the C–Cl bond dipoles do not point in opposite directions. In the middle isomer, the C–Cl bonds and dipoles are pointing in opposite directions (as are the C–H bonds), the molecule is nonpolar and has a measured dipole moment of zero.

Orbital Overlap; Hybrid Orbitals

9.29   (a)   *Orbital overlap* occurs when a valence atomic orbital on one atom shares the same region of space with a valence atomic orbital on an adjacent atom.

       (b)   In valence bond theory, overlap of orbitals allows the two electrons in a chemical bond to mutually occupy the space between the bonded nuclei.

       (c)   Valence bond theory is a combination of the atomic orbital concept with the Lewis model of electron pair bonding.

9.31   *Analyze/Plan.* Given electron domain geometry, list the appropriate orbital hybridization and associated bond angles; refer to Table 9.4. *Solve*:

     (a)   sp -- 180°   (b) sp^3 -- 109°   (c) sp^2 -- 120°

     (d) sp^3d^2 -- 90° and 180°   (e) sp^3d -- 90°, 120° and 180°

9.33   *Analyze/Plan.* Follow the logic in Sample Exercise 9.5. *Solve:*

SO_3^{2-}, 26 e⁻, 13 e⁻ pr

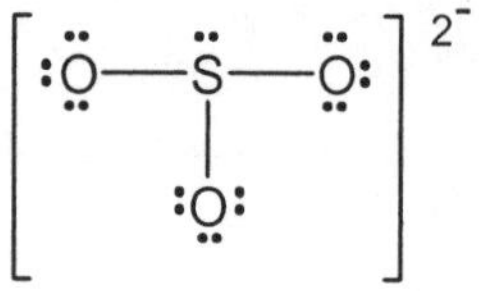

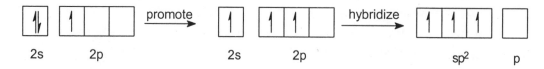

4 e⁻ domains around S; tetrahedral e⁻ domain geometry;
trigonal pyramidal molecular geometry;
sp³ hybrid orbitals (based on e⁻ domain geometry)
"ideal" O–S–O angle ~107° (The nonbonding e⁻ domain
will close down the tetrahedral angles somewhat.)

9.35   (a)   B: $[He]2s^2 2p^1$

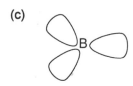

2s   2p   2s   2p   sp²   p

(b)   The hybrid orbitals are called sp².   (c)

(d)   A single 2p orbital is unhybridized.
It lies perpendicular to the trigonal
plane of the sp² hybrid orbitals.

9.37   *Analyze/Plan.* Given the molecular (or ionic) formula, draw the correct Lewis structure and
determine the electron domain geometry, which determines hybridization. *Solve:*

(a)   24 e⁻, 12 e⁻ pairs   (b)   32 e⁻, 16 e⁻ pairs

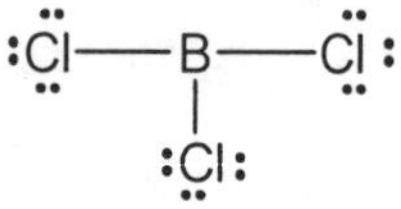

3 e⁻ pairs around B
trigonal planar e⁻ domain
geometry, sp² hybrid orbitals

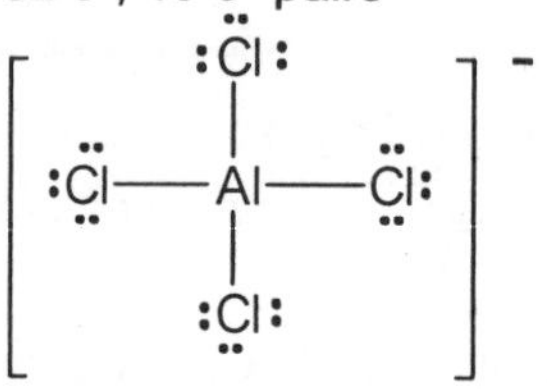

4 e⁻ domains around Al
tetrahedral e⁻ domain geometry
sp³ hybrid orbitals

(c)   16 e⁻, 8 e⁻ pairs   (d)   22 e⁻, 11 e⁻ pairs

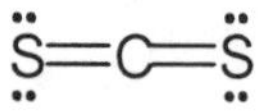

2 e⁻ domains around C
linear e⁻ domain geometry
sp hybrid orbitals

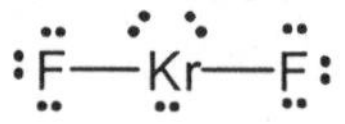

5 e⁻ pairs around Kr
trigonal bipyramidal e⁻ domain
geometry, sp³d hybrid orbitals

(e)   48 e⁻, 24 e⁻ pairs

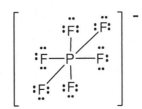

6 e⁻ pairs around P,
octahedral e⁻ domain
geometry, sp^3d^2 orbitals

Multiple Bonds

9.39   (a)    (b)

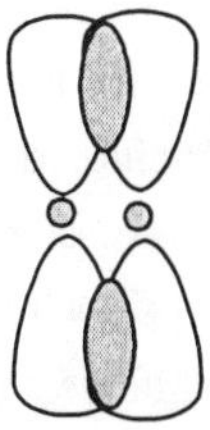

                        σ   π

     (c)   A σ bond is generally stronger than a π bond, because there is more extensive orbital overlap.

9.41   (a)

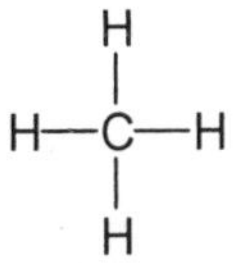

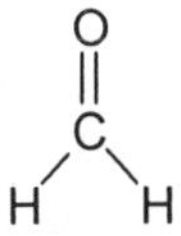

     (b) sp^3 sp^2

     (c)   The C atom in CH_4 is sp^3 hybridized; there are no unhybridized p orbitals available for the π overlap required by multiple bonds. In CH_2O, the C atom is sp^2 hybridized, with 1 p atomic orbital available to form the π overlap in the C=O double bond.

9.43   *Analyze/Plan.* Single bonds are σ bonds, double bonds consist of 1 σ and 1 π bond. Each bond is formed by a pair of valence electrons. *Solve:*

     (a) C_3H_6O has 3(4) + 6(1) + 6 = 24 valence electrons
     (b)   9 pairs or 18 total valence electrons form σ bonds
     (c)   1 pair or 2 total valence electrons form π bonds
     (d)   2 pairs or 4 total valence electrons are nonbonding
     (e)   The central C atom is sp^2 hybridized

9.45   *Analyze/Plan.* Given the correct Lewis structure, analyze the electron domain geometry at **each central atom**. This determines the hybridization and bond angles at that atom. *Solve:*

     (a)   ~109° about the left most C, sp^3; ~120° about the right-hand C, sp^2

     (b)   The doubly bonded O can be viewed as sp^2, the other as sp^3; the nitrogen is sp^3 with approximately 109° bond angles.

(c)   nine σ bonds, one π bond

9.47   (a)   In a localized π bond, the electron density is concentrated strictly between the two atoms forming the bond. In a delocalized π bond, parallel p orbitals on more than two adjacent atoms overlap and the electron density is spread over all the atoms that contribute p orbitals to the network. There are still two regions of overlap, above and below the σ framework of the molecule.

(b)   The existence of more than one resonance form is a good indication that a molecule will have delocalized π bonding.

(c)

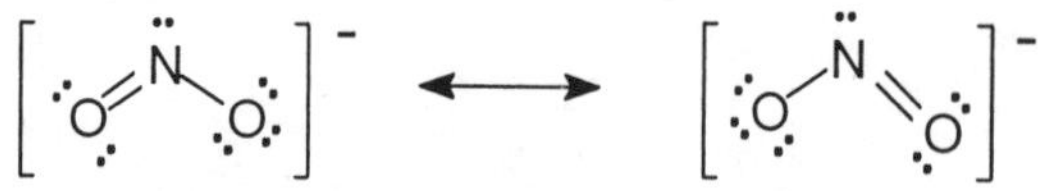

$$\left[\ddot{O} = \ddot{N} - \ddot{\ddot{O}} \right]^{-} \longleftrightarrow \left[\ddot{\ddot{O}} - \ddot{N} = \ddot{O} \right]^{-}$$

The existence of more than one resonance form for NO_2^- indicates that the π bond is delocalized. From an orbital perspective, the electron-domain geometry around N is trigonal planar, so the hybridization at N is sp^2. This leaves a p orbital on N and one on each O atom perpendicular to the trigonal plane of the molecule, in the correct orientation for delocalized π overlap. Physically, the two N-O bond lengths are equal, indicating that the two N-O bonds are equivalent, rather than one longer single bond and one shorter double bond.

Molecular Orbitals

9.49   (a)   Both atomic and molecular orbitals have a characteristic energy and shape (region where there is a high probability of finding an electron). Each atomic or molecular orbital can hold a maximum of two electrons. Atomic orbitals are localized on single atoms and their energies are the result of interactions between the subatomic particles in a single atom. MOs can be delocalized over several or even all the atoms in a molecule and their energies are influenced by interactions between electrons on several atoms.

(b)   There is a net stabilization (lowering in energy) that accompanies bond formation because the bonding electrons in H_2 are strongly attracted to both H nuclei.

(c)   2

9.51   (a)

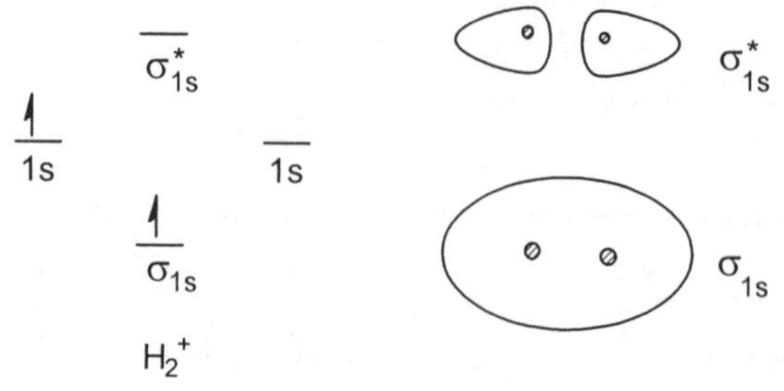

(b)   There is 1 electron in H_2^+.

(c) $\boxed{}$ σ^*_{1s} (d) Bond order = 1/2 (1-0) = 1/2

$\boxed{\uparrow}$ σ_{1s}

(e) Yes. The stability of H_2^+ is due to the lower energy state of the σ bonding molecular orbital relative to the energy of a H 1s atomic orbital. If the single electron in H_2^+ is excited to the σ^*_{1s} orbital, its energy is higher than the energy of a H 1s atomic orbital and H_2^+ will decompose into a hydrogen atom and a hydrogen ion.

$$H_2^+ \xrightarrow{h\nu} H + H^+.$$

9.53   *Analyze/Plan.* In a σ molecular orbital, the electron density is spherically symmetric about the internuclear axis and is concentrated along this axis. In a π MO, the electron density is concentrated above and below the internuclear axis and zero along it. *Solve:*

(a)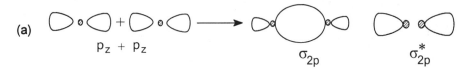

$p_z + p_z \longrightarrow \sigma_{2p} \qquad \sigma^*_{2p}$

(b)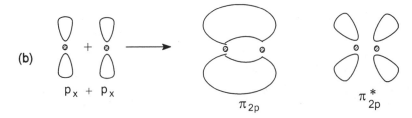

$p_x + p_x \longrightarrow \pi_{2p} \qquad \pi^*_{2p}$

(c) σ_{2p} is lower in energy than π_{2p} due to greater extent of orbital overlap in the σ MO. $\sigma_{2p} < \pi_{2p} < \pi^*_{2p} < \sigma^*_{2p}$

9.55   (a) When comparing the same two bonded atoms, the greater the bond order, the shorter the bond length and the greater the bond energy. That is, bond order and bond energy are directly related, while bond order and bond length are inversely related. When comparing different bonded nuclei, there are no simple relationships (see Solution 8.86).

(b) Be_2, 4 e⁻ Be_2^+, 3 e⁻

     $\boxed{\uparrow\downarrow}$ σ^*_{2s} $\boxed{\uparrow}$ σ^*_{2s}

     $\boxed{\uparrow\downarrow}$ σ_{2s} $\boxed{\uparrow\downarrow}$ σ_{2s}

     BO = 1/2(2-2) = 0   BO = 1/2(2-1) = 0.5

Be$_2$ has a bond order of zero and is not energetically favored over isolated Be atoms; it is not expected to exist. Be$_2^+$ has a bond order of 0.5 and is slightly lower in energy than isolated Be atoms. It will probably exist under special experimental conditions, but be unstable.

9.57   (a), (b) Substances with no unpaired electrons are weakly repelled by a magnetic field. This property is called *diamagnetism*.

     (c)   O$_2^{2-}$, Be$_2^{2+}$ (see Figure 9.41)

9.59

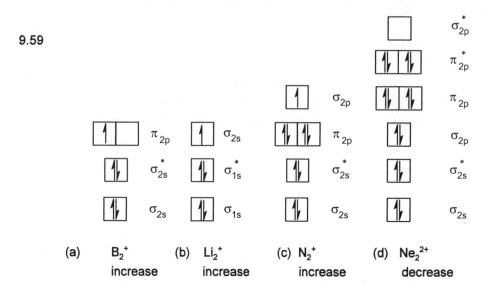

     (a)   B$_2^+$ (b)   Li$_2^+$ (c)   N$_2^+$ (d)   Ne$_2^{2+}$

         increase   increase   increase   decrease

Addition of an electron increases bond order if it occupies a bonding MO and decreases stability if it occupies an antibonding MO.

9.61   *Analyze/Plan.* Determine the number of 'valence' (non-core) electrons in each molecule or ion. Use the homonuclear diatomic MO diagram from Figure 9.38 (shown below) to calculate bond order and magnetic properties of each species. The electronegativity difference between heteroatomics increases the energy difference between the 2s AO on one atom and the 2p AO on the other, rendering the 'no interaction' MO diagram in Figure 9.38 appropriate. *Solve:*

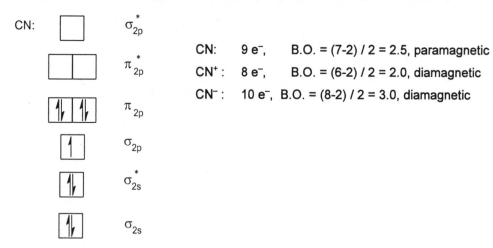

CN: 9 e$^-$,   B.O. = (7-2) / 2 = 2.5, paramagnetic

CN$^+$:   8 e$^-$,   B.O. = (6-2) / 2 = 2.0, diamagnetic

CN$^-$:   10 e$^-$, B.O. = (8-2) / 2 = 3.0, diamagnetic

9.63   (a) $3s$, $3p_x$, $3p_y$, $3p_z$ (b) π_{3p} (c) 2

        (d)   If the MO diagram for P_2 is similar to that of N_2, P_2 will have no unpaired electrons and be diamagnetic.

Additional Exercises

9.65   (a) $8\ e^-$, $4\ e^-$ pairs   (b) $32\ e^-$, $16\ e^-$ pairs

H—Se—H

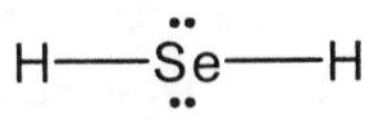

4 e^- domains
tetrahedral domain geometry
bent molecular geometry

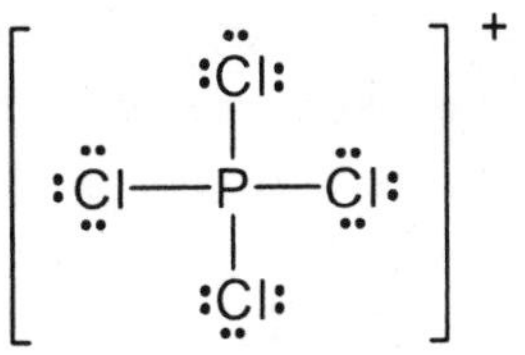

4 e^- domains
tetrahedral domain and
molecular geometry

     (c) $18\ e^-$, $9\ e^-$ pairs   (d) $28\ e^-$, $14\ e^-$ pairs

$$\left[\ \ddot{O}=\ddot{N}-\ddot{O}\colon\right]^- \longleftrightarrow \left[\colon\ddot{O}-\ddot{N}=\ddot{O}\ \right]^-$$

3 e^- domains
trigonal planar domain geometry

bent molecular geometry

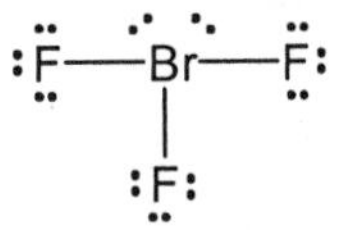

5 e^- domains
trigonal bipyramidal e^- domain geometry,

T-shaped molecular geometry (in a trigonal bipyramid, nonbonded domains lie in the trigonal plane)

     (e) $22\ e^-$ $11\ e^-$ pairs

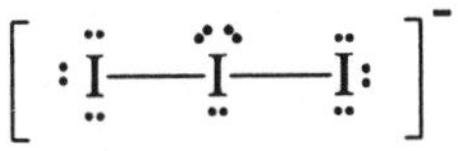

$$\left[\ \colon\ddot{I}-\ddot{I}-\ddot{I}\colon\ \right]^-$$

5 e^- domains
trigonal bipyramidal e^- domain geometry
linear molecular geometry (In a trigonal
bipyramid, nonbonded domains lie in
the trigonal plane.)

9.67

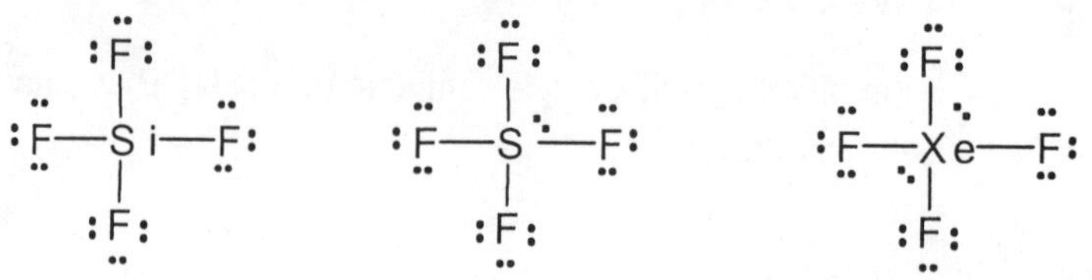

:F:
:F—Si—F:
:F:

:F:
:F—S⁻—F:
:F:

:F:
:F—Xe—F:
:F:

e- domain geometry	td	tbp	octahedral (oh)
molecular geometry	td	seesaw (ss)	square planar (s)

Although there are four bonding electron domains in each molecule, the number of nonbonding domains is different in each case. The bond angles and thus the molecular shape are influenced by the total number of electron domains.

9.69 (a) CO_2, 16 valence e⁻   (b)   NCS⁻, 16 valence e⁻

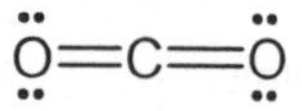

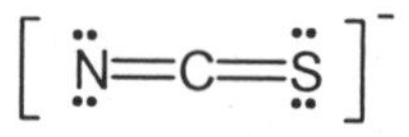

$$\ddot{O}=C=\ddot{O}$$

    2 σ   2 π

$$\left[\ddot{N}=C=\ddot{S} \right]^{-} \quad + \quad$$ two other resonance structures

      2 σ   2 π   (for any of the resonance structures)

(c) H_2CO, 12 valence e⁻   (d)   HCO(OH), 18 valence e⁻

    3 σ, 1 π

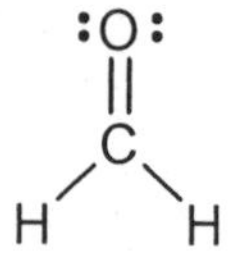

H—C (=O, O—H)

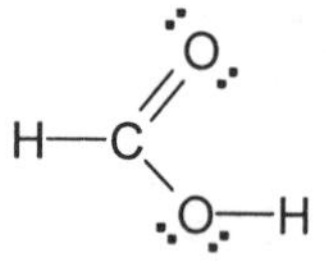

    4 σ, 1 π

9.72   The compound on the right has a dipole moment. In the square planar *trans* structure on the left, all equivalent bond dipoles can be oriented opposite each other, for a net dipole moment of zero.

9.74

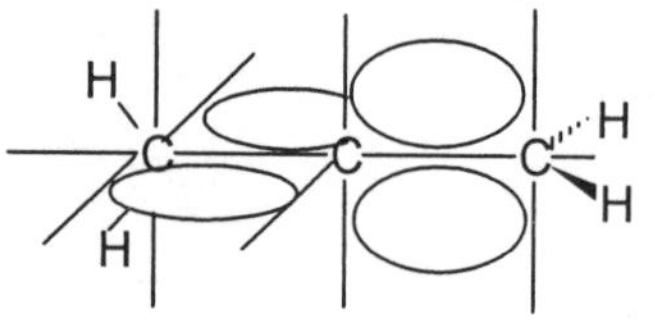

H, C C C H, H

(a)   The molecule is nonplanar. The CH_2 planes at each end are twisted 90° from one another.

(b)   Allene has no dipole moment.

(c)   The bonding in allene would not be described as delocalized. The π electron clouds of the two adjacent C=C are mutually perpendicular. The mechanism for delocalization of π electrons is mutual overlap of parallel p atomic orbitals on adjacent atoms. If adjacent π electron clouds are mutually perpendicular, there is no overlap and no delocalization of π electrons.

9.77   (a)   Ö=Ö–Ö: ⟷   :Ö–Ö=Ö

To accommodate the π bonding by all 3 O atoms indicated in the resonance structures above, all O atoms are sp^2 hybridized.

(b)   For the first resonance structure, both sigma bonds are formed by overlap of sp^2 hybrid orbitals, the π bond is formed by overlap of atomic p orbitals, one of the nonbonded pairs on the right terminal O atom is in a p atomic orbital, and the remaining 5 nonbonded pairs are in sp^2 hybrid orbitals.

(c)   Only unhybridized p atomic orbitals can be used to form a delocalized π system.

(d)   The unhybridized p orbital on each O atom is used to form the delocalized π system, and in both resonance structures one nonbonded electron pair resides in a p atomic orbital. The delocalized π system then contains 4 electrons, 2 from the π bond and 2 from the nonbonded pair in the p orbital.

9.79

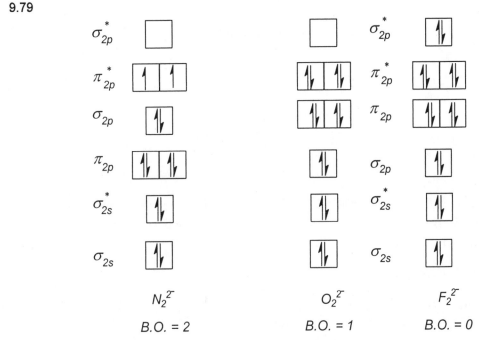

N_2^{2-} and O_2^{2-} are likely to be stable species, F_2^{2-} is not.

Integrative Exercises

9.82   (a)   Assume 100 g of compound

$$2.1 \text{ g H} \times \frac{1 \text{ mol H}}{1.008 \text{ g H}} = 2.1 \text{ mol H}; \quad 2.1 / 2.1 = 1$$

$$29.8 \text{ g N} \times \frac{1 \text{ mol N}}{14.01 \text{ g N}} = 2.13 \text{ mol N}; \quad 2.13 / 2.1 \approx 1$$

$$68.1 \text{ g O} \times \frac{1 \text{ mol O}}{16.00 \text{ g O}} = 4.26 \text{ mol O}; \quad 4.26 / 2.1 \approx 2$$

The empirical formula is HNO_2; formula weight = 47. Since the approximate molecular weight is 50, the **molecular formula is HNO_2.**

(b)   Assume N is central, since it is unusual for O to be central, and part (d) indicates as much. HNO_2: 18 valence e^-

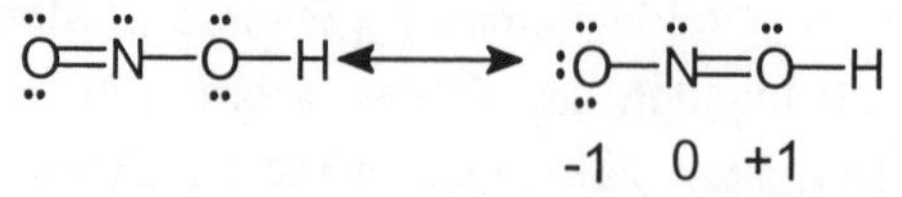

$$\ddot{O} = \ddot{N} - \ddot{O} - H \longleftrightarrow :\ddot{O} - \ddot{N} = \ddot{O} - H$$
$$\qquad\qquad\qquad\qquad\quad -1 \quad 0 \quad +1$$

The second resonance form is a minor contributor due to unfavorable formal charges.

(c)   The electron pair geometry around N is trigonal planar; if the resonance structure on the right makes a significant contribution to the molecular structure, all 4 atoms would lie in a plane. If only the left structure contributes, the H could rotate in and out of the molecular plane. The relative contributions of the two resonance structures could be determined by measuring the O–N–O and N–O–H bond angles.

(d)   3 VSEPR e^- domains around N, sp^2 hybridization

(e)   3 σ, 1 π for both structures (or for H bound to N).

9.87

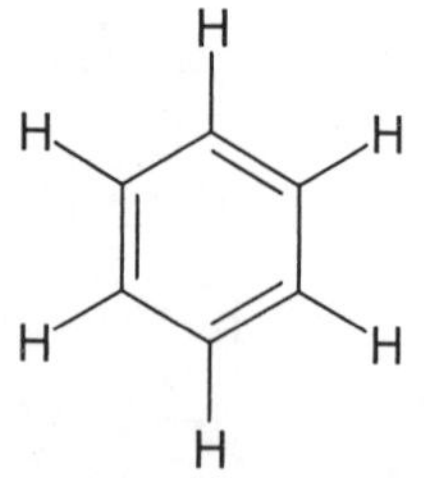

$$(g) \longrightarrow 6C(g) + 6H(g)$$

$\Delta H = 6D(C–H) + 3D(C–C) + 3D(C=C) - 0$ (The products are isolated atoms;
   $= 6(413 \text{ kJ}) + 3(348 \text{ kJ}) + 3(614 \text{ kJ})$ there is no bond making.)
   $= 5364 \text{ kJ}$

According to Hess's Law:

$\Delta H^{\circ} = 6\Delta H_f^{\circ} \text{ C}(g) + 6\Delta H_f^{\circ} \text{ H}(g) - \Delta H_f^{\circ} \text{ C}_6\text{H}_6(g)$
   $= 6(718.4 \text{ kJ}) + 6(217.94 \text{ kJ}) - (+82.9 \text{ kJ})$
   $= 5535 \text{ kJ}$

The difference in the two results, 171 kJ/mol C_6H_6 is due to the resonance stabilization in benzene. That is, because the π electrons are delocalized, the molecule has a lower overall energy than that predicted for the presence of 3 localized C–C and C=C bonds. Thus, the amount of energy actually required to decompose 1 mole of $C_6H_6(g)$, represented by the Hess's Law calculation, is greater than the sum of the localized bond enthalpies (not taking resonance into account) from the first calculation above.

10 Gases

Gas Characteristics; Pressure

10.1   In the gas phase molecules are far apart, while in the liquid they are touching.

   (a)   A gas is much less dense than a liquid because most of the volume of a gas is empty space.

   (b)   A gas is much more compressible because of the distance between molecules.

   (c)   Gaseous molecules are so far apart that there is no barrier to mixing, regardless of the identity of the molecule. All mixtures of gases are homogeneous. Liquid molecules are touching. In order to mix, they must displace one another. Similar molecules displace each other and form homogeneous mixtures. Very dissimilar molecules form heterogeneous mixtures.

10.3   (a)   F = m × a. Since both people have the same mass and both experience the acceleration of gravity, the forces they exert on the floor are exactly equal.

   (b)   P = F / A. The two forces are equal, but the person standing on one foot exerts this force over a smaller area. Thus, the person standing on one foot exerts a greater pressure on the floor.

10.5   *Analyze*. Given: 760 mm column of Hg, densities of Hg and H_2O. Find: height of a column of H_2O at same pressure.

   Plan. We must develop a relationship between pressure, height of a column of liquid, and density of the liquid. Relationships that might prove useful: P = F/A; F = m × a; m = d × V(density)(volume); V = A × height   *Solve*:

   $$P = \frac{F}{A} = \frac{m \times a}{A} = \frac{d \times V \times a}{A} = \frac{d \times A \times h \times a}{A} = d \times h \times a$$

   (a) $P_{Hg} = P_{H_2O}$; Using the relationship derived above: $(d \times h \times a)_{H_2O} = (d \times h \times a)_{Hg}$

   Since a, the acceleration due to gravity, is equal in both liquids,

   $(d \times h)_{H_2O} = (d \times h)_{Hg}$

   1.00 g/mL × h_{H_2O} = 13.6 g/mL × 760 mm

   $$h_{H_2O} = \frac{13.6 \text{ g/mL} \times 760 \text{ mm}}{1.00 \text{ g/mL}} = 1.034 \times 10^4 = 1.03 \times 10^4 \text{ mm} = 10.3 \text{ m}$$

(b)   Pressure due to H_2O:

$1 \text{ atm} = 1.034 \times 10^4 \text{ mm } H_2O$ (from part (a))

$$36 \text{ ft } H_2O \times \frac{12 \text{ in}}{1 \text{ ft}} \times \frac{2.54 \text{ cm}}{1 \text{ in}} \times \frac{10 \text{ mm}}{1 \text{ cm}} \times \frac{1 \text{ atm}}{1.034 \times 10^4 \text{ mm}} = 1.061 = 1.1 \text{ atm}$$

$P_{total} = P_{atm} + P_{H_2O} = 0.95 \text{ atm} + 1.061 \text{ atm} = 2.011 = 2.0 \text{ atm}$

10.7   (a)   The tube can have **any** cross-sectional area. (The height of the Hg column in a barometer is independent of the cross-sectional area. See the expression for pressure derived in Solution 10.5.)

        (b)   At equilibrium, the force of gravity per unit area acting on the mercury column at the level of the outside mercury is **not** equal to the force of gravity per unit area acting on the atmosphere. (F = ma; the acceleration due to gravity is equal for the two substances, but the mass of Hg for a given cross-sectional area is different than the mass of air for this same area.)

        (c)   The column of mercury is held up by the pressure of the atmosphere applied to the exterior pool of mercury.

10.9   *Analyze/Plan.* Follow the logic in sample Exercise 10.1. *Solve*:

        (a) $265 \text{ torr} \times \dfrac{1 \text{ atm}}{760 \text{ torr}} = 0.349 \text{ atm}$

        (b) $265 \text{ torr} \times \dfrac{1 \text{ mm Hg}}{1 \text{ torr}} = 265 \text{ mm Hg}$

        (c) $265 \text{ torr} \times \dfrac{1.01325 \times 10^5 \text{ Pa}}{760 \text{ torr}} = 3.53 \times 10^4 \text{ Pa}$

        (d) $265 \text{ torr} \times \dfrac{1.01325 \times 10^5 \text{ Pa}}{760 \text{ torr}} \times \dfrac{1 \text{ bar}}{1 \times 10^5 \text{ Pa}} = 0.353 \text{ bar}$

10.11   *Analyze/Plan.* Follow the logic in Sample Exercise 10.1. *Solve*:

        (a) $30.45 \text{ in Hg} \times \dfrac{25.4 \text{ mm}}{1 \text{ in}} \times \dfrac{1 \text{ torr}}{1 \text{ mm Hg}} = 773.4 \text{ torr}$

           [The result has 4 sig figs because 25.4 mm/in is considered to be an exact number. (Section 1.5)]

        (b)   The pressure in Chicago is greater than **standard atmospheric pressure**, 760 torr, so it makes sense to classify this weather system as a "high pressure system."

10.13   *Analyze.* Given: mass, area. Find: pressure. *Plan.* P = F/A = m × a/A; use this relationship, paying attention to units. *Solve*:

$$1 \text{ Pa} = \frac{1 \text{ N}}{\text{m}^2} = \frac{1 \text{ kg} \cdot \text{m}}{\text{s}^2} \times \frac{1}{\text{m}^2} = \frac{1 \text{ kg}}{\text{m} \cdot \text{s}^2} \qquad \text{Change mass to kg and area to m}^2.$$

$$P = \frac{m \times a}{A} = \frac{125\,lb}{0.50\,in^2} \times \frac{9.81\,m}{1\,s^2} \times \frac{0.454\,kg}{1\,lb} \times \frac{39.4^2\,in^2}{1\,m^2} = 1.7 \times 10^6 \frac{kg}{m \cdot s^2}$$

$$= 1.7 \times 10^6\,Pa = 1.7 \times 10^3\,kPa$$

Check. $[1.25 \times 10 \times 0.5 \times (40)^2/0.5] \approx (125 \times 16,000) \approx 2.0 \times 10^6\,Pa \approx 2.0 \times 10^3\,kPa$. The units are correct.

10.15   *Analyze/Plan.* Follow the logic in Sample Exercise 10.2.   *Solve*:

(i)   The Hg level is lower in the open end than the closed end, so the gas pressure is less than atmospheric pressure.

$$P_{gas} = 0.975\,atm - \left(52\,cm \times \frac{1\,atm}{76\,cm}\right) = 0.29\,atm$$

(ii)   The Hg level is higher in the open end, so the gas pressure is greater than atmospheric pressure.

$$P_{gas} = 0.975\,atm + \left(67\,mm\,Hg \times \frac{1\,atm}{760\,mm\,Hg}\right) = 1.063\,atm$$

(iii)   This is a closed-end manometer so $P_{gas} = h$.

$$P_{gas} = 10.3\,cm \times \frac{1\,atm}{76\,cm} = 0.136\,atm$$

The Gas Laws

10.17   (a) $V_1/T_1 = V_2/T_2$ (b) $P_1V_1 = P_2V_2$

$V_1/300\,K = V_2/500\,K$ $1\,atm \times V_1 = 2\,atm \times V_2$

$V_2 = 5/3\,V_1$ $V_2 = 1/2\,V_1$

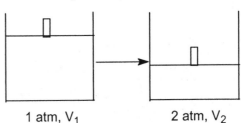

300 K, V_1 500 K, V_2 1 atm, V_1 2 atm, V_2

10.19   *Analyze.* Given: initial P, V, T. Find: final values of P, V, T for certain changes of condition.   *Plan.* Select the appropriate Gas Law relationships from Section 10.3; solve for final conditions, paying attention to units.   *Solve*:

(a) $P_1V_1 = P_2V_2$; the proportionality holds true for any pressure or volume units.

$P_1 = 748\,torr$, $V_1 = 10.3\,L$, $P_2 = 1.88\,atm$

$$V_2 = \frac{P_1V_1}{P_2} = \frac{748\,torr \times 10.3\,L}{1.88\,atm} \times \frac{1\,atm}{760\,torr} = 5.39\,L$$

Check. As pressure increases, volume should decrease; our result agrees with this.

(b) $V_1/T_1 = V_2/T_2$;   T must be in Kelvins for the relationship to be true.

$V_1 = 10.3$ L, $T_1 = 23°C = 296$ K, $T_2 = 165°C = 438$ K

$$V_2 = \frac{V_1 T_2}{T_1} = \frac{10.3\ L \times 438\ K}{296\ K} = 15.2\ L$$

Check. As temperature increases, volume should increase; our result is consistent with this.

10.21   (a)   Avogadro's hypothesis states that equal volumes of gases at the same temperature and pressure contain equal numbers of molecules. Since molecules react in the ratios of small whole numbers, it follows that the volumes of reacting gases (at the same temperature and pressure) are in the ratios of small whole numbers.

       (b)   Since the two gases are at the same temperature and pressure, the ratio of the numbers of atoms is the same as the ratio of volumes. There are 1.5 times as many Xe atoms as Ne atoms.

The Ideal-Gas Equation

(In *Solutions to Exercises*, the symbol for molar mass is $\mathscr{M}$.)

10.23   (a)   PV = nRT;   P in atmospheres, V in liters, n in moles, T in kelvins

           (b)   An ideal gas exhibits pressure, volume and temperature relationships which are described by the equation PV = nRT. (An ideal gas obeys the ideal-gas equation.)

10.25   PV = nRT. At constant volume and temperature, P is directly proportional to n.

For samples with equal masses of gas, the gas with $\mathscr{M} = 30$ will have twice as many moles of particles and twice the pressure. Thus, flask A contains the gas with $\mathscr{M} = 30$ and flask B contains the gas with $\mathscr{M} = 60$.

10.27   *Analyze/Plan*. Follow the strategy for calculations involving many variables. *Solve*:

(a)   n = 2.46 mol, P = 1.28 atm, T = –6°C = 267 K

$$V = \frac{nRT}{P} = 2.46\ mol \times \frac{0.08206\ L \cdot atm}{K \cdot mol} \times \frac{267\ K}{1.28\ atm} = 42.1\ L$$

(b)   n = 4.79×10^{-2} mol, V = 135 mL = 0.135 L

$$P = 720\ torr \times \frac{1\ atm}{760\ torr} = 0.9474 = 0.947\ atm$$

$$T = \frac{PV}{nR} = 0.9474\ atm \times \frac{0.135\ L}{0.0479\ mol} \times \frac{1\ K \cdot mol}{0.08206\ L \cdot atm} = 32.5\ K$$

(c) $n = 5.52 \times 10^{-2}$ mol, $V = 413$ mL $= 0.413$ L, $T = 88°C = 361$ K

$$P = \frac{nRT}{V}; = 0.0552 \text{ mol} \times \frac{0.08206 \text{ L} \cdot \text{atm}}{\text{K} \cdot \text{mol}} \times \frac{361 \text{ K}}{0.413 \text{ L}} = 3.96 \text{ atm}$$

(d) $V = 88.4$ L, $T = 54°C = 327$ K,

$$P = 9.84 \text{ kPa} \times \frac{1 \text{ atm}}{101.325 \text{ kPa}} = 0.09711 = 0.0971 \text{ atm}$$

$$n = \frac{PV}{RT} = 0.09711 \text{ atm} \times \frac{\text{K} \cdot \text{mol}}{0.08206 \text{ L} \cdot \text{atm}} \times \frac{88.4 \text{ L}}{327 \text{ K}} = 0.320 \text{ mol}$$

10.29   *Analyze/Plan.* Follow the strategy for calculations involving many variables. *Solve*:

$n = g / \mathscr{M}$; $PV = nRT$; $PV = gRT / \mathscr{M}$; $g = \mathscr{M} PV / RT$

$P = 1.0$ atm, $T = 23°C = 296$ K, $V = 2.0 \times 10^5$ m^3. Change m^3 to L, then calculate grams (or kg).

$$2.0 \times 10^5 \text{ m}^3 \times \frac{10^3 \text{ dm}^3}{1 \text{ m}^3} \times \frac{1 \text{ L}}{1 \text{ dm}^3} = 2.0 \times 10^8 \text{ L H}_2$$

$$g = \frac{2.02 \text{ g H}_2}{1 \text{ mol H}_2} \times \frac{\text{K} \cdot \text{mol}}{0.08206 \text{ L} \cdot \text{atm}} \times \frac{1.0 \text{ atm} \times 2.0 \times 10^8 \text{ L}}{296 \text{ K}} = 1.7 \times 10^7 \text{ g} = 1.7 \times 10^4 \text{ kg H}_2$$

10.31   *Analyze/Plan.* Follow the strategy for calculations involving many variables. *Solve*:

(a) $P = \dfrac{nRT}{V}$; $n = 0.29 \text{ kg O}_2 \times \dfrac{1000 \text{ g}}{1 \text{ kg}} \times \dfrac{1 \text{ mol O}_2}{32.00 \text{ g O}_2} = 9.0625 = 9.1 \text{ mol}$; $V = 2.3$ L;

$T = 273 + 9°C = 282$ K

$$P = \frac{9.0625 \text{ mol}}{2.3 \text{ L}} \times \frac{0.08206 \text{ L} \cdot \text{atm}}{\text{K} \cdot \text{mol}} \times 282 \text{ K} = 91 \text{ atm}$$

(b) $V = \dfrac{nRT}{P}$; $= \dfrac{9.0625 \text{ mol}}{0.95 \text{ atm}} \times \dfrac{0.08206 \text{ L} \cdot \text{atm}}{\text{K} \cdot \text{mol}} \times 299 \text{ K} = 2.3 \times 10^2$ L

10.33   *Analyze/Plan.* Follow the strategy for calculations involving many variables. *Solve*:

(a) $g = \dfrac{\mathscr{M} PV}{RT}$; $V = 9.22$ L, $T = 24°C = 297$ K, $P = 1124 \text{ torr} \times \dfrac{1 \text{ atm}}{760 \text{ torr}} = 1.4789$

$$= 1.479 \text{ atm}$$

$$g = \frac{70.91 \text{ g Cl}_2}{1 \text{ mol Cl}_2} \times \frac{\text{K} \cdot \text{mol}}{0.08206 \text{ L} \cdot \text{atm}} \times \frac{1.4789 \text{ atm}}{297 \text{ K}} \times 9.22 \text{ L} = 39.7 \text{ g Cl}_2$$

(b) $V_2 = \dfrac{P_1 V_1 T_2}{T_1 P_2} = \dfrac{1124 \text{ torr} \times 9.22 \text{ L} \times 273 \text{ K}}{297 \text{ K} \times 760 \text{ torr}} = 12.5$ L

(c) $T_2 = \dfrac{P_2 V_2 T_1}{P_1 V_1} = \dfrac{876 \text{ torr} \times 15.00 \text{ L} \times 297 \text{ K}}{1124 \text{ torr} \times 9.22 \text{ L}} = 377$ K

(d) $P_2 = \dfrac{P_1 V_1 T_2}{V_2 T_1} = \dfrac{1124 \text{ torr} \times 9.22 \text{ L} \times 331 \text{ K}}{6.00 \text{ L} \times 297 \text{ K}} = 1.92 \times 10^3 \text{ torr} = 2.53 \text{ atm}$

10.35   *Analyze.* Given: mass of cockroach, rate of O_2 consumption, temperature, percent O_2 in air, volume of air. Find: mol O_2 consumed per hour; mol O_2 in 1 quart of air; mol O_2 consumed in 48 hr.

     (a)   *Plan/Solve.* V of O_2 consumed = rate of consumption × mass × time. n = PV/RT.

$$5.2 \text{ g} \times 1 \text{ hr} \times \frac{0.8 \text{ mL O}_2}{1 \text{ g} \cdot \text{hr}} = 4.16 = 4 \text{ mL O}_2 \text{ consumed}$$

$$n = \frac{PV}{RT} = 1 \text{ atm} \times \frac{K \cdot mol}{0.08206 \text{ L} \cdot \text{atm}} \times \frac{0.00416 \text{ L}}{297 \text{ K}} = 1.71 \times 10^{-4} = 2 \times 10^{-4} \text{ mol O}_2$$

     (b)   *Plan/Solve.* qt air → L air → L O_2 available. mol O_2 available = PV/RT. mol O_2/hr (from part (a)) → total mol O_2 consumed. Compare O_2 available and O_2 consumed.

$$1 \text{ qt air} \times \frac{0.946 \text{ L}}{1 \text{ qt}} \times 0.21 \text{ O}_2 \text{ in air} = 0.199 \text{ L O}_2 \text{ available}$$

$$n = 1 \text{ atm} \times \frac{K \cdot mol}{0.08206 \text{ L} \cdot \text{atm}} \times \frac{0.199 \text{ L}}{297 \text{ K}} = 8.16 \times 10^{-3} = 8 \times 10^{-3} \text{ mol O}_2 \text{ available}$$

$$\text{roach uses } \frac{1.71 \times 10^{-4} \text{ mol}}{1 \text{ hr}} \times 48 \text{ hr} = 8.19 \times 10^{-3} = 8 \times 10^{-3} \text{ mol O}_2 \text{ consumed}$$

        Not only does the roach use 20% of the available O_2, it needs all the O_2 in the jar.

Further Applications of the Ideal-Gas Equation

10.37   (c) $Cl_2(g)$ is the most dense at 1.00 at and 298 K. Gas density is directly proportional to molar mass and pressure, and inversely proportional to temperature [Equation 10.10]. For gas samples at the same conditions, molar mass determines density. Of the three gases listed, Cl_2 has the largest molar mass.

10.39   (c) Because the helium atoms are of lower mass than the average air molecule, the helium gas is less dense than air. The balloon thus weighs less than the air displaced by its volume.

10.41   *Analyze/Plan.* Conditions (P, V, T) and amounts of gases are given. Rearrange the relationship PV$\mathcal{M}$ = gRT to obtain the desired of quantity, paying attention (as always!) to units. *Solve:*

     (a) $d = \dfrac{\mathcal{M} P}{RT}$; $\mathcal{M}$ = 46.0 g/mol; P = 0.970 atm, T = 35°C = 308 K

$$d = \frac{46.0 \text{ g NO}_2}{1 \text{ mol}} \times \frac{K \cdot mol}{0.08206 \text{ L} \cdot \text{atm}} \times \frac{0.970 \text{ atm}}{308 \text{ K}} = 1.77 \text{ g/L}$$

     (b) $\mathcal{M} = \dfrac{gRT}{PV} = \dfrac{2.50 \text{ g}}{0.875 \text{ L}} \times \dfrac{0.08206 \text{ L} \cdot \text{atm}}{K \cdot mol} \times \dfrac{308 \text{ K}}{685 \text{ torr}} \times \dfrac{760 \text{ torr}}{1 \text{ atm}} = 80.1 \text{ g/mol}$

10.43 *Analyze/Plan.* Given: mass, conditions (P, V, T) of unknown gas. Find: molar mass.
$\mathcal{M}$ = gRT/PV. *Solve:*

$$\mathcal{M} = \frac{gRT}{PV} = \frac{1.012\ g}{0.354\ L} \times \frac{0.08206\ L \cdot atm}{K \cdot atm} \times \frac{372\ K}{742\ torr} \times \frac{760\ torr}{1\ atm} = 89.4\ g/mol$$

10.45 *Analyze/Plan.* Follow the logic in Sample Exercise 10.9. *Solve:*

$$mol\ O_2 = \frac{PV}{RT} = 3.5 \times 10^{-6}\ torr \times \frac{1\ atm}{760\ torr} \times \frac{K \cdot mol}{0.08206\ L \cdot atm} \times \frac{0.382\ L}{300\ K} = 7.146 \times 10^{-11}$$

$$= 7.1 \times 10^{-11}\ mol\ O_2$$

$$7.146 \times 10^{-11}\ mol\ O_2 \times \frac{2\ mol\ Mg}{1\ mol\ O_2} \times \frac{24.3\ g\ Mg}{1\ mol\ Mg} = 3.5 \times 10^{-9}\ g\ Mg$$

10.47 *Analyze/Plan.* kg H_2SO_4 → g H_2SO_4 → mol H_2SO_4 → mol NH_3 → V NH_3 *Solve:*

$$87\ kg \times \frac{1000\ g}{1\ kg} = 8.7 \times 10^4\ g\ H_2SO_4 \times \frac{1\ mol}{98.08\ g} = 887.03 = 887\ mol\ H_2SO_4$$

$$887.03\ mol\ H_2SO_4 \times \frac{2\ mol\ NH_3}{1\ mol\ H_2SO_4} = 1.774 \times 10^3 = 1.77 \times 10^3\ mol\ NH_3$$

$$V_{NH_3} = \frac{nRT}{P} = 1.774 \times 10^3\ mol \times \frac{0.08206\ L \cdot atm}{K \cdot mol} \times \frac{315\ K}{15.6\ atm} = 2.94 \times 10^3\ L\ NH_3$$

10.49 *Analyze/Plan.* The gas sample is a mixture of $H_2(g)$ and $H_2O(g)$. Find the partial pressure of $H_2(g)$ and then the moles of $H_2(g)$ and Zn(s). *Solve:*

$$P_t = 738\ torr = P_{H_2} + P_{H_2O}$$

From Appendix B, the vapor pressure of H_2O at 24°C = 22.38 torr

$$P_{H_2} = (738\ torr - 22.38\ torr) \times \frac{1\ atm}{760\ torr} = 0.9416 = 0.942\ atm$$

$$n_{H_2} = \frac{P_{H_2}V}{RT} = 0.9416\ atm \times \frac{K \cdot mol}{0.08206\ L \cdot atm} \times \frac{0.159\ L}{297\ K} = 0.006143 = 0.00614\ mol\ H_2$$

$$0.006143\ mol\ H_2 \times \frac{1\ mol\ Zn}{1\ mol\ H_2} \times \frac{65.39\ g\ Zn}{1\ mol\ Zn} = 0.402\ g\ Zn$$

Partial Pressures

10.51 (a)   When the stopcock is opened, the volume occupied by $N_2(g)$ increases from 2.0 L to 5.0 L. At constant T, $P_1V_1 = P_2V_2$. 1.0 atm × 2.0 L = P_2 × 5.0 L; P_2 = 0.40 atm

    (b)   When the gases mix, the volume of $O_2(g)$ increases from 3.0 L to 5.0 L. At constant T, $P_1V_1 = P_2V_2$. 2.0 atm × 3.0 L = P_2 × 5.0 L; P_2 = 1.2 atm

    (c) $P_T = P_{N_2} + P_{O_2}$ = 0.40 atm + 1.2 atm = 1.6 atm

10.53 *Analyze.* Given: amount, V, T of 3 gases. Find: P of each gas, total P.

Plan. $P = nRT/V$; $P_T = P_1 + P_2 + P_3 + ...$ *Solve:*

(a) $P_{He} = \dfrac{nRT}{V} = 0.538 \text{ mol} \times \dfrac{0.08206 \text{ L} \cdot \text{atm}}{\text{K} \cdot \text{atm}} \times \dfrac{298 \text{ K}}{7.00 \text{ L}} = 1.88 \text{ atm}$

$P_{Ne} = \dfrac{nRT}{V} = 0.315 \text{ mol} \times \dfrac{0.08206 \text{ L} \cdot \text{atm}}{\text{K} \cdot \text{atm}} \times \dfrac{298 \text{ K}}{7.00 \text{ L}} = 1.10 \text{ atm}$

$P_{Ar} = \dfrac{nRT}{V} = 0.103 \text{ mol} \times \dfrac{0.08206 \text{ L} \cdot \text{atm}}{\text{K} \cdot \text{atm}} \times \dfrac{298 \text{ K}}{7.00 \text{ L}} = 0.360 \text{ atm}$

(b) $P_t = 1.88 \text{ atm} + 1.10 \text{ atm} + 0.360 \text{ atm} = 3.34 \text{ atm}$

10.55 *Analyze/Plan.* The partial pressure of each component is equal to the mole fraction of that gas times the total pressure of the mixture. Find the mole fraction of each component and then its partial pressure. *Solve:*

$n_t = 0.75 \text{ mol } N_2 + 0.30 \text{ mol } O_2 + 0.15 \text{ mol } CO_2 = 1.20 \text{ mol}$

$\chi_{N_2} = \dfrac{0.75}{1.20} = 0.625 = 0.63; \quad P_{N_2} = 0.625 \times 1.56 \text{ atm} = 0.98 \text{ atm}$

$\chi_{O_2} = \dfrac{0.30}{1.20} = 0.250 = 0.25; \quad P_{O_2} = 0.250 \times 1.56 \text{ atm} = 0.39 \text{ atm}$

$\chi_{CO_2} = \dfrac{0.15}{1.20} = 0.125 = 0.13; \quad P_{CO_2} = 0.125 \times 1.56 \text{ atm} = 0.20 \text{ atm}$

10.57 *Analyze/Plan.* Mole fraction = pressure fraction. Find the desired mole fraction of O_2 and change to mole percent. *Solve:*

$\chi_{O_2} = \dfrac{P_{O_2}}{P_t} = \dfrac{0.21 \text{ atm}}{8.38 \text{ atm}} = 0.025;$ mole % $= 0.025 \times 100 = 2.5\%$

10.59 *Analyze/Plan.* $N_2(g)$ and $O_2(g)$ undergo changes of conditions and are mixed. Calculate the new pressure of each gas and add them to obtain the total pressure of the mixture.

$P_2 = P_1 V_1 T_2 / V_2 T_1$; $P_T = P_{N_2} + P_{O_2}$.   *Solve:*

$P_{N_2} = \dfrac{P_1 V_1 T_2}{V_2 T_1} = \dfrac{3.80 \text{ atm} \times 1.00 \text{ L} \times 293 \text{ K}}{10.0 \text{ L} \times 299 \text{ K}} = 0.372 \text{ atm}$

$P_{O_2} = \dfrac{P_1 V_1 T_2}{V_2 T_1} = \dfrac{4.75 \text{ atm} \times 5.00 \text{ L} \times 293 \text{ K}}{10.0 \text{ L} \times 299 \text{ K}} = 2.33 \text{ atm}$

$P_T = 0.372 \text{ atm} + 2.33 \text{ atm} = 2.70 \text{ atm}$

Kinetic - Molecular Theory; Graham's Law

10.61 (a) Increase in temperature at constant volume, decrease in volume, increase in pressure
(b) decrease in temperature   (c) increase in volume   (d) increase in temperature

10.63 The fact that gases are readily compressible supports the assumption that most of the volume of a gas sample is empty space.

10.65 *Analyze/Plan.* We have samples of two different gases at different pressures and temperatures. Compare the two samples by considering the postulates of the kinetic-molecular theory that pertain to the quantities in (a)-(d). *Solve*:

(a) $n \propto P/T$ (V/R is the same for A and B.) Since P is greater and T is smaller for vessel A, it has more molecules.

(b)   Vessel A has more molecules but the molar mass of CO is smaller than the molar mass of SO_2, so we need to calculate the masses. Since volume is not specified, calculate g/L.

$$\frac{g_A}{V} = \frac{\mathcal{m}\,P}{RT} = \frac{28.01\,g\,CO}{1\,mol\,CO} \times \frac{K \cdot mol}{0.08206\,L \cdot atm} \times \frac{1\,atm}{273\,K} = 1.25\,g\,CO/L$$

$$\frac{g_B}{V} = \frac{\mathcal{m}\,P}{RT} = \frac{64.07\,g\,SO_2}{1\,mol\,SO_2} \times \frac{K \cdot mol}{0.08206\,L \cdot atm} \times \frac{0.5\,atm}{293\,K} = 1.33\,g\,SO_2/L$$

Vessel B has more mass.

(c)   Vessel B is at a higher temperature so the average kinetic energy of its molecules is higher.

(d)   The two factors that affect rms speed are temperature and molar mass.   The molecules in vessel A have smaller molar mass but are at the lower temperature, so we must calculate the rms speeds.

Mathematically, according to Equation 10.24,

$$\frac{u_A}{u_B} = \sqrt{\frac{T_A / \mathcal{m}_A}{T_B / \mathcal{m}_B}} = \sqrt{\frac{273/28.01}{293/64.07}} = 1.46$$

The ratio is greater than 1; vessel A has the greater rms speed.

10.67 (a)   *Plan.* The greater the molecular (and molar) mass, the smaller the rms speed of the molecules. *Solve*: In order of increasing speed (and decreasing molar mass):

$$CO_2 \approx N_2O < F_2 < HF < H_2$$

(b)   *Plan*. Follow the logic of Sample Exercise 10.14. *Solve*:

$$u_{H_2} = \sqrt{\frac{3RT}{\mathscr{M}}} = \left(\frac{3 \times 8.314\ kg \cdot m^2/s^2 \cdot K \cdot mol \times 300\ K}{2.02 \times 10^{-3}\ kg/mol} \right)^{1/2} = 1.92 \times 10^3\ m/s$$

$$u_{CO_2} = \left(\frac{3 \times 8.314\ kg \cdot m^2/s^2 \cdot K \cdot mol \times 300\ K}{44.0 \times 10^{-3}\ kg/mol} \right)^{1/2} = 4.12 \times 10^2\ m/s$$

As expected, the lighter molecule moves at the greater speed.

10.69   *Plan*. The heavier the molecule, the slower the rate of effusion. Thus, the order for increasing rate of effusion is in the order of decreasing mass. *Solve*:

rate $^2H^{37}Cl$ < rate $^1H^{37}Cl$ < rate $^2H^{35}Cl$ < rate $^1H^{35}Cl$

10.71   *Analyze*. Given: relative effusion rates of two gases at same temperature. Find: molecular formula of one of the gases. *Plan*. Use Graham's law to calculate the formula weight of arsenic (III) sulfide, and thus the molecular formula. *Solve*:

$$\frac{rate\ (sulfide)}{rate\ (Ar)} = \left[\frac{39.9}{\mathscr{M}(sulfide)} \right]^{1/2} = 0.28$$

$\mathscr{M}$ (sulfide) = $(39.9 / 0.28)^2$ = 510 g/mol (two significant figures)

The empirical formula of arsenic(III) sulfide is As_2S_3, which has a formula mass of 246.1. Twice this is 490 g/mol, close to the value estimated from the effusion experiment. Thus, the formula of the vapor phase molecule is As_4S_6.

Nonideal-Gas Behavior

10.73   (a)   Nonideal gas behavior is observed at very high pressures and/or low temperatures.

       (b)   The real volumes of gas molecules and attractive intermolecular forces between molecules cause gases to behave nonideally.

10.75   The ratio PV/RT is equal to the number of moles of molecules in an ideal-gas sample; this number should be a constant for all pressure, volume and temperature conditions. If the value of this ratio changes with increasing pressure, the gas sample is not behaving ideally (according to the ideal-gas equation).

10.77   *Plan*. The constants *a* and *b* are part of the correction terms in the van der Waals equation. The smaller the values of *a* and *b*, the smaller the corrections and the more ideal the gas. *Solve*:

Ar (*a* = 1.34, *b* = 0.0322) will behave more like an ideal gas than CO_2 (*a* = 3.59, *b* = 0.0427) at high pressures.

10.79   *Analyze.* Conditions and amount of $CCl_4(g)$ are given. *Plan.* Use ideal-gas equation and van der Waals equation to calculate pressure of gas at these conditions. *Solve:*

(a) $P = 1.00 \text{ mol} \times \dfrac{0.08206 \text{ L} \cdot \text{atm}}{\text{K} \cdot \text{mol}} \times \dfrac{313 \text{ K}}{28.0 \text{ L}} = 0.917 \text{ atm}$

(b) $P = \dfrac{nRT}{V - nb} - \dfrac{an^2}{V^2} = \dfrac{1.00 \times 0.08206 \times 313}{28.0 - (1.00 \times 0.1383)} - \dfrac{20.4(1.00)^2}{(28.0)^2} = 0.896 \text{ atm}$

Check. The van der Waals result indicates that the real pressure will be less than the ideal pressure. That is, intermolecular forces reduce the effective number of particles and the real pressure. This is reasonable for 1 mole of gas at relatively low temperature and pressure.

Additional Exercises

10.81   Over time, the gases will mix perfectly. Each bulb will contain 4 blue and 3 red atoms.

10.83 $P_1V_1 = P_2V_2$; $V_2 = P_1V_1/P_2$

$V_2 = \dfrac{3.0 \text{ atm} \times 1.0 \text{ mm}^3}{695 \text{ torr}} \times \dfrac{760 \text{ torr}}{1 \text{ atm}} = 3.3 \text{ mm}^3$

10.86   If the air in the room is at STP, the partial pressure of O_2 is $0.2095 \times 1 \text{ atm} = 0.2095 \text{ atm}$. Since the gases in air are perfectly mixed, the volume of O_2 is the volume of the room.

$V = 10.0 \text{ ft} \times 8.0 \text{ ft} \times 8.0 \text{ ft} \times \dfrac{(12)^3 \text{ in}^3}{\text{ft}^3} \times \dfrac{(2.54)^3 \text{cm}^3}{\text{in}^3} \times \dfrac{1 \text{ L}}{1000 \text{ cm}^3} = 1.812 \times 10^4$
$$= 1.8 \times 10^4 \text{ L}$$

$g = \dfrac{\mathcal{M} PV}{RT} = \dfrac{32.00 \text{ g } O_2}{\text{mol } O_2} \times \dfrac{\text{K} \cdot \text{mol}}{0.08026 \text{ L} \cdot \text{atm}} \times \dfrac{0.2095 \text{ atm} \times 1.812 \times 10^4 \text{ L}}{273 \text{ K}} = 5.4 \times 10^3 \text{ g } O_2$

10.90   (a) $5.00 \text{ g HCl} \times \dfrac{1 \text{ mol HCl}}{36.46 \text{ g HCl}} = 0.1371 = 0.137 \text{ mol HCl}$

               $5.00 \text{ g } NH_3 \times \dfrac{1 \text{ mol } NH_3}{17.03 \text{ g } NH_3} = 0.2936 = 0.294 \text{ mol } NH_3$

The gases react in a 1:1 mole ratio, HCl is the limiting reactant and is completely consumed. $(0.2936 \text{ mol} - 0.1371 \text{ mol}) = 0.1565 = 0.157 \text{ mol } NH_3$ remain in the system. $NH_3(g)$ is the only gas remaining after reaction. $V_t = 4.00 \text{ L}$

   (b) $P = \dfrac{nRT}{V} = 0.1565 \text{ mol} \times \dfrac{0.08206 \text{ L} \cdot \text{atm}}{\text{K} \cdot \text{mol}} \times \dfrac{298 \text{ K}}{4.00 \text{ L}} = 0.957 \text{ atm}$

10.92 $\mathcal{M}_{avg} = \dfrac{dRT}{P} = \dfrac{1.104 \text{ g}}{1 \text{ L}} \times \dfrac{0.08206 \text{ L} \cdot \text{atm}}{\text{K} \cdot \text{mol}} \times \dfrac{300 \text{ K}}{435 \text{ torr}} \times \dfrac{760 \text{ torr}}{1 \text{ atm}}$

                                         $= 47.48 = 47.5 \text{ g/mol}$

χ = mole fraction O_2; 1 - χ = mole fraction Kr

47.48 g = χ(32.00) + (1-χ)(83.80)

36.3 = 51.8 χ; χ = 0.701; 70.1% O_2

10.95 Only item (b) is satisfactory. Item (c) would not have supported a column of Hg because it is open at both ends. The atmosphere would exert pressure on the top of the column as well as on the reservoir; the column would only be as high as the reservoir and the height would not change with changing pressure. Item (d) is not tall enough to support a nearly 760 mm Hg column. Items (a) and (e) are inappropriate for the same reason: they don't have a uniform cross-sectional area. The height of the Hg column is a direct measure of atmospheric pressure only if the cross-sectional area is constant over the entire tube.

10.98 (a) The effect of intermolecular attraction becomes more significant as a gas is compressed to a smaller volume at constant temperature. This compression causes the pressure, and thus the number of intermolecular collisions, to increase. Intermolecular attraction causes some of these collisions to be inelastic, which amplifies the deviation from ideal behavior.

      (b) The effect of intermolecular attraction becomes less significant as the temperature of a gas is increased at constant volume. When the temperature of a gas is increased at constant volume, the pressure of the gas, the number of intermolecular collisions and the average kinetic energy of the gas particles increases. This higher average kinetic energy means that a larger fraction of the molecules has sufficient kinetic energy to overcome intermolecular attractions, even though there are more total collisions. This increases the fraction of elastic collisions, and the gas more closely obeys the ideal-gas equation.

Integrative Exercises

10.101 $n = \dfrac{PV}{RT} = 1.00 \text{ atm} \times \dfrac{K \cdot mol}{0.08206 \, L \cdot atm} \times \dfrac{2.7 \times 10^{12} \, L}{273 \, K} = 1.205 \times 10^{11} = 1.2 \times 10^{11}$ mol CH_4

$CH_4(g) + 2O_2(g) \rightarrow CO_2(g) + 2H_2O(l)$ $\Delta H° = -890.4$ kJ

(At STP, H_2O is in the liquid state.)

$\Delta H^{\circ}_{rxn} = \Delta H^{\circ}_f \, CO_2(g) + 2\Delta H^{\circ}_f \, H_2O(l) - \Delta H^{\circ}_f \, CH_4(g) - \Delta H^{\circ}_f \, O_2(g)$

$\Delta H^{\circ}_{rxn} = -393.5$ kJ + 2(-285.83 kJ) - (-74.8 kJ) - 0 = -890.4 kJ

$\dfrac{-890.4 \text{ kJ}}{1 \text{ mol } CH_4} \times 1.205 \times 10^{11} \text{ mol } CH_4 = -1.073 \times 10^{14} = -1.1 \times 10^{14}$ kJ

The negative sign indicates heat evolved by the combustion reaction.

10.105 After reaction, the flask contains $IF_5(g)$ and whichever reactant is in excess. Determine the limiting reactant, which regulates the moles of IF_5 produced and moles of excess reactant.

$$I_2(s) + 5F_2(g) \rightarrow 2\ IF_5(g)$$

$$10.0\ g\ I_2 \times \frac{1\ mol\ I_2}{253.8\ g\ I_2} \times \frac{5\ mol\ F_2}{1\ mol\ I_2} = 0.1970 = 0.197\ mol\ F_2$$

$$10.0\ g\ F_2 \times \frac{1\ mol\ F_2}{38.00\ g\ F_2} = 0.2632 = 0.263\ mol\ F_2\ available$$

I_2 is the limiting reactant; F_2 is in excess.

0.263 mol F_2 available - 0.197 mol F_2 reacted = 0.066 mol F_2 remain.

$$10.0\ g\ I_2 \times \frac{1\ mol\ I_2}{253.8\ g\ I_2} \times \frac{2\ mol\ IF_5}{1\ mol\ I_2} = 0.0788\ mol\ IF_5\ produced$$

(a) $\quad P_{IF_5} = \dfrac{nRT}{V} = 0.0788\ mol \times \dfrac{0.08206\ L \bullet atm}{K \bullet mol} \times \dfrac{398\ K}{5.00\ L} = 0.515\ atm$

(b) $\quad \chi_{IF_5} = \dfrac{mol\ IF_5}{mol\ IF_5\ +\ mol\ F_2} = \dfrac{0.0788}{0.0788\ +\ 0.066} = 0.544$

11 Intermolecular Forces, Liquids and Solids

Kinetic-Molecular Theory

11.1   (a)   solid < liquid < gas   (b)   gas < liquid < solid

11.3   Density is the ratio of the mass of a substance to the volume it occupies. For the same substance in different states, mass will be the same. In the liquid and solid states, the particles are touching and there is very little empty space, so the volumes occupied by a unit mass are very similar and the densities are similar. In the gas phase, the molecules are far apart, so a unit mass occupies a much greater volume than the liquid or solid, and the density of the gas phase is much less.

11.5   As the temperature of a substance is increased, the average kinetic energy of the particles increases. In a collection of particles (molecules), the state is determined by the strength of interparticle forces relative to the average kinetic energy of the particles. As the average kinetic energy increases, more particles are able to overcome intermolecular attractive forces and move to a less ordered state, from solid to liquid to gas.

Intermolecular Forces

11.7   (a)   London-dispersion forces   (b) dipole-dipole and London-dispersion forces
       (c)   dipole-dipole or in certain cases hydrogen bonding

11.9   (a) Br_2 is a nonpolar covalent molecule, so only London-dispersion forces must be overcome to convert the liquid to a gas.

       (b) CH_3OH is a polar covalent molecule that experiences London-dispersion, dipole-dipole and hydrogen-bonding (O–H bonds) forces. All of these forces must be overcome to convert the liquid to a gas.

       (c) H_2S is a polar covalent molecule that experiences London-dispersion and dipole-dipole forces, so these must be overcome to change the liquid into a gas. (H–S bonds do not lead to hydrogen-bonding interactions.)

11.11 (a)   *Polarizability* is the ease with which the charge distribution (electron cloud) in a molecule can be distorted to produce a transient dipole.

(b)   Te is most polarizable because its valence electrons are farthest from the nucleus and least tightly held.

(c)   Polarizability increases as molecular size (and thus molecular weight) increases. In order of increasing polarizability: $CH_4 < SiH_4 < SiCl_4 < GeCl_4 < GeBr_4$

(d)   The magnitude of London-dispersion forces and thus the boiling points of molecules increase as polarizability increases. The order of increasing boiling points is the order of increasing polarizability: $CH_4 < SiH_4 < SiCl_4 < GeCl_4 < GeBr_4$

11.13   *Analyze/Plan.* For molecules with similar structures, the strength of dispersion forces increases with molecular size (molecular weight and number of electrons in the molecule).

Solve: (a) H_2S (b) CO_2 (c) CCl_4

11.15   Both hydrocarbons experience dispersion forces. Rod-like butane molecules can contact each other over the length of the molecule, while spherical 2-methylpropane molecules can only touch tangentially. The larger contact surface of butane produces greater polarizability and a higher boiling point.

11.17   Molecules with N–H, O–H and F–H bonds form hydrogen bonds with like molecules. **CH_3NH_2** and **CH_3OH** have N–H and O–H bonds, respectively. (CH_3F has C–F and C–H bonds, but no H–F bonds.)

11.19 (a)   HF has the higher boiling point because hydrogen bonding is stronger than dipole-dipole forces.

(b) $CHBr_3$ has the higher boiling point because it has the higher molar mass which leads to greater polarizability and stronger dispersion forces.

(c)   ICl has the higher boiling point because it is a polar molecule. For molecules with similar structures and molar masses, dipole-dipole forces are stronger than dispersion forces.

11.21   Surface tension (Section 11.3), high boiling point (relative to H_2S, H_2Se, H_2Te, Figure 11.7), high heat capacity per gram, high enthalpy of vaporization; the solid is less dense than the liquid; it is a liquid at room temperature despite its low molar mass.

Viscosity and Surface Tension

11.23 (a) Viscosities and surface tensions of liquids both increase as intermolecular forces become stronger.

(b) As temperature increases, the average kinetic energy of the molecules increases and intermolecular attractions are more easily overcome. Surface tensions and viscosities decrease.

11.25 (a) $CHBr_3$ has a higher molar mass, is more polarizable and has stronger dispersion forces, so the surface tension is greater (see Solution 11.19(b)).

(b) As temperature increases, the viscosity of the oil decreases because the average kinetic energies of the molecules increase (Solution 11.23(b)).

(c) Adhesive forces between polar water and nonpolar car wax are weak, so the large surface tension of water draws the liquid into the shape with the smallest surface area, a sphere.

Changes of State

11.27 Endothermic: melting (s → l), vaporization (l → g), sublimation (s → g)
Exothermic: condensation (g → l), freezing (l → s), deposition (g → s)

11.29 The heat energy required to increase the kinetic energy of molecules enough to melt the solid does not produce a large separation of molecules. The specific order is disrupted, but the molecules remain close together. On the other hand, when a liquid is vaporized, the intermolecular forces which maintain close molecular contacts must be overcome. Because molecules are being separated, the energy requirement is higher than for melting.

11.31 *Analyze.* the heat required to vaporize 50 g of H_2O equals the heat lost by the cooled water. *Plan.* Using the enthalpy of vaporization, calculate the heat required to vaporize 50 g of H_2O in this temperature range. Using the specific heat capacity of water, calculate the mass of water than can be cooled 13°C if this much heat is lost.

Solve. Evaporation of 50 g of water requires:

$$50 \text{ g } H_2O \times \frac{2.4 \text{ kJ}}{1 \text{ g } H_2O} = 1.2 \times 10^2 \text{ kJ or } 1.2 \times 10^5 \text{ J}$$

Cooling a certain amount of water by 13°C:

$$1.2 \times 10^5 \text{ J} \times \frac{1 \text{ g} \cdot \text{K}}{4.184 \text{ J}} \times \frac{1}{13°C} = 2206 = 2.2 \times 10^3 \text{ g } H_2O$$

Check. The units are correct. A surprisingly large mass of water (2200 g ≈ 2.2 L) can be cooled by this method.

11.33   *Analyze/Plan.* Follow the logic in Sample Exercise 11.4.   *Solve*:

Heat the solid from -120°C to -114°C (153 K to 159 K), using the specific heat of the solid.

$$75.0 \text{ g } C_2H_5OH \times \frac{0.97 \text{ J}}{\text{g} \cdot \text{K}} \times 6 \text{ K} \times \frac{1 \text{ kJ}}{1000 \text{ J}} = 0.4365 = 0.4 \text{ kJ}$$

At -114°C (159 K), melt the solid, using its enthalpy of fusion.

$$75.0 \text{ g } C_2H_5OH \times \frac{1 \text{ mol } C_2H_5OH}{46.07 \text{ g } C_2H_5OH} \times \frac{5.02 \text{ kJ}}{1 \text{ mol}} = 8.172 = 8.17 \text{ kJ}$$

Heat the liquid from -114°C to 78°C (159 K to 351 K), using the specific heat of the liquid.

$$75.0 \text{ g } C_2H_5OH \times \frac{2.3 \text{ J}}{\text{g} \cdot \text{K}} \times 192 \text{ K} \times \frac{1 \text{ kJ}}{1000 \text{ J}} = 33.12 = 33 \text{ kJ}$$

At 78°C (351 K), vaporize the liquid, using its enthalpy of vaporization.

$$75.0 \text{ g } C_2H_5OH \times \frac{1 \text{ mol } C_2H_5OH}{46.07 \text{ g } C_2H_5OH} \times \frac{38.56 \text{ kJ}}{1 \text{ mol}} = 62.77 = 62.8 \text{ kJ}$$

The total energy required is 0.4365 kJ + 8.172 kJ + 33.12 kJ + 62.77 kJ = 104.50 = 105 kJ. (The result has zero decimal places, from 33 kJ required to heat the liquid.)

Check. The relative energies of the various steps are reasonable; vaporization is the largest.

11.35   (a)   The critical pressure is the pressure required to cause liquefaction at the critical temperature. The critical temperature is the highest temperature at which a gas can be liquefied, regardless of pressure.

(b)   As the force of attraction between molecules increases, the critical temperature of the compound increases.

(c)   The temperature of $N_2(l)$ is 77 K. All of the gases in Table 11.4 have critical temperatures higher than 77 K, so all of them can be liquefied at this temperature, given sufficient pressure.

Vapor Pressure and Boiling Point

11.37   (a)   No effect.   (b)   No effect.

(c)   Vapor pressure decreases with increasing intermolecular attractive forces because fewer molecules have sufficient kinetic energy to overcome the attractive forces and escape to the vapor phase.

(d)   Vapor pressure increases with increasing temperature because average kinetic energies of molecules increase.

11.39   *Analyze/Plan*. Given the molecular formulae of several substances, determine the kind of intermolecular forces present, and rank the strength of these forces. The weaker the forces, the more volatile the substance. *Solve*:

$CBr_4 < CHBr_3 < CH_2Br_2 < CH_2Cl_2 < CH_3Cl < CH_4$

The weaker the intermolecular forces, the higher the vapor pressure, the more volatile the compound.   The order of increasing volatility is the order of decreasing strength of intermolecular forces. By analogy to the boiling points of HCl and HBr (Section 11.2), the trend will be dominated by dispersion forces, even though four of the molecules ($CHBr_3$, CH_2Br_2, CH_2Cl_2 and CH_3Cl) are polar. Thus, the order of increasing volatility is the order of decreasing molar mass and decreasing strength of dispersion forces.

11.41   (a)   The water in the two pans is at the same temperature, the boiling point of water at the atmospheric pressure of the room. During a phase change, the temperature of a system is constant. All energy gained from the surroundings is used to accomplish the transition, in this case to vaporize the liquid water. The pan of water that is boiling vigorously is gaining more energy and the liquid is being vaporized more quickly than in the other pan, but the temperature of the phase change is the same.

        (b)   Vapor pressure does not depend on either volume or surface area of the liquid. As long as the containers are at the same temperature, the vapor pressures of water in the two containers are the same.

11.43   The boiling point is the temperature at which the vapor pressure of a liquid equals atmospheric pressure.

        (a)   The boiling point of diethyl ether at 400 torr is ~17°C, or, at 17°C, the vapor pressure of diethyl ether is 400 torr.

        (b)   At a pressure of 25 torr, water would boil at ~28°C, or, the vapor pressure of water at 28°C is 25 torr.

11.45   (a)   From Appendix B, a vapor pressure of 340 torr is in the 70-80°C range. By linear interpolation,

        $$\text{b.p.} = 70°C + \left[\frac{340 - 234}{355 - 234} \times 10°C \right] \approx 79°C$$

        (b)   According to Figure 11.22, the vapor pressure of diethyl ether at 12°C is approximately 325 torr. This is a substantial vapor pressure, but still less than the atmospheric pressure of 340 torr. In an open end manometer such as the one in Figure 10.3, the arm open to the atmosphere would be lower than the arm open to the container.

Phase Diagrams

11.47   The liquid/gas line of a phase diagram ends at the critical point, the temperature and pressure beyond which the gas and liquid phases are indistinguishable. At temperatures higher than the critical temperature, a gas cannot be liquefied, regardless of pressure.

11.49   **(a)**   The water vapor would condense to form a solid at a pressure of around 4 torr. At higher pressure, perhaps 5 atm or so, the solid would melt to form liquid water. This occurs because the melting point of ice, which is 0°C at 1 atm, decreases with increasing pressure.

     (b)   In thinking about this exercise, keep in mind that the **total** pressure is being maintained at a constant 0.50 atm. That pressure is composed of water vapor pressure and some other pressure, which could come from an inert gas. At 100°C and 0.50 atm, water is in the vapor phase. As it cools, the water vapor will condense to the liquid at the temperature where the vapor pressure of liquid water is 0.50 atm. From Appendix B, we see that condensation occurs at approximately 82°C. Further cooling of the liquid water results in freezing to the solid at approximately 0°C. The freezing point of water increases with decreasing pressure, so at 0.50 atm, the freezing temperature is very slightly above 0°C.

11.51   **(a)**

     (b)   The solid-liquid line on the phase diagram is normal and the melting point of Xe(s) increases with increasing pressure. This means that Xe(s) is denser than Xe(l).

     (c)   Cooling Xe(g) at 100 torr will cause deposition of the solid. A pressure of 100 torr is below the pressure of the triple point, so the gas will change directly to the solid upon cooling.

Structures of Solids

11.53 In a crystalline solid, the component particles (atoms, ions or molecules) are arranged in an ordered repeating pattern. In an amorphous solid, there is no orderly structure. Quartz glass (Figure 11.30(b)) is an example of an amorphous solid. Paraffin wax is another example of an amorphous solid. Also, most plastics show no long range order and are amorphous overall, although they can show regions of order (see Section 12.2).

11.55 The unit cell is the building block of the crystal lattice. When repeated in three dimensions, it produces the crystalline solid. It is a parallelepiped with characteristic distances and angles. Unit cells can be primitive (lattice points only at the corners of the parallelepiped) or centered (lattice points at the corners and at the middle of faces or the middle of the parallelepiped).

11.57 In a metallic solid such as gold, the atoms are held in their very orderly arrangement by metallic bonding, the result of valence electrons delocalized throughout the three-dimensional lattice. A large amount of kinetic energy is required to disrupt this delocalized bonding network and allow the atoms to translate relative to each, so the melting point of Au(s) is quite high. Xe atoms are held in a cubic close-packed arrangement by London-dispersion forces much weaker than metallic bonding. Very little kinetic energy is required for Xe atoms to overcome these forces and melt, so the melting point of Xe is quite low.

11.59 *Analyze.* Given the cubic unit cell edge length and arrangement of Ir atoms, calculate the atomic radius and the density of the metal. *Plan.* There is space between the atoms along the unit cell edge, but they touch along the face diagonal. Use the geometry of the right equilateral triangle to calculate the atomic radius. From the definition of density and paying attention to units, calculate the density of Ir(s). *Solve:*

(a) The length of the face diagonal of a face-centered cubic unit cell is four times the radius of the atom and $\sqrt{2}$ times the unit cell dimension or edge length, usually designated *a* for cubic unit cells.

$$4\,r = \sqrt{2}\;a; \; r = \sqrt{2}\;a/4 = \frac{\sqrt{2}\times 3.833\,\text{Å}}{4} = 1.3552 = 1.355\,\text{Å}$$

(b) The density of iridium is the mass of the unit cell contents divided by the unit cell volume. There are 4 Ir atoms in a face-centered cubic unit cell.

$$\frac{4\;\text{Ir atoms}}{(3.833\times 10^{-8}\,\text{cm})^3} \times \frac{192.22\;\text{g Ir}}{6.022\times 10^{23}\;\text{Ir atoms}} = 22.67\;\text{g/cm}^3$$

Check. The units of density are correct. Note that Ir is quite dense.

11.61 *Analyze.* Given the atomic arrangement, length of the cubic unit cell edge and density of the solid, calculate the atomic weight of the element. *Plan.* If we calculate the mass of a single unit cell, and determine the number of atoms in one unit cell, we can calculate the mass of a single atom and of a mole of atoms. *Solve:*

The volume of the unit cell is $(2.86\times 10^{-8}\,\text{cm})^3$. The mass of the unit cell is:

$$\frac{7.92 \text{ g}}{\text{cm}^3} \times \frac{(2.86 \times 10^{-8})^3 \text{ cm}^3}{\text{unit cell}} = 1.853 \times 10^{-22} \text{ g/unit cell}$$

There are two atoms of the element present in the body-centered cubic unit cell. Thus the atomic weight is:

$$\frac{1.853 \times 10^{-22} \text{ g}}{\text{unit cell}} \times \frac{1 \text{ unit cell}}{2 \text{ atoms}} \times \frac{6.022 \times 10^{23} \text{ atoms}}{1 \text{ mol}} = 55.8 \text{ g/mol}$$

Check. The result is a reasonable atomic weight and the units are correct. The element could be iron.

11.63 (a)   Each sphere is in contact with 12 nearest neighbors; its coordination number is thus 12.

(b)   Each sphere has a coordination number of six.

(c)   Each sphere has a coordination number of eight.

11.65 *Analyze*. Given the atomic arrangement and density of the solid, calculate the unit cell edge length. *Plan*. Calculate the mass of a single unit cell and then use density to find the volume of a single unit cell. The edge length is the cube-root of the volume of a cubic cell. *Solve*:

There are four PbSe units in the unit cell. The unit cell edge is designated *a*.

$$8.27 \text{ g/cm}^3 = \frac{4 \text{ PbSe units}}{a^3} \times \frac{286.2 \text{ g}}{6.022 \times 10^{23} \text{ PbSe units}} \times \left(\frac{1 \text{ Å}}{1 \times 10^{-8} \text{ cm}}\right)^3$$

$a^3 = 229.87 \text{ Å}^3$, $a = 6.13 \text{ Å}$

11.67 (a)   The U ions in UO_2 are represented by the smaller spheres in Figure 11.42(c). The chemical formula requires twice as many O^{2-} ions as U^{4+} ions. There are eight complete large spheres and four total (8 × 1/8 + 6 ×1/2) small spheres, so the small ones must represent U^{4+}. (It is probably true that O^{2-} has a physically larger radius than U^{4+}, but the elements' large separation on the periodic chart makes the relative radii difficult to estimate from trends.)

(b)   According to Figure 11.42(c), there are four UO_2 units in the "fluorite" unit cell.

$$\frac{4 \text{ } UO_2 \text{ units}}{(5.468 \text{ Å})^3} \times \frac{270.03 \text{ g}}{6.022 \times 10^{23} \text{ } UO_2 \text{ units}} \times \left(\frac{1 \text{ Å}}{1 \times 10^{-8} \text{ cm}}\right)^3 = 10.97 \text{ g/cm}^3$$

Bonding in Solids

11.69 (a)   Hydrogen bonding, dipole-dipole forces, London dispersion forces

(b)   covalent chemical bonds (mainly)

(c)   ionic bonds (mainly)

(d)   metallic bonds

11.71   In molecular solids, relatively weak intermolecular forces (hydrogen bonding, dipole-dipole, dispersion) bind the molecules in the lattice, so relatively little energy is required to disrupt these forces. In covalent-network solids, covalent bonds join atoms into an extended network. Melting or deforming a covalent-network solid means breaking these covalent bonds, which requires a large amount of energy.

11.73   Because of its relatively high melting point and properties as a conducting solution, the solid must be ionic.

11.75   (a)   B – nonmetallic element likely to adopt covalent-network lattice like C(s), versus weak dispersion forces in BF_3

         (b)   NaCl – ionic versus metallic bonding; Na(s) has only one valence electron and is a relatively soft, low-melting alkali metal.

         (c) TiO_2 – due to higher charge on O^{2-} than Cl^-. [In fact, $TiCl_4$ is molecular, with a very low melting point, but this is difficult to predict.]

         (d) MgF_2 – due to higher charge on Mg^{2+} than Na^+.

Additional Exercises

11.78   (a)   Dipole-dipole attractions (polar covalent molecules): SO_2, IF, HBr

         (b)   Hydrogen bonding (O–H, N–H or F–H bonds): CH_3NH_2, HCOOH

11.80   (a)   The *cis* isomer has stronger dipole-dipole forces; the *trans* isomer is nonpolar. The higher boiling point of the *cis* isomer supports this conclusion.

         (b)   While boiling points are primarily a measure of strength of intermolecular forces, melting points are influenced by crystal packing efficiency as well as intermolecular forces. Since the nonpolar *trans* isomer with weaker intermolecular forces has the higher melting point, it must pack more efficiently.

11.83   (a) Decrease   (b) increase   (c) increase   (d) increase
            (e) increase   (f) increase   (g) increase

11.86   The two O–H groups in ethylene glycol are involved in many hydrogen bonding interactions, leading to its high boiling point and viscosity, relative to pentane, which experiences only dispersion forces.

11.88   The vacuum pump reduces the pressure of the atmosphere (air + water vapor) above the water. Eventually, atmospheric pressure equals the vapor pressure of water and the water boils. Boiling is an endothermic process, and the temperature drops if the system is not able to absorb heat from the surroundings fast enough. As the temperature of the water decreases, the water freezes. (On a molecular level, the evaporation of water removes the molecules with the highest kinetic energies from the liquid. This decrease in average kinetic energy is what we experience as a temperature decrease.)

11.93　(a)　　8 corners × 1/8 atom/corner = 1 atom

　　　　(b)　　8 corners × 1/8 atom/corner + 1 center × 1atom/center = 2 atoms

　　　　(c)　　8 corners × 1/8 atom/corner + 6 faces × 1/2 atom/face = 4 atoms

11.95　The most effective diffraction of light by a grating occurs when the wavelength of light and the separation of the slits in the grating are similar. When X-rays are diffracted by a crystal, layers of atoms serve as the "slits." The most effective diffraction occurs when the distances between layers of atoms are similar to the wavelength of the X-rays. Typical interlayer distances in crystals range from 2 Å to 20 Å. Visible light, 400-700 nm or 4,000 to 7,000 Å, is too long to be diffracted effectively by crystals. Molybdenum X-rays of 0.71 Å are on the same order of magnitude as interlayer distances in crystals and are diffracted.

Integrative Exercises

11.100　(a)　　In order for butane to be stored as a liquid at temperatures above its boiling point (-5°C), the pressure in the tank must be greater than atmospheric pressure. In terms of the phase diagram of butane, the pressure must be high enough so that, at tank conditions, the butane is "above" the gas-liquid line and in the liquid region of the diagram.

　　　　　　　The pressure of a gas is described by the ideal gas law as P = nRT/V; pressure is directly proportional to moles of gas. The more moles of gas present in the tank the greater the pressure, until sufficient pressure is achieved for the gas to liquify. At the point where liquid and gas are in equilibrium and temperature is constant, liquid will vaporize or condense to maintain the equilibrium vapor pressure. That is, as long as some liquid is present, the gas pressure in the tank will be constant.

　　　　(b)　　If butane gas escapes the tank, butane liquid will vaporize (evaporate) to maintain the equilibrium vapor pressure. Vaporization is an endothermic process, so the butane will absorb heat from the surroundings. The temperature of the tank and the liquid butane will decrease.

　　　　(c)　　$155 \text{ g C}_4\text{H}_{10} \times \dfrac{1 \text{ mol C}_4\text{H}_{10}}{58.12 \text{ g C}_4\text{H}_{10}} \times \dfrac{21.3 \text{ kJ}}{\text{mol}} = 56.8 \text{ kJ}$

　　　　　　　$V = \dfrac{nRT}{P} = 155 \text{ g} \times \dfrac{1 \text{ mol}}{58.12 \text{ g}} \times \dfrac{0.08206 \text{ L} \cdot \text{atm}}{\text{mol} \cdot \text{K}} \times \dfrac{308 \text{ K}}{755 \text{ torr}} \times \dfrac{760 \text{ torr}}{1 \text{ atm}}$

　　　　　　　　　　　　　　　　　　　　　　　　　　　　$= 67.851 = 67.9 \text{ L}$

11.103　$P = \dfrac{nRT}{V} = \dfrac{g \, RT}{\mathscr{m} \, V}$;　T = 273 + 26°C = 299 K;　V = 5.00 L

　　　g C_6H_6(g) = 7.2146 - 5.1493 = 2.0653 g C_6H_6(g)

　　　$P \text{ (vapor)} = \dfrac{2.0653 \text{ g}}{78.11 \text{ g/mol}} \times \dfrac{299 \text{ K}}{5.00 \text{ L}} \times \dfrac{0.08206 \text{ L} \cdot \text{atm}}{\text{K} \cdot \text{mol}} \times \dfrac{760 \text{ torr}}{1 \text{ atm}} = 98.6 \text{ torr}$

12 Modern Materials

Liquid Crystals

12.1   Both an ordinary liquid and a nematic liquid crystal phase are fluids; they are converted directly to the solid phase upon cooling. The nematic phase is cloudy and more viscous than an ordinary liquid. Upon heating, the nematic phase is converted to an ordinary liquid.

12.3   In the solid state, there is three-dimensional order; the relative orientation of the molecules is fixed and repeating in all three dimensions. Essentially no translational or rotational motion is allowed. When a substance changes to the nematic liquid-crystalline phase, the molecules remain aligned in one dimension (the long dimension of the molecule). Translational motion is allowed, but rotational motion is restricted. Transformation to the isotropic-liquid phase destroys the one-dimensional order. Free translational and rotational motion result in random molecular orientations that change continuously.

12.5   The presence of polar groups or nonbonded electron pairs leads to relatively strong dipole-dipole interactions between molecules. These are a significant part of the orienting forces necessary for liquid crystal formation.

12.7   In the nematic phase, molecules are aligned in one dimension, the long dimension of the molecule. In a smectic phase (A or C), molecules are aligned in two dimensions. Not only are the long directions of the molecules aligned, but the ends are also aligned. The molecules are organized into layers; the height of the layer is related to the length of the molecule.

12.9   A nematic phase is composed of sheets of molecules aligned along their lengths, but with no additional order within the sheet or between sheets. A cholesteric phase also contains this kind of sheet, but with some ordering between sheets. In a cholesteric phase, there is a characterisitic angle between molecules in one sheet and those in an adjacent sheet. That is, one sheet of molecules is twisted at some characteristic angle relative to the next, producing a "screw" axis perpendicular to the sheets.

Polymers

12.11   *n* -decane does not have a sufficiently high chain length or molecular mass to be considered a polymer.

12.13 *Analyze.* Given two types of reactant molecules, we are asked to write a condensation reaction with an ester product. *Plan.* A condensation reaction occurs when two smaller molecules combine to form a larger molecule and a small molecule, often water. Consider the structures of the two reactants and how they could combine to join the larger fragments and split water. *Solve*:

A carboxylic acid contains the $\overset{\overset{\displaystyle O}{\|}}{-C-OH}$ functional group; an alcohol contains the –OH functional group. These can be arranged to form the $\overset{\overset{\displaystyle O}{\|}}{-C-O-C-}$ ester functional group

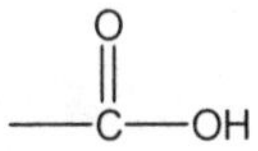

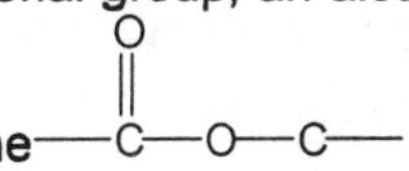

and H_2O.   Condensation reaction to form an ester:

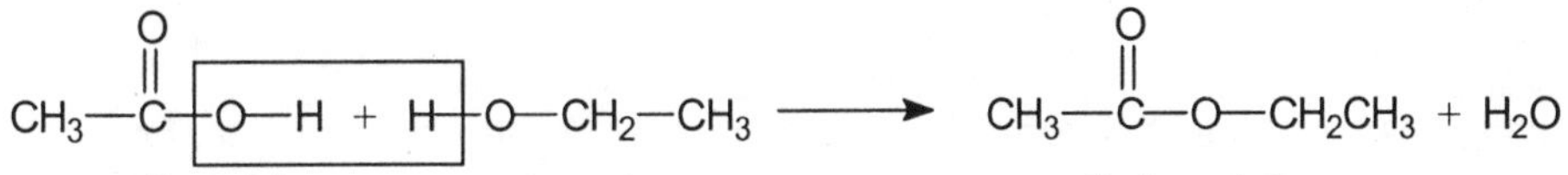

$$CH_3-\overset{\overset{\displaystyle O}{\|}}{C}\boxed{-O-H \; + \; H}-O-CH_2-CH_3 \longrightarrow CH_3-\overset{\overset{\displaystyle O}{\|}}{C}-O-CH_2CH_3 \; + \; H_2O$$

         acetic acid   ethanol   ethyl acetate

If a dicarboxylic acid (two –COOH groups, usually at opposite ends of the molecule) and a dialcohol (two –OH groups, usually at opposite ends of the molecule) are combined, there is the potential for propagation of the polymer chain at both ends of both monomers. Polyethylene terephthalate (Table 12.1) is an example of a polyester formed from the monomers ethylene glycol and terephthalic acid.

12.15 *Analyze/Plan.* Decide whether the given polymer is an addition or condensation polymer. Select the smallest repeat unit and deconstruct it into the monomer(s) with the specific functional group(s) that would form the stated polymer. *Solve*:

(a)

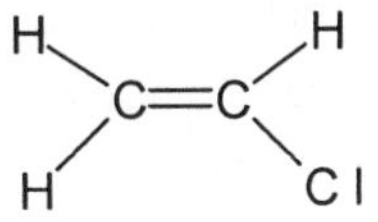

vinyl chloride (chloroethylene or chloroethene)

(b)

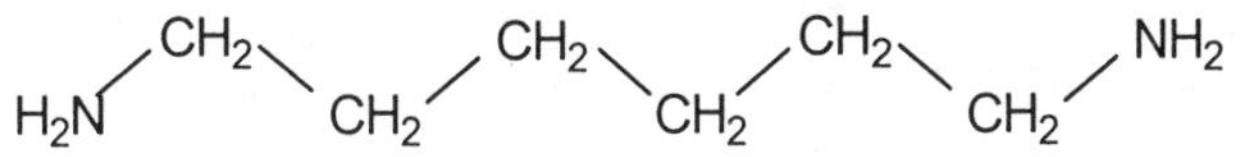

hexanediamine

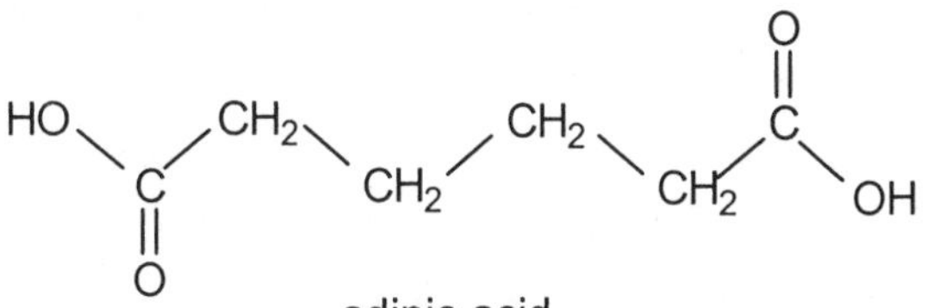

adipic acid

(Formulas given in Equation 12.3.)

(c)

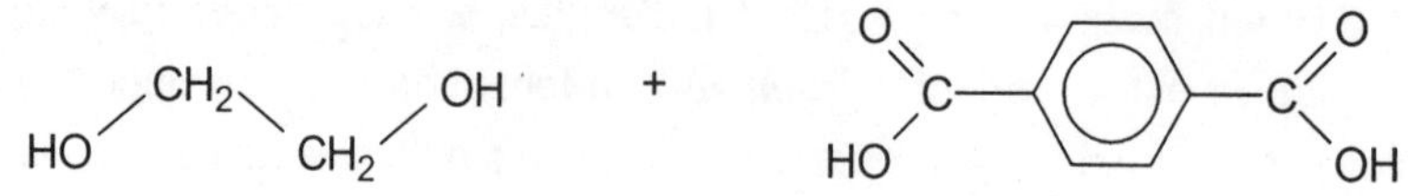

ethylene glycol   terephthalic acid

12.17 *Plan/Solve.* When nylon polymers are made, H_2O is produced as the C–N bonds are formed. Reversing this process (adding H_2O across the C–N bond), we see that the monomers used to produce Nomex™ are:

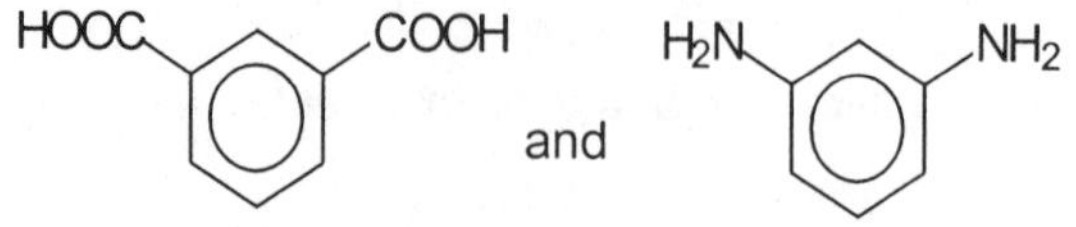

and

12.19 *Analyze/Plan.* Given the formula of a monomer, write the equation for condensation polymerization. The monomers are aligned so that the caroboxyl-end of one monomer joins the amine-end of another molecule. *Solve*:

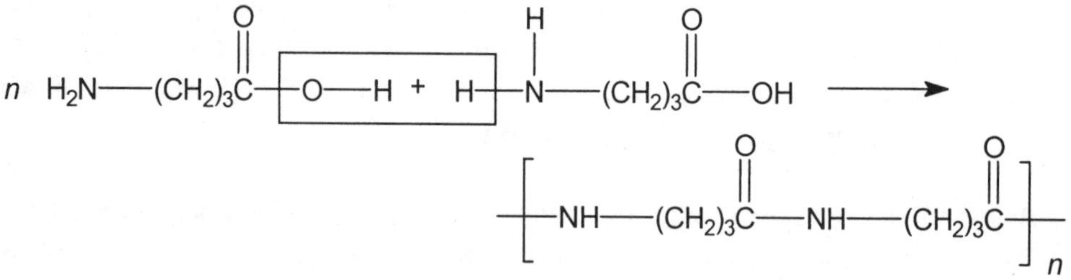

12.21 Most of a polymer backbone is composed of σ bonds. The geometry around individual atoms is tetrahedral with bond angles of 109°, so the polymer is not flat, and there is relatively free rotation around the σ bonds. The flexibility of the molecular chains causes flexibility of the bulk material. Flexibility is enhanced by molecular features that inhibit order, such as branching, and diminished by features that encourage order, such as crosslinking or delocalized π electron density.

Crosslinking is the formation of chemical bonds between polymer chains. It reduces flexibility of the molecular chains and increases the hardness of the material. Crosslinked polymers are less chemically reactive because of the links.

12.23 The function of the material (polymer) determines whether high molecular mass and high degree of crystallinity are desirable properties. If the material will be formed into containers or pipes, rigidity and structural strength are required. If the polymer will be used as a flexible wrapping or as a garment material, rigidity is an undesirable property.

Biomaterials

12.25   Is the neoprene biocompatible: is the surface smooth enough and is the chemical composition appropriate so that there are no inflammatory reactions in the body? Does neoprene meet the physical requirements of a flexible lead: will it remain resistant to degradation by body fluids over a long time period; will it maintain elasticity over the same time period? Can neoprene be prepared in sufficiently pure form (free of trace amounts of monomer, catalyst, etc.) so that it can be classified as *medical grade*?

12.27   Current vascular-graft materials cannot be lined with cells similar to those in the native artery. The body detects that the graft is "foreign" and platelets attach to the inside surfaces, causing blood clots. The inside surfaces of the future vascular implants need to accommodate a lining of cells that do not attract or attach to platelets.

12.29   In order for skin cells in a culture medium to develop into synthetic skin, a mechanical matrix must be present that holds the cells in contact with one another and allows them to differentiate. The matrix must be mechanically strong, biocompatible and biodegradable. It probably has polar functional groups that are capable of hydrogen bonding with biomolecules in the tissue cells.

Ceramics

12.31   Ceramics are not readily recyclable because of their extremely high melting points and rigid ionic or covalent-network structures. According to Table 12.4, the melting points of ceramic materials are much higher than those of Al and Fe. This makes recycling ceramics technologically difficult and expensive. Crystalline ceramics have rigid, precise three-dimensional structures. If and when these materials can be melted, either covalent or ionic bonds are broken. The precise structures are usually not reformed upon cooling. Recyclable ceramics such as bottle glass are amorphous; there is no exact repeating structure that must be reformed after melting.

12.33   Very small, uniformly sized and shaped particles are required for the production of a strong ceramic object by sintering. During sintering, the small ceramic particles are heated to a high temperature below the melting point of the solid. This high temperature initiates condensation reactions between atoms at the surfaces of the spheres; the spheres are then connected by chemical bonds between atoms in different spheres. The more uniform the particle size and the greater the total surface area of the solid, the more chemical bonds are formed, and the stronger the ceramic object.

12.35   Concrete is a typically brittle ceramic that is susceptible to catastrophic fracture. Steel reinforcing rods are added to resist stress applied along the long direction of the rod. By analogy, the shape of the reinforcing material in the ceramic composite should be rod-like, with a length much greater than its diameter. This is the optimal shape because rods have great strength when the load or stress is applied parallel to the long direction of the rod. Rods can be oriented in many directions, so that the material (concrete or ceramic composite) is strengthened in all directions.

12.37   By analogy to the ZnS structure, the C atoms form a face-centered cubic array with Si atoms occupying **alternate** tetrahedral holes in the lattice. This means that the coordination numbers of both Si and C are 4; each Si is bound to 4 C atoms in a tetrahedral arrangement, and each C is bound to 4 Si atoms in a tetrahedral arrangement, producing an extended three-dimensional network. ZnS, an ionic solid, sublimes at 1185° and 1 atm pressure and melts at 1850° and 150 atm pressure. The considerably higher melting point of SiC, 2800° at 1 atm, indicates that SiC is probably not a purely ionic solid and that the Si–C bonding network has significant covalent character. This is reasonable, since the electronegativities of Si and C are similar (Figure 8.7). SiC is high-melting because a great deal of chemical energy is stored in the covalent Si–C bonds, and it is hard because the three-dimensional lattice resists any change that would weaken the Si–C bonding network.

Superconductivity

12.39   A superconducting material offers no resistance to the flow of electrical current; *superconductivity* is the frictionless flow of electrons. Superconductive materials could transmit electricity with no heat loss and therefore much greater efficiency than current carriers. Because of the Meisner effect, they are also potential materials for magnetically levitated trains.

12.41   Below 39 K, MgB_2 conducts electricity with zero resistivity, the definition of a superconductor. Above 39 K, the material is not superconducting. The sharp drop in resistivity of MgB_2 near 39 K is the superconducting transition temperature, T_c.

12.43   Because they are brittle ceramics, it is difficult to mold superconductors into useful shapes such as wires and these wires would be fragile at best. For presently known superconductors, the amount of current per cross-sectional area that can be carried by these wires is limited. The low temperatures required for superconductivity render today's superconducting ceramics impractical for widespread use.

Thin Films

12.45   Adhesion is due to attractive intermolecular forces. These include ion-dipole, dipole-dipole, dispersion and hydrogen bonding. Adhesive interactions will be strongest between substances with similar intermolecular forces, so the bonding characteristics (that determine intermolecular forces) of the thin film material should be matched to those of the substrate.

12.47   The coating in Figure 12.31 is a metallic film that reflects most of the incident sunlight. The exclusion of sunlight from the interior of the building reduces glare and cooling load. The opacity of the film provides privacy.

Additional Exercises

12.49   A dipole moment (permanent, partial charge separation) roughly parallel to the long dimension of the molecule would cause the molecules to reorient when an electric field is applied perpendicular to the usual direction of molecular orientation.

12.52   At the temperature where a substance changes from the solid to the liquid-crystalline phase, kinetic energy sufficient to overcome most of the long range order in the solid has been supplied. A few van der Waals forces have sufficient attractive energy to impose the one-dimensional order characteristic of the liquid-crystalline state. Very little additional kinetic energy (and thus a relatively small increase in temperature) is required to overcome these aligning forces and produce an isotropic liquid.

12.54   In a liquid crystal display (Figure 12.7), the molecules must be free to rotate by 90°. The long directions of molecules remain aligned but any attractive forces between the ends of molecules are disrupted. At low Antarctic temperatures, the liquid crystalline phase is closer to its freezing point. The molecules have less kinetic energy due to temperature and the applied voltage may not be sufficient to overcome orienting forces among the ends of molecules. If some or all of the molecules do not rotate when the voltage is applied, the display will not function properly.

12.58   (a)

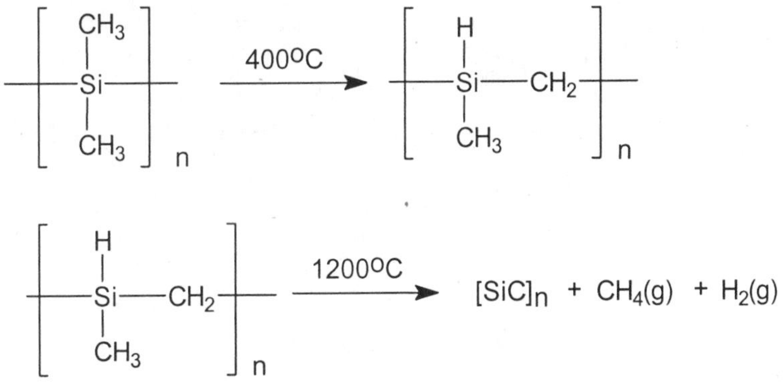

(b) $2NbBr_5(g) + 5H_2(g) \rightarrow 2Nb(s) + 10HBr(g)$

(c) $SiCl_4(l) + 4C_2H_5OH(l) \rightarrow Si(OC_2H_5)_4(s) + 4HCl(g)$

(d)

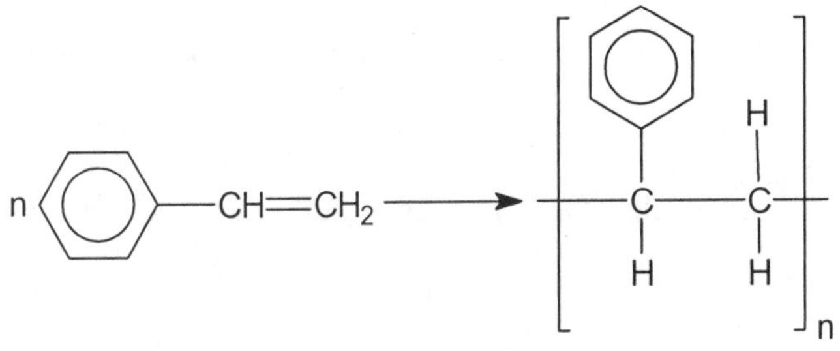

12.62   The formula of the compound deposited as a thin film is indicated by boldface type.

(a) $SiH_4(g) + 2H_2(g) + 2CO_2(g) \rightarrow \textbf{SiO}_2\textbf{(s)} + 4H_2(g) + 2CO(g)$

(b) $TiCl_4(g) + 2H_2O(g) \rightarrow \textbf{TiO}_2\textbf{(s)} + 4HCl(g)$

(c) $GeCl_4(g) \rightarrow Ge(s) + 2Cl_2(g)$

The H_2 carrier gas dilutes the $GeCl_4(g)$ so the reaction occurs more evenly and at a controlled rate; it does not participate in the reaction.

Integrative Exercises

12.64   (a)

HDPE

$\Delta H = D(C=C) - 2D(C-C) = 614 - 2(348) = -82$ kJ/mol C_2H_4

(b) $(n+1)$ HOOC—$(CH_2)_6$—COOH + $(n+1)$ H_2N—$(CH_2)_6$—NH_2 $\longrightarrow$

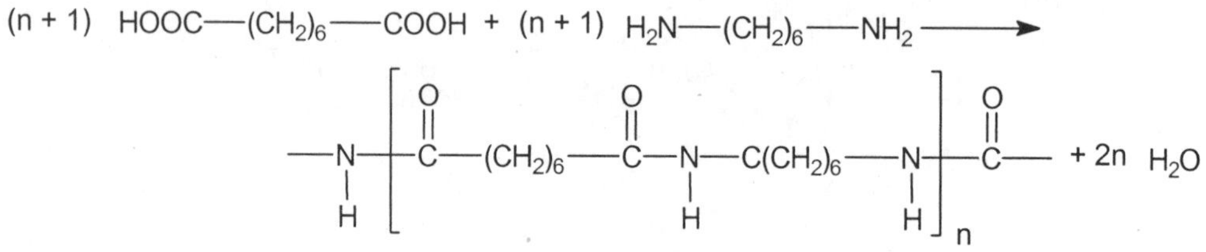

Nylon 6,6

$\Delta H = 2D(C-O) + 2D(N-H) - 2D(C-N) - 2D(H-O)$

$\Delta H = 2(358) + 2(391) - 2(293) - 2(463) = -14$ kJ/mol

(This is -14 kJ/mol of either reactant.)

(c) $(n+1)$ HOOC—⬡—COOH + $(n+1)$ HO—CH_2—CH_2—OH $\longrightarrow$

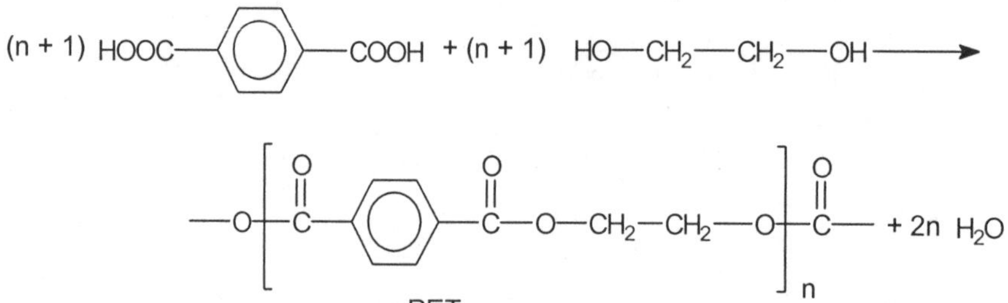

PET

$\Delta H = 2D(C-O) + 2D(O-H) - 2D(C-O) - 2D(O-H) = 0$ kJ

12.68   (a)   The data (14.99%) has 4 sig figs, so use molar masses to 5 sig figs.

mass % O = $14.99 = \dfrac{(8+x)15.999}{746.04 + (8+x)15.999} \times 100$

rounded (to show sig figs)   **unrounded**

(8+x)15.999   (8+x)15.999
   = 0.1499 [746.04 + (8+x) 15.999]   = 0.1499 [746.04 + (8+x) 15.999]
127.99 + 15.999x   127.992 + 15.999x
   = 0.1499(874.04 + 15.999x)   = 0.1499 (874.036 + 15.999x
15.999x - 2.398x   15.999x - 2.3983x
   = 131.0 - 127.99   = 131.018 - 127.992
13.601x = 3.0; x = 0.22   13.6007x = 3.026;   x = 0.2225

(b)   **Hg** and **Cu** both have more than one stable oxidation state. If different Cu ions (or Hg ions) in the solid lattice have different charges, then the average charge is a noninteger value. Ca and Ba are stable only in the +2 oxidation state; they are unlikely to have noninteger average charge.

(c) Ba^{2+} is largest; Cu^{2+} is smallest. For ions with the same charge, size decreases going up or across the periodic table. In the +2 state, Hg is smaller than Ba. If Hg has an average charge greater than 2+, it will be smaller yet. The same argument is true for Cu and Ca.

13 Properties of Solutions

The Solution Process

13.1 If the enthalpy released due to solute-solvent attractive forces (ΔH_3) is at least as large as the enthalpy required to separate the solute particles (ΔH_1), the overall enthalpy of solution (ΔH_{soln}) will be either slightly endothermic (owing to $+\Delta H_2$) or exothermic. Even if ΔH_{soln} is slightly endothermic, the increase in disorder due to mixing will cause a significant amount of solute to dissolve. If the magnitude of ΔH_3 is small relative to the magnitude of ΔH_1, ΔH_{soln} will be large and endothermic (energetically unfavorable) and not much solute will dissolve.

13.3 *Analyze/Plan.* Decide whether the solute and solvent in question are ionic, polar covalent or nonpolar covalent. Draw Lewis structures as needed. Then, state the appropriate type of solute-solvent interaction. *Solve*:

(a) CCl_4, nonpolar; benzene, nonpolar; dispersion forces

(b) $CaCl_2$, ionic; water, polar; ion-dipole forces

(c)   propanol, polar with hydrogen bonding; water, polar with hydrogen bonding; hydrogen bonding

(d)   HCl, polar; CH_3CN, polar; dipole-dipole forces

13.5 (a)   Lattice energy is the amount of energy required to completely separate a mole of solid ionic compound into its gaseous ions (Section 8.2). For ionic solutes, this corresponds to ΔH_1 (solute-solute interactions) in Equation 13.1.

(b)   In Equation 13.1, ΔH_3 is always exothermic. Formation of attractive interactions, no matter how weak, always lowers the energy of the system, relative to the energy of the isolated particles.

13.7 (a) ΔH_{soln} is determined by the relative magnitudes of the "old" solute-solute (ΔH_1) and solvent-solvent (ΔH_2) interactions and the new solute-solvent interactions (ΔH_3); $\Delta H_{soln} = \Delta H_1 + \Delta H_2 + \Delta H_3$. Since the solute and solvent in this case experience very similar London dispersion forces, the energy required to separate them individually and the energy released when they are mixed are approximately equal. $\Delta H_1 + \Delta H_2 \approx -\Delta H_3$. Thus, ΔH_{soln} is nearly zero.

(b)   Mixing hexane and heptane produces a homogeneous solution from two pure substances, and the randomness of the system increases. Since no strong intermolecular forces prevent the molecules from mixing, they do so spontaneously due to the increase in disorder.

Saturated Solutions; Factors Affecting Solubility

13.9   (a)   Supersaturated

(b)   Add a seed crystal. Supersaturated solutions exist because not enough solute molecules are properly aligned for crystallization to occur. A seed crystal provides a nucleus of already aligned molecules, so that ordering of the dissolved particles is more facile.

13.11   *Analyze/Plan*. On Figure 13.17, find the solubility curve for the appropriate solute. Find the intersection of 40°C and 40 g solute on the graph. If this point is below the solubility curve, more solute can dissolve and the solution is unsaturated. If the intersection is on or above the curve, the solution is saturated. *Solve*:

(a) unsaturated   (b) saturated   (c) saturated   (d) unsaturated

13.13   The liquids water and glycerol form homogenous mixtures (solutions), regardless of the relative amounts of the two components. Glycerol has an –OH group on each C atom in the molecule. This structure facilitates strong hydrogen bonding similar to that in water. Like dissolves like and the two liquids are miscible in all proportions.

13.15   For small *n* values, the dominant interactions among acid molecules will be hydrogen-bonding. As n increases, dispersion forces between carbon chains become more important and eventually dominate. Thus, as *n* increases, water solubility decreases and hexane solubility increases.

13.17   *Analyze/Plan*. Water, H_2O, is a polar solvent that forms hydrogen bonds with other H_2O molecules. The more soluble solute in each case will have intermolecular interactions that are most similar to the hydrogen bonding in H_2O. *Solve*:

(a)   Ionic $CaCl_2$ is more soluble because ion-dipole solute-solvent interactions are more similar to ionic solute-solute and hydrogen bonding solvent-solvent interactions than the weak dispersion forces between CCl_4 and H_2O.

(b) C_6H_5OH is more soluble because it is capable of hydrogen bonding. Nonpolar C_6H_6 is capable only of dispersion force interactions and does not have strong intermolecular interactions with polar (hydrogen bonding) H_2O.

13.19 (a) Carbonated beverages are stored with a partial pressure of $CO_2(g)$ greater than 1 atm above the liquid. A sealed container is required to maintain this CO_2 pressure.

(b) Since the solubility of gases increases with decreasing temperature, some $CO_2(g)$ will remain dissolved in the beverage if it is kept cool.

13.21 *Analyze/Plan.* Follow the logic in Sample Exercise 13.2. *Solve:*

$$S_{He} = 3.7 \times 10^{-4} \ M/atm \times 1.5 \ atm = 5.6 \times 10^{-4} \ M$$

$$S_{N_2} = 6.0 \times 10^{-4} \ M/atm \times 1.5 \ atm = 9.0 \times 10^{-4} \ M$$

Concentrations of Solutions

13.23 *Analyze/Plan.* Follow the logic in Sample Exercise 13.3. *Solve:*

(a) $\text{mass \%} = \dfrac{\text{mass solute}}{\text{total mass solution}} \times 100 = \dfrac{11.7 \ g \ Na_2SO_4}{11.7 \ g \ Na_2SO_4 + 443 \ g \ H_2O} \times 100 = 2.57\%$

(b) $\text{ppm} = \dfrac{\text{mass solute}}{\text{total mass solution}} \times 10^6; \ \dfrac{5.95 \ g \ Ag}{1 \ ton \ ore} \times \dfrac{1 \ ton}{2000 \ lb} \times \dfrac{1 \ lb}{453.6 \ g} \times 10^6$

$$= 6.56 \ \text{ppm}$$

13.25 *Analyze/Plan.* Given masses of CH_3OH and H_2O, calculate moles of each component.
(a) Mole fraction CH_3OH = (mol CH_3OH)/(total mol) (b) mass % CH_3OH = [(g CH_3OH)/(total mass)] × 100 (c) molality CH_3OH = (mol CH_3OH)/(kg H_2O). *Solve:*

(a) $7.5 \ g \ CH_3OH \times \dfrac{1 \ mol \ CH_3OH}{32.04 \ g \ CH_3OH} = 0.234 = 0.23 \ mol \ CH_3OH$

$245 \ g \ H_2O \times \dfrac{1 \ mol \ H_2O}{18.02 \ g \ H_2O} = 13.60 = 13.6 \ mol \ H_2O$

$\chi_{CH_3OH} = \dfrac{0.234}{0.234 + 13.60} = 0.0169 = 0.017$

(b) $\text{mass \% } CH_3OH = \dfrac{7.5 \ g \ CH_3OH}{7.5 \ g \ CH_3OH + 245 \ g \ H_2O} \times 100 = 3.0\% \ CH_3OH$

(c) $m = \dfrac{0.234 \ mol \ CH_3OH}{0.245 \ kg \ H_2O} = 0.955 = 0.96 \ m \ CH_3OH$

13.27 *Analyze/Plan.* Given mass solute and volume solution, calculate mol solute, then molarity = mol solute/L solution. Or, for dilution, $M_c \times L_c = M_d \times L_d$ *Solve:*

(a) $M = \dfrac{\text{mol solute}}{\text{L soln}}; \ \dfrac{10.5 \ g \ Mg(NO_3)_2}{0.2500 \ L \ soln} \times \dfrac{1 \ mol \ Mg(NO_3)_2}{148.3 \ g \ Mg(NO_3)_2} = 0.283 \ M \ Mg(NO_3)_2$

(b) $\dfrac{22.4 \text{ g LiClO}_4 \cdot 3\text{H}_2\text{O}}{0.125 \text{ L soln}} \times \dfrac{1 \text{ mol LiClO}_4 \cdot 3\text{H}_2\text{O}}{160.4 \text{ g LiClO}_4 \cdot 3\text{H}_2\text{O}} = 1.12 \ M \text{ LiClO}_4 \cdot 3\text{H}_2\text{O}$

(c) $M_c \times L_c = M_d \times L_d$; $3.50 \ M \text{ HNO}_3 \times 0.0250 \text{ L} = ?M \text{ HNO}_3 \times 0.250 \text{ L}$

250 mL of 0.350 M HNO$_3$

13.29 *Analyze/Plan.* Follow the logic in Sample Exercise 13.4. *Solve*:

(a) $m = \dfrac{\text{mol solute}}{\text{kg solvent}}$; $\dfrac{10.5 \text{ g C}_6\text{H}_6}{18.5 \text{ g CCl}_4} \times \dfrac{1 \text{ mol C}_6\text{H}_6}{78.11 \text{ g C}_6\text{H}_6} \times \dfrac{1000 \text{ g CCl}_4}{1 \text{ kg CCl}_4} = 7.27 \ m \ \text{C}_6\text{H}_6$

(b) The density of H$_2$O = 0.997 g/mL = 0.997 kg/L.

$\dfrac{4.15 \text{ g NaCl}}{0.250 \text{ L H}_2\text{O}} \times \dfrac{1 \text{ mol NaCl}}{58.44 \text{ g NaCl}} \times \dfrac{1 \text{ L H}_2\text{O}}{0.997 \text{ kg H}_2\text{O}} = 0.285 \ m \text{ NaCl}$

13.31 *Analyze/Plan.* Assume 1 L of solution. Density gives the total mass of 1 L of solution. The g H$_2$SO$_4$/L are also given in the problem. Mass % = mass solute/total mass solution. Calculate mass solvent from mass solution and mass solute. Calculate moles solute and solvent and use the appropriate definitions to calculate mole fraction, molality and molarity. *Solve*:

(a) $\dfrac{571.6 \text{ g H}_2\text{SO}_4}{1 \text{ L soln}} \times \dfrac{1 \text{ L soln}}{1329 \text{ g soln}} = 0.430098 \text{ g H}_2\text{SO}_4/\text{g soln}$

mass percent is thus 0.4301 × 100 = 43.01% H$_2$SO$_4$

(b) In a liter of solution there are 1329 − 571.6 = 757.4 = 757 g H$_2$O.

$\dfrac{571.6 \text{ g H}_2\text{SO}_4}{98.09 \text{ g/mol}} = 5.827 \text{ mol H}_2\text{SO}_4$; $\dfrac{757.4 \text{ g H}_2\text{O}}{18.02 \text{ g/mol}} = 42.03 = 42.0 \text{ mol H}_2\text{O}$

$\chi_{\text{H}_2\text{SO}_4} = \dfrac{5.827}{42.03 + 5.827} = 0.122$

(The result has 3 sig figs because 42.0 mol H$_2$O limits the denominator to 3 sig figs.)

(c) molality = $\dfrac{5.827 \text{ mol H}_2\text{SO}_4}{0.7574 \text{ kg H}_2\text{O}} = 7.693 = 7.69 \ m \text{ H}_2\text{SO}_4$

(d) molarity = $\dfrac{5.827 \text{ mol H}_2\text{SO}_4}{1 \text{ L soln}} = 5.827 \ M \text{ H}_2\text{SO}_4$

13.33 *Analyze/Plan.* Given: 90.0 mL of CH$_3$CN(l), 0.786 g/mL; 15.0 mL CH$_3$OH, 0.791 g/mL. Use the density and volume of each component to calculate mass and then moles of each component. Use the definitions to calculate mole fraction, molality and molarity. *Solve*:

(a) $\text{mol CH}_3\text{CN} = \dfrac{0.786\ g}{1\ mL} \times 90.0\ mL \times \dfrac{1\ \text{mol CH}_3\text{CN}}{41.05\ g\ \text{CH}_3\text{CN}} = 1.7233 = 1.72\ mol$

$\text{mol CH}_3\text{OH} = \dfrac{0.791\ g}{1\ mL} \times 15.0\ mL \times \dfrac{1\ \text{mol CH}_3\text{OH}}{32.04\ g\ \text{CH}_3\text{OH}} = 0.3703 = 0.370\ mol$

$\chi_{\text{CH}_3\text{OH}} = \dfrac{0.3703\ \text{mol CH}_3\text{OH}}{1.7233\ \text{mol CH}_3\text{CN} + 0.3703\ \text{mol CH}_3\text{OH}} = 0.177$

(b)   Assuming CH_3OH is the solute and CH_3CN is the solvent,

$90.0\ mL\ \text{CH}_3\text{CN} \times \dfrac{0.786\ g}{1\ mL} \times \dfrac{1\ kg}{1000\ g} = 0.07074 = 0.0707\ kg\ \text{CH}_3\text{CN}$

$m_{\text{CH}_3\text{OH}} = \dfrac{0.3703\ \text{mol CH}_3\text{OH}}{0.7074\ kg\ \text{CH}_3\text{CN}} = 5.2347 = 5.23\ m\ \text{CH}_3\text{OH}$

(c)   The total volume of the solution is 105.0 mL, assuming volumes are additive.

$M = \dfrac{0.3703\ \text{mol CH}_3\text{OH}}{0.1050\ L\ \text{solution}} = 3.53\ M\ \text{CH}_3\text{OH}$

13.35 *Analyze/Plan.* Given concentration and volume of solution use definitions of the appropriate concentration units to calculate amount of solute; change amount to moles if needed. *Solve*:

(a) $mol = M \times L$; $\dfrac{0.250\ \text{mol CaBr}_2}{1\ L\ soln} \times 0.255\ L = 6.38 \times 10^{-2}\ \text{mol CaBr}_2$

(b)   Assume that for dilute aqueous solutions, the mass of the solvent is the mass of solution. Use proportions to get mol KCl.

$\dfrac{0.150\ \text{mol KCl}}{1\ kg\ H_2O} = \dfrac{x\ \text{mol KCl}}{0.0500\ kg\ H_2O}$; $x = 7.50 \times 10^{-3}\ \text{mol KCl}$

(c)   Use proportions to get mass of glucose, then change to mol glucose.

$\dfrac{2.50\ g\ \text{C}_6\text{H}_{12}\text{O}_6}{100\ g\ soln} = \dfrac{x\ g\ \text{C}_6\text{H}_{12}\text{O}_6}{50.0\ g\ soln}$; $x = 1.25\ g\ \text{C}_6\text{H}_{12}\text{O}_6$

$1.25\ g\ \text{C}_6\text{H}_{12}\text{O}_6 \times \dfrac{1\ \text{mol C}_6\text{H}_{12}\text{O}_6}{180.2\ g\ \text{C}_6\text{H}_{12}\text{O}_6} = 6.94 \times 10^{-3}\ \text{mol C}_6\text{H}_{12}\text{O}_6$

13.37 *Analyze/Plan.* When preparing solution, we must know amount of solute and solvent. Use the appropriate concentration definition to calculate amount of solute. If this amount is in moles, use molar mass to get grams; use mass in grams directly. Amount of solvent can be expressed as total volume or mass of solution. Combine mass solute and solvent to produce required amount (mass or volume) of solution. *Solute*:

(a) $mol = M \times L$; $\dfrac{1.50 \times 10^{-2}\ \text{mol KBr}}{1\ L\ soln} \times 0.75\ L \times \dfrac{119.0\ g\ \text{KBr}}{1\ \text{mol KBr}} = 1.3\ g\ \text{KBr}$

Weigh out 1.5 g KBr, dissolve in water, dilute with stirring to 0.75 L (750 mL).

(b)   Mass of solution is required, but density is not specified. Use molality to calculate mass fraction, and then the masses of solute and solvent needed for 125 g of solution.

$$\frac{0.180 \text{ mol KBr}}{1000 \text{ g H}_2\text{O}} \times \frac{119.0 \text{ g KBr}}{1 \text{ mol KBr}} = 21.42 = 21.4 \text{ g KBr/kg H}_2\text{O}$$

Thus, mass fraction $= \dfrac{21.42 \text{ g KBr}}{1000 + 21.42} = 0.02097 = 0.0210$

In 125 g of the 0.180 m solution, there are

$$(125 \text{ g soln}) \times \frac{0.02097 \text{ g KBr}}{1 \text{ g soln}} = 2.621 = 2.62 \text{ g KBr}$$

Weigh out 2.62 g KBr, dissolve it in 125 - 2.62 = 122.38 = 122 g H_2O to make exactly 125 g of 0.180 m solution.

(c)   Using solution density, calculate the total mass of 1.85 L of solution, and from the mass % of KBr, the mass of KBr required.

$$1.85 \text{ L soln} \times \frac{1000 \text{ mL}}{1 \text{ L}} \times \frac{1.10 \text{ g soln}}{1 \text{ mL}} = 2035 = 2.04 \times 10^3 \text{ g soln}$$

$$0.120 \, (2035 \text{ g soln}) = 244.2 = 244 \text{ g KBr}$$

Dissolve 244 g KBr in water, dilute with stirring to 1.85 L.

(d)   Calculate moles KBr needed to precipitate 16.0 g AgBr. $AgNO_3$ is present in excess.

$$16.0 \text{ g AgBr} \times \frac{1 \text{ mol AgBr}}{187.8 \text{ g AgBr}} \times \frac{1 \text{ mol KBr}}{1 \text{ mol AgBr}} = 0.08520 = 0.0852 \text{ mol KBr}$$

$$0.0852 \text{ mol KBr} \times \frac{1 \text{ L soln}}{0.150 \text{ mol KBr}} = 0.568 \text{ L soln}$$

Weigh out 0.0852 mol KBr (10.1 g KBr), dissolve it in a small amount of water and dilute to 0.568 L.

13.39   *Analyze/Plan.* Assume 1.00 L of solution. Calculate mass of 1 L of solution using density. Calculate mass of NH_3 using mass %, then mol NH_3 in 1.00 L.   *Solve*:

$$1.00 \text{ L soln} \times \frac{1000 \text{ mL}}{1 \text{ L}} \times \frac{0.90 \text{ g soln}}{1 \text{ mL soln}} = 9.0 \times 10^2 \text{ g soln/L}$$

$$\frac{900 \text{ g soln}}{1.00 \text{ L soln}} \times \frac{28 \text{ g NH}_3}{100 \text{ g soln}} \times \frac{1 \text{ mol NH}_3}{17.03 \text{ g NH}_3} = 14.80 = 15 \text{ mol NH}_3/\text{L soln} = 15 \, M \text{ NH}_3$$

13.41 *Analyze/Plan.*

$$\chi_{C_3H_6(OH)_2} = 0.100 = \frac{mol\ C_3H_6(OH)_2}{mol\ C_3H_6(OH)_2 + mol\ H_2O}$$

$0.100\ [mol\ C_3H_6(OH)_2 + mol\ H_2O] = mol\ C_3H_6(OH)_2$

$0.100\ mol\ H_2O = 0.900\ mol\ C_3H_6(OH)_2;\ mol\ H_2O = 9[mol\ C_3H_6(OH)_2]$

The solution has nine times as many moles of H_2O as moles of $C_3H_6(OH)_2$. Assume 1.00 mol $C_3H_6(OH)_2$ and 9.00 mol H_2O. Calculate mass of $C_3H_6(OH)_2$ and H_2O. Use definitions to calculate mass % and molality. *Solve:*

(a)   76.09 = 76.1 g $C_3H_6(OH)_2$;   9.00 mol H_2O × 18.02 g H_2O/mol = 162.18 = 162 g H_2O

$$mass\ \% = \frac{76.09\ g\ C_3H_6(OH)_2}{76.09\ g\ C_3H_6(OH)_2 + 162.18\ g\ H_2O} \times 100 = 31.9\%\ C_3H_6(OH)_2\ by\ mass$$

(b) $m = \dfrac{mol\ C_3H_6(OH)_2}{kg\ H_2O};\ \dfrac{1.00\ mol\ C_3H_6(OH)_2}{0.16218\ kg\ H_2O} = 6.166 = 6.17\ m\ C_3H_6(OH)_2$

Colligative Properties

13.43   freezing point depression, $\Delta T_f = K_f(m)$; boiling point elevation, $\Delta T_b = K_b(m)$;

osmotic pressure, $\pi = M\,RT$;   vapor pressure lowering, $P_A = \chi_A P_A^\circ$

13.45   (a)   An *ideal solution* is a solution that obeys Raoult's Law.

       (b)   *Analyze/Plan.* Calculate the vapor pressure predicted by Raoult's law and compare it to the experimental vapor pressure. Assume ethylene glycol (eg) is the solute. *Solve:*

         $\chi_{H_2O} = \chi_{eg} = 0.500;\ P_A = \chi_A P_A^\circ = 0.500(149)\ mm\ Hg = 74.5\ mm\ Hg$

         The experimental vapor pressure (P_A), 67 mm Hg, is less than the value predicted by Raoult's law for an ideal solution. The solution is not ideal.

         Check. An ethylene glycol-water solution has extensive hydrogen bonding, which causes deviation from ideal behavior. We expect the experimental vapor pressure to be less than the ideal value and it is.

13.47   (a)   *Analyze/Plan.* H_2O vapor pressure will be determined by the mole fraction of H_2O in the solution. The vapor pressure of pure H_2O at 338 K (65°C) = 187.5 torr. *Solve:*

         $\dfrac{15.0\ g\ C_{12}H_{22}O_{11}}{342.3\ g/mol} = 0.04382 = 0.0438\ mol;\ \dfrac{100.0\ g\ H_2O}{18.02\ g/mol} = 5.5494 = 5.549\ mol$

         $P_{H_2O} = \chi_{H_2O}\ P_{H_2O}^\circ = \dfrac{5.5494\ mol\ H_2O}{5.5494 + 0.04382} \times 187.5\ torr = 186.0\ torr$

(b)   *Analyze/Plan.* For this problem, it will be convenient to express Raoult's law in terms of the lowering of the vapor pressure of the solvent, ΔP_A.

$\Delta P_A = P_A{}^\circ - \chi_A P_A{}^\circ = P_A{}^\circ (1 - \chi_A)$. $1 - \chi_A = \chi_B$, the mole fraction of the *solute* particles $\Delta P_A{}^\circ = \chi_B P_A{}^\circ$; the vapor pressure of the solvent (A) is lowered according to the mole fraction of solute (B) particles present.   *Solve:*

$$P_{H_2O} \text{ at } 40°C = 55.3 \text{ torr}; \quad \frac{500 \text{ g H}_2\text{O}}{18.02 \text{ g/mol}} = 27.747 = 27.7 \text{ mol H}_2\text{O}$$

$$\chi_{C_3H_8O_2} = \frac{4.60 \text{ torr}}{55.3 \text{ torr}} = \frac{y \text{ mol C}_3\text{H}_8\text{O}_2}{y \text{ mol C}_3\text{H}_8\text{O}_2 + 27.747 \text{ mol H}_2\text{O}} = 0.08318 = 0.0832$$

$$0.08318 = \frac{y}{y + 27.747}; \; 0.08318 \, y + 2.308 = y; \; 0.9168 \, y = 2.308,$$

$$y = 2.517 = 2.52 \text{ mol C}_3\text{H}_8\text{O}_2$$

This result has 3 sig figs because (27.7 × 0.0832 = 2.31) has 3 sig figs.

$$2.517 \text{ mol C}_3\text{H}_8\text{O}_2 \times \frac{76.09 \text{ g C}_3\text{H}_8\text{O}_2}{\text{mol C}_3\text{H}_8\text{O}_2} = 191.52 = 192 \text{ g C}_3\text{H}_8\text{O}_2$$

13.49   *Analyze/Plan.* At 63.5°C, $P_{H_2O}^{\,o} = 175$ torr, $P_{Eth}^{\,o} = 400$ torr. Let G = the mass of H_2O and/or C_2H_5OH.   *Solve:*

(a) $$\chi_{Eth} = \cfrac{\cfrac{G}{46.07 \text{ g C}_2\text{H}_5\text{OH}}}{\cfrac{G}{46.07 \text{ g C}_2\text{H}_5\text{OH}} + \cfrac{G}{18.02 \text{ g H}_2\text{O}}}$$

Multiplying top and bottom of the right side of the equation by 1/G gives:

$$\chi_{Eth} = \frac{1/46.07}{1/46.07 + 1/18.02} = \frac{0.02171}{0.02171 + 0.05549} = 0.2812$$

(b) $P_T = P_{Eth} + P_{H_2O}$; $P_{Eth} = \chi_{Eth} \times P_{Eth}^{\,o}$; $P_{H_2O} = \chi_{H_2O} \, P_{H_2O}^{\,o}$

$\chi_{Eth} = 0.2812$, $P_{Eth} = 0.2812 \, (400 \text{ torr}) = 112.48 = 112$ torr

$\chi_{H_2O} = 1 - 0.2812 = 0.7188$; $P_{H_2O} = 0.7188(175 \text{ torr}) = 125.8 = 126$ torr

$P_T = 112.5$ torr + 125.8 torr = 238.3 = 238 torr

(c) $$\chi_{Eth} \text{ in vapor} = \frac{P_{Eth}}{P_{total}} = \frac{112.5 \text{ torr}}{238.3 \text{ torr}} = 0.4721 = 0.472$$

13.51   (a)   Because NaCl is a soluble ionic compound and a strong electrolyte, there are 2 mol dissolved particles for every 1 mol of NaCl solute. $C_6H_{12}O_6$ is a molecular solute, so there is 1 mol of dissolved particles per mol solute. Boiling point elevation is directly related to total moles of dissolved particles; 0.10 *m* NaCl has more dissolved particles so its boiling point is higher than 0.10 *m* $C_6H_{12}O_6$.

(b)   *Analyze/Plan.* $\Delta T = K_b \, m$; K_b for H_2O is 0.51 °C/m (Table 13.4)   *Solve*:

0.10 *m* NaCl: $\Delta T = \dfrac{0.51°C}{m} \times 0.20 \, m = 0.102 \, °C$; $T_b = 100.0 + 0.102 = 100.1°C$

0.10 *m* $C_6H_{12}O_6$: $\Delta T = \dfrac{0.51°C}{m} \times 0.10 \, m = 0.051 \, °C$; $T_b = 100.0 + 0.051 = 100.1°C$

Check. Because K_b for H_2O is so small, there is little real difference in the boiling points of the two solutions.

13.53   0.030 *m* phenol > 0.040 *m* glycerin = 0.020 *m* KBr. Phenol is very slightly ionized in water, but not enough to match the number of particles in a 0.040 *m* glycerin solution. The KBr solution is 0.040 *m* in particles, so it has the same freezing point as 0.040 glycerin, which is a nonelectrolyte.

13.55   *Analyze/Plan.* $\Delta T = K \, (m)$; first, calculate the **molality** of each solution

(a)   0.35 *m*   (b)   14.2 mol CHCl$_3$ $\times \dfrac{119.4 \text{ g CHCl}_3}{\text{mol CHCl}_3} = 1.6955 = 1.70$ kg;

$$\dfrac{1.58 \text{ mol } C_{10}H_8}{1.6955 \text{ kg CHCl}_3} = 0.9319 = 0.932 \, m$$

(c)   5.13 g KBr $\times \dfrac{1 \text{ mol KBr}}{119.0 \text{ g KBr}} \times \dfrac{2 \text{ mol particles}}{1 \text{ mol KBr}} = 0.08622 = 0.0862$ mol particles

6.85 g $C_6H_{12}O_6 \times \dfrac{1 \text{ mol } C_6H_{12}O_6}{180.2 \text{ g } C_6H_{12}O_6} = 0.03801 = 0.0380$ mol particles

$$m = \dfrac{(0.08622 + 0.03801) \text{ mol particles}}{0.255 \text{ kg } H_2O} = 0.48718 = 0.487 \, m$$

Solve: Then, f.p. = $T_f - K_f(m)$; b.p. = $T_b + K_b(m)$; T in °C

	m	T_f	-$K_f(m)$	f.p.	T_b	+$K_b(m)$	b.p.
(a)	0.35	-114.6	-1.99(0.35) = -0.70	-115.3	78.4	1.22(0.35) = 0.43	78.8
(b)	0.932	-63.5	-4.68(0.932) = -4.36	-67.9	61.2	3.63(0.932) = 3.38	64.6
(c)	0.487	0.0	-1.86(0.487) = -0.906	-0.91	100.0	0.52(0.487) = 0.25	100.3

13.57   *Analyze/Plan.* $\pi = M$ RT; T = 25°C + 273 = 298 K; M = mol $C_9H_8O_4$/L soln   *Solve*:

$$M = \dfrac{50.0 \text{ mg } C_9H_8O_4}{0.250 \text{ L}} \times \dfrac{1 \text{ g}}{1000 \text{ mg}} \times \dfrac{1 \text{ mol } C_9H_8O_4}{180.2 \text{ g } C_9H_8O_4} = 1.1099 \times 10^{-3} = 1.11 \times 10^{-3} \, M$$

$$\pi = \dfrac{1.1099 \times 10^{-3} \text{ mol}}{L} \times \dfrac{0.08206 \text{ L} \cdot \text{atm}}{K \cdot \text{mol}} \times 298 \text{ K} = 0.02714 = 0.0271 \text{ atm}$$

13.59   *Analyze/Plan.* Follow the logic in Sample Exercise 13.11. *Solve*:

$$\Delta T_b = K_b\, m\,;\quad m = \frac{\Delta T_b}{K_b} = \frac{+0.49}{5.02} = 0.0976 = 0.098\ m\ \text{adrenaline}$$

$$m = \frac{\text{mol adrenaline}}{\text{kg CCl}_4} = \frac{\text{g adrenaline}}{\mathscr{M}\ \text{adrenaline} \times\ \text{kg CCl4}}$$

$$\mathscr{M}\ \text{adrenaline} = \frac{\text{g adrenaline}}{m \times\ \text{kg CCl}_4} = \frac{0.64\ \text{g adrenaline}}{0.0976\ m \times 0.0360\ \text{kg CCl}_4} = 1.8 \times 10^2\ \text{g/mol adrenaline}$$

13.61   *Analyze/Plan.* Follow the logic in Sample Exercise 13.12. *Solve*:

$$\pi = MRT;\quad M = \frac{\pi}{RT}\ ;\quad T = 25°\text{C} + 273 = 298\ \text{K}$$

$$M = 0.953\ \text{torr} \times \frac{1\ \text{atm}}{760\ \text{torr}} \times \frac{\text{K} \bullet \text{mol}}{0.08206\ \text{L} \bullet \text{atm}} \times \frac{1}{298\ \text{K}} = 5.128 \times 10^{-5} = 5.13 \times 10^{-5}\ M$$

$$\text{mol} = M \times L = 5.128 \times 10^{-5}\ \times 0.210\ \text{L} = 1.077 \times 10^{-5} = 1.08 \times 10^{-5}\ \text{mol lysozyme}$$

$$\mathscr{M} = \frac{\text{g}}{\text{mol}} = \frac{0.150\ \text{g}}{1.077 \times 10^{-5}\ \text{mol}} = 1.39 \times 10^4\ \text{g/mol lysozyme}$$

13.63   (a)   *Analyze/Plan.* $i = \pi$ (measured) / π (calculated for a nonelectrolyte);

         π (calculated) = M RT. *Solve*:

$$\pi\ (\text{calculated}) = 0.010\ \frac{\text{mol}}{\text{L}} \times \frac{0.08206\ \text{L} \bullet \text{atm}}{\text{mol} \bullet \text{K}} \times 298\ \text{K} = 0.2445 = 0.24\ \text{atm}$$

         $i = 0.674\ \text{atm}/0.2445\ \text{atm} = 2.756 = 2.76$

     (b)   The van't Hoff factor is the effective number of particles per mole of solute. The closer the measured i value is to a theoretical integer value, the more ideal the solution. Ion-pairing and other interparticle attractive forces reduce the effective number of particles in solution and reduce the measured value of i. The more concentrated the solution, the greater the ion-pairing and the smaller the measured value of i.

Colloids

13.65   (a)   In the gaseous state, the particles are far apart and intermolecular attractive forces are small. When two gases combine, all terms in Equation 13.1 are essentially zero and the mixture is always homogeneous.

     (b)   The outline of a light beam passing through a colloid is visible, whereas light passing through a true solution is invisible unless collected on a screen. This is the Tyndall effect. To determine whether Faraday's (or anyone's) apparently homogeneous dispersion is a true solution or a colloid, shine a beam of light on it and see if the light is scattered.

13.67   (a) hydrophobic   (b) hydrophilic   (c) hydrophobic

13.69   Colloid particles are stabilized by attractive intermolecular forces with the dispersing medium (solvent) and do not coalesce because of electrostatic repulsions between groups at the surface of the dispersed particles. Colloids can be coagulated by heating (more collisions, greater chance that particles will coalesce); hydrophilic colloids can be coagulated by adding electrolytes, which neutralize surface charges allowing the colloid particles to collide more freely.

Additional Exercises

13.71   The outer periphery of the BHT molecule is mostly hydrocarbon-like groups, such as $-CH_3$. The one $-OH$ group is rather buried inside, and probably does little to enhance solubility in water. Thus, BHT is more likely to be soluble in the nonpolar hydrocarbon hexane, C_6H_{14}, than in polar water.

13.73   Assume that the density of the solution is 1.00 g/mL.

    (a) $4 \text{ ppm } O_2 = \dfrac{4 \text{ mg } O_2}{1 \text{ kg soln}} = \dfrac{4 \times 10^{-3} \text{ g } O_2}{1 \text{ L soln}} \times \dfrac{1 \text{ mol } O_2}{32.0 \text{ g } O_2} = 1.25 \times 10^{-4} = 1 \times 10^{-4} M$

    (b) $C_{O_2} = kP_{O_2}; \; P_{O_2} = C_{O_2}/k = \dfrac{1.25 \times 10^{-4} \text{ mol}}{L} \times \dfrac{L \cdot atm}{1.71 \times 10^{-3} \text{ mol}} = 0.0731 = 0.07 \text{ atm}$

    $0.0731 \text{ atm} \times \dfrac{760 \text{ mm Hg}}{1 \text{ atm}} = 55.6 = 60 \text{ mm Hg}$

13.76 $15 \text{ ppm KBr} = \dfrac{15 \text{ mg KBr}}{1 \text{ kg soln}} = \dfrac{15 \times 10^{-3} \text{ g KBr}}{1 \text{ L soln}} \times \dfrac{1 \text{ mol KBr}}{119.0 \text{ g KBr}} = 1.26 \times 10^{-4} = 1.3 \times 10^{-4} M$

    $12 \text{ ppm KCl} = \dfrac{12 \text{ mg KBr}}{1 \text{ kg soln}} = \dfrac{12 \times 10^{-3} \text{ g KCl}}{1 \text{ L soln}} \times \dfrac{1 \text{ mol KCl}}{74.55 \text{ g KCl}} = 1.61 \times 10^{-4} = 1.6 \times 10^{-4} M$

    A solution that is 12 ppm KCl has the higher molarity of K^+ ions.

13.79   (a) $m = \dfrac{\text{mol Na(s)}}{\text{kg Hg(l)}}; \; 1.0 \text{ cm}^3 \text{ Na(s)} \times \dfrac{0.97 \text{ g}}{1 \text{ cm}^3} \times \dfrac{1 \text{ mol}}{23.0 \text{ g Na}} = 0.0422 = 0.042 \text{ mol Na}$

    $20.0 \text{ cm}^3 \text{ Hg(l)} \times \dfrac{13.6 \text{ g}}{1 \text{ cm}^3} \times \dfrac{1 \text{ kg}}{1000 \text{ g}} = 0.272 \text{ kg Hg(l)}; \; m = \dfrac{0.0422 \text{ mol Na}}{0.272 \text{ kg Hg(l)}}$

    $= 0.155 = 0.16 \; m \text{ Na}$

    (b) $M = \dfrac{\text{mol Na(s)}}{\text{L soln}} = \dfrac{0.0422 \text{ mol Na}}{0.021 \text{ L soln}} = 2.01 = 2.0 \; M \text{ Na}$

    (c)   Clearly, molality and molarity are not the same for this amalgam. Only in the instance that one kg solvent and the mass of one liter solution are nearly equal do the two concentration units have similar values. In this example, one kg Hg has a volume much less than one liter.

13.82   (a)   0.100 m K_2SO_4 is 0.300 m in particles. H_2O is the solvent.

           $\Delta T_f = K_f m = -1.86(0.300) = -0.558$; $T_f = 0.0 - 0.558 = -0.558°C = -0.6°C$

      (b) ΔT_f (nonelectrolyte) $= -1.86(0.100) = -0.186$; $T_f = 0.0 - 0.186 = -0.186°C = -0.2°C$

           T_f (measured) $= i \times T_f$ (nonelectrolyte)

           From Table 13.5, i for 0.100 m $K_2SO_4 = 2.32$

           T_f (measured) $= 2.32(-0.186°C) = -0.432°C = -0.4°C$

13.85   (a) $K_b = \dfrac{\Delta T_b}{m}$; $\Delta T_b = 47.46°C - 46.30°C = 1.16°C$

           $m = \dfrac{\text{mol solute}}{\text{kg } CS_2} = \dfrac{0.250 \text{ mol}}{400.0 \text{ mL } CS_2} \times \dfrac{1 \text{ mL } CS_2}{1.261 \text{ g } CS_2} \times \dfrac{1000 \text{ g}}{1 \text{ kg}} = 0.4956 = 0.496 \ m$

           $K_b = \dfrac{1.16°C}{0.4956 \ m} = 2.34°C/m$

      (b) $m = \dfrac{\Delta T_b}{K_b} = \dfrac{(47.08 - 46.30)°C}{2.34°C/m} = 0.333 = 0.33 \ m$

           $m = \dfrac{\text{mol unknown}}{\text{kg } CS_2}$; $m \times \text{kg } CS_2 = \dfrac{\text{g unknown}}{\mathscr{M} \text{ unknown}}$; $\mathscr{M} = \dfrac{\text{g unknown}}{m \times \text{kg } CS_2}$

           $50.0 \text{ mL } CS_2 \times \dfrac{1.261 \text{ g } CS_2}{1 \text{ mL}} \times \dfrac{1 \text{ kg}}{1000 \text{ g}} = 0.06305 = 0.0631 \text{ kg } CS_2$

           $\mathscr{M} = \dfrac{5.39 \text{ g unknown}}{0.333 \ m \times 0.06305 \text{ kg } CS_2} = 257 = 2.6 \times 10^2 \text{ g/mol}$

Integrative Exercises

13.89   Since these are very dilute solutions, assume that the density of the solution $\approx$ the density of $H_2O \approx 1.0$ g/mL at 25°C. Then, 100 g solution = 100 g H_2O = 0.100 kg H_2O.

      (a) CF_4: $\dfrac{0.0015 \text{ g } CF_4}{0.100 \text{ kg } H_2O} \times \dfrac{1 \text{ mol } CF_4}{88.00 \text{ g } CF_4} = 1.7 \times 10^{-4} \ m$

           $CClF_3$: $\dfrac{0.009 \text{ g } CClF_3}{0.100 \text{ kg } H_2O} \times \dfrac{1 \text{ mol } CClF_3}{104.46 \text{ g } CClF_3} = 8.6 \times 10^{-4} \ m = 9 \times 10^{-4} \ m$

           CCl_2F_2: $\dfrac{0.028 \text{ g } CCl_2F_2}{0.100 \text{ kg } H_2O} \times \dfrac{1 \text{ mol } CCl_2F_2}{120.9 \text{ g } CCl_2F_2} = 2.3 \times 10^{-3} \ m$

           $CHClF_2$: $\dfrac{0.30 \text{ g } CHClF_2}{0.100 \text{ kg } H_2O} \times \dfrac{1 \text{ mol } CHClF_2}{86.47 \text{ g } CHClF_2} = 3.5 \times 10^{-2} \ m$

      (b) $m = \dfrac{\text{mol solute}}{\text{kg solvent}}$; $M = \dfrac{\text{mol solute}}{\text{L solution}}$

Molality and molarity are numerically similar when kilograms solvent and liters solution are nearly equal. This is true when solutions are dilute, so that the density of the solution is essentially the density of the solvent, and when the density of the solvent is nearly 1 g/mL. That is, for dilute aqueous solutions such as the ones in this problem, $M \approx m$.

(c)   Water is a polar solvent; the solubility of solutes increases as their polarity increases. All the fluorocarbons listed have tetrahedral molecular structures. CF_4, a symmetrical tetrahedron, is nonpolar and has the lowest solubility. As more different atoms are bound to the central carbon, the electron density distribution in the molecule becomes less symmetrical and the molecular polarity increases. The most polar fluorocarbon, $CHClF_2$, has the greatest solubility in H_2O. It may act as a weak hydrogen bond acceptor for water.

(d) $S_g = k\, P_g$. Assume $M = m$ for $CHClF_2$. $P_g = 1$ atm

$$k = \frac{S_g}{P_g} = \frac{M}{P_g}; \quad k = \frac{3.5 \times 10^{-2}\, M}{1.0\, \text{atm}} = 3.5 \times 10^{-2}\ \text{mol/L} \cdot \text{atm}$$

This value is greater than the Henry's law constant for $N_2(g)$, because $N_2(g)$ is nonpolar and of lower molecular mass than $CHClF_2$. In fact, the Henry's law constant for nonpolar CF_4, 1.7×10^{-4} mol/L $\cdot$ atm is similar to the value for N_2, 6.8×10^{-4} mol L $\cdot$ atm.

13.93   (a)

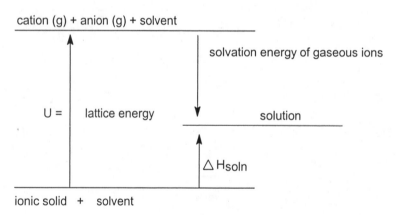

(b)   If the lattice energy (U) of the ionic solid (ion-ion forces) is too large relative to the solvation energy of the gaseous ions (ion-dipole forces), ΔH_{soln} will be too large and positive (endothermic) for solution to occur. This is the case for solutes like NaBr.

Lattice energy is inversely related to the distance between ions, so salts with large cations like $(CH_3)_4N^+$ have smaller lattice energies than salts with simple cations like Na^+. The smaller lattice energy of $(CH_4)_3NBr$ causes it to be more soluble in nonaqueous polar solvents. Also, the $-CH_3$ groups in the large cation are capable of dispersion interactions with the $-CH_3$ (or other nonpolar groups) of the solvent molecules. This produces a more negative solvation energy for the salts with large cations.

Overall, for salts with larger cations, U is smaller (less positive), the solvation energy of the gaseous ions is more negative, and ΔH_{soln} is less endothermic. These salts are more soluble in polar nonaqueous solvents.

13.96   *Plan*. Assume 100 g sample. Calculate empirical formula from mass % data. Calculate molar mass from osmotic pressure. Deduce molecular formula.

$$61.00 \text{ g C} \times \frac{1 \text{ mol C}}{12.01 \text{ g C}} = 5.079 \text{ mol C}; \; 5.079/0.8467 = 6.0$$

$$6.83 \text{ g H} \times \frac{1 \text{ mol H}}{1.008 \text{ g H}} = 6.776 \text{ mol H}; \; 6.776/0.8467 = 8.0$$

$$11.86 \text{ g N} \times \frac{1 \text{ mol N}}{14.007 \text{ g N}} = 0.8467 \text{ mol N}; \; 0.8467/0.8467 = 1$$

$$20.32 \text{ g O} \times \frac{1 \text{ mol O}}{16.00 \text{ g O}} = 1.270 \text{ mol O}; \; 1.270/0.8467 = 1.5$$

Multiplying by 2 to obtain an integer ratio, the empirical formula is $C_{12}H_{16}N_2O_3$. The formula weight is 236.3 g.

$$\pi = M \, RT; \; M = \text{mol/L}; \; \text{mol} = g/\mathcal{M}; \; M = \frac{g}{\mathcal{M} \times L}; \; \pi = \frac{g}{\mathcal{M} \times L} \times RT; \; \mathcal{M} = \frac{g\,RT}{\pi \times L}$$

$$\mathcal{M} = \frac{2.505 \times 10^{-3} \text{ g}}{0.01000 \text{ L}} \times \frac{0.08206 \text{ L} \cdot \text{atm}}{\text{mol} \cdot \text{K}} \times \frac{298 \text{ K}}{19.7 \text{ torr}} \times \frac{760 \text{ torr}}{1 \text{ atm}} = 236 \text{ g/mol}$$

Since the formula weight and molar mass are equal, the empirical and molecular formula is $C_{12}H_{16}N_2O_3$.

14 Chemical Kinetics

Reaction Rates

14.1 (a) *Reaction rate* is the change in the amount of products or reactants in a given amount of time; it is the speed of a chemical reaction.

(b) Rates depend on concentration of reactants, surface area of reactants, temperature and presence of catalyst.

(c) The stoichiometry of the reaction (mole ratios of reactants and products) must be known to relate rate of disappearance of reactants to rate of appearance of products.

14.3 *Analyze/Plan*. Given mol A at a series of times in minutes calculate mol B produced, molarity of A at each time, change in M of A at each 10 min interval, and ΔM A/s. For this reaction, mol B produced equals mol A consumed. M of A or [A] = mol A/0.100 L. The average rate of disappearance of A for each 10 minute interval is

$$\frac{\Delta[A]}{s} = \frac{[A]_0 - [A]_1}{10 \text{ min}} \times \frac{1 \text{ min}}{60 \text{ s}}$$

Solve:

Time(min)	Mol A	(a) Mol B	[A]	Δ [A]	(b) Rate (Δ [A]/s)
0	0.065	0.000	0.65		
10	0.051	0.014	0.51	-0.14	2.3×10^{-4}
20	0.042	0.023	0.42	-0.09	1.5×10^{-4}
30	0.036	0.029	0.36	-0.06	1.0×10^{-4}
40	0.031	0.034	0.31	-0.05	0.8×10^{-4}

(c) $$\frac{\Delta M_B}{\Delta t} = \frac{(0.029 - 0.014) \text{ mol}/0.100 \text{ L}}{(30 - 10) \text{ min}} \times \frac{1 \text{ min}}{60 \text{ s}} = 1.25 \times 10^{-4} = 1.3 \times 10^{-4} \text{ } M/s$$

14.5   *Analyze/Plan.* Follow the logic in Sample Exercise 14.1.   *Solve:*

Time (sec)	Time Interval (sec)	Concentration (M)	Δ M	Rate (M /s)
0		0.0165		
2,000	2,000	0.0110	-0.0055	28 × 10⁻⁷
5,000	3,000	0.00591	-0.0051	17 × 10⁻⁷
8,000	3,000	0.00314	-0.00277	9.23 × 10⁻⁷
12,000	4,000	0.00137	-0.00177	4.43 × 10⁻⁷
15,000	3,000	0.00074	-0.00063	2.1 × 10⁻⁷

14.7   From the slopes of the lines in the figure at right, the rates are -1.2×10^{-6} *M* /s at 5000 s, -5.8×10^{-7} *M* /s at 8000 s.

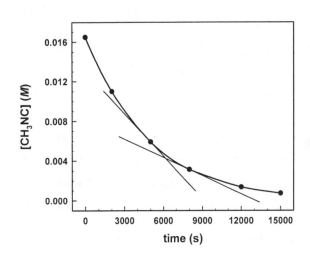

14.9   *Analyze/Plan.* Follow the logic in Sample Exercise 14.3.   *Solve:*

(a) $-\Delta[H_2O_2]/\Delta t = \Delta[H_2]/\Delta t = \Delta[O_2]/\Delta t$

(b) $-\Delta[N_2O]/2\Delta t = \Delta[N_2]/2\Delta t = \Delta[O_2]/\Delta t$
        $-\Delta[N_2O]/\Delta t = \Delta[N_2]/\Delta t = 2\Delta[O_2]/\Delta t$

(c) $-\Delta[N_2]/\Delta t = \Delta[NH_3]/2\Delta t$; $-\Delta[H_2]/3\Delta t = \Delta[NH_3]/2\Delta t$
        $-2\Delta[N_2]/\Delta t = \Delta[NH_3]/\Delta t$; $-\Delta[H_2]/\Delta t = 3\Delta[NH_3]/2\Delta t$

14.11   *Analyze/Plan.* Use Equation 14.4 to relate the rate of disappearance of reactants to the rate of appearance of products. Use this relationship to calculate desired quantities. *Solve:*

(a) $\Delta[H_2O]/2\Delta t = -\Delta[H_2]/2\Delta t = -\Delta[O_2]/\Delta t$

        H_2 is burning, $-\Delta[H_2]/\Delta t = 0.85$ mol/s

        O_2 is consumed, $-\Delta[O_2]/\Delta t = -\Delta[H_2]/2\Delta t = 0.85$ mol/s/2 = 0.43 mol/s

        H_2O is produced, $+\Delta[H_2O]/\Delta t = -\Delta[H_2]/\Delta t = 0.85$ mol/s

(b)   The change in total pressure is the sum of the changes of each partial pressure. NO and Cl_2 are disappearing and NOCl is appearing.

$-\Delta P_{NO} / \Delta t = -23$ torr/min

$-\Delta P_{Cl_2} / \Delta t = \Delta P_{NO} / 2\Delta t = -12$ torr/min

$+\Delta P_{NOCl} / \Delta t = -\Delta P_{NO} / \Delta t = +23$ torr/min

$\Delta P_T / \Delta t = -23$ torr/min $- 12$ torr/min $+ 23$ torr/min $= -12$ torr/min

Rate Laws

14.13   (a)   If [A] doubles, the rate will increase by a factor of four; the rate constant, k, is unchanged. Rate is proportional to $[A]^2$, so when the value of [A] doubles, rate changes by 2^2 or 4. The rate constant, k, is the proportionality constant that does not change (unless the temperature changes).

      (b)   The reaction is second order in A, first order in B, and third order overall.

      (c)   Units of k = $\dfrac{M/s}{M^3} = M^{-2}\,s^{-1}$

14.15   *Analyze/Plan.* Follow the logic in Sample Exercise 14.6. *Solve:*

      (a)   rate = $k[N_2O_5] = 4.82 \times 10^{-3}\,s^{-1}\,[N_2O_5]$

      (b)   rate = $4.82 \times 10^{-3}\,s^{-1}\,(0.0240\,M) = 1.16 \times 10^{-4}\,M/s$

      (c)   rate = $4.82 \times 10^{-3}\,s^{-1}\,(0.0480\,M) = 2.31 \times 10^{-4}\,M/s$

             When the concentration of N_2O_5 doubles, the rate of the reaction doubles.

14.17   *Analyze/Plan.* Write the rate law and rearrange to solve for k. Use the given data to calculate k, including units. *Solve:*

      (a, b)   rate = $k[CH_3Br][OH^-]$; k = $\dfrac{rate}{[CH_3Br][OH^-]}$

           at 298 K, k = $\dfrac{0.0432\,M/s}{(5.0 \times 10^{-3}\,M)(0.050\,M)} = 1.7 \times 10^2\,M^{-1}\,s^{-1}$

      (c)   Since the rate law is first order in $[OH^-]$, if $[OH^-]$ is tripled, the rate triples.

14.19   *Analyze/Plan.* Substitute relative values into the rate law and solve for x. *Solve:*

      (a)   rate = $[A]^x$; $3 = [3]^x$;   x = 1

      (b) $8 = [2]^x$,   x = 3

      (c) $1 = [3]^x$;   x = 0   (The rate does not depend on [A].)

14.21   *Analyze/Plan.* Follow the logic in Sample Exercise 14.6. *Solve:*

      (a)   From the data given, when $[OCl^-]$ doubles, rate doubles. When $[I^-]$ doubles, rate doubles. The reaction is first order in both $[OCl^-]$ and $[I^-]$. rate = $[OCl^-][I^-]$

      (b)   Using the first set of data:

           k = $\dfrac{rate}{[OCl^-][I^-]} = \dfrac{1.36 \times 10^4\,M/s}{(1.5 \times 10^{-3}\,M)(1.5 \times 10^{-3}\,M)} = 6.0444 \times 10^9 = 6.04 \times 10^9\,M^{-1}\,s^{-1}$

(c) $\text{rate} = \dfrac{6.044 \times 10^9}{M \cdot s} \, (1.0 \times 10^{-3}\, M)(5.0 \times 10^{-4}\, M) = 3.02 \times 10^3\, \text{M/s}$

14.23   *Analyze/Plan.* Follow the logic in Sample Exercise 4.6 to deduce the rate law. Rearrange the rate law to solve for k and deduce units. Calculate a k value for each set of concentrations and then average the three values. *Solve*:

(a)   Doubling [NO] while holding [O_2] constant increases the rate by a factor of 4 (experiments 1 and 3). Reducing [O_2] by a factor of 2 while holding [NO] constant reduces the rate by a factor of 2 (experiments 2 and 3). The rate is second order in [NO] and first order in [O_2]. $\text{rate} = k[NO]^2[O_2]$

(b, c) From experiment 1: $k_1 = \dfrac{1.41 \times 10^{-2}\, M/s}{(0.0126\, M)^2 (0.0125\, M)} = 7105 = 7.11 \times 10^3\, M^{-2}\,s^{-1}$

$k_2 = 0.113/(0.0252)^2(0.0250) = 7118 = 7.12 \times 10^3\, M^{-2}\,s^{-1}$
$k_3 = 5.64 \times 10^{-2}/(0.0252)^2(0.125) = 7105 = 7.11 \times 10^3\, M^{-2}\,s^{-1}$
$k_{avg} = (7105 + 7118 + 7105)/3 = 7109 = 7.11 \times 10^3\, M^{-2}\,s^{-1}$

14.25   *Analyze/Plan.* Follow the logic in Sample Exercise 4.6 to deduce the rate law. Rearrange the rate law to solve for k and deduce units. Calculate a k value for each set of concentrations and then average the three values. *Solve*:

(a)   Increasing [NO] by a factor of 2.5 while holding [Br_2] constant (experiments 1 and 2) increases the rate by a factor 6.25 or $(2.5)^2$. Increasing [Br_2] by a factor of 2.5 while holding [NO] constant increases the rate by a factor of 2.5. The rate law for the appearance of NOBr is: $\text{rate} = \Delta[NOBr]/\Delta t = k[NO]^2[Br_2]$.

(b)   From experiment 1: $k_1 = \dfrac{24\, M/s}{(0.10\, M)^2 (0.20\, M)} = 1.20 \times 10^4 = 1.2 \times 10^4\, M^{-2}\,s^{-1}$

$k_2 = 150/(0.25)^2(0.20) = 1.20 \times 10^4 = 1.2 \times 10^4\, M^{-2}\,s^{-1}$

$k_3 = 60/(0.10)^2(0.50) = 1.20 \times 10^4 = 1.2 \times 10^4\, M^{-2}\,s^{-1}$

$k_4 = 735/(0.35)^2(0.50) = 1.2 \times 10^4 = 1.2 \times 10^4\, M^{-2}\,s^{-1}$

$k_{avg} = (1.2 \times 10^4 + 1.2 \times 10^4 + 1.2 \times 10^4 + 1.2 \times 10^4)/4 = 1.2 \times 10^4\, M^{-2}\,s^{-1}$

(c)   Use the reaction stoichiometry and Equation 14.4 to relate the designated rates. $\Delta[NOBr]/2\Delta t = -\Delta[Br_2]/\Delta t$; the rate of disappearance of Br_2 is half the rate of appearance of NOBr.

(d)   Note that the data is given in terms of appearance of NOBr.

$\dfrac{-\Delta[Br_2]}{\Delta t} = \dfrac{k[NO]^2[Br_2]}{2} = \dfrac{1.2 \times 10^4}{2\, M^2\,s} \times (0.075\, M)^2 \times (0.25\, M) = 8.4\, M/s$

Change of Concentration with Time

14.27 (a) $[A]_0$ is the molar concentration of reactant A at time zero, the initial concentration of A. $[A]_t$ is the molar concentration of reactant A at time t. $t_{1/2}$ is the time required to reduce $[A]_0$ by a factor of 2, the time when $[A]_t = [A]_0/2$. k is the rate constant for a particular reaction. k is independent of reactant concentration but varies with reaction temperature.

       (b)   A graph of ln[A] vs time yields a straight line for a first-order reaction.

14.29   *Analyze/Plan.* The half-life of a first-order reaction depends only on the rate constant, $t_{1/2} = 0.693/k$. Use this relationship to calculate k for a given $t_{1/2}$, and, at a different temperature, $t_{1/2}$ given k. *Solve*:

       (a) $t_{1/2} = 2.3 \times 10^5$ s; $t_{1/2} = 0.693/k$, $k = 0.693/t_{1/2}$

             $k = 0.693/2.3 \times 10^5$ s $= 3.0 \times 10^{-6}$ s^{-1}

       (b) $k = 2.2 \times 10^{-5}$ s^{-1}. $t_{1/2} = 0.693/2.2 \times 10^{-5}$ s^{-1} $= 3.15 \times 10^4 = 3.2 \times 10^4$ s

14.31   *Analyze/Plan.* Follow the logic in Sample Exercise 14.7. In this reaction, pressure is a measure of concentration. In (a) we are given k, $[A]_0$, t and asked to find $[A]_t$, using Equation 14.13, the integrated form of the first-order rate law. In (b), $[A_t] = 0.1[A_0]$, find t. *Solve*:

       (a) $\ln P_t = -kt + \ln P_0$; $P_0 = 375$ torr; $t = 65$ s

             $\ln P_{65} = -4.5 \times 10^{-2}$ s$^{-1}(65) + \ln(375) = -2.925 + 5.927 = 3.002$

             $P_{65} = 20.12 = 20$ torr

       (b) $P_t = 0.10\ P_0$; $\ln(P_t/P_0) = -kt$

             $\ln(0.10\ P_0/P_0) = -kt$, $\ln(0.10) = -kt$; $-\ln(0.10)/k = t$

             $t = -(-2.303)/4.5 \times 10^{-2}$ s^{-1} $= 51.2 = 51$ s

      Check. From part (a), the pressure at 65 s is 20 torr, $P_t \sim 0.05\ P_0$. In part (b) we calculate the time where $P_t = 0.10\ P_0$ to be 51 s. This time should be smaller than 65 s, and it is. Data and results in the two parts are consistent.

14.33   *Analyze/Plan.* Given reaction order, various values for t, P_t, find the rate constant for the reaction at this temperature. For a first-order reaction, a graph of ln P vs t is linear with a slope of -k. *Solve*:

t(s)	$P_{SO_2Cl_2}$	$\ln P_{SO_2Cl_2}$
0	1.000	0
2500	0.947	-0.0545
5000	0.895	-0.111
7500	0.848	-0.165
10000	0.803	-0.219

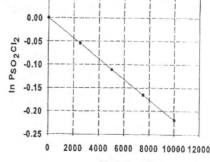

Graph $\ln P_{SO_2Cl_2}$ vs. time. (Pressure is a satisfactory unit for a gas, since the concentration in moles/liter is proportional to P.) The graph is linear with slope -2.19×10^{-5} s^{-1} as shown on the figure. The rate constant $k = -$slope $= 2.19 \times 10^{-5}$ s^{-1}.

14.35 *Analyze/Plan.* Given: mol A, t. Change mol to *M* at various times. Make both first- and second-order plots to see which is linear. *Solve:*

(a)

time(min)	mol A	[A] (*M*)	ln[A]	1/mol A
0	0.065	0.65	-0.43	1.5
10	0.051	0.51	-0.67	2.0
20	0.042	0.42	-0.87	2.4
30	0.036	0.36	-1.02	2.8
40	0.031	0.31	-1.17	3.2

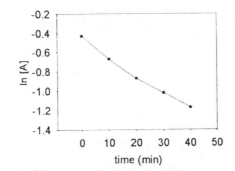 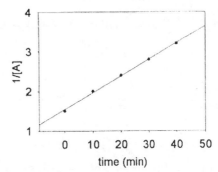

The plot of 1/[A] vs time is linear, so the reaction is second-order in [A].

(b) For a second-order reaction, a plot of 1/[A] vs. t is linear with slope k.

$k = $ slope $= (3.2 - 2.0)$ M^{-1} / 30 min $= 0.040$ M^{-1} min^{-1}

(The best fit to the line yields slope $= 0.042$ $M^{-1}min^{-1}$.)

(c) $t_{1/2} = 1/k[A]_0 = 1/(0.040$ M^{-1} $min^{-1})(0.65$ $M) = 38.46 = 38$ min

(Using the "best-fit" slope, $t_{1/2} = 37$ min.)

14.37 Analyze/Plan. Follow the logic in Solution 14.35. Make both first and second order plots to see which is linear. *Solve:*

(a)

time(s)	[NO$_2$](*M*)	ln[NO$_2$]	1/[NO$_2$]
0.0	0.100	-2.303	10.0
5.0	0.017	-4.08	59
10.0	0.0090	-4.71	110
15.0	0.0062	-5.08	160
20.0	0.0047	-5.36	210

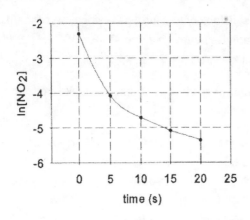 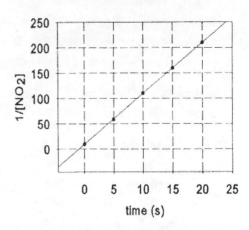

The plot of $1/[NO_2]$ vs time is linear, so the reaction is second order in NO_2.

(b)   The slope of the line is (210 - 59) M^{-1} / 15.0 s = 10.07 = 10 $M^{-1}s^{-1}$ = k.
(The slope of the best-fit line is 10.02 = 10 $M^{-1}s^{-1}$.)

Temperature and Rate

14.39   (a)   The central idea of the *collision model* is that molecules must collide to react.

        (b)   The energy of the collision and the orientation of the molecules when they collide determine whether a reaction will occur.

        (c)   According to the Kinetic Molecular Theory (Chapter 10), the higher the temperature, the greater the speed and kinetic energy of the molecules. Therefore, at a higher temperature, there are more total collisions and each collision is more energetic.

14.41   *Analyze/Plan.* Given the temperature and energy, use Equation 14.18 to calculate the fraction of Ar atoms that have at least this energy. *Solve*:

$f = e^{-E_a/RT}$ $E_a = 12.5$ kJ/mol $= 1.25 \times 10^4$ J/mol; T = 400 K (127°C)

$$-E_a/RT = -\frac{1.25 \times 10^4 \text{ J/mol}}{400 \text{ K}} \times \frac{\text{mol} \cdot \text{K}}{8.314 \text{ J}} = -3.7587 = -3.76$$

$f = e^{-3.7587} = 2.33 \times 10^{-2}$

At 400 K, approximately 1 out of 43 molecules has this kinetic energy.

14.43 *Analyze/Plan.* Use the definitions of activation energy ($E_{max} - E_{react}$) and ΔE ($E_{prod} - E_{react}$) to sketch the graphs and calculate E_a for the reverse reaction. *Solve:*

(a)

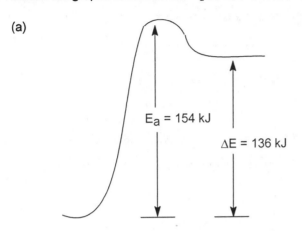

$E_a = 154$ kJ

$\Delta E = 136$ kJ

(b) E_a(reverse) = 18 kJ/mol

14.45 Assuming all collision factors (A) to be the same, reaction rate depends only on E_a; it is independent of ΔE. Based on the magnitude of E_a, reaction (b) is fastest and reaction (c) is slowest.

14.47 *Analyze/Plan.* Given k_1, at T_1, calculate k_2 at T_2. Change T to Kelvins, then use the Ahrrenius equation [14.21] to calculate k_2. *Solve:*

$T_1 = 20°C + 273 = 293$ K; $T_2 = 60°C + 273 = 333$ K; $k_1 = 2.75 \times 10^{-2} s^{-1}$

(a) $\ln\left(\dfrac{k_1}{k_2}\right) = \dfrac{E_a}{R}\left(\dfrac{1}{333} - \dfrac{1}{293}\right) = \dfrac{75.5 \times 10^3 \text{ J/mol}}{8.314 \text{ J/mol}}(-4.100 \times 10^{-4})$

$\ln(k_1/k_2) = -3.7229 = -3.72$; $k_1/k_2 = 0.0242 = 0.024$; $k_2 = \dfrac{0.0275 \text{ s}^{-1}}{0.0242} = 1.1 \text{ s}^{-1}$

(b) $\ln\left(\dfrac{k_1}{k_2}\right) = \dfrac{105 \times 10^3 \text{ J/mol}}{8.314 \text{ J/mol}}\left(\dfrac{1}{333} - \dfrac{1}{293}\right) = -5.1776 = -5.18$

$k_1/k_2 = 5.642 \times 10^{-3} = 5.6 \times 10^{-3}$; $k_2 = \dfrac{0.0275 \text{ s}^{-1}}{5.642 \times 10^{-3}} = 4.9 \text{ s}^{-1}$

14.49 *Analyze/Plan.* Follow the logic in Sample Exercise 14.11. *Solve:*

k	ln k	T(K)	1/T($\times 10^3$)
0.0521	-2.955	288	3.47
0.101	-2.293	298	3.36
0.184	-1.693	308	3.25
0.332	-1.103	318	3.14

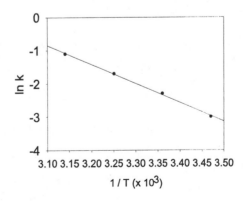

The slope, -5.71×10^3, equals $-E_a/R$. Thus,
$E_a = 5.71 \times 10^3 \times 8.314$ J/mol = 47.5 kJ/mol.

14.51   *Analyze/Plan.* Given E_a, find the ratio of rates for a reaction at two temperatures. Assuming initial concentrations are the same at the two temperatures, the ratio of rates will be the ratio of rate constants, k_1/k_2. Use Equation [14.21] to calculate this ratio. *Solve:*

$T_1 = 50°C + 273 = 323$ K; $T_2 = 0°C + 273 = 273$ K

$$\ln\left(\frac{k_1}{k_2}\right) = \frac{E_a}{R}\left[\frac{1}{T_2} - \frac{1}{T_1}\right] = \frac{65.7 \text{ kJ/mol}}{8.314 \text{ J/mol}} \times \frac{1000 \text{ J}}{1 \text{ kJ}}\left[\frac{1}{273} - \frac{1}{323}\right]$$

$\ln(k_1/k_2) = 7.902 \times 10^3\,(5.670 \times 10^{-4}) = 4.481 = 4.48$; $k_1/k_2 = 88.3 = 88$

The reaction will occur 88 times faster at 50°C, assuming equal initial concentrations.

Reaction Mechanisms

14.53   (a)   An *elementary step* is a process that occurs in a single event; the order is given by the coefficients in the balanced equation for the step.

(b)   A *unimolecular* elementary step involves only one reactant molecule; the activated complex is derived from a single molecule. A *bimolecular* elementary step involves two reactant molecules in the activated complex and the overall process.

(c)   A *reaction mechanism* is a series of elementary steps that describe how an overall reaction occurs and explain the experimentally determined rate law.

14.55   *Analyze/Plan.* Elementary processes occur as a single step, so the molecularity is determined by the number of reactant molecules; the rate law reflects reactant stoichiometry. *Solve:*

(a)   unimolecular, rate = $k[Cl_2]$

(b)   bimolecular, rate = $k[OCl^-][H_2O]$

(c)   bimolecular, rate = $k[NO][Cl_2]$

14.57   This is the profile of a two-step mechanism, A → B and B → C. There is one intermediate, B. Because there are two energy maxima, there are two transition states. The B → C step is faster, because its activation energy is smaller. The reaction is exothermic because the energy of the products is lower than the energy of the reactants.

14.59   (a) $H_2(g) + ICl(g) \rightarrow HI(g) + HCl(g)$

$HI(g) + ICl(g) \rightarrow I_2(g) + HCl(g)$

$H_2(g) + 2ICl(g) \rightarrow I_2(g) + 2HCl(g)$

(b)   Intermediates are produced and consumed during reaction. HI is the intermediate.

(c)   Follow the logic in Sample Exercise 14.13.
First step: rate = $k[H_2][ICl]$
Second step: rate = $k[HI][ICl]$

(d)   The slow step determines the rate law for the overall reaction. If the first step is slow, the observed rate law is: rate = $k[H_2][HCl]$.

14.61   *Analyze/Plan.* Given a proposed mechanism and an observed rate law, determine which step is rate determining. *Solve*:

     (a)   If the first step is slow, the observed rate law is the rate law for this step.
               rate = $k[NO][Cl_2]$

     (b)   Since the observed rate law is second-order in [NO], the second step must be slow relative to the first step; the second step is rate determining.

Catalysis

14.63   (a)   A catalyst increases the rate of reaction by decreasing the activation energy, E_a, or increasing the frequency factor A. Lowering the activation energy is more common and more dramatic.

     (b)   A *homogeneous catalyst* is in the same phase as the reactants; a *heterogeneous catalyst* is in a different phase and is usually a solid.

14.65   (a) $2[NO_2(g) + SO_2(g) \rightarrow NO(g) + SO_3(g)]$
                 $2NO(g) + O_2(g) \rightarrow 2NO_2(g)$
              _____
               $2SO_2(g) + O_2(g) \rightarrow 2SO_3(g)$

     (b) $NO_2(g)$ is a catalyst because it is consumed and then reproduced in the reaction sequence. ($NO(g)$ is an intermediate because it is produced and then consumed.)

     (c)   Since NO_2 is in the same state as the other reactants, this is homogeneous catalysis.

14.67   Use of chemically stable supports such as alumina and silica makes it possible to obtain very large surface areas per unit mass of the precious metal catalyst. This is so because the metal can be deposited in a very thin, even monomolecular, layer on the surface of the support.

14.69   As illustrated in Figure 14.21, the two C–H bonds that exist on each carbon of the ethylene molecule before adsorption are retained in the process in which a D atom is added to each C (assuming we use D_2 rather than H_2). To put two deuteriums on a single carbon, it is necessary that one of the already existing C–H bonds in ethylene be broken while the molecule is adsorbed, so the H atom moves off as an adsorbed atom, and is replaced by a D. This requires a larger activation energy than simply adsorbing C_2H_4 and adding one D atom to each carbon.

14.71 (a)   Living organisms operate efficiently in a very narrow temperature range; heating to increase reaction rate is not an option. Therefore, the role of enzymes as homogeneous catalysts that speed up desirable reactions without heating and undesirable side-effects is crucial for biological systems.

      (b)   *catalase*: $2H_2O_2 \rightarrow 2H_2O + O_2$; *nitrogenase*: $N_2 \rightarrow 2NH_3$ (nitrogen fixation)

14.73 *Analyze/Plan.* Let k = the rate constant for the uncatalyzed reaction,

                k_c = the rate constant for the catalyzed reaction

According to Equation [14.22], $\ln k = -E_a/RT + \ln A$

Subtracting $\ln k$ from $\ln k_c$,

$$\ln k_c - \ln k = -\left[\frac{55\,kJ/mol}{RT} + \ln A\right] - \left[-\frac{95\,kJ/mol}{RT} + \ln A\right]. \quad Solve:$$

      (a)   RT = 8.314 J/K•mol × 298 K × 1 kJ/1000 J = 2.478 kJ/mol; $\ln A$ is the same for both reactions.

$$\ln (k_c/k) = \frac{95\,kJ/mol - 55\,kJ/mol}{2.478\,kJ/mol}; \quad k_c/k = 1.0 \times 10^7$$

The catalyzed reaction is approximately 10,000,000 (ten million) times faster at 25°C.

      (b)   RT = 8.314 J/K•mol × 398 K × 1 kJ/1000 J = 3.309 kJ/mol

$$\ln (k_c/k) = \frac{40\,kJ/mol}{3.309\,kJ/mol}; \quad k_c/k = 1.8 \times 10^5$$

The catalyzed reaction is 180,000 times faster at 125°C.

Additional Exercises

14.75   rate $= \dfrac{-\Delta[H_2S]}{\Delta t} = \dfrac{\Delta[Cl^-]}{2\Delta t} = k[H_2S][Cl_2]$

$$\frac{-\Delta[H_2S]}{\Delta t} = (3.5 \times 10^{-2}\ M^{-1}s^{-1})(1.6 \times 10^{-4}\ M)(0.070\ M) = 3.92 \times 10^{-7} = 3.9 \times 10^{-7}\ M/s$$

$$\frac{\Delta[Cl^-]}{\Delta t} = \frac{2\Delta[H_2S]}{\Delta t} = 2(3.92 \times 10^{-7}\ M/s) = 7.8 \times 10^{-7}\ M/s$$

14.78 (a)   The rate increases by a factor of nine when $[C_2O_4^{2-}]$ triples (compare experiments 1 and 2). The rate doubles when $[HgCl_2]$ doubles (compare experiments 2 and 3). The rate law is apparently: rate $= k[HgCl_2][C_2O_4^{2-}]^2$

      (b) $k = \dfrac{rate}{[HgCl_2][C_2O_4^{2-}]^2}$ Using the data for Experiment 1,

$$k = \frac{(3.2 \times 10^{-5}\ M/s)}{[0.164\ M][0.15\ M]^2} = 8.672 \times 10^{-3} = 8.7 \times 10^{-3}\ M^{-2}\,s^{-1}$$

(c)   rate = $(8.672 \times 10^{-3} \, M^{-2}s^{-1})(0.12 \, M)(0.10 \, M)^2 = 1.0 \times 10^{-5} \, M/s$

14.80   (a) $k = (8.56 \times 10^{-5} \, M/s)/(0.200 \, M) = 4.28 \times 10^{-4} \, s^{-1}$

        (b)   ln [urea] = $-(4.28 \times 10^{-4}s^{-1} \times 5.00 \times 10^3 \, s) + $ ln (0.500)

                  ln [urea] = $-2.14 - 0.693 = -2.833 = -2.83$;   [urea] = $0.0588 = 0.059 \, M$

        (c) $t_{1/2} = 0.693/k = 0.693/4.28 \times 10^{-4} \, s^{-1} = 1.62 \times 10^3 \, s$

14.84   **ln k**   **1/T**

        -24.17 3.33×10^{-3}

        -20.72 3.13×10^{-3}

        -17.32 2.94×10^{-3}

        -15.24 2.82×10^{-3}

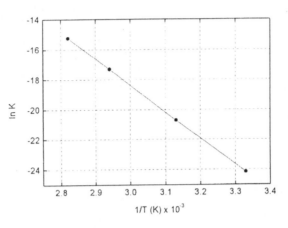

The calculated slope is -1.751×10^4.
The activation energy E_a, equals
$-$ (slope) $\times$ (8.314 J/mol). Thus,
$E_a = 1.8 \times 10^4 \, (8.314) = 1.5 \times 10^5$ J/mol
$= 1.5 \times 10^2$ kJ/mol. (The best-fit slope is
$-1.76 \times 10^4 = -1.8 \times 10^4$ and the value
of E_a is 1.5×10^2 kJ/mol.)

14.87   (a)

$$Cl_2(g) \rightleftharpoons 2Cl(g)$$
$$Cl(g) + CHCl_3(g) \rightarrow HCl(g) + CCl_3(g)$$
$$Cl(g) + CCl_3(g) \rightarrow CCl_4(g)$$

$$Cl_2(g) + 2Cl(g) + CHCl_3(g) + CCl_3(g) \rightarrow 2Cl(g) + HCl(g) + CCl_3(g) + CCl_4(g)$$
$$Cl_2(g) + CHCl_3(g) \rightarrow HCl(g) + CCl_4(g)$$

        (b) $Cl(g)$, $CCl_3(g)$

        (c)   Step 1 - unimolecular, Step 2 - bimolecular, Step 3 - bimolecular

        (d)   Step 2, the slow step, is rate determining.

        (e)   If Step 2 is rate determining, rate = $k_2[CHCl_3][Cl]$. Cl is an intermediate formed in
              Step 1, an equilibrium. By definition, the rates of the forward and reverse processes
              are equal; $k_1 [Cl_2] = k_{-1} [Cl]^2$. Solving for [Cl] in terms of $[Cl_2]$,

$$[Cl]^2 = \frac{k_1}{k_{-1}} [Cl_2]; \;\; [Cl] = \left(\frac{k_1}{k_{-1}} [Cl_2] \right)^{1/2}$$

            Substituting into the overall rate law

$$\text{rate} = k_2 \left(\frac{k_1}{k_{-1}} \right)^{1/2} [CHCl_3][Cl_2]^{1/2} = k[CHCl_3][Cl_2]^{1/2} \quad \text{(The overall order is 3/2.)}$$

14.89   Enzyme: carbonic anhydrase; substrate: carbonic acid (H_2CO_3); turnover number:
         1×10^7 molecules/s.

Integrative Exercises

14.91   *Analyze/Plan.* $2N_2O_5 \rightarrow 4NO_2 + O_2$ rate $= k[N_2O_5] = 1.0 \times 10^{-5} \text{ s}^{-1} [N_2O_5]$
Use the integrated rate law for a first-order reaction, Equation 14.13, to calculate $k[N_2O_5]$ at 20.0 hr. Build a stoichiometry table to determine mol O_2 produced in 20.0 hr. Assuming that $O_2(g)$ is insoluble in chloroform, calculate the pressure of O_2 in the 10.0 L container. *Solve:*

$$20.0 \text{ hr} \times \frac{60 \text{ min}}{1 \text{ hr}} \times \frac{60 \text{ s}}{1 \text{ min}} = 7.20 \times 10^4 \text{ s}; \ [N_2O_5]_0 = 0.600 \ M$$

$$\ln[A]_t - \ln[A]_0 = -kt; \ \ln[N_2O_5]_t = -kt + \ln[N_2O_5]_0$$

$$\ln[N_2O_5]_t = -1.0 \times 10^{-5} \text{ s}^{-1} (7.20 \times 10^4 \text{ s}) + \ln(0.600) = -0.720 - 0.511 = -1.231$$

$$[N_2O_5]_t = e^{-1.231} = 0.292 \ M$$

N_2O_5 was present initially as 1.00 L of 0.600 *M* solution.

mol $N_2O_5 = M \times L = 0.600$ mol N_2O_5 initial, 0.292 mol N_2O_5 at 20.0 hr

	$2N_2O_5$	$\rightarrow$	$4NO_2$	+	O_2
t = 0	0.600 mol		0		0
change	-0.308 mol		0.616 mol		0.154 mol
t = 20 hr	0.292 mol		0.616 mol		0.154 mol

[Note that the reaction stoichiometry is applied to the 'change' line.]

$PV = nRT; \ P = nRT/V; \ V = 10.0 \text{ L}, \ T = 45°C = 318 \text{ K}, \ n = 0.154 \text{ mol}$

$$P = 0.154 \text{ mol} \times \frac{318 \text{ K}}{10.0 \text{ L}} \times \frac{0.08206 \text{ L} \cdot \text{atm}}{\text{mol} \cdot \text{K}} = 0.402 \text{ atm}$$

14.93   (a)   Use an apparatus such as the one pictured in Figure 10.3 (c) (an open-end manometer), a clock, a rule and a constant temperature bath. Since $P = (n/V)RT$, $\Delta P/\Delta t$ at constant temperature is an acceptable measure of reaction rate.

         Load the flask with HCl(aq) and read the height of the Hg in both arms of the manometer. Quickly add Zn(s) to the flask and record time = 0 when the Zn(s) contacts the acid. Record the height of the Hg in one arm of the manometer at convenient time intervals such as 5 sec. (The decrease in the short arm will be the same as the increase in the tall arm). Calculate the pressure of $H_2(g)$ at each time.

     (b)   Keep the amount of Zn(s) constant and vary the concentration of HCl(aq) to determine the reaction order for H^+ and Cl^-. Keep the concentration of HCl(aq) constant and vary the amount of Zn(s) to determine the order for Zn(s). Combine this information to write the rate law.

     (c) $-\Delta[H^+]/2\Delta t = \Delta[H_2]/\Delta t; \ -\Delta[H^+]/\Delta t = 2\Delta[H_2]/\Delta t$

         $[H_2] = $ mol H_2/L $H_2 = n/V; \ [H_2] = P$ (in atm)$/RT$

         Then, the rate of disappearance of H^+ is twice the rate of appearance of $H_2(g)$.

(d)   By changing the temperature of the constant temperature bath, measure the rate data at several (at least three) temperatures and calculate the rate constant k at these temperatures. Plot ln k vs 1/T. The slope of the line is $-E_a/R$ and E_a = -slope (R).

(e)   Measure rate data at constant temperature, HCl concentration and mass of Zn(s), varying only the form of the Zn(s). Compare the rate of reaction for metal strips and granules.

14.96   In the lock and key model of enzyme action, the active site is the specific location in the enzyme where reaction takes place. The precise geometry (size and shape) of the active site both accommodates and activates the substrate (reactant). Proteins are large biopolymers, with the same structural flexibility as synthetic polymers (Chapter 12). The three-dimensional shape of the protein in solution, including the geometry of the active site, is determined by many intermolecular forces of varying strengths.

Changes in temperature change the kinetic energy of the various groups on the enzyme and their tendency to form intermolecular associations or break free from them. Thus, changing the temperature changes the overall shape of the protein and specifically the shape of the active site. At the operating temperature of the enzyme, the competition between kinetic energy driving groups apart and intermolecular attraction pulling them together forms an active site that is optimum for a specific substrate. At temperatures above the temperature of maximum activity, sufficient kinetic energy has been imparted so that the forces driving groups apart win the competition, and the three-dimensional structure of the enzyme is destroyed. This is the process of *denaturation*. The activity of the enzyme is destroyed because the active site has collapsed. The protein or enzyme is denatured, because it is no longer capable of its "natural" activity.

15 Chemical Equilibrium

The Concept of Equilibrium; Equilibrium - Constant Expressions

15.1   Yes. The first box is pure reactant A. As the reaction proceeds, some A changes to B. In the fourth and fifth boxes, the relative amounts (concentrations) of A and B are constant. Although the reaction is ongoing the rates of A → B and B → A are equal, and the relative amounts of A and B are constant.

15.3   *Analyze/Plan.* Given the forward and reverse rate constants, calculate the equilibrium constant using Equation [15.5]. At equilibrium, the rates of the forward and reverse reactions are equal. Write the rate laws for the forward and reverse reactions and use their equality to answer part (b). *Solve*:

    (a) $K_{eq} = \dfrac{k_f}{k_r}$, Equation [15.5]; $K_{eq} = \dfrac{4.2 \times 10^{-3}\,\text{s}^{-1}}{1.5 \times 10^{-1}\,\text{s}^{-1}} = 2.8 \times 10^{-2}$

    (b) $\text{rate}_f = \text{rate}_r$; $k_f[A] = k_r[B]$

        Since $k_f < k_r$, in order for the two rates to be equal, [A] must be greater than [B].

15.5   (a)   The *law of mass action* expresses the relationship between the concentrations of reactants and products at equilibrium for any reaction. The law of mass action is a generic equilibrium expression.

        $K_{eq} = \dfrac{P_{NOBr_2}}{P_{NO} \times P_{Br_2}}$

    (b)   The *equilibrium-constant expression* is an algebraic equation where the variables are the equilibrium concentrations of the reactants and products for a specific chemical reaction. The *equilibrium constant* is a number; it is the ratio calculated from the equilibrium expression for a particular chemical reaction. For any reaction, there are an infinite number of sets of equilibrium concentrations, depending on initial concentrations, but there is only one equilibrium constant.

    (c)   Introduce a known quantity of $NOBr_2(g)$ into a vessel of known volume at constant (known) temperature. After equilibrium has been established, measure the total pressure in the flask. Using an equilibrium table, such as the one in Sample Exercise 15.8, calculate equilibrium pressures and concentrations of $NO(g)$, $Br_2(g)$ and $NOBr_2(g)$ and calculate K_{eq}.

15.7 *Analyze/Plan.* Follow the logic in Sample Exercises 15.1 and 15.5. *Solve:*

(a) $K_{eq} = \dfrac{P_{N_2O} \times P_{NO_2}}{P_{NO}^3}$ (b) $K_{eq} = \dfrac{P_{CS_2} \times P_{H_2}^4}{P_{CH_4} \times P_{H_2S}^2}$

(c) $K_{eq} = \dfrac{P_{CO}^4}{P_{Ni(CO)_4}}$ (d) $K_{eq} = \dfrac{[H^+][F^-]}{[HF]}$ e) $K_{eq} = \dfrac{[Ag^+]^2}{[Zn^{2+}]}$

homogeneous: (a), (b), (d);   heterogeneous: (c), (e)

15.9 *Analyze/Plan.* Follow the logic in Sample exercise 15.2. *Solve:*

(a) mostly reactants ($K_{eq} \ll 1$)

(b) mostly products ($K_{eq} \gg 1$)

15.11 *Analyze/Plan.* Follow the logic in Sample Exercise 15.3. *Solve:*

(a) $2SO_2(g) + O_2(g) \rightleftharpoons 2SO_3(g)$ is the reverse of the reaction given.

$K_{eq}' = (K_{eq})^{-1} = 1/2.4 \times 10^{-3} = 4.2 \times 10^2$

(b) Since $K_{eq} < 1$ (when SO_3 is the reactant) and $K_{eq}' > 1$ (when SO_3 is the product), the equilibrium favors SO_3 at this temperature.

15.13 *Analyze/Plan.* Follow the logic in Sample Exercise 15.3. *Solve:*

(a) $K_{eq}' = 1/K_{eq} = 1/0.112 = 8.93$

(b) $K_{eq}' = 1/K_{eq}^2 = (0.112)^2 = 1.25 \times 10^{-2}$

(c) $K_{eq}' = 1/K_{eq}^2 = 1/(0.112)^2 = 79.7$

15.15 *Analyze/Plan.* Follow the logic in Sample Exercise 15.3. *Solve:*

(a) $K_{eq}' = (K_{eq})^{1/2} = (1.1 \times 10^{-2})^{1/2} = 0.1049 = 0.10$

(b) $K_{eq}' = (K_{eq})^2 = (1.1 \times 10^{-2})^2 = 1.2 \times 10^{-4}$

(c) $K_{eq}' = 1/(K_{eq})^2 = 1/(1.1 \times 10^{-2})^2 = 8.3 \times 10^3$

15.17 *Analyze/Plan.* Follow the logic in Sample Exercise 15.5. *Solve:*

(a) $K_{eq} = \dfrac{[Hg]^4 P_{O_2}}{[Hg_2O]^2}$

(b) The molar concentration, the ratio of moles of a substance to volume occupied by the substance, is a constant for pure solids and liquids.

(c) $K_{eq} = P_{O_2}$

Calculating Equilibrium Constants

15.19 *Analyze/Plan.* Follow the logic in Sample Exercise 15.7. *Solve*:

$$K_{eq} = \frac{P_{H_2} \times P_{I_2}}{P_{HI}^2} = \frac{(0.0274)(0.0274)}{(0.202)^2} = 1.84 \times 10^{-2}$$

15.21 *Analyze/Plan.* Follow the logic in Sample Exercise 15.7. *Solve*:

$$2NO(g) + Cl_2(g) \rightleftharpoons 2NOCl(g)$$

$$K_{eq} = \frac{P_{NOCl}^2}{P_{NO}^2 \times P_{Cl_2}} = \frac{(0.28)^2}{(0.095)^2(0.171)} = 50.80 = 51$$

15.23 *Analyze/Plan.* Follow the logic in Sample Exercise 15.8, using pressure rather than concentration as a measure of amount. Change mol of substances present initially to pressures and construct an equilibrium table. *Solve*:

(a) $P = nRT/V$; $P_{NO} = 0.10$ mol $\times \dfrac{300\ K}{1.0\ L} \times \dfrac{0.08206\ L\bullet atm}{K\bullet mol} = 2.462 = 2.5$ atm

$P_{H_2} = 0.050$ mol $\times \dfrac{300\ K}{1.0\ L} \times \dfrac{0.08206\ L\bullet atm}{K\bullet mol} = 1.231 = 1.2$ atm;

$P_{H_2O} = P_{NO} = 2.462 = 2.5$ atm

First calculate the change in P_{NO}, 2.462 - 1.53 = 0.932 = 0.9 atm. From the stoichiometry of the reaction, calculate the change in the other pressures. Finally, calculate the equilibrium pressures.

	2NO(g)	+	2H₂(g)	⇌	N₂(g)	+	2H₂O(g)
initial	2.462 atm		1.231 atm		0 atm		2.462 atm
change	-0.932 atm		-0.932 atm		+0.466 atm		+0.932 atm
equil.	1.53 atm		0.299 atm		0.466 atm		3.394 atm

Strictly speaking, the change in P_{NO} has one decimal place and thus one sig fig. This limits equilibrium pressures to one decimal place, and K_{eq} to one sig fig. We compute the extra figures and then round.

(b) $K_{eq} = \dfrac{P_{N_2} \times P_{H_2O}^2}{P_{NO}^2 \times P_{H_2}^2} = \dfrac{(0.466)(3.394)^2}{(1.53)^2(0.299)^2} = \dfrac{(0.5)(3.4)^2}{(1.5)^2(0.3)^2} = 25.65 = 3 \times 10^1$

15.25 *Analyze/Plan.* Follow the logic in Sample Exercise 15.8 and Solution 15.23. *Solve*:

(a) $P = nRT/V$; $P_{CO_2} = 0.2000$ mol $\times \dfrac{500\ K}{2.000L} \times \dfrac{0.08206\ L\bullet atm}{K\bullet mol} = 4.1030 = 4.10$ atm

$P_{H_2} = 0.1000$ mol $\times \dfrac{500\ K}{2.000L} \times \dfrac{0.08206\ L\bullet atm}{K\bullet mol} = 2.0515 = 2.05$ atm

$P_{H_2O} = 0.1600 \times \dfrac{500\ K}{2.000L} \times \dfrac{0.08206\ L\bullet atm}{K\bullet mol} = 3.2824 = 3.28$ atm

The change in P_{H_2O} is 3.51 - 3.28 = 0.2276 = 0.23 atm. From the reaction stoichiometry, calculate the change in the other pressures, and the equilibrium pressures.

	$CO_2(g)$ +	$H_2(g)$	$\rightleftharpoons$	$CO(g)$ +	$H_2O(g)$
initial	4.10 atm	2.05 atm		0 atm	3.28 atm
change	-0.23 atm	-0.23 atm		+0.23	+0.23 atm
equil	3.87 atm	1.82 atm		0.23 atm	3.51 atm

(b) $K_{eq} = \dfrac{P_{CO} \times P_{H_2O}}{P_{CO_2} \times P_{H_2}} = \dfrac{(0.23)(3.51)}{(3.87)(1.82)} = 0.1146 = 0.11$

Without intermediate rounding, equilibrium pressures are $P_{H_2O} = 3.51$, $P_{CO} = 0.2276$, $P_{H_2} = 1.8239$, $P_{CO_2} = 3.8754$ and $K_{eq} = 0.1130 = 0.11$, in good agreement with the value above.

Applications of Equilibrium Constants

15.27   (a)   A *reaction quotient* is the result of the law of mass action for a general set of concentrations, whereas the equilibrium constant requires equilibrium concentrations.

      (b)   In the direction of more products, to the right.

      (c)   If Q = K, the system is at equilibrium; the concentrations used to calculate Q must be equilibrium concentrations.

15.29   *Analyze/Plan.* Follow the logic in Sample Exercise 15.9. We are given partial pressures so we can calculate Q directly and decide on the direction to equilibrium.

    Solve: $K_{eq} = \dfrac{P_{CO} \times P_{Cl_2}}{P_{COCl_2}} = 6.71 \times 10^{-9}$ at 100°C

      (a) $Q = \dfrac{(1.01 \times 10^{-4})(2.03 \times 10^{-4})}{(6.12 \times 10^{-2})} = 3.35 \times 10^{-7}$; $Q > K_{eq}$

      The reaction will proceed to the left to attain equilibrium.

      (b) $Q = \dfrac{(3.37 \times 10^{-6})(6.89 \times 10^{-5})}{(1.38)} = 1.68 \times 10^{-10}$; $Q < K_{eq}$

      The reaction will proceed to the right to attain equilibrium.

      (c) $Q = \dfrac{(4.53 \times 10^{-5})^2}{(3.06 \times 10^{-1})} = 6.71 \times 10^{-9}$, $Q = K_{eq}$

      The reaction is at equilibrium.

15.31 *Analyze/Plan.* Follow the logic in Sample Exercise 15.10. *Solve:*

$$K_{eq} = \frac{P_{SO_2} \times P_{Cl_2}}{P_{SO_2Cl_2}}; \quad P_{Cl_2} = \frac{K_{eq} \times P_{SO_2Cl_2}}{P_{SO_2}} = \frac{(2.39)(3.31)}{(1.59)} = 4.9754 = 4.98 \text{ atm}$$

Check. $K_{eq} = \frac{(1.59)(4.98)}{(3.31)} = 2.39.$ Our values are self-consistent.

15.33 *Analyze/Plan.* Follow the logic in Sample Exercise 15.10. In each case, change given masses to pressures, solve for the equilibrium pressure of the desired component, and calculate mass of that substance present at equilibrium. *Solve:*

(a) $K_{eq} = \dfrac{P_{Br}^2}{P_{Br_2}} = 0.133; \quad P = \dfrac{gRT}{\mathcal{M} V}; \quad T = 273 + 1285°C = 1558 \text{ K}$

$$P_{Br_2} = \frac{0.245 \text{ g}}{159.8 \text{ g/mol}} \times \frac{1558 \text{ K}}{0.200 \text{ L}} \times \frac{0.08206 \text{ L} \cdot \text{atm}}{\text{K} \cdot \text{mol}} = 0.9801 = 0.980 \text{ atm}$$

$$P_{Br} = (K_{eq} \times P_{Br_2})^{1/2} = (0.133 \times 0.9801)^{1/2} = 0.36104 = 0.361 \text{ atm}$$

$$g_{Br} = \frac{\mathcal{M}_{Br} P_{Br} V}{RT} = \frac{79.904 \text{ g/mol} \times 0.36104 \text{ atm} \times 0.200 \text{ L}}{1558 \text{ K} \times 0.08206 \text{ L} \cdot \text{atm/mol} \cdot \text{K}} = 0.04513 = 0.0451 \text{ g Br}$$

(b) $PV = nRT; \quad P = gRT/(\mathcal{M} \times V)$

$$P_{H_2} = \frac{0.056 \text{ g H}_2}{2.016 \text{ g/mol}} \times \frac{0.08206 \text{ L} \cdot \text{atm}}{\text{K} \cdot \text{mol}} \times \frac{700 \text{ K}}{2.000 \text{ L}} = 0.7978 = 0.80 \text{ atm}$$

$$P_{I_2} = \frac{4.36 \text{ g I}_2}{253.8 \text{ g / mol}} \frac{0.08206 \text{ L} \cdot \text{atm}}{\text{K} \cdot \text{mol}} \times \frac{700 \text{ K}}{2.000 \text{ L}} = 0.4934 = 0.494 \text{ atm}$$

$K_p = 55.3 = ; \dfrac{P_{HI}^2}{P_{H_2} \times I_2} \quad P_{HI} = [55.3 \, (P_{H_2})(P_{I_2})]^{1/2} = [55.3(0.7978)(0.4934)]^{1/2}$
$$= 4.666 = 4.7 \text{ atm}$$

$$g_{HI} = \frac{\mathcal{M}_{HI} P_{HI} V}{RT} = \frac{128.0 \text{ g HI}}{\text{mol HI}} \times \frac{\text{K} \cdot \text{mol}}{0.08206 \text{ L} \cdot \text{atm}} \times \frac{4.666 \text{ atm} \times 2.000 \text{ L}}{700 \text{ K}}$$
$$= 20.79 = 21 \text{ g HI}$$

15.35 *Analyze/Plan.* Follow the logic in Sample Exercise 15.11. Since pressure of NO is given directly, we can construct the equilibrium table straight away. *Solve:*

	2NO(g)	⇌	N₂(g)	+	O₂(g)
initial	37.3 atm		0		0
change	-2x		+x		+x
equil.	37.3 - 2x		+x		+x

$$K_{eq} = \frac{P_{N_2} \times P_{O_2}}{P_{NO}^2} = 2.4 \times 10^{-3}$$

$$2.4 \times 10^3 = \frac{x^2}{(37.3-2x)^2}; \quad (2.4 \times 10^3)^{1/2} = \frac{x}{37.3-2x}$$

$x = (2.4 \times 10^3)^{1/2}\,(37.3 - 2x);\ x = 1827.3 - 97.98x;\ 98.98x = 1827.3,\ x = 18.46 = 18\ \text{atm}$

$P_{N_2} = P_{O_2} = 18\ \text{atm};\ P_{NO} = 37.3 - 2(18.46) = 0.377 = 0.4\ \text{atm}$

Strictly speaking, 18 atm has 2 sig figs and no decimal places, so P_{NO} should have no decimal places, or $P_{NO} = 0$ atm. This result is not very useful.

Check. $K_{eq} = \dfrac{(18)^2}{(0.4)^2} = 2 \times 10^3$; more sig figs are needed for closer agreement.

15.37   *Analyze/Plan.* Write the K_{eq} expression, substitute the stated pressure relationship and solve for P_{Br_2}. *Solve:*

$$K_{eq} = \frac{P_{NO}^2 \times P_{Br_2}}{P_{NOBr}^2}$$

When $P_{NOBr} = P_{NO}$, these terms cancel and $P_{Br_2} = K_{eq} = 0.416$ atm. This is true for all cases where $P_{NOBr} = P_{NO}$.

15.39   (a)   *Analyze/Plan.* If only $PH_3BCl_3(s)$ is present initially, the equation requires that the equilibrium partial pressures of $PH_3(g)$ and $BCl_3(g)$ are equal. Write the K_{eq} expression and solve for $x = P_{PH_3} = P_{BCl_3}$. *Solve:*

$K_{eq} = P_{PH_3} \times P_{BCl_3};\ 5.42 \times 10^{-2} = x^2;\ x = 0.2328 = 0.233$ atm PH_3 and BCl_3

      (b)   Since the mole ratios are 1:1:1, mol $PH_3BCl_3(s)$ required = mol PH_3 or BCl_3 produced.

$$n_{PH_3} = P_{PH_3}\,V/RT = \frac{0.2328\ \text{atm} \times 0.500\ \text{L}}{353\ \text{K} \times 0.08206\ \text{L} \cdot \text{atm/K} \cdot \text{mol}}$$

$$= 4.018 \times 10^{-3} = 4.02 \times 10^{-3}\ \text{mol}\ PH_3$$

$$4.018 \times 10^{-3}\ \text{mol}\ PH_3 = 4.018 \times 10^{-3}\ \text{mol}\ PH_3BCl_3 \times \frac{151.2\ \text{g}\ PH_3BCl_3}{1\ \text{mol}\ PH_3BCl_3}$$

$$= 0.6076 = 0.608\ \text{g}\ PH_3BCl_3$$

In fact, some $PH_3BCl_3(s)$ must remain for the system to be in equilibrium, so a bit more than 0.608 g PH_3BCl_3 is needed.

15.41   *Analyze/Plan.* Follow the approach in Solution 15.35. Calculate P_{IBr} from mol IBr and construct the equilibrium table.

$$K_{eq} = \frac{P_{IBr}^2}{P_{I_2} \times P_{Br_2}} = 280;\ P_{IBr} = \frac{nRT}{V} = \frac{0.500\ \text{mol}}{1.000\ \text{L}} \times 423\ \text{K} \times 0.08206\ \frac{\text{L} \cdot \text{atm}}{\text{K} \cdot \text{mol}}$$

$$= 17.356 = 17.4\ \text{atm}$$

Since no I_2 or Br_2 were present initially, the amounts present at equilibrium are produced by the reverse reaction and stoichiometrically equal. Let these amounts equal x. The amount of HBr that reacts is then 2x. Substitute the equilibrium pressures (in terms of x) into the equilibrium expression and solve for x.

$$I_2 \quad + \quad Br_2 \quad \rightleftharpoons \quad 2IBr$$

initial	0 atm	0 atm	17.356
change	+x atm	+x atm	-2x
equil.	x atm	x atm	(17.356 - 2x) atm

$K_{eq} = 280 = \dfrac{(17.356 - 2x)^2}{x^2}$; taking the square root of both sides

$16.733 = \dfrac{17.356 - 2x}{x}$; $16.733x + 2x = 17.356$; $18.733x = 17.356$

$x = 0.92647 = 0.926$ atm; $P_{I_2} = 0.926$ atm; $P_{Br_2} = 0.926$ atm

$P_{IBr} = 17.356 - 2x = 17.356 - 1.853 = 15.503 = 15.5$ atm

Check. $\dfrac{(15.5)^2}{(0.926)^2} = 280$. Our values are self-consistent.

LeChâtelier's Principle

15.43   *Analyze/Plan.* Follow the logic in Sample Exercise 15.12. *Solve*:

(a)   Shift equilibrium to the right; more $SO_3(g)$ is formed, the amount of $SO_2(g)$ decreases.

(b)   Heating an exothermic reaction decreases the value of K. More SO_2 and O_2 will form, the amount of SO_3 will decrease.

(c)   Since, $\Delta n = -1$, a change in volume will affect the equilibrium position and favor the side with more moles of gas. The amounts of SO_2 and O_2 increase and the amount of SO_3 decreases.

(d)   No effect. Speeds up the forward and reverse reactions equally.

(e)   No effect. Does not appear in the equilibrium expression.

(f)   Shift equilibrium to the right; amounts of SO_2 and O_2 decrease.

15.45   *Analyze/Plan.* Given certain changes to a reaction system, determine the effect on K_{eq}, if any. Only changes in temperature cause changes to the value of K_{eq}. *Solve*:

(a)   No effect   (b) no effect   (c) increase equilibrium constant   (d) no effect

15.47   *Analyze/Plan.* Use Hess's Law, $\Delta H° = \Sigma \Delta H_f°$ products - $\Sigma \Delta H_f°$ reactants, to calculate $\Delta H°$. According to the sign of $\Delta H°$, describe the effect of temperature on the value of K_{eq}.

According to the value of Δn, describe the effect of changes to container volume. *Solve*:

(a) $\Delta H° = \Delta H°_f\ NO_2(g) + \Delta H°_f\ N_2O(g) - 3\Delta H°_f\ NO(g)$

$\Delta H° = 33.84\ kJ + 81.6\ kJ - 3(90.37\ kJ) = -155.7\ kJ$

(b)   The reaction is exothermic (-ΔH°), so the equilibrium constant will decrease with increasing temperature.

(c)   Δn does not equal zero, so a change in volume at constant temperature will affect the fraction of products in the equilibrium mixture. An increase in container volume would favor reactants, while a decrease in volume would favor products.

Additional Exercises

15.49 (a)   Since both the forward and reverse processes are elementary steps, we can write the rate laws directly from the chemical equation.

$rate_f = k_f\ [CO][Cl_2] = rate_r = k_r\ [COCl][Cl]$

$$\frac{k_f}{k_r} = \frac{[COCl][Cl]}{[CO][Cl_2]} = K$$

$$K_{eq} = \frac{k_f}{k_r} = \frac{1.4 \times 10^{-28}\ M^{-1}\ s^{-1}}{9.3 \times 10^{10}\ M^{-1}\ s^{-1}} = 1.5 \times 10^{-39}$$

For a homogeneous equilibrium in the gas phase, we usually write K_{eq} in terms of partial pressures. In this exercise, concentrations are more convenient because the rate constants are expressed in terms of molarity. For this reaction, the value of K_{eq} is the same regardless of how K_{eq} is expressed, because there is no change in the moles of gas in going from reactants to products.

(b)   Since the K is quite small, reactants are much more plentiful than products at equilibrium.

15.51 $K_{eq} = \dfrac{P_{SO_2} \times P_{Cl_2}}{P_{SO_2Cl_2}}$; $P_{SOCl_2} = \dfrac{nRT}{V} = \dfrac{2.00\ mol}{2.00\ L} \times 303\ K \times \dfrac{0.08206\ L\bullet atm}{K\bullet mol}$

$= 24.864 = 24.9\ atm$

The change in $P_{SOCl_2} = x = 0.56(24.864) = 13.924 = 14\ atm$

	$SO_2Cl_2(g)$	⇌	$SO_2(g)$	+	$Cl_2(g)$
initial	24.9 atm		0		0
change	-14 atm		+14 atm		+14 atm
equil.	11 atm		+14 atm		+14 atm

$$K_{eq} = \frac{(13.924)^2}{10.940} = 17.72 = 18$$

15.54 (a)

$$A(g) \quad \rightleftharpoons \quad 2B(g)$$

initial	0.55 atm	0
change	-0.19 atm	+0.38 atm
equil.	0.36 atm	0.38 atm

$$P_t = P_A + P_B = 0.36 \text{ atm} + 0.38 \text{ atm} = 0.74 \text{ atm}$$

(b) $\quad K_{eq} = \dfrac{(P_B)^2}{P_A} = \dfrac{(0.38)^2}{0.36} = 0.4011 = 0.40$

15.57 $\quad P_{BCl_3} = \dfrac{nRT}{V} = \dfrac{0.0128 \text{ mol} \times 333 \text{ K}}{0.500 \text{ L}} \times \dfrac{0.08206 \text{ L} \cdot \text{atm}}{\text{mol} \cdot \text{K}} = 0.69955 = 0.700 \text{ atm}$

PH_3BCl_3 is a solid and its concentration is taken as a constant, C.

$$PH_3BCl_3 \quad \rightleftharpoons \quad PH_3 \quad + \quad BCl_3$$

initial	C	0 atm	0.700 atm
change		+x atm	+x atm
equil.	C	+x atm	0.700 atm

$K_{eq} = P_{PH_3} \times P_{BCl_3} = 0.052(0.700+x); \quad x^2 + 0.700 - 0.052 = 0$

$$x = \frac{-0.700 \pm [(0.700)^2 - 4(-0.052)]^{1/2}}{2} = 0.06773 = 6.8 \times 10^{-2} \text{ atm PH}_3$$

Check: $(0.068)(0.700 + 0.068) = 0.052$; the solution is correct to two significant figures.

15.60 In general, the reaction quotient is of the form $Q = \dfrac{P_{NOCl}^2}{P_{NO}^2 \times P_{Cl_2}}$.

(a) $\quad Q = \dfrac{(0.11)^2}{(0.15)^2(0.31)} = 1.7$

$Q > K_{eq}$. Therefore, the reaction will shift toward reactants, to the left, in moving toward equilibrium.

(b) $\quad Q = \dfrac{(0.050)^2}{(0.12)^2(0.10)} = 1.7$

$Q > K_{eq}$. Therefore, the reaction will shift toward reactants, to the left, in moving toward equilibrium.

(c) $\quad Q = \dfrac{(5.10 \times 10^{-3})^2}{(0.15)^2(0.20)} = 5.8 \times 10^{-3}$

$Q < K_{eq}$. Therefore, the reaction mixture will shift in the direction of more product, to the right, in moving toward equilibrium.

15.63 $K_{eq} = \dfrac{P_{CO_2}}{P_{CO}} = 6.0 \times 10^2$

If P_{CO} is 150 torr, P_{CO_2} can never exceed 760 - 150 = 610 torr. Then Q = 610/150 = 4.1. Since this is far less than K, the reaction will shift in the direction of more product. Reduction will therefore occur.

15.66   *Analyze/Plan.* Equilibrium pressures of H_2, I_2, HI → K_{eq} → equilibrium table → new equilibrium concentrations.   *Solve*:

$P = \dfrac{nRT}{V}$; $\dfrac{RT}{V} = \dfrac{0.08206 \text{ L} \cdot \text{atm}}{\text{mol} \cdot \text{K}} \times \dfrac{731 \text{ K}}{5.00 \text{ L}} = 11.997 = 12.0 \text{ atm/mol}$

$P_{H_2} = P_{I_2} = 0.112 \text{ mol} \times 11.997 \dfrac{\text{atm}}{\text{mol}} = 1.344 = 1.34 \text{ atm}$

$P_{HI} = 0.775 \text{ mol} \times 11.997 \dfrac{\text{atm}}{\text{mol}} = 9.298 = 9.30 \text{ atm}$

$H_2(g) + I_2(g) \rightleftharpoons 2HI(g)$; $K_{eq} = \dfrac{P_{HI}^2}{P_{H_2} \times P_{I_2}} = \dfrac{(9.298)^2}{(1.344)^2} = 47.861 = 47.9$

$P_{HI} \text{ (added)} = 0.100 \text{ mol} \times \dfrac{11.997 \text{ atm}}{\text{mol}} = 1.1997 = 1.20 \text{ atm}$

	$H_2(g)$	+	$I_2(g)$	$\rightleftharpoons$	$2HI(g)$
initial	1.34 atm		1.34 atm		9.30 atm + 1.20 atm
change	+x atm		+x atm		-2x atm
equil.	(1.34+x) atm		(1.34+x) atm		(10.50-2x) atm

$K_{eq} = 47.86 = \dfrac{(10.50 - 2x)^2}{(1.34 + x)^2}$.   Take the square root of both sides:

$6.918 = \dfrac{10.50 - 2x}{1.34 + x}$; 9.270 + 6.918 x = 10.50 - 2x; 8.918 x = 1.230, x = 0.1379 = 0.140

$P_{H_2} = P_{I_2} = 1.34 + 0.140 = 1.48 \text{ atm}$; $P_{HI} = 10.50 - 2(0.140) = 10.22 \text{ atm}$

Check: $\dfrac{(10.22)^2}{(1.48)^2} = 47.68 = 47.7$

15.69   The patent claim is false. A catalyst does not alter the position of equilibrium in a system, only the rate of approach to the equilibrium condition.

Integrative Exercises

15.70   (a)   (i) $K_{eq} = [Na^+]/[Ag^+]$ (ii) $K_{eq} = [Hg^{2+}]^3 / [Al^{3+}]^2$

(iii) $K_{eq} = [Zn^{2+}] P_{H_2} / [H^+]^2$

(b)   According to Table 4.5, the activity series of the metals, a metal can be oxidized by any metal cation below it on the table.

       (i) Ag^+ is far below Na, so the reaction will proceed to the right and K_{eq} will be large.

       (ii) Al^{3+} is above Hg, so the reaction will not proceed to the right and K_{eq} will be small.

       (iii) H^+ is below Zn, so the reaction will proceed to the right and K_{eq} will be large.

(c) $K_{eq} < 1$ for this reaction, so Fe^{2+} (and thus Fe) is above Cd on the table. In other words, Cd is below Fe. The value of K_{eq}, 0.06, is small but not extremely small, so Cd will be only a few rows below Fe.

15.72   (a)   At equilibrium, the forward and reverse reactions occur at **equal** rates.

       (b)   One expects the reactants to be favored at equilibrium since they are lower in energy.

       (c)   A catalyst lowers the activation energy for both the forward and reverse reactions; the "hill" would be lower.

       (d)   Since the activation energy is lowered for both processes, the new rates would be equal and the ratio of the rate constants, k_f / k_r, would remain unchanged.

       (e)   Since the reaction is endothermic (the energy of the reactants is lower than that of the products, ΔE is positive), the value of K should increase with increasing temperature.

15.75 $K_{eq} = P_{CO}^2 / P_{CO_2}$. mole % = pressure %. Since the total pressure is 1 atm, mol %/100 = mol fraction = partial pressure.

Temp (K)	P_{CO_2} (atm)	P_{CO} (atm)	K_{eq}
1123	0.0623	0.9377	14.1
1223	0.0132	0.9868	78.8
1323	0.0037	0.9963	2.7×10^2
1473	0.0006	0.9994	1.7×10^3 (2×10^3 to 1 sig fig)

Because K_{eq} grows larger with increasing temperature, the reaction must be endothermic in the forward direction.

16 Acid-Base Equilibria

Arrhenius and Brønsted-Lowry Acids and Bases

16.1   Solutions of HCl and H_2SO_4 taste sour, turn litmus paper red (are acidic), neutralize solutions of bases, react with active metals to form $H_2(g)$ and conduct electricity. The two solutions have these properties in common because both solutes are strong acids. That is, they both ionize completely in H_2O to form $H^+(aq)$ and an anion. (The first ionization step for H_2SO_4 is complete, but the second is not.) The presence of ions enables the solutions to conduct electricity; the presence of $H^+(aq)$ in excess of 1×10^{-7} M accounts for all the other listed properties.

16.3   (a)   According to the Arrhenius definition, an acid when dissolved in water increases $[H^+]$. According to the Brønsted-Lowry definition, an acid is capable of donating H^+, regardless of physical state. The Arrhenius definition of an acid is confined to an aqueous solution; the Brønsted-Lowry definition applies to any physical state.

(b) $HCl(g) + NH_3(g) \rightarrow NH_4^+Cl^-(s)$ HCl is the B-L (Brønsted-Lowry) acid; it donates an H^+ to NH_3 to form NH_4^+. NH_3 is the B-L base; it accepts the H^+ from HCl.

16.5   *Analyze/Plan.* Follow the logic in Sample Exercise 16.1. A conjugate base has one less H^+ than its conjugate acid. *Solve:*

(a) HSO_3^- (b) $C_2H_3O_2^-$ (c) $HAsO_4^{2-}$ (d) NH_3

16.7   *Analyze/Plan.* Use the definitions of B-L acids and bases, and conjugate acids and bases to make the designations. Evaluate the changes going from reactant to product to inform your choices. *Solve:*

	__B-L acid__	+	__B-L base__	$\rightleftharpoons$	__Conjugate acid__	+	__Conjugate base__
(a)	$NH_4^+(aq)$		$CN^-(aq)$		$HCN(aq)$		$NH_3(aq)$
(b)	$H_2O(l)$		$(CH_3)_3N(aq)$		$(CH_3)_3NH^+(aq)$		$OH^-(aq)$
(c)	$HCHO_2(aq)$		$PO_4^{3-}(aq)$		$HPO_4^{2-}(aq)$		$CHO_2^-(aq)$

16.9   *Analyze/Plan.* Follow the logic in Sample Exercise 16.2. *Solve:*

(a)   Acid: $HC_2O_4^-$ (aq) $+$ $H_2O(l)$ $\rightleftharpoons$ $C_2O_4^{2-}(aq)$ $+$ $H_3O^+(aq)$
         B-L acid   B-L base   conj. base   conj. acid

Base: $HC_2O_4^-(aq)$ $+$ $H_2O(l)$ $\rightleftharpoons$ $H_2C_2O_4(aq)$ $+$ $OH^-(aq)$
         B-L base   B-L acid   conj. acid   conj. base

(b) $H_2C_2O_4$ is the conjugate acid of $HC_2O_4^-$.

$C_2O_4^{2-}$ is the conjugate base of $HC_2O_4^-$.

16.11   *Analyze/Plan.* Based on the chemical formula, decide whether the acid is strong, weak or negligible. Is it one of the known seven strong acids (Section 16.5)? Also check Figure 16.4. Remove a single H and decrease the particle charge by one to write the formula of the conjugate base. *Solve*:

(a) weak, NO_2^- (b) strong, HSO_4^- (c) weak, PO_4^{3-}
(d) negligible, CH_3^- (e) weak, CH_3NH_2

16.13   *Analyze/Plan.* Given chemical formula, determine strength of acids and bases by checking the known strongs (Section 16.5). Recall the paradigm 'The **stronger** the acid, the **weaker** its conjugate base, and vice versa!' *Solve*:

(a)   HBr. It is one of the seven strong acids (Section 16.5).

(b) F^-. HCl is a stronger acid than HF, so F^- is the stronger conjugate base.

16.15   *Analyze/Plan.* Acid-base equilibria favor formation of the weaker acid and base. Compare the relative strengths of the substances acting as acids on opposite sides of the equation. (Bases can also be compared; the conclusion should be the same.) *Solve*:

	Base	**+**	**Acid**	$\rightleftharpoons$	**Conjugate acid**	**+**	**Conjugate base**
(a)	F^- (aq)	+	HCO_3^-(aq)		HF(aq)	+	CO_3^{2-}(aq)

HF is a stronger acid than HCO_3^-, so the equilibrium lies to the left.

(b) O^{2-}(aq)   + $H_2O(l)$ $\rightleftharpoons$ OH^-(aq)   + OH^-(aq)

H_2O is a stronger acid than OH^-, so the equilibrium lies to the right.

(c) HS^-(aq)   + $HC_2H_3O_2$(aq) $\rightleftharpoons$ H_2S(aq)   + $C_2H_3O_2^-$(aq)

$HC_2H_3O_2$ is a stronger acid than H_2S, so the equilibrium lies to the right.

Autoionization of Water

16.17   (a)   *Autoionization* is the ionization of a neutral molecule (in the absence of any other reactant) into an anion and a cation. The equilibrium expression for the autoionization of water is $H_2O(l) \rightleftharpoons H^+(aq) + OH^-(aq)$.

(b)   Pure water is a poor conductor of electricity because it contains very few ions. Ions, mobile charged particles, are required for the conduction of electricity in liquids.

(c)   If a solution is *acidic*, it contains more H^+ than OH^- ($[H^+] > [OH^-]$).

16.19 *Analyze/Plan.* Follow the logic in Sample Exercise 16.5. In pure water at 25°C, $[H^+] = [OH^-] = 1 \times 10^{-7}$ *M*. If $[H^+] > 1 \times 10^{-7}$ *M*, the solution is acidic; if $[H^+] < 1 \times 10^{-7}$ *M*, the solution is basic. *Solve:*

(a) $[H^+] = \dfrac{K_w}{[OH^-]} = \dfrac{1.0 \times 10^{-14}}{5 \times 10^{-5} \, M} = \mathbf{2 \times 10^{-10} \, M} < 1 \times 10^{-7}$ *M*; basic

(b) $[H^+] = \dfrac{K_w}{[OH^-]} = \dfrac{1.0 \times 10^{-14}}{3.2 \times 10^{-9} \, M} = \mathbf{3.1 \times 10^{-6} \, M} > 1 \times 10^{-7}$ *M*; acidic

(c) $[OH^-] = 100[H^+]$; $K_w = [H^+] \times 100[H^+] = 100[H^+]^2$;

$[H^+] = (K_w/100)^{1/2} = \mathbf{1.0 \times 10^{-8} \, M} < 1 \times 10^{-7}$ *M*; basic

16.21 *Analyze/Plan.* Follow the logic in Sample Exercise 16.4. Note that the value of the equilibrium constant (in this case, K_w) changes with temperature. *Solve:*

At 0°C, $K_w = 1.2 \times 10^{-15} = [H^+][OH^-]$.

In pure water, $[H^+] = [OH^-]$; $2.4 \times 10^{-14} = [H^+]^2$; $[H^+] = (1.2 \times 10^{-15})^{1/2}$

$[H^+] = [OH^-] = 3.5 \times 10^{-8}$ *M*

The pH Scale

16.23 *Analyze/Plan.* A change of one pH unit (in either direction) is:

$\Delta pH = pH_2 - pH_1 = -(\log[H^+]_2 - \log[H^+]_1) = -\log\dfrac{[H^+]_2}{[H^+]_1} = \pm 1$. The antilog of +1 is 10; the antilog of -1 is 1×10^{-1}. Thus, a ΔpH of one unit represents an increase or decrease in $[H^+]$ by a factor of 10. *Solve:*

(a) $\Delta pH = \pm 2.00$ is a change of $10^{2.00}$; $[H^+]$ changes by a factor of 100.

(b) $\Delta pH = \pm 0.5$ is a change of $10^{0.50}$; $[H^+]$ changes by a factor of 3.2.

16.25 (a) $K_w = [H^+][OH^-]$. If NaOH is added to water, it dissociates into $Na^+(aq)$ and $OH^-(aq)$. This increases $[OH^-]$ and necessarily decreases $[H^+]$. When $[H^+]$ decreases, pH increases.

(b) $0.00003 \, M = 3 \times 10^{-5}$ *M*. On figure 16.5, this is $[H^+] > 1 \times 10^{-5}$ but $< 1 \times 10^{-4}$. The pH is between 4 and 5. by calculation:

$pH = -\log[H^+] = -\log(3 \times 10^{-5}) = 4.5$ If pH < 7, the solution is acidic.

(c) pH = 7.8 is between pH 7 and pH 8 on Figure 16.5, closer to pH = 8. A pH = 8, $[H^+] = 1 \times 10^{-8}$; at pH = 7, $[H^+] = 1 \times 10^{-7} = 10 \times 10^{-8}$. A good estimate is $3 \times 10^{-8} \, M \, H^+$.

By calculation: $[H^+] = 10^{-pOH} = 10^{-7.8} = 2 \times 10^{-8}$ *M*

At pH = 7, $[OH^-] = 1 \times 10^{-7}$; at pH = 8, $[OH^-] = 1 \times 10^{-6} = 10 \times 10^{-7}$.

Since pH = 7.8 is closer to pH = 8, we estimate 7×10^{-7} M OH$^-$.

By calculation: pOH = 14.0 - 7.8 = 6.2

[OH$^-$] = 10^{-pOH} = $10^{-6.2}$ = 6×10^{-7} M OH$^-$

16.27   *Analyze/Plan.* At 25°C, [H$^+$][OH$^-$] = 1×10^{-14}; pH = pOH = 14. Use these relationships to complete the table. If pH < 7, the solution is acidic; if pH > 7, the solution is basic. *Solve*:

[H$^+$]	[OH$^-$]	pH	pOH	acidic or basic
7.5×10^{-3} M	1.3×10^{-12} M	2.12	11.88	acidic
2.8×10^{-5} M	3.6×10^{-10} M	4.56	9.44	acidic
5.6×10^{-9} M	1.8×10^{-6} M	8.25	5.75	basic
5.0×10^{-9} M	2.0×10^{-6} M	8.30	5.70	basic

16.29   *Analyze/Plan.* Given pH and a new value of the equilibrium constant K$_w$, calculate equilibrium concentrations of H$^+$(aq) and OH$^-$(aq). The definition of pH remains pH = -log[H$^+$]. *Solve*:

pH = 7.40; [H$^+$] = 10^{-pH} = $10^{-7.40}$ = 4.0×10^{-8} M

K$_w$ = 2.4×10^{-14} = [H$^+$][OH$^-$]; [OH$^-$] = 2.4×10^{-14} / [H$^+$]

[OH$^-$] = 2.4×10^{-14} / 4.0×10^{-8} = 6.0×10^{-7} M

Alternately, pH + pOH = pK$_w$. At 37°C, pH + pOH = -log(2.4×10^{-14})

pH + pOH = 13.62; pOH = 13.62 - 7.40 = 6.22

[OH$^-$] = 10^{-pOH} = $10^{-6.22}$ = 6.0×10^{-7} M

Strong Acids and Bases

16.31   (a)   A *strong* acid is completely ionized in aqueous solution; a strong acid is a strong electrolyte.

(b)   For a strong acid such as HCl, [H$^+$] = initial acid concentration. [H$^+$] = 0.500 M

(c)   HCl, HBr, H I

16.33   *Analyze/Plan.* Follow the logic in Sample Exercise 16.8. Strong acids are completely ionized, so [H$^+$] = original acid concentration, and pH = -log[H$^+$]. For the solutions obtained by dilution, use the 'dilution' formula, $M_1V_1 = M_2V_2$, to calculate molarity of the acid. *Solve:*

(a) 8.5×10^{-3} M HBr = 8.5×10^{-3} M H$^+$; pH = -log (8.5×10^{-3}) = 2.07

(b) $\dfrac{1.52 \text{ g HNO}_3}{0.575 \text{ L soln}} \times \dfrac{1 \text{ mol HNO}_3}{63.02 \text{ g HNO}_3} = 0.041947 = 0.0419$ M HNO$_3$

[H$^+$] = 0.0419 M; pH = -log (0.041947) = 1.377

(c) $M_c \times V_c = M_d \times V_d$; 0.250 $M \times 0.00500$ L = ? $M \times 0.0500$ L

$$M_d = \frac{0.250\ M \times 0.00500\ L}{0.0500\ L} = 0.0250\ M\ HCl$$

[H$^+$] = 0.0250 M; pH = -log (0.0250) = 1.602

(d) $[H^+]_{total} = \dfrac{\text{mol H}^+ \text{ from HBr + mol H}^+ \text{ from HCl}}{\text{total L solution}}$

$$[H^+]_{total} = \frac{(0.100\ M\ HBr \times 0.0100\ L) + (0.200\ M \times 0.0200\ L)}{0.0300\ L}$$

$$[H^+]_{total} = \frac{1.00 \times 10^{-3}\ \text{mol H}^+ + 4.00 \times 10^{-3}\ \text{mol H}^+}{0.0300\ L} = 0.1667 = 0.167\ M$$

pH = -log (0.1667 M) = 0.778

16.35   *Analyze/Plan.* Follow the logic in Sample Exercise 16.9. Strong bases dissociate completely upon dissolving. pOH = -log[OH$^-$]; pH = 14 - pOH.

(a)   Pay attention to the formula of the base to get [OH$^-$]. *Solve*:

[OH$^-$] = 2[Sr(OH)$_2$] = 2(1.5 $\times 10^{-3}$ M) = 3.0 $\times 10^{-3}$ M OH$^-$ (see Exercise 16.32(b))

pOH = -log (3.0 $\times 10^{-3}$) = 2.52; pH = 14 - pOH = 11.48

(b)   mol/LiOH = g LiOH/molar mass LiOH. [OH$^-$] = [LiOH]. *Solve*:

$$\frac{2.250\ \text{g LiOH}}{0.2500\ \text{L soln}} \times \frac{1\ \text{mol LiOH}}{23.948\ \text{g LiOH}} = 0.37581 = 0.3758\ M\ LiOH = [OH^-]$$

pOH = -log (0.37581) = 0.4250; pH = 14 - pOH = 13.5750

(c)   Use the dilution formula to get the [NaOH] = [OH$^-$]. *Solve*:

$M_c \times V_c = M_d \times V_d$; 0.175 $M \times 0.00100$ L = ? $M \times 2.00$ L

$$M_d = \frac{0.0175\ M \times 0.00100\ L}{2.00\ L} = 8.75 \times 10^{-5}\ M\ NaOH = [OH^-]$$

pOH = -log (8.75 $\times 10^{-5}$) = 4.058; pH = 14 - pOH = 9.942

(d)   Consider total mol OH$^-$ from KOH and Ca(OH)$_2$, as well as total solution volume. *Solve*:

$$[OH^-]_{total} = \frac{\text{mol OH}^- \text{ from KOH + mol OH}^- \text{ from Ca(OH)}_2}{\text{total L soln}}$$

$$[OH^-]_{total} = \frac{(0.105\ M \times 0.00500\ L) + 2(9.5 \times 10^{-2} \times 0.0150\ L)}{0.0200\ L}$$

$$[OH^-]_{total} = \frac{0.525 \times 10^{-3}\ \text{mol OH}^- + 2.85 \times 10^{-3}\ \text{mol OH}^-}{0.0200\ L} = 0.16875 = 0.17\ M$$

$pOH = -\log (0.16875) = 0.77;$ $pH = 14 - pOH = 13.23$

(9.5×10^{-2} M has 2 sig figs, so the [OH⁻] has 2 sig figs and pH and pOH have 2 decimal places.)

16.37 *Analyze/Plan.* pH → pOH → [OH⁻] = [NaOH]. *Solve:*

$pOH = 14 - pH = 14.00 - 11.50 = 2.50$

$pOH = 2.50 = -\log[OH^-]; [OH^-] = 10^{-2.50} = 3.2 \times 10^{-3}$ M

$[OH^-] = [NaOH] = 3.2 \times 10^{-3}$ M

16.39 *Analyze/Plan.* $NaH(aq) \rightarrow Na^+(aq) + H^-(aq)$

$H^-(aq) + H_2O(l) \rightarrow H_2(g) + OH^-(aq)$

Thus, initial [NaH] = [OH⁻]; [NaH] = g NaH/[$\mathcal{M}$(NaH) × V]. *Solve:*

$$[NaH] = \frac{mol\ NaH}{L\ solution} = 15.00\ g\ NaH \times \frac{1\ mol\ NaH}{24.00\ g\ NaH} \times \frac{1}{2.50\ L} = 0.250\ M$$

$[OH^-] = 0.250$ M; $pOH = -\log (0.250) = 0.602$, $pH = 14 - pOH = 13.400$

Weak Acids

16.41 *Analyze/Plan.* Remember that K_{eq} = [products]/[reactants]. If $H_2O(l)$ appears in the equilibrium reaction, it will **not** appear in the K_a expression, because it is a pure liquid. *Solve:*

(a) $HBrO_2(aq) \rightleftharpoons H^+(aq) + BrO_2^-(aq);$ $K_a = \dfrac{[H^+][BrO_2^-]}{[HBrO_2]}$

         $HBrO_2(aq) + H_2O(l) \rightleftharpoons H_3O^+(aq) + BrO_2^-(aq);$ $K_a = \dfrac{[H_3O^+][BrO_2^-]}{[HBrO_2]}$

(b) $HC_3H_5O_2(aq) \rightleftharpoons H^+(aq) + C_3H_5O_2^-(aq);$ $K_a = \dfrac{[H^+][C_3H_5O_2^-]}{[HC_3H_5O_2]}$

         $HC_3H_5O_2(aq) + H_2O(l) \rightleftharpoons H_3O^+(aq) + C_3H_5O_2^-(aq);$ $K_a = \dfrac{[H_3O^+][C_3H_5O_2^-]}{[HC_3H_5O_2]}$

16.43 *Analyze/Plan.* Follow the logic in Sample Exercise 16.10. *Solve:*

$HC_3H_5O_3(aq) \rightleftharpoons H^+(aq) + C_3H_5O_3^-(aq);$ $K_a = \dfrac{[H^+][C_3H_5O_3^-]}{[HC_3H_5O_3]}$

$[H^+] = [C_3H_5O_3^-] = 10^{-2.44} = 3.63 \times 10^{-3} = 3.6 \times 10^{-3}$ M

$[HC_3H_5O_3] = 0.10 - 3.63 \times 10^{-3} = 0.0964 = 0.096$ M

$$K_a = \frac{(3.63 \times 10^{-3})^2}{(0.0964)} = 1.4 \times 10^{-4}$$

16.45   *Analyze/Plan.* Write the equilibrium reaction and the K_a expression. Use % ionization to get equilibrium concentration of $[H^+]$, and by stoichiometry, $[X^-]$ and $[HX]$. Calculate K_a. *Solve:*

$[H^+] = 0.094 \times [HX]_{initial} = 0.0188 = 0.019\ M$

$$HX(aq) \rightleftharpoons H^+(aq) + X^-(aq)$$

initial	0.200 *M*	0	0
equil.	(0.200 - 0.019) *M*	0.019 *M*	0.019 *M*

$$K_a = \frac{[H^+][X^-]}{[HX]} = \frac{(0.0188)^2}{0.181} = 2.0 \times 10^{-3}$$

16.47   *Analyze/Plan.* Write the equilibrium reaction and the K_a expression.

$[H^+] = 10^{-pH} = [C_2H_3O_2^-]$ $[HC_2H_3O_2] = x - [H^+]$.

Substitute into the K_a expression and solve for x. *Solve:*

$[H^+] = 10^{-pH} = 10^{-2.90} = 1.26 \times 10^{-3} = 1.3 \times 10^{-3}\ M$

$$K_a = 1.8 \times 10^{-5} = \frac{[H^+][C_2H_3O_2^-]}{[HC_2H_3O_2]} = \frac{(1.26 \times 10^{-3})^2}{(x - 1.26 \times 10^{-3})}$$

$1.8 \times 10^{-5}(x - 1.26 \times 10^{-3}) = (1.26 \times 10^{-3})^2;$

$1.8 \times 10^{-5}x = 1.585 \times 10^{-6} + 2.266 \times 10^{-8} = 1.608 \times 10^{-6};$

$x = 0.08931 = 0.089\ M\ HC_2H_3O_2$

16.49   *Analyze/Plan.* Follow the logic in Sample Exercise 16.11. Write K_a, construct the equilibrium table, solve for $x = [H^+]$, then get equilibrium $[C_7H_5O_2^-]$ and $[HC_7H_5O_2]$ by substituting $[H^+]$ for x. *Solve:*

$$HC_7H_5O_2(aq) \rightleftharpoons H^+(aq) + C_7H_5O_2^-(aq)$$

initial	0.050 *M*	0	0
equil.	(0.050 - x) *M*	x *M*	x *M*

$$K_a = \frac{[H^+][C_7H_5O_2^-]}{[HC_7H_5O_2]} = \frac{x^2}{(0.050 - x)} \approx \frac{x^2}{0.050} = 6.3 \times 10^{-5}$$

$x^2 = 0.050\ (6.3 \times 10^{-5}\ );\ \ x = 1.8 \times 10^{-3}\ M = [H^+] = [H_3O^+] = [C_7H_5O_2^-]$

$[HC_7H_5O_2] = 0.050 - 0.0018 = 0.048\ M$

Check. $\dfrac{1.8 \times 10^{-3}\ M\ H^+}{0.050\ M\ HC_7H_5O_2} \times 100 = 3.6\%$ ionization; the assumption is valid

16.51   *Analyze/Plan.* Follow the logic in Sample Exercise 16.11.

(a)   *Solve:*

$$HC_3H_5O_2(aq) \rightleftharpoons H^+(aq) + C_3H_5O_2^-(aq)$$

initial	0.095 *M*	0	0
equil	(0.095 - x) *M*	x *M*	x *M*

$$K_a = \frac{[H^+][C_3H_5O_2^-]}{[HC_3H_5O_2]} = \frac{x^2}{(0.095-x)} \approx \frac{x^2}{0.095} = 1.3 \times 10^{-5}$$

$x^2 = 0.095(1.3 \times 10^{-5})$; $x = 1.111 \times 10^{-3} = 1.1 \times 10^{-3}$ M H^+; pH = 2.95

Check. $\dfrac{1.1 \times 10^{-3} M H^+}{0.095 M HC_3H_5O_2} \times 100 = 1.2\%$ ionization; the assumption is valid

(b)   *Solve*:

$$K_a = \frac{[H^+][CrO_4^{2-}]}{[HCrO_4^-]} = \frac{x^2}{(0.100-x)} \approx \frac{x^2}{0.100} = 3.0 \times 10^{-7}$$

$x^2 = 0.100(3.0 \times 10^{-7})$; $x = 1.732 \times 10^{-4} = 1.7 \times 10^{-4}$ M H^+

pH = $-\log(1.732 \times 10^{-4}) = 3.7614 = 3.76$

Check. $\dfrac{1.7 \times 10^{-4} M H^+}{0.100 M HCrO_4^-} \times 100 = 0.17\%$ ionization; the assumption is valid

(c)   Follow the logic in Sample Exercise 16.14. pOH = $-\log[OH^-]$. pH = 14 - pOH

Solve:

$$C_5H_5N(aq) + H_2O(l) \rightleftharpoons C_5H_5NH^+(aq) + OH^-$$

initial	0.120 M	0	0
equil	(0.120 - x) M	x M	x M

$$K_b = \frac{[C_5H_5NH^+][OH^-]}{[C_5H_5N]} = \frac{x^2}{(0.120-x)} \approx \frac{x^2}{0.120} = 1.7 \times 10^{-9}$$

$x^2 = 0.120(1.7 \times 10^{-9})$; $x = 1.428 \times 10^{-5} = 1.4 \times 10^{-5}$ M OH^-; pH = 9.15

Check. $\dfrac{1.4 \times 10^{-5} M OH^-}{0.120 M C_5H_5N} \times 100 = 0.011\%$ ionization; the assumption is valid

16.53   *Analyze/Plan.* $K_a = 10^{-pK_a}$. Follow the logic in Sample Exercise 16.11. *Solve*:

Let $[H^+] = [NC_7H_4SO_3^-] = z$. $K_a =$ antilog (-2.32) $= 4.79 \times 10^{-3} = 4.8 \times 10^{-3}$

$\dfrac{z^2}{0.10 - z} = 4.79 \times 10^{-3}$. Since K_a is relatively large, solve the quadratic.

$z^2 = 4.79 \times 10^{-3} z - 4.79 \times 10^{-4} = 0$

$$z = \frac{-4.79 \times 10^{-3} \pm \sqrt{(4.79 \times 10^{-3})^2 - 4(1)(-4.79 \times 10^{-4})}}{2(1)} = \frac{-4.79 \times 10^{-3} \pm \sqrt{1.937 \times 10^{-3}}}{2}$$

$z = 1.96 \times 10^{-2} = 2.0 \times 10^{-2}$ M H^+; pH = $-\log (1.96 \times 10^{-2}) = 1.71$

16.55   *Analyze/Plan.* Follow the logic in Sample Exercise 16.12. *Solve:*

(a) $HN_3(aq)$ $\rightleftharpoons$ $H^+(aq) + N_3^-(aq)$

      initial $0.400\ M$ 0 0

      equil $(0.400 - x)\ M$ $x\ M$ $x\ M$

$$K_a = \frac{[H^+][N_3^-]}{[HN_3]} = 1.9 \times 10^{-5};\ \frac{x^2}{(0.400-x)} \approx \frac{x^2}{0.400} = 1.9 \times 10^{-5}$$

$$x = 0.00276 = 2.8 \times 10^{-3}\ M = [H^+];\ \%\ \text{ionization} = \frac{2.76 \times 10^{-3}}{0.400} \times 100 = 0.69\%$$

(b) $1.9 \times 10^{-5} \approx \dfrac{x^2}{0.100}$; $x = 0.00138 = 1.4 \times 10^{-3}\ M\ H^+$

     $\%\ \text{ionization} = \dfrac{1.38 \times 10^{-3}\ M\,H^+}{0.100\ M\,HN_3} \times 100 = 1.4\%$

(c) $1.9 \times 10^{-5} \approx \dfrac{x^2}{0.0400}$; $x = 8.72 \times 10^{-4} = 8.7 \times 10^{-4}\ M\ H^+$

     $\%\ \text{ionization} = \dfrac{8.72 \times 10^{-4}\ M\,H^+}{0.0400\ M\,HN_3} \times 100 = 2.2\%$

Check. Notice that a tenfold dilution [part (a) versus part (c)] leads to a slightly more than threefold increase in percent ionization.

16.57   *Analyze/Plan.* Let the weak acid be HX. $HX(aq) \rightleftharpoons H^+(aq) + X^-(aq)$. Solve the K_a expression symbolically for $[H^+]$ in terms of $[HX]$. Substitute into the formula for % ionization, $([H^+]/[HX]) \times 100$. *Solve:*

$$K_a = \frac{[H^+][X^-]}{[HX]};\ [H^+] = [X^-] = y;\ K_a = \frac{y^2}{[HX] - y};\ \text{assume that \% ionization is small}$$

$$K_a = \frac{y^2}{[HX]};\ y = K_a^{1/2}\,[HX]^{1/2}$$

$$\%\ \text{ionization} = \frac{y}{[HX]} \times 100 = \frac{K_a^{1/2}[HX]^{1/2}}{[HX]} \times 100 = \frac{K_a^{1/2}}{[HX]^{1/2}} \times 100$$

That is, percent ionization varies inversely as the square root of concentration HX.

16.59   Analyze/Plan. Follow the logic in Sample Exercise 16.13. Citric acid is a triprotic acid with three K_a values that do not differ by more than 10^3. We must consider all three steps. Also, $C_6H_5O_7^{3-}$ is only produced in step 3. *Solve:*

$H_3C_6H_5O_7(aq) \rightleftharpoons H^+(aq) + H_2C_6H_5O_7^-(aq)$	$K_{a1} = 7.4 \times 10^{-4}$
$H_2C_6H_5O_7^-(aq) \rightleftharpoons H^+(aq) + HC_6H_5O_7^{2-}(aq)$	$K_{a2} = 1.7 \times 10^{-5}$
$HC_6H_5O_7^{2-}(aq) \rightleftharpoons H^+(aq) + C_6H_5O_7^{3-}(aq)$	$K_{a3} = 4.0 \times 10^{-7}$

To calculate the pH of a 0.050 *M* solution, assume initially that only the first ionization is important:

$$H_3C_6H_5O_7(aq) \rightleftharpoons H^+(aq) + H_2C_6H_5O_7^-(aq)$$

initial	0.050 M	0	0
equil.	(0.050 - x) M	x M	x M

$$K_{a1} = \frac{[H^+][H_2C_6H_5O_7^-]}{[H_3C_6H_5O_7]} = \frac{x^2}{(0.050 - x)} = 7.4 \times 10^{-4}$$

$x^2 = (0.050 - x)(7.4 \times 10^{-4})$; $x^2 \approx (0.050)(7.4 \times 10^{-4})$; $x = 0.00608 = 6.1 \times 10^{-3}$ M

Since this value for x is rather large in relation to 0.050, a better approximation for x can be obtained by substituting this first estimate into the expression for x^2, then solving again for x:

$$x^2 = (0.050 - x)(7.4 \times 10^{-4}) = (0.050 - 6.08 \times 10^{-3})(7.4 \times 10^{-4})$$
$$x^2 = 3.2 \times 10^{-5}; \quad x = 5.7 \times 10^{-3} M$$

(This is the same result obtained from the quadratic formula.)

The correction to the value of x, though not large, is significant. Does the second ionization produce a significant additional concentration of H^+?

$$H_2C_6H_5O_7^-(aq) \rightleftharpoons H^+(aq) + HC_6H_5O_7^{2-}(aq)$$

initial	5.7×10^{-5} M	5.7×10^{-3} M	0
equil.	$(5.7 \times 10^{-3} - y)$	$(5.7 \times 10^{-3} + y)$	y

$$K_{a2} = \frac{[H^+][HC_6H_5O_7^{2-}]}{[H_2C_6H_5O_7^-]} = 1.7 \times 10^{-5}; \quad \frac{(5.7 \times 10^{-3} + y)(y)}{(5.7 \times 10^{-3} - y)} = 1.7 \times 10^{-5}$$

Assume that y is small relative to 5.7×10^{-3}; that is, that additional ionization of $H_2C_6H_5O_7^-$ is small, then

$$\frac{(5.7 \times 10^{-3})y}{(5.7 \times 10^{-3})} = 1.7 \times 10^{-5} M; \quad y = 1.7 \times 10^{-5} M$$

This value is indeed small compared to 5.7×10^{-3} M; [H^+] and pH are determined by the first ionization step. If we were only interested in pH, we could stop here. However, to calculate [$C_6H_5O_7^{3-}$], we must consider the third ionization, with adjusted

[H^+] = $5.7 \times 10^{-3} + 1.7 \times 10^{-5} = 5.72 \times 10^{-5}$ M (= 5.7×10^{-5})

$$HC_6H_5O_7^{2-} \rightleftharpoons H^+(aq) + HC_6H_5O_7^{3-}(aq)$$

initial	1.75×10^{-5} M	5.72×10^{-3} M	0
equil.	$1.7 \times 10^{-5} - z$	$5.72 \times 10^{-3} + z$	z

$$K_{a3} = \frac{[H^+][C_6H_5O_7^{3-}]}{[HC_6H_5O_7^{2-}]} = \frac{(5.72 \times 10^{-3} + z)(z)}{(1.7 \times 10^{-5} - z)} = 4.0 \times 10^{-7}$$

Assume z is small relative to 5.72×10^{-3}, but not relative to 1.7×10^{-5}.

$(4.0 \times 10^{-7})(1.7 \times 10^{-5} - z) = 5.72 \times 10^{-3} z$; $6.8 \times 10^{-12} - 4.0 \times 10^{-7} z = 5.72 \times 10^{-3} z$;

$6.8 \times 10^{-12} = 5.72 \times 10^{-3} z + 4.0 \times 10^{-7} z = 5.72 \times 10^{-3} z; \ z = 1.19 \times 10^{-9} = 1.2 \times 10^{-9} \ M$

$[C_6H_5O_7^{3-}] = 1.2 \times 10^{-9} \ M; \ [H^+] = 5.72 \times 10^{-3} \ M + 1.2 \times 10^{-9} \ M = 5.72 \times 10^{-3} \ M$

$pH = -\log(5.72 \times 10^{-3}) = 2.24$

Note that neither the second nor third ionizations contributed significantly to $[H^+]$ and pH.

Weak Bases

16.61   All Brønsted-Lowry bases contain at least one nonbonded (lone) pair of electrons to attract H^+.

16.63   *Analyze/Plan.* Remember that $K_{eq} = $ [products]/[reactants]. If $H_2O(l)$ appears in the equilibrium reaction, it will **not** appear in the K_b expression, because it is a pure liquid. *Solve*:

(a) $(CH_3)_2NH(aq) + H_2O(l) \rightleftharpoons (CH_3)_2NH_2^+(aq) + OH^-(aq); \ K_b = \dfrac{[(CH_3)_2NH_2^+][OH^-]}{[(CH_3)_2NH]}$

(b) $CO_3^{2-}(aq) + H_2O(l) \rightleftharpoons HCO_3^-(aq) + OH^-(aq); \ K_b = \dfrac{[HCO_3^-][OH^-]}{[CO_3^{2-}]}$

(c) $CHO_2^-(aq) + H_2O(l) \rightleftharpoons HCHO_2(aq) + OH^-(aq); \ K_b = \dfrac{[HCHO_2][OH^-]}{[CHO_2^-]}$

16.65   *Analyze/Plan.* Follow the logic in Sample Exercise 16.14. *Solve*:

$$C_2H_5NH_2(aq) + H_2O(l) \rightleftharpoons C_2H_5NH_3^+(aq) + OH^-(aq)$$

initial	0.075 M	0	0
equil.	(0.075 - x) M	x M	x M

$K_b = \dfrac{[C_2H_5NH_3^+][OH^-]}{[C_2H_5NH_2]} = \dfrac{(x)(x)}{(0.075 - x)} \approx \dfrac{x^2}{0.075} = 6.4 \times 10^{-4}$

$x^2 = 0.075 \ (6.4 \times 10^{-4}); \ x = [OH^-] = 6.9 \times 10^{-3} \ M; \ pH = 11.84$

Check. $\dfrac{6.9 \times 10^{-3} \ M \ OH^-}{0.075 \ M \ C_2H_5NH_2} \times 100 = 9.2\%$ ionization; the assumption is **not** valid

To obtain a more precise result, the K_b expression is rewritten in standard quadratic form and solved via the quadratic formula.

$\dfrac{x^2}{0.075 - x} = 6.4 \times 10^{-4}; \ x^2 + 6.4 \times 10^{-4} x - 4.8 \times 10^{-5} = 0$

$x = \dfrac{b \pm \sqrt{b^2 - 4ac}}{2a} = \dfrac{-6.4 \times 10^{-4} \pm \sqrt{(6.4 \times 10^{-4})^2 - 4(1)(-4.8 \times 10^{-5})}}{2}$

$x = 6.61 \times 10^{-3} = 6.6 \times 10^{-3} \ M \ OH^-; \ pOH = 2.18, \ pH = 14.00 - pOH = 11.82$

Note that the pH values obtained using the two algebraic techniques are very similar.

16.67 *Analyze/Plan.* Given pH and initial concentration of base, calculate all equilibrium concentrations. pH → pOH → [OH⁻] at equilibrium. Construct the equilibrium table and calculate other equilibrium concentrations. Substitute into the K_b expression and calculate K_b. *Solve:*

(a) $[OH^-] = 10^{-pOH}$; pOH = 14 - pH = 14.00 - 11.33 = 2.67

        $[OH^-] = 10^{-2.67} = 2.138 \times 10^{-3} = 2.1 \times 10^{-3}$ M

$$C_{10}H_{15}ON(aq) + H_2O(l) \rightleftharpoons C_{10}H_{15}ONH^+(aq) + OH^-(aq)$$

initial	0.035 M	0	0
equil.	0.033 M	2.1×10^{-3} M	2.1×10^{-3} M

(b) $K_b = \dfrac{[C_{10}H_{15}ONH^+][OH^-]}{[C_{10}H_{15}ON]} = \dfrac{(2.138 \times 10^{-3})^2}{(0.03286)} = 1.4 \times 10^{-4}$

The K_a - K_b Relationship; Acid-Base Properties of Salts

16.69 (a)   For a conjugate acid/conjugate base pair such as $C_6H_5OH/C_6H_5O^-$, K_b for the conjugate base is always K_w/K_a for the conjugate acid. K_b for the conjugate base can always be calculated from K_a for the conjugate acid, so a separate list of K_b values is not necessary.

(b) $K_b = K_w/K_a = 1.0 \times 10^{-14}/1.3 \times 10^{-10} = 7.7 \times 10^{-5}$

(c) K_b for phenolate (7.7×10^{-5}) > K_b for ammonia (1.8×10^{-5}).

        Phenolate is a stronger base than NH_3.

16.71 *Analyze/Plan.* Given K_a, determine relative strengths of the acids and their conjugate bases. The greater the magnitude of K_a, the stronger the acid and the weaker the conjugate base. K_b (conjugate base) = K_w/K_a. *Solve:*

(a)   Acetic acid is stronger, because it has the larger K_a value.

(b)   Hypochlorite ion is the stronger base because the weaker acid, hypochlorous acid, has the stronger conjugate base.

(c) K_b for $C_2H_3O_2^- = K_w/K_a$ for $HC_2H_3O_2 = 1.0 \times 10^{-14}/1.8 \times 10^{-5} = 5.6 \times 10^{-10}$

        K_b for $ClO^- = K_w/K_a$ for HClO = $1 \times 10^{-14}/3.0 \times 10^{-8} = 3.3 \times 10^{-7}$

        Note that K_b for ClO^- is greater than K_b for $C_2H_3O_2^-$.

16.73 *Analyze.* When the solute in an aqueous solution is a salt, evaluate the acid/base properties of the component ions.

(a)   *Plan.* NaCN is a soluble salt and thus a strong electrolyte. When it is dissolved in H_2O, it dissociates completely into Na^+ and CN^-. [NaCN] = [Na^+] = [CN^-] = 0.10 M. Na^+ is the conjugate acid of the strong base NaOH and thus does not influence the pH of the solution. CN^-, on the other hand, is the conjugate base of the weak acid

HCN and **does** influence the pH of the solution. Like any other weak base, it hydrolyzes water to produce OH^- (aq). Solve the equilibrium problem to determine $[OH^-]$. *Solve*:

$$CN^-(aq) + H_2O(l) \rightleftharpoons HCN(aq) + OH^-(aq)$$

initial	0.10 M	0	0
equil.	(0.10 - x) M	x M	x M

$$K_b \text{ for } CN^- = \frac{[HCN][OH^-]}{[CN^-]} = \frac{K_w}{K_a \text{ for } HCN} = \frac{1 \times 10^{-14}}{4.9 \times 10^{-10}} = 2.04 \times 10^{-5} = 2.0 \times 10^{-5}$$

$2.04 \times 10^{-5} = \dfrac{(x)(x)}{(0.10 - x)}$; assume the percent of CN^- that hydrolyzes is small

$x^2 = 0.10 \,(2.04 \times 10^{-5})$; $x = [OH^-] = 0.00143 = 1.4 \times 10^{-3} \, M$

$pOH = 2.85$; $pH = 14 - 2.85 = 11.15$

(b)   *Plan*. $Na_2CO_3(aq) \rightarrow 2Na^+(aq) + CO_3^{2-}(aq)$

CO_3^{2-} is the conjugate base of HCO_3^- and its hydrolysis reaction will determine the $[OH^-]$ and pH of the solution (see similar explanation for NaCN in part (a)). We will assume the process $HCO_3^-(aq) + H_2O(l) \rightleftharpoons H_2CO_3(aq) + OH^-$ will not add significantly to the $[OH^-]$ in solution because $[HCO_3^-$ (aq)] is so small. Solve the equilibrium problem for $[OH^-]$. *Solve*:

$$CO_3^{2-}(aq) + H_2O(l) \rightleftharpoons HCO_3^-(aq) + OH^-(aq)$$

initial	0.080 M	0	0
equil.	(0.080 - x) M	x	x

$$K_b = \frac{[HCO_3^-][OH^-]}{[CO_3^{2-}]} = \frac{K_w}{K_a \text{ for } HCO_3^-} = \frac{1.0 \times 10^{-14}}{5.6 \times 10^{-11}} = 1.79 \times 10^{-4} = 1.8 \times 10^{-4}$$

$1.8 \times 10^{-4} = \dfrac{x^2}{(0.080 - x)}$; $x^2 = 0.080 \,(1.79 \times 10^{-4})$; $x = 0.00378 = 3.8 \times 10^{-3} \, M \, OH^-$

(Assume x is small compared to 0.080); $pOH = 2.42$; $pH = 14 - 2.42 = 11.58$

Check. $\dfrac{3.8 \times 10^{-3} \, M \, OH^-}{0.080 \, M \, CO_3^{2-}} \times 100 = 4.75\%$ hydrolysis; the assumption is valid

(c)   *Plan*. For the two salts present, Na^+ and Ca^{2+} are negligible acids. NO_2^- is the conjugate base of HNO_2 and will determine the pH of the solution. *Solve*:

Calculate total $[NO_2^-]$ present initially.

$[NO_2^-]_{total} = [NO_2^-]$ from $NaNO_2 + [NO_2^-]$ from $Ca(NO_2)_2$

$[NO_2^-]_{total} = 0.10 \, M + 2(0.20 \, M) = 0.50 \, M$

The hydrolysis equilibrium is:

$$NO_2^-(aq) + H_2O(l) \rightleftharpoons HNO_2 + OH^-(aq)$$

initial	0.50 M	0	0
equil.	(0.50 - x) M	x M	x M

$$K_b = \frac{[HNO_2][OH^-]}{[NO_2^-]} = \frac{K_w}{K_a \text{ for } HNO_2} = \frac{1.0 \times 10^{-14}}{4.5 \times 10^{-4}} = 2.22 \times 10^{-11} = 2.2 \times 10^{-11}$$

$$2.2 \times 10^{-11} = \frac{x^2}{(0.50 - x)} \approx \frac{x^2}{0.50}; \quad x^2 = 0.50 \,(2.22 \times 10^{-11})$$

$$x = 3.33 \times 10^{-6} = 3.3 \times 10^{-6} \, M \, OH^-; \quad pOH = 5.48; \quad pH = 14 - 5.48 = 8.52$$

16.75 *Analyze/Plan.* Given the formula of a salt, predict whether an aqueous solution will be acidic, basic or neutral. Evaluate the acid base properties of both ions and determine the overall effect on solution pH. *Solve*:

(a) acidic; NH_4^+ is a weak acid, Br^- is negligible.

(b) acidic; Fe^{3+} is a highly charged metal cation and a Lewis acid; Cl^- is negligible.

(c) basic; CO_3^{2-} is the conjugate base of HCO_3^-; Na^+ is negligible.

(d) neutral; both K^+ and ClO_4^- are negligible.

(e) acidic; $HC_2O_4^-$ is amphoteric, but K_a for the acid dissociation (6.4×10^{-5}) is much greater than K_b for the base hydrolysis $(1.0 \times 10^{-14} / 5.9 \times 10^{-2} = 1.7 \times 10^{-13})$.

16.77 *Plan.* Estimate pH using relative base strength and then calculate to confirm prediction. NaCl is a neutral salt, so it is not the unknown. The unknown is a relatively weak base, because a pH of 8.08 is not very basic. Since F^- is a weaker base than OCl^-, the unknown is probably NaF. Calculate K_b for the unknown from the data provided. *Solve*:

$$[OH^-] = 10^{-pOH}; \quad pOH = 14.00 - pH = 14.00 - 8.08 = 5.92$$

$$[OH^-] = 10^{-5.92} = 1.202 \times 10^{-6} = 1.2 \times 10^{-6} \, M = [HX]$$

$$[NaX] = [X^-] = 0.050 \text{ mol salt}/0.500 \, L = 0.10 \, M$$

$$K_b = \frac{[OH^-][HX]}{[X^-]} = \frac{(1.202 \times 10^{-6})^2}{(0.10 - 1.2 \times 10^{-6})} \approx \frac{(1.202 \times 10^{-6})^2}{0.10} = 1.4 \times 10^{-11}$$

K_b for $F^- = K_w/K_a$ for $HF = 1.0 \times 10^{-14}/6.8 \times 10^{-4} = 1.5 \times 10^{-11}$

The unknown is NaF.

16.79 *Analyze/Plan.* The solution will be basic because of the hydrolysis of the sorbate anion, $C_6H_7O_2^-$. Calculate the initial molarity of $C_6H_7O_2^-$. Calculate K_b from K_w/K_a. Solve the K_b expression for $[OH^-]$. *Solve*:

$$\frac{11.25 \text{ g } KC_6H_7O_2}{1.75 \, L} \times \frac{1 \text{ mol } KC_6H_7O_2}{150.2 \text{ g } KC_6H_7O_2} = 0.04280 = 0.0428 \, M \, KC_6H_7O_2$$

$$[C_6H_7O_2^-] = [KC_6H_7O_2] = 0.0428 \, M$$

$$C_6H_7O_2^-(aq) \; + \; H_2O(l) \; \rightleftharpoons \; HC_6H_7O_2(aq) \; + \; OH^-(aq)$$

initial	0.0428 M	0	0
equil.	(0.0428 - x) M	x M	x M

$$K_b = \frac{[HC_6H_7O_2][OH^-]}{[C_6H_7O_2^-]} = \frac{K_w}{K_a \text{ for } HC_6H_7O_2} = \frac{1.0 \times 10^{-14}}{1.7 \times 10^{-5}} = 5.88 \times 10^{-10} = 5.9 \times 10^{-10}$$

$$5.88 \times 10^{-10} = \frac{x^2}{0.0428 - x} \approx \frac{x^2}{0.0428}; \; x^2 = 0.0428 \, (5.88 \times 10^{-10})$$

$$x = [OH^-] = 5.018 \times 10^{-6} = 5.0 \times 10^{-6} \; M; \; pOH = 5.30; \; pH = 14 - pOH = 8.70$$

Acid-Base Character and Chemical Structure

16.81 (a) As the electronegativity of the central atom (X) increases, more electron density is withdrawn from the X–O and O–H bonds, respectively. In water, the O–H bond is ionized to a greater extent and the strength of the oxyacid increases.

(b) As the number of nonprotonated oxygen atoms in the molecule increases, they withdraw electron density from the other bonds in the molecule and the strength of the oxyacid increases.

16.83 (a) HNO_3 is a stronger acid than HNO_2 because it has one more nonprotonated oxygen atom, and thus a higher oxidation number on N.

(b) For binary hydrides, acid strength increases going down a family, so H_2S is a stronger acid than H_2O.

(c) H_2SO_4 is a stronger acid because H^+ is much more tightly held by the anion HSO_4^-.

(d) For oxyacids, the greater the electronegativity of the central atom, the stronger the acid, so H_2SO_4 is a stronger acid than H_2SeO_4.

(e) CCl_3COOH is stronger because the electronegative Cl atoms withdraw electron density from other parts of the molecule, which weakens the O-H bond and makes H^+ easier to remove.

16.85 (a) BrO^- (HClO is the stronger acid due to a more electronegative central atom, so BrO^- is the stronger base.)

(b) BrO^- ($HBrO_2$ has more nonprotonated O atoms and is the stronger acid, so BrO^- is the stronger base.)

(c) HPO_4^{2-} (larger negative charge, greater attraction for H^+)

16.87 (a)   True

     (b)   False. In a series of acids that have the same central atom, acid strength increases with the number of nonprotonated oxygen atoms bonded to the central atom.

     (c)   False. H_2Te is a stronger acid than H_2S because the H–Te bond is longer, weaker and more easily dissociated than the H–S bond.

Lewis Acids and Bases

16.89   Yes. If a substance is an Arrhenius base, it must also be a Brønsted base and a Lewis base. The Arrhenius definition (hydroxide ion) is the most restrictive, the Brønsted (H^+ acceptor) more general and the Lewis (electron pair donor) most general. Since a hydroxide ion is both an H^+ acceptor and an electron pair donor, any substance that fits the narrow Arrhenius definition will fit the broader Brønsted and Lewis definitions.

16.91   *Analyze/Plan.* Identify each reactant as an electron pair donor (Lewis base) or electron pair acceptor (Lewis acid). Remember that a Brønsted acid is necessarily a Lewis acid, and a Brønsted base is necessarily a Lewis base (Solution 16.89). *Solve:*

	Lewis Acid	**Lewis Base**
(a)	$Fe(ClO_4)_3$ or Fe^{3+}	H_2O
(b)	H_2O	CN^-
(c)	BF_3	$(CH_3)_3N$
(d)	HIO	NH_2^-

16.93 (a) Cu^{2+}, higher cation charge

     (b) Fe^{3+}, higher cation charge

     (c) Al^{3+}, smaller cation radius, same charge

Additional Exercises

16.95 (a)   Correct.

     (b)   Incorrect. A Brønsted acid must have ionizable hydrogen. Lewis acids are electron pair acceptors, but need not have ionizable hydrogen.

     (c)   Correct.

     (d)   Incorrect. K^+ is a negligible Lewis acid because it is the conjugate of strong base KOH. Its relatively large ionic radius and low positive charge render it a poor attractor of electron pairs.

     (e)   Correct.

16.98   Assume T = 25°C. For acid or base solute concentrations less than 1×10^{-6} M, we must consider the autoionization of water as a source of $[OH^-]$ and $[H^+]$.

$$H_2O(l) \rightleftharpoons [H^+] + [OH^-]$$

initial	C	0	2.5×10^{-9} M
equil	C	x	$(x + 2.5 \times 10^{-9})$ M

$K_w = 1.0 \times 10^{-14} = [H^+][OH^-] = (x)(x + 2.5 \times 10^{-9})$; $x2 + 2.5 \times 10^{-9} x - 1.0 \times 10^{-14} = 0$

From the quadratic formula, $x = \dfrac{-2.5 \times 10^{-9} \pm \sqrt{(2.5 \times 10^{-9})^2 - 4(-1 \times 10^{-14})}}{2}$

$$= 9.876 \times 10^{-8} = 9.9 \times 10^{-8} \text{ M H}^+$$

$[H^+] = 9.9 \times 10^{-8}$ M; $[OH^-] = 9.9 \times 10^{-8} + 2.5 \times 10^{-9}) = 1.013 \times 10^{-7} = 1.0 \times 10^{-7}$ M

pH = 7.0054 = 7.01

Check: $[9.876 \times 10^{-8}][1.013 \times 10^{-7}] = 1.0 \times 10^{-14}$

16.99   The solution with the higher pH has the lower $[H^+]$.

(a)   For solutions with equal concentrations, the weaker acid will have a lower $[H^+]$ and higher pH.

(b)   The acid with $K_a = 8 \times 10^{-6}$ is the weaker acid, so it has the higher pH.

(c)   The base with $pK_b = 4.5$ is the stronger base, has greater $[OH^-]$ and smaller $[H^+]$, so higher pH.

16.101 (a) $H_2X \rightarrow H^+ + HX^-$

           Assuming HX^- does not ionize, $[H^+] = 0.050$ M, pH = 1.30

(b) $H_2X \rightarrow 2H^+ + X^-$;   0.050 M H_2X = 0.10 M H^+; pH = 1.00

(c)   The observed pH of a 0.050 M solution of H_2X is only slightly less than 1.30, the pH assuming no ionization of HX^-. HX^- is not completely ionized; H_2X, which is completely ionized, is a stronger acid than HX^-.

(d)   Since H_2X is a strong acid, HX^- has no tendency to act like a base. HX^- does act like a weak acid, so a solution of NaHX would be acidic.

16.104   Call each compound in the neutral form Q.

         Then, $Q(aq) + H_2O(l) \rightleftharpoons QH^+(aq) + OH^-$. $K_b = [QH^+][OH^-] / [Q]$

The ratio in question is $[QH^+] / [Q]$, which equals $K_b / [OH^-]$ for each compound. At pH = 2.5, pOH = 11.5, $[OH^-]$ = antilog (-11.5) = $3.16 \times 10^{-12} = 3 \times 10^{-12}$ M. Now calculate $K_b / [OH^-]$ for each compound:

Nicotine $\dfrac{[QH^+]}{[Q]} = 7 \times 10^{-7} / 3.16 \times 10^{-12} = 2 \times 10^5$

Caffeine $\dfrac{[QH^+]}{[Q]} = 4 \times 10^{-14} / 3.16 \times 10^{-12} = 1 \times 10^{-2}$

Strychnine $\dfrac{[QH^+]}{[Q]} = 1 \times 10^{-6} / 3.16 \times 10^{-12} = 3 \times 10^5$

Quinine $\dfrac{[QH^+]}{[Q]} = 1.1 \times 10^{-6} / 3.16 \times 10^{-12} = 3.5 \times 10^5$

For all the compounds except caffeine the protonated form has a much higher concentration than the neutral form. However, for caffeine, a very weak base, the neutral form dominates.

Integrative Exercises

16.107 At 25°C, $[H^+] = [OH^-] = 1.0 \times 10^{-7}$ M

$$\frac{1.0 \times 10^{-7} \text{ mol H}^+}{1\,\text{L}\,H_2O} \times 0.0010\,\text{L} \times \frac{6.022 \times 10^{23}\,\text{H}^+\text{ ions}}{\text{mol H}^+} = 6.0 \times 10^{13}\,\text{H}^+\text{ ions}$$

16.109 *Analyze.* If pH were directly related to CO_2 concentration, this exercise would be simple. Unfortunately, we must solve the equilibrium problem for the diprotic acid H_2CO_3 to calculate $[H^+]$ and pH. We are given ppm CO_2 **in the atmosphere** at two different times, and the pH that corresponds to one of these CO_2 levels. We are asked to find pH at the other atmospheric CO_2 level.

Plan. Assume all dissolved CO_2 is present as H_2CO_3 (aq) (Sample Exercise 16.13). pH → $[H^+]$ → $[H_2CO_3]$. While H_2CO_3 is a diprotic acid, the two K_a values differ by more than 10^3, so we can ignore the second ionization when calculating $[H_2CO_3]$. Change 375 ppm CO_2 to pressure and calculate the Henry's law constant for CO_2. Calculate the dissolved $[CO_2] = [H_2CO_3]$ at 315 ppm, then solve the K_{a1} expression for $[H^+]$ and pH.

(a) *Solve:* $H_2CO_3(aq) \rightleftharpoons H^+(aq) + HCO_3^-$ (aq)

$K_{a1} = 4.3 \times 10^{-7} = \dfrac{[H^+][HCO_3^-]}{[H_2CO_3]}$; $[H^+] = 10^{-5.4} = 3.98 \times 10^{-6} = 4 \times 10^{-6}$ M

$[H^+] = [HCO_3^-]$; $[H_2CO_3] = x - 4 \times 10^{-6}$

$4.3 \times 10^{-7} = \dfrac{(3.98 \times 10^{-6})^2}{(x - 3.98 \times 10^{-6})}$; $4.3 \times 10^{-7} x = 1.585 \times 10^{-11} + 1.712 \times 10^{-12}$

$x = 1.756 \times 10^{-11} / 4.3 \times 10^{-7} = 4.084 \times 10^{-5} = 4 \times 10^{-5}$ M H_2CO_3

375 ppm = 375 mol CO_2/1 × 10^6 mol air = 0.000375 mol % CO_2

Because of the properties of gases, mol % = pressure %. P_{CO_2} = 0.000375 atm. According to Equation 13.4, $S_{CO_2} = kP_{CO_2}$; 4.084×10^{-5} mol/L = k(3.75×10^{-4} atm) k = 0.1089 = 0.1 mol/L•atm.

Forty years ago, S_{CO_2} = 0.1089 $\dfrac{mol}{L•atm}$ × 3.15×10^{-4} atm = 3.4305×10^{-5}

$$= 3.4 \times 10^{-5} M$$

Now solve K_{a1} for [H$^+$] at this [H$_2$CO$_3$]. [H$^+$] = x
We cannot assume x is small, because [H$_2$CO$_3$] is so low.

4.3×10^{-7} = x^2/(3.4305×10^{-5} - x); x^2 + 4.3×10^{-7} x - 1.475×10^{-11} = 0

$$x = \frac{-4.3 \times 10^{-7} \pm \sqrt{(4.3 \times 10^{-7})^2 - 4(-1.475 \times 10^{-11})}}{2} = \frac{-4.3 \times 10^{-7} + 7.693 \times 10^{-6}}{2}$$

$$= 3.632 \times 10^{-6} = 3.6 \times 10^{-6} M \, H^+$$

[H$^+$] = 3.6×10^{-6} M, pH = 5.440 = 5.4

[Note that, to the precision that the pH data is reported, the change in atmospheric CO$_2$ leads to no change in pH.]

(b)   From part (a), [H$_2$CO$_3$] today = 4.084×10^{-5} M

$$\frac{4.084 \times 10^{-5} \, mol \, H_2CO_3}{1 \, L} \times 20.0 \, L = 8.168 \times 10^{-4} = 8 \times 10^{-4} \, mol \, CO_2$$

$$V = \frac{nRT}{P} = 8.168 \times 10^{-5} \, mol \times \frac{298 \, K}{1.0 \, atm} \times \frac{0.08206 \, L•atm}{mol•K} = 0.01997 = 0.02 \, L = 20 \, mL$$

16.112 Calculate M of the solution from osmotic pressure, and K$_b$ using the equilibrium expression for the hydrolysis of cocaine. Let Coc = cocaine and CocH$^+$ be the conjugate acid of cocaine.

$$\pi = M \, RT; \quad M = \pi/RT = \frac{52.7 \, torr}{288 \, K} \times \frac{1 \, atm}{760 \, torr} \times \frac{mol•K}{0.08206 \, L•atm}$$

$$= 0.002934 = 2.93 \times 10^{-3} M \, Coc$$

pH = 8.53; pOH = 14 - pH = 5.47; [OH$^-$] = $10^{-5.47}$ = 3.39×10^{-6} = 3.4×10^{-6} M

	Coc(aq) + H$_2$O(l) ⇌	CocH$^+$(aq) +	OH$^-$(aq)
initial	2.93×10^{-3} M	0	0
equil.	(2.93×10^{-3} - 3.4×10^{-6}) M	3.4×10^{-6} M	3.4×10^{-6} M

$$K_b = \frac{[CocH^+][OH^-]}{[Coc]} = \frac{(3.39 \times 10^{-6})^2}{(2.934 \times 10^{-3} - 3.39 \times 10^{-6})} = 3.9 \times 10^{-9}$$

Note that % hydrolysis is small in this solution, so "x", 3.4×10^{-6} M, is small compared to 2.93×10^{-3} M and could be ignored in the denominator of the calculation.

16.114 (a)   (i) $HCO_3^-(aq) \rightleftharpoons H^+(aq) + CO_3^{2-}(aq)$ $K_1 = K_{a2}$ for $H_2CO_3 = 5.6 \times 10^{-11}$

                    $H^+(aq) + OH^-(aq) \rightleftharpoons H_2O(l)$ $K_2 = 1/K_w = 1 \times 10^{14}$

                    $HCO_3^-(aq) + OH^-(aq) \rightleftharpoons CO_3^{2-}(aq) + H_2O(l)$ $K = K_1 \times K_2 = 5.6 \times 10^3$

         (ii) $NH_4^+(aq) \rightleftharpoons H^+(aq) + NH_3(aq)$ $K_1 = K_a$ for $NH_4^+ = 5.6 \times 10^{-10}$

                    $CO_3^{2-}(aq) + H^+(aq) \rightleftharpoons HCO_3^-(aq)$ $K_2 = 1/K_{a2}$ for $H_2CO_3 = 1.8 \times 10^{10}$

                    $NH_4^+(aq) + CO_3^{2-}(aq) \rightleftharpoons HCO_3^-(aq) + NH_3(aq)$ $K = K_1 \times K_2 = 10$

     (b)   Both (i) and (ii) have K > 1, although K = 10 is not **much** greater than 1. Both could be written with a single arrow. (This is true in general when a strong acid or strong base, $H^+(aq)$ or $OH^-(aq)$, is a reactant.)

17 Additional Aspects of Aqueous Equilibria

Common-Ion Effect

17.1 (a) The extent of ionization of a weak electrolyte is decreased when a strong electrolyte containing an ion in common with the weak electrolyte is added to it.

(b) $NaNO_2$

17.3 *Analyze/Plan.* Given the formula of two substances, determine the effect on pH when one is added to the other. In general, when an acid is added to a solution, pH decreases; when a base is added to a solution, pH increases. Based on its formula, determine whether the substance being added is an acid or a base and predict the change in pH of the solution. *Solve:*

(a) pH increases; NO_2^- decreases the ionization of HNO_2 and decreases $[H^+]$.

(b) pH decreases; $CH_3NH_3^+$ decreases the ionization (hydrolysis) of CH_3NH_2 and decreases $[OH^-]$.

(c) pH increases; CHO_2^- decreases the ionization of $HCHO_2$ and decreases $[H^+]$.

(d) no change; Br^- is a negligible base and does not affect the 100% ionization of the strong acid HBr.

(e) pH decreases; the pertinent equilibrium is
$C_2H_3O_2^-(aq) + H_2O(l) \rightleftharpoons HC_2H_3O_2 + OH^-(aq)$.
HCl reacts with $OH^-(aq)$, decreasing $[OH^-]$ and pH.

17.5 *Analyze/Plan.* Follow the logic in Sample Exercise 17.1.

$$HC_3H_5O_2(aq) \rightleftharpoons H^+(aq) + C_3H_5O_2^-(aq)$$

i	0.085 M		0.060 M
c	-x	+x	+x
e	(0.085 - x) M	+x M	(0.060 + x) M

$$K_a = 1.3 \times 10^{-5} = \frac{[H^+][C_3H_5O_2^-]}{[HC_3H_5O_2]} = \frac{(x)(0.060 + x)}{(0.085 - x)}$$

Assume x is small compared to 0.060 and 0.085.

$$1.3 \times 10^{-5} = \frac{0.060\, x}{0.085}; \quad x = 1.8 \times 10^{-5} = [H^+], \text{ pH} = 4.73$$

$$[C_3H_5O_2^-] = 0.060 + 1.8 \times 10^{-5} = 6.002 \times 10^{-2} = 6.0 \times 10^{-2}\ M$$

17.7 *Analyze/Plan.* Follow the logic in Sample Exercise 17.1. This exercise is more straightforward than the sample, because we are given concentrations directly. *Solve:*

(a) $HCHO_2$ is a weak acid, and $NaCHO_2$ contains the common ion CHO_2^-, the conjugate base of $HCHO_2$. Solve the common-ion equilibrium problem.

$$HCHO_2(aq) \rightleftharpoons H^+(aq) + CHO_2^-(aq)$$

i	0.260 M		0.160 M
c	-x	+x	+x
e	(0.260 - x) M	+x M	(0.160 + x) M

$$K_a = 1.8 \times 10^{-4} = \frac{[H^+][CHO_2^-]}{[HCHO_2]} = \frac{(x)(0.160 + x)}{(0.260 - x)} \approx \frac{0.160\,x}{0.260}$$

$x = 2.93 \times 10^{-4} = 2.9 \times 10^{-4}\ M = [H^+]$, pH = 3.53

Check: Since the extent of ionization of a weak acid or base is suppressed by the presence of a conjugate salt, the 5% rule usually holds true in buffer solutions.

(b) C_5H_5N is a weak base, and C_5H_5NHCl contains the common ion $C_5H_5NH^+$, which is the conjugate acid of C_5H_5N. Solve the common ion equilibrium problem.

$$C_5H_5N(aq) + H_2O(l) \rightleftharpoons C_5H_5NH^+(aq) + OH^-(aq)$$

i	0.210 M	0.350 M	
c	-x	+x	+x
e	(0.210 - x) M	(0.0350 + x) M	+x M

$$K_b = 1.7 \times 10^{-9} = \frac{[C_5H_5NH^+][OH^-]}{[C_5H_5N]} = \frac{(0.350 + x)(x)}{(0.210 - x)} \approx \frac{0.350\,x}{0.210}$$

$x = 1.02 \times 10^{-9} = 1.0 \times 10^{-9}\ M = [OH^-]$, pOH = 8.991, pH = 14.00 - 8.991 = 5.01

Check. In a buffer, if [conj. acid] > [conj. base], pH < pK_a of the conj. acid. If [conj. acid] < [conj. base], pH > pK_a of the conj. acid. In this buffer, pK_a of $C_5H_5NH^+$ is 5.23. $[C_5H_5NH^+]$ > $[C_5H_5N]$ and pH = 5.009, less than 5.23.

17.9 *Analyze/Plan.* We are asked to calculate % ionization of (a) a weak acid and (b) a weak acid in a solution containing a common ion, its conjugate base. Calculate % ionization as in Sample Exercise 16.12. In part (b), the concentration of the common ion is 0.085 M, not x, as in part (a). *Solve:*

$$HBu(aq) \rightleftharpoons H^+(aq) + Bu^-(aq) \qquad K_a = \frac{[H^+][Bu^-]}{[HBu]} = 1.5 \times 10^{-5}$$

equil (a)	$0.0075 - x\ M$	$x\ M$	$x\ M$
equil (b)	$0.0075 - x\ M$	$x\ M$	$0.085 + x\ M$

(a) $K_a = 1.5 \times 10^{-5} = \dfrac{x^2}{0.0075 - x} \approx \dfrac{x^2}{0.0075}$; $x = [H^+] = 3.354 \times 10^{-4} = 3.4 \times 10^{-4}\ M\ H^+$

$\%$ ionization $= \dfrac{3.4 \times 10^{-4}\ M\ H^+}{0.0075\ M\ HBu} \times 100 = 4.5\%$ ionization

(b) $K_a = 1.5 \times 10^{-5} = \dfrac{(x)(0.085 + x)}{0.0075 - x} \approx \dfrac{0.085\,x}{0.0075}$; $x = 1.3 \times 10^{-6}\ M\ H^+$

$\%$ ionization $= \dfrac{1.3 \times 10^{-6}\ M\ H^+}{0.0075\ M\ HBu} \times 100 = 0.018\%$ ionization

Check. Percent ionization is much smaller when the 'common ion' is present.

Buffers

17.11 $HC_2H_3O_2$ and $NaC_2H_3O_2$ are a weak conjugate acid/conjugate base pair which act as a buffer because unionized $HC_2H_3O_2$ reacts with added base, while $C_2H_3O_2^-$ combines with added acid, leaving $[H^+]$ relatively unchanged. Although HCl and NaCl are a conjugate acid/conjugate base pair, Cl^- is a negligible base. That is, it has no tendency to combine with added acid to form unionized HCl. Any added acid simply increases $[H^+]$ in an HCl/NaCl mixture. In general, the conjugate bases of strong acids are negligible and mixtures of strong acids and their conjugate salts do not act as buffers.

17.13   *Analyze/Plan.* Follow the logic in Sample Exercise 17.3. Assume that $\%$ ionization is small in these buffers (Solutions 17.9 and 17.10). *Solve:*

(a) $K_a = \dfrac{[H^+][Lac^-]}{[HLac]}$; $[H^+] = \dfrac{[K_a][HLac]}{[Lac^-]} = \dfrac{1.4 \times 10^{-4}\,(0.12)}{(0.11)}$

$[H^+] = 1.53 \times 10^{-4} = 1.5 \times 10^{-4}$; pH = 3.82

(b)   mol $= M \times L$; total volume $= 85\ mL + 95\ mL = 180\ mL$

$[H^+] = \dfrac{K_a[HLac]}{[Lac^-]} = \dfrac{1.4 \times 10^{-4}\,(0.13\ M \times 0.085\ L)/0.180\ L}{(0.15\ M \times 0.095\ L)/0.180\ L} = \dfrac{1.4 \times 10^{-4}\,(0.13 \times 0.085)}{(0.15 \times 0.095)}$

$[H^+] = 1.086 \times 10^{-4} = 1.1\ M\ H^+$; pH = 3.96

17.15   (a)   *Analyze/Plan.* Follow the logic in Sample Exercises 17.1 and 17.3. As in Sample Exercise 17.1, start by calculating concentrations of the components. *Solve:*

$$HC_2H_3O_2(aq) \rightleftharpoons H^+(aq) + C_2H_3O_2^-(aq); \quad K_a = 1.8 \times 10^{-5} = \frac{[H^+][C_2H_3O_2^-]}{[HC_2H_3O_2]}$$

$[HC_2H_3O_2] = \dfrac{20.0\ g\ HC_2H_3O_2}{2.00\ L\ soln} \times \dfrac{1\ mol\ HC_2H_3O_2}{60.05\ g\ HC_2H_3O_2} = 0.167\ M$

$$[C_2H_3O_2^-] = \frac{20.0 \text{ g NaC}_2H_3O_2}{2.00 \text{ L soln}} \times \frac{1 \text{ mol NaC}_2H_3O_2}{82.04 \text{ g NaC}_2H_3O_2} = 0.122 \text{ M}$$

$$[H^+] = \frac{K_a[HC_2H_3O_2]}{[C_2H_3O_2^-]} = \frac{1.8 \times 10^{-5}(0.167 - x)}{(0.122 + x)} \approx \frac{1.8 \times 10^{-5}(0.167)}{(0.122)}$$

$[H^+] = 2.4843 \times 10^{-5} = 2.5 \times 10^{-5}$ M, pH = 4.60

(b) *Plan.* On the left side of the equation, write all ions present in solution after HCl or NaOH is added to the buffer. Using acid-base properties and relative strengths, decide which ions will combine to form new products. *Solve:*

$$Na^+(aq) + C_2H_3O_2^-(aq) + H^+(aq) + Cl^-(aq) \rightarrow HC_2H_3O_2(aq) + Na^+(aq) + Cl^-(aq)$$

(c) $HC_2H_3O_2(aq) + Na^+(aq) + OH^-(aq) \rightarrow C_2H_3O_2^-(aq) + H_2O(l) + Na^+(aq)$

17.17 *Analyze/Plan.* Follow the logic in Sample Exercise 17.4. *Solve:*

In this problem, $[BrO^-]$ is the unknown.

pH = 9.15, $[H^+] = 10^{-9/15} = 7.0795 \times 10^{-10} = 7.1 \times 10^{-10}$ M

$[HBrO] = 0.050 - 7.1 \times 10^{-10} \approx 0.050$ M

$$K_a = 2.5 \times 10^{-9} = \frac{7.0795 \times 10^{-10}[BrO^-]}{0.050}; \quad [BrO^-] = 0.1766 = 0.18 \text{ M}$$

For 1.00 L, 0.18 mol NaBrO are needed.

17.19 *Analyze/Plan.* Follow the logic in Sample Exercise 17.5. *Solve:*

(a) $$K_a = \frac{[H^+][C_2H_3O_2^-]}{[HC_2H_3O_2]}; \quad [H^+] = \frac{K_a[HC_2H_3O_2]}{[C_2H_3O_2^-]}$$

$$[H^+] \approx \frac{1.8 \times 10^{-5}(0.10)}{(0.13)} = 1.385 \times 10^{-5} = 1.4 \times 10^{-5} \text{ M}; \quad pH = 4.86$$

(b) $HC_2H_3O_2(aq) + KOH(aq) \rightarrow C_2H_3O_2^-(aq) + H_2O(l) + K^+(aq)$

0.10 mol	0.02 mol	0.13 mol
-0.02 mol	-0.02 mol	+0.02 mol
0.08 mol	0 mol	0.15 mol

$$[H^+] = \frac{1.8 \times 10^{-5}(0.08 \text{ mol}/0.100 \text{ L})}{(0.15 \text{ mol}/0.100 \text{ L})} = 9.60 \times 10^{-6} = 1 \times 10^{-5} \text{ M}; \quad pH = 5.02 = 5.0$$

(c) $C_2H_3O_2^-(aq) + HNO_3(aq) \rightarrow HC_2H_3O_2(aq) + Cl^-(aq)$

0.13 mol	0.02 mol	0.10 mol
-0.02 mol	-0.02 mol	+0.02 mol
0.11 mol	0 mol	0.12 mol

$$[H^+] = \frac{1.8 \times 10^{-5}(0.12 \text{ mol}/0.100 \text{ L})}{(0.11 \text{ mol}/0.100 \text{ L})} = 1.96 \times 10^{-5} = 2.0 \times 10^{-5} \text{ M}; \quad pH = 4.71$$

17.21 *Analyze/Plan.* Calculate the [conj. base]/[conj. acid] ratio in the H_2CO_3/HCO_3^- blood buffer. Write the acid dissociation equilibrium and K_a expression. Find K_a for H_2CO_3 in Appendix D. Calculate [H$^+$] from the pH and solve for the ratio. *Solve:*

$$H_2CO_3(aq) \rightleftharpoons H^+(aq) + HCO_3^-(aq) \quad K_a = \frac{[H^+][HCO_3^-]}{[H_2CO_3]}; \quad \frac{[HCO_3^-]}{[H_2CO_3]} = \frac{K_a}{[H^+]}$$

(a) at pH = 7.4, [H$^+$] = $10^{-7.4}$ = 4.0×10^{-8} M; $\quad \dfrac{[HCO_3^-]}{[H_2CO_3]} = \dfrac{4.3 \times 10^{-7}}{4.0 \times 10^{-8}} = 11$

(b) at pH = 7.1, [H$^+$] = 7.9×10^{-8} M; $\quad \dfrac{[HCO_3^-]}{[H_2CO_3]} = 5.4$

Acid-Base Titrations

17.23 (a) Curve B. The initial pH is lower and the equivalence point region is steeper.

(b) pH at the approximate equivalence point of curve A = 8.0
pH at the approximate equivalence point of curve B = 7.0

(c) Volume of base required to reach the equivalence point depends only on moles of acid present; it is independent of acid strength. Since acid B requires 40 mL and acid A requires only 30 mL, more moles of acid B are being titrated. For equal volumes of A and B, the concentration of acid B is greater.

17.25 (a) HX is weaker. The pH at the equivalence point is determined by the identity and concentration of the conjugate base, X^- or Y^-. The higher the pH at the equivalence point, the stronger the conjugate base (X^-) and the weaker the conjugate acid (HX).

(b) Phenolphthalein, which changes color in the pH 8-10 range, is perfect for HX and probably appropriate for HY. Bromthymol blue changes from 6-7.5, and thymol blue between from 8-9.5, but these are two-color indicators. One-color indicators such as phenolphthalein are preferred because detection of the color change is more reproducible.

17.27 *Analyze/Plan.* We are asked to calculate the volume of 0.0850 M NaOH required to titrate various acid solutions to their equivalence point. At the equivalence point, moles base added equals moles acid initially present. Solve the stoichiometry problem, recalling that mol = $M \times$ L. In part (c) calculate molarity of HCl from g/L and proceed as outlined above. *Solve:*

(a) $40.0 \text{ mL HNO}_3 \times \dfrac{0.0900 \text{ mol HNO}_3}{1000 \text{ mL soln}} \times \dfrac{1 \text{ mol NaOH}}{1 \text{ mol HNO}_3} \times \dfrac{1000 \text{ mL soln}}{0.0850 \text{ mol NaOH}}$

$= 42.353 = 42.4 \text{ mL NaOH soln}$

(b) $35.0 \text{ mL HBr} \times \dfrac{0.0720 \ M \text{ HBr}}{1000 \text{ mL soln}} \times \dfrac{1 \text{ mol NaOH}}{1 \text{ mol HBr}} \times \dfrac{1000 \text{ mL soln}}{0.0850 \text{ mol NaOH}}$

$= 29.645 = 29.6 \text{ mL NaOH soln}$

(c) $\dfrac{1.85 \text{ g HCl}}{1 \text{ L soln}} \times \dfrac{1 \text{ mol HCl}}{36.46 \text{ g HCl}} = 0.05074 = 0.0507 \ M \text{ HCl}$

$50.0 \text{ mL HCl} \times \dfrac{0.05074 \text{ mol HCl}}{1000 \text{ mL}} \times \dfrac{1 \text{ mol NaOH}}{1 \text{ mol HCL}} \times \dfrac{1000 \text{ mL soln}}{0.0850 \text{ mol NaOH}}$

$= 29.847 = 29.8 \text{ mL NaOH soln}$

17.29 *Analyze/Plan.* Follow the logic in Sample Exercise 17.6 for the titration of a strong acid with a strong base. *Solve:*

moles $H^+ = M_{HBr} \times L_{HBr} = 0.200 \ M \times 0.0200 \text{ L} = 4.00 \times 10^{-3} \text{ mol}$

moles $OH^- = M_{NaOH} \times L_{NaOH} = 0.200 \ M \times L_{NaOH}$

	mL_{HBr}	mL_{NaOH}	Total Volume	Moles H^+	Moles OH^-	Molarity Excess Ion	pH
(a)	20.0	15.0	35.0	4.00×10^{-3}	3.00×10^{-3}	$0.0286(H^+)$	1.544
(b)	20.0	19.9	39.9	4.00×10^{-3}	3.98×10^{-3}	$5 \times 10^{-4}(H^+)$	3.3
(c)	20.0	20.0	40.0	4.00×10^{-3}	4.00×10^{-3}	$1 \times 10^{-7}(H^+)$	7.0
(d)	20.0	20.1	40.1	4.00×10^{-3}	4.02×10^{-3}	$5 \times 10^{-4}(H^+)$	10.7
(e)	20.0	35.0	55.0	4.00×10^{-3}	7.00×10^{-3}	$0.0545(OH^-)$	12.737

molarity of excess ion = moles ion / total vol in L

(a) $\dfrac{4.00 \times 10^{-3} \text{ mol H}^+ - 3.00 \times 10^{-3} \text{ mol OH}^-}{0.0350 \text{ L}} = 0.0286 \ M \text{ H}^+$

(b) $\dfrac{4.00 \times 10^{-3} \text{ mol H}^+ - 3.98 \times 10^{-3} \text{ mol OH}^-}{0.0339 \text{ L}} = 5.01 \times 10^{-4} = 5 \times 10^{-4} \ M \text{ H}^+$

(c)   equivalence point, mol $H^+ =$ mol OH^-

NaBr does not hydrolyze, so $[H^+] = [OH^-] = 1 \times 10^{-7} \ M$

(d) $\dfrac{4.02 \times 10^{-3} \text{ mol H}^+ - 4.00 \times 10^{-3} \text{ mol OH}^-}{0.041 \text{ L}} = 4.88 \times 10^{-4} = 5 \times 10^{-4} \ M \text{ OH}^-$

(e) $\dfrac{7.00 \times 10^{-3} \text{ mol H}^+ - 4.00 \times 10^{-3} \text{ mol OH}^-}{0.0550 \text{ L}} = 0.054545 = 0.0545 \ M \text{ OH}^-$

17.31 *Analyze/Plan.* Follow the logic in Sample Exercise 17.7 for the titration of a weak acid with a strong base. *Solve:*

(a)   At 0 mL, only weak acid, $HC_2H_3O_2$, is present in solution. Using the acid ionization equilibrium

$$HC_2H_3O_2(aq) \rightleftharpoons H^+(aq) + C_2H_3O_2^-(aq)$$

initial	0.150 M	0	0
equil	0.150 - x M	x M	x M

$$K_a = \frac{[H^+][C_2H_3O_2^-]}{[HC_2H_3O_2]} = 1.8 \times 10^{-5} \text{ (Appendix D)}$$

$$1.8 \times 10^{-5} = \frac{x^2}{(0.150 - x)} \approx \frac{x^2}{0.150}; \quad x^2 = 2.7 \times 10^{-6}; \quad x = [H^+] = 0.001643$$
$$= 1.6 \times 10^{-3}; \quad pH = 2.78$$

(b)-(f)   Calculate the moles of each component after the acid-base reaction takes place.
Moles $HC_2H_3O_2$ originally present = $M \times L$ = 0.150 $M \times$ 0.0350 L = 5.25 × 10^{-3} mol.
Moles NaOH added = $M \times L$ = 0.150 $M \times$ y mL.

$$NaOH(aq) \quad + \quad HC_2H_3O_2(aq) \quad \rightarrow \quad Na^+C_2H_3O_2^-(aq) + H_2O(l)$$

(b)

	(0.150 M × 0.0175 L) =		
before rx	2.625 × 10^{-3} mol	5.25 × 10^{-3} mol	
after rx	0	2.625 × 10^{-3} mol	2.63 × 10^{-3} mol

(c)

	(0.150 M × 0.0345 L) =		
before rx	5.175 × 10^{-3} mol	5.25 × 10^{-3} mol	
after rx	0	0.075 × 10^{-3} mol	5.18 × 10^{-3} mol

(d)

	(0.150 M × 0.0350 L) =		
before rx	5.25 × 10^{-3} mol	5.25 × 10^{-3} mol	
after rx	0	0	5.25 × 10^{-3} mol

(e)

	(0.150 M × 0.0355 L) =		
before rx	5.325 × 10^{-3} mol	5.25 × 10^{-3} mol	
after rx	0.075 × 10^{-3} mol	0	5.25 × 10^{-3} mol

(f)

	(0.150 M × 0.0500 L) =		
before rx	7.50 × 10^{-3} mol	5.25 × 10^{-3} mol	
after rx	2.25 × 10^{-3} mol	0	5.25 × 10^{-3} mol

Calculate the molarity of each species (M = mol/L) and solve the appropriate equilibrium problem in each part.

(b) V_T = 35.0 mL $HC_2H_3O_2$ + 17.5 mL NaOH = 52.5 mL = 0.0525 L

$$[HC_2H_3O_2] = \frac{2.625 \times 10^{-3} \text{ mol}}{0.0525} = 0.0500 \text{ M}$$

$$[C_2H_3O_2^-] = \frac{2.625 \times 10^{-3} \text{ mol}}{0.0525} = 0.0500 \text{ M}$$

$$HC_2H_3O_2(aq) \rightleftharpoons H^+(aq) + C_2H_3O_2^-(aq)$$

equil $0.0500 - x$ M x M $0.0500 + x$ M

$$K_a = \frac{[H^+][C_2H_3O_2^-]}{[HC_2H_3O_2]}; \quad [H^+] = \frac{K_a[HC_2H_3O_2]}{[C_2H_3O_2^-]}$$

$$[H^+] = \frac{1.8 \times 10^{-5}(0.0500 - x)}{(0.0500 + x)} = 1.8 \times 10^{-5} \ M \ H^+; \quad pH = 4.74$$

(c) $$[HC_2H_3O_2] = \frac{7.5 \times 10^{-5} \ \text{mol}}{0.0695 \ \text{L}} = 0.001079 = 1.1 \times 10^{-3} \ M$$

$$[C_2H_3O_2^-] = \frac{5.175 \times 10^{-3} \ \text{mol}}{0.0695 \ \text{L}} = 0.07446 = 0.074 \ M$$

$$[H^+] = \frac{1.8 \times 10^{-5}(1.079 \times 10^{-3} - x)}{(0.07446 + x)} \approx 2.6 \times 10^{-7} \ M \ H^+; \quad pH = 6.58$$

(d)   At the equivalence point, only $C_3H_5O_2^-$ is present.

$$[C_2H_3O_2^-] = \frac{5.25 \times 10^{-3} \ \text{mol}}{0.0700 \ \text{L}} = 0.0750 \ M$$

The pertinent equilibrium is the base hydrolysis of $C_2H_3O_2^-$.

$$C_2H_3O_2^-(aq) + H_2O(l) \rightleftharpoons HC_2H_3O_2(aq) + OH^-(aq)$$

initial $0.0750 \ M$ 0 0
equil $0.0750 - x \ M$ x x

$$K_b = \frac{K_w}{K_a \ \text{for} \ HC_2H_3O_2} = \frac{1.0 \times 10^{-14}}{1.8 \times 10^{-5}} = 5.56 \times 10^{-10} = 5.6 \times 10^{-10} = \frac{[HC_2H_3O_2][OH^-]}{[C_2H_3O_2^-]}$$

$$5.56 \times 10^{-10} = \frac{x^2}{0.0750 - x}; \quad x^2 \approx 5.56 \times 10^{-10}(0.0750); \quad x = 6.458 \times 10^{-6}$$

$$= 6.5 \times 10^{-10} \ M \ OH^-$$

$$pOH = -\log(6.458 \times 10^{-6}) = 5.19; \quad pH = 14.00 - pOH = 8.81$$

(e)   After the equivalence point, the excess strong base determines the pOH and pH. The $[OH^-]$ from the hydrolysis of $C_2H_3O_2^-$ is small and can be ignored.

$$[OH^-] = \frac{0.075 \times 10^{-3} \ \text{mol}}{0.0705 \ \text{L}} = 1.064 \times 10^{-3} = 1.1 \times 10^{-3} \ M; \quad pOH = 2.97$$

$$pH = 14.00 - 2.97 = 11.03$$

(f) $$[OH^-] = \frac{2.25 \times 10^{-3} \ \text{mol}}{0.0850 \ \text{L}} = 0.0265 \ M \ OH^-; \quad pOH = 1.577; \quad pH = 14.00 - 1.577 = 12.423$$

17.33 *Analyze/Plan.* Calculate the pH at the equivalence point for the titration of several bases with 0.200 M HBr. The volume of 0.200 M HBr required in all cases equals the volume of base and the final volume $= 2V_{base}$. The concentration of the salt produced at the equivalence point is

$$\frac{0.200\, M \times V_{base}}{2V_{base}} = 0.100\ M.$$

In each case, identify the salt present at the equivalence point, determine its acid-base properties (Section 16.9), and solve the pH problem. *Solve:*

(a) NaOH is a strong base; the salt present at the equivalence point, NaBr, does not affect the pH of the solution. 0.100 M NaBr, pH = 7.00

(b) $HONH_2$ is a weak base, so the salt present at the equivalence point is $HONH_3^+Br^-$. This is the salt of a strong acid and a weak base, so it produces an acidic solution.

$$0.100\ M\ HONH_3^+Br^-;\qquad\qquad HONH_3^+(aq) \rightleftharpoons H^+(aq) + HONH_2$$
$$[\text{equil}]\quad 0.100 - x \qquad\qquad x \qquad\quad x$$

$$K_a = \frac{[H^+][HONH_2]}{[HONH_3^+]} = \frac{K_w}{K_b} = \frac{1.0 \times 10^{-14}}{1.1 \times 10^{-8}} = 9.09 \times 10^{-7} = 9.1 \times 10^{-7}$$

Assume x is small with respect to [salt].

$K_a = x^2 / 0.100;\ x = [H^+] = 3.02 \times 10^{-4} = 3.0 \times 10^{-4}\ M,\ pH = 3.52$

(c) $C_6H_5NH_2$ is a weak base and $C_6H_5NH_3^+Br^-$ is an acidic salt.

0.100 M $C_6H_5NH_3^+Br^-$. Proceeding as in (b):

$$K_a = \frac{[H^+][C_6H_5NH_2]}{[C_6H_5NH_3^+]} = \frac{K_w}{K_b} = 2.33 \times 10^{-5} = 2.3 \times 10^{-5}$$

$[H^+]^2 = 0.100(2.33 \times 10^{-5});\ [H^+] = 1.52 \times 10^{-3} = 1.5 \times 10^{-3}\ M,\ pH = 2.82$

Solubility Equilibria and Factors Affecting Solubility

17.35 (a) The concentration of undissolved solid does not appear in the solubility product expression because it is constant as long as there is solid present. Concentration is a ratio of moles solid to volume of the solid; solids occupy a specific volume not dependent on the solution volume. As the amount (moles) of solid changes, the volume changes proportionally, so that the ratio of moles solid to volume solid is constant.

(b) *Analyze/Plan.* Follow the example in Sample Exercise 17.9. *Solve:*

$K_{sp} = [Ag^+][I^-];\ \ K_{sp} = [Sr^{2+}][SO_4^{2-}];\ \ K_{sp} = [Fe^{2+}][OH^-]^2;\ \ K_{sp} = [Hg_2^{2+}][Br^-]^2$

17.37 *Analyze/Plan.* Follow the logic in Sample Exercise 17.10. *Solve:*

(a) $CaF_2(s) \rightleftharpoons Ca^{2+}(aq) + 2F^-(aq)$; $K_{sp} = [Ca^{2+}][F^-]^2$

The molar solubility is the moles of CaF_2 that dissolve per liter of solution. Each mole of CaF_2 produces **1** mol $Ca^{2+}(aq)$ and **2** mol $F^-(aq)$.

$[Ca^{2+}] = 1.24 \times 10^{-3}$ M; $[F^-] = 2 \times 1.24 \times 10^{-3}$ $M = 2.48 \times 10^{-3}$ M

$K_{sp} = (1.24 \times 10^{-3})(2.48 \times 10^{-3})^2 = 7.63 \times 10^{-9}$

(b) $SrF_2(s) \rightleftharpoons Sr^{2+}(aq) + 2F^-(aq)$; $K_{sp} = [Sr^{2+}][F^-]^2$

Transform the gram solubility to molar solubility.

$$\frac{1.1 \times 10^{-2} \text{ g SrF}_2}{0.100 \text{ L}} \times \frac{1 \text{ mol SrF}_2}{125.6 \text{ g SrF}_2} = 8.76 \times 10^{-4} = 8.8 \times 10^{-4} \text{ mol SrF}_2/\text{L}$$

$[Sr^{2+}] = 8.76 \times 10^{-4}$ M; $[F^-] = 2(8.76 \times 10^{-4}$ $M)$

$K_{sp} = (8.76 \times 10^{-4})(2(8.76 \times 10^{-4}))^2 = 2.7 \times 10^{-9}$

(c) $Ba(IO_3)_2(s) \rightleftharpoons Ba^{2+}(aq) + 2IO_3^-(aq)$; $K_{sp} = [Ba^{2+}][IO_3^-]^2$

Since 1 mole of dissolved $Ba(IO_3)_2$ produces 1 mole of Ba^{2+}, the molar solubility of

$Ba(IO_3)_2 = [Ba^{2+}]$. Let $x = [Ba^{2+}]$; $[IO_3^-] = 2x$

$K_{sp} = 6.0 \times 10^{-10} = (x)(2x)^2$; $4x^3 = 6.0 \times 10^{-10}$; $x^3 = 1.5 \times 10^{-10}$; $x = 5.3 \times 10^{-4}$ M

The molar solubility of $Ba(IO_3)_2$ is 5.3×10^{-4} mol/L.

17.39 *Analyze/Plan.* Given gram solubility of a compound, calculate K_{sp}. Write the dissociation equilibrium and K_{sp} expression. change gram solubility to molarity of the individual ions, taking the stoichiometry of the compound into account. Calculate K_{sp}. *Solve*:

$CaC_2O_4(s) \rightleftharpoons Ca^{2+}(aq) + C_2O_4^{2-}(aq)$; $K_{sp} = [Ca^{2+}][C_2O_4^{2-}]$

$$[Ca^{2+}] = [C_2O_4^{2-}] = \frac{0.0061 \text{ g CaC}_2O_4}{1.00 \text{ L soln}} \times \frac{1 \text{ mol CaC}_2O_4}{128.1 \text{ g CaC}_2O_4} = 4.76 \times 10^{-5} = 4.8 \times 10^{-5} \text{ } M$$

$K_{sp} = (4.76 \times 10^{-5} M)(4.76 \times 10^{-5} M) = 2.3 \times 10^{-9}$

17.41 *Analyze/Plan.* Follow the logic in Sample Exercises 17.11 and 17.12. *Solve*:

(a) $AgBr(s) \rightleftharpoons Ag^+(aq) + Br^-(aq)$; $K_{sp} = [Ag^+][Br^-] = 5.0 \times 10^{-13}$

molar solubility $= x = [Ag^+] = [Br^-]$; $K_{sp} = x^2$

$x = (5.0 \times 10^{-13})^{1/2}$; $x = 7.1 \times 10^{-7}$ mol AgBr/L

(b) Molar solubility $= x = [Br^-]$; $[Ag^+] = 0.030$ $M + x$

$K_{sp} = (0.030 + x)(x) \approx 0.030(x)$

$5.0 \times 10^{-13} = 0.030(x)$; $x = 1.7 \times 10^{-11}$ mol AgBr/L

(c)   Molar solubility = x = $[Ag^+]$

There are two sources of Br^-: $NaBr(0.10\ M)$ and $AgBr(x\ M)$

$K_{sp} = (x)(0.10 + x)$; Assuming x is small compared to $0.10\ M$

$5 \times 10^{-13} = 0.10(x)$; $x \approx 5.0 \times 10^{-12}$ mol AgBr/L

17.43   *Analyze/Plan.* We are asked to calculate the solubility of a slightly-soluble hydroxide salt at various pH values. This is a common ion problem; pH tells us not only $[H^+]$ but also $[OH^-]$, which is an ion common to the salt. Use pH to calculate $[OH^-]$, then proceed as in Sample Exercise 17.12. *Solve*:

$Mn(OH)_2(s) \rightleftharpoons Mn^{2+}(aq) + 2OH^-(aq)$; $K_{sp} = 1.6 \times 10^{-13}$

Since $[OH^-]$ is set by the pH of the solution, the solubility of $Mn(OH)_2$ is just $[Mn^{2+}]$.

(a)   pH = 7.0, pOH = 14 - pH = 7.0, $[OH^-] = 10^{-pOH} = 1.0 \times 10^{-7}\ M$

$K_{sp} = 1.6 \times 10^{-13} = [Mn^{2+}](1.0 \times 10^{-7})^2$; $[Mn^{2+}] = \dfrac{1.6 \times 10^{-13}}{1.0 \times 10^{-14}} = 16\ M$

$\dfrac{16\ mol\ Mn(OH)_2}{1\ L} \times \dfrac{88.95\ g\ Mn(OH)_2}{1\ mol\ Mn(OH)_2} = 1423 = 1.4 \times 10^3\ g\ Mn(OH)_2/L$

Check: Note that the solubility of $Mn(OH)_2$ in pure water is $3.6 \times 10^{-5}\ M$, and the pH of the resulting solution is 9.0. The relatively low pH of a solution buffered to pH 7.0 actually increases the solubility of $Mn(OH)_2$.

(b)   pH = 9.5, pOH = 4.5, $[OH^-] = 3.16 \times 10^{-5} = 3.2 \times 10^{-5}\ M$

$K_{sp} = 1.6 \times 10^{-13} = [Mn^{2+}](3.16 \times 10^{-5})^2$; $[Mn^{2+}] = \dfrac{1.6 \times 10^{-13}}{1.0 \times 10^{-9}} = 1.6 \times 10^{-4}\ M$

$1.6 \times 10^{-4}\ M\ Mn(OH)_2 \times 88.95\ g/mol = 0.0142 = 0.014\ g/L$

(c)   pH = 11.8, pOH = 2.2, $[OH^-] = 6.31 \times 10^{-3} = 6.3 \times 10^{-3}\ M$

$K_{sp} = 1.6 \times 10^{-13} = [Mn^{2+}](6.31 \times 10^{-3})^2$; $[Mn^{2+}] = \dfrac{1.6 \times 10^{-13}}{3.98 \times 10^{-5}} = 4.0 \times 10^{-9}\ M$

$4.02 \times 10^{-9}\ M\ Mn(OH)_2 \times 88.95\ g/mol = 3.575 \times 10^{-7} = 3.6 \times 10^{-7}\ g/L$

17.45   *Analyze/Plan.* Follow the logic in Sample Exercise 17.13. *Solve*:

If the anion of the salt is the conjugate base of a weak acid, it will combine with H^+, reducing the concentration of the free anion in solution, thereby causing more salt to dissolve.

More soluble in acid: (a) $ZnCO_3$ (b) ZnS   (d) AgCN   (e) $Ba_3(PO_4)_2$

17.47 *Analyze/Plan.* Follow the logic in Sample Exercise 17.14. *Solve:*

The formation equilibrium is

$$Cu^{2+}(aq) + 4NH_3(aq) \rightleftharpoons Cu(NH_3)_4{}^{2+}(aq) \quad K_f = \frac{[Cu(NH_3)_4{}^{2+}]}{[Cu^{2+}][NH_3]^4} = 5 \times 10^{12}$$

Assuming that nearly all the Cu^{2+} is in the form $Cu(NH_3)_4{}^{2+}$

$$[Cu(NH_3)_4{}^{2+}] = 1 \times 10^{-3} \, M; \quad [Cu^{2+}] = x; \quad [NH_3] = 0.10 \, M$$

$$5 \times 10^{12} = \frac{(1 \times 10^{-3})}{x(0.10)^4}; \quad x = 2 \times 10^{-12} \, M = [Cu^{2+}]$$

17.49 *Analyze/Plan.* We are asked to calculate K_{eq} for a particular reaction, making use of pertinent K_{sp} and K_f values from Appendix D and Table 17.1. Write the dissociation equilibrium for AgI and the formation reaction for $Ag(CN)_2^-$. Use algebra to manipulate these equations and their associated equilibrium constants to obtain the desired reaction and its equilibrium constant. *Solve:*

$$Ag\,I(s) \rightleftharpoons Ag^+(aq) + I^-(aq)$$
$$Ag^+(aq) + 2CN^-(aq \rightleftharpoons Ag(CN)_2^-(aq)$$

$$Ag\,I(s) + 2CN^-(aq) \rightleftharpoons Ag(CN)_2^-(aq) + I^-(aq)$$

$$K = K_{sp} \times K_f = [Ag^+][I^-] \times \frac{[Ag(CN)_2^-]}{[Ag^+][CN^-]^2} = (8.3 \times 10^{-17})(1 \times 10^{21}) = 8 \times 10^4$$

Precipitation; Qualitative Analysis

17.51 *Analyze/Plan.* Follow the logic in Sample Exercise 17.15. Precipitation conditions: will Q (see Chapter 15) exceed K_{sp} for the compound? *Solve:*

(a) In base, Ca^{2+} can form $Ca(OH)_2(s)$.

$$Ca(OH)_2(s) \rightleftharpoons Ca^{2+}(aq) + 2OH^-(aq); \quad K_{sp} = [Ca^{2+}][OH^-]^2$$

$$Q = [Ca^{2+}][OH^-]^2; \quad [Ca^{2+}] = 0.050 \, M; \quad pOH = 6; \quad [OH^-] = 10^{-6} = 1 \times 10^{-6} \, M$$

$$Q = (0.050)(1 \times 10^{-6})^2 = 5 \times 10^{-14}; \quad K_{sp} = 6.5 \times 10^{-6} \quad \text{(Appendix D)}$$

$Q < K_{sp}$, no $Ca(OH)_2$ precipitates.

(b) $Ag_2SO_4(s) \rightleftharpoons 2Ag^+(aq) + SO_4{}^{2-}(aq); \quad K_{sp} = [Ag^+]^2[SO_4{}^{2-}]$

$$[Ag^+] = \frac{0.050 \, M \times 100 \, mL}{110 \, mL} = 4.545 \times 10^{-2} = 4.5 \times 10^{-2} \, M$$

$$[SO_4{}^{2-}] = \frac{0.050 \, M \times 10 \, mL}{110 \, mL} = 4.545 \times 10^{-3} = 4.5 \times 10^{-3} \, M$$

$$Q = (4.545 \times 10^{-2})^2(4.545 \times 10^{-3}) = 9.4 \times 10^{-6}; \quad K_{sp} = 1.5 \times 10^{-5}$$

$Q < K_{sp}$, no Ag_2SO_4 precipitates.

17.53 *Analyze/Plan.* We are asked which ion will precipitate first from a solution containing Pb^{2+}(aq) and Ag^+(aq) when I^-(aq) is added. Follow the logic in Sample Exercise 17.16.

$Mn(OH)_2(s) \rightleftharpoons Mn^{2+}$(aq) $+ 2OH^-$ (aq); $K_{sp} = [Mn^{2+}][OH^-]^2 = 1.6 \times 10^{-13}$

At equilibrium, $[Mn^{2+}][OH^-]^2 = 1.6 \times 10^{-13}$. Change $[Mn^{2+}]$ to mol/L and solve for $[OH^-]$.
Solve:

$$\frac{1\ \mu g\ Mn^{2+}}{1\ L} \times \frac{1 \times 10^{-6}\ g}{1\ \mu g} \times \frac{1\ mol\ Mn^{2+}}{54.94\ g\ Mn^{2+}} = 1.82 \times 10^{-8} = 2 \times 10^{-8}\ M\ Mn^{2+}$$

$1.6 \times 10^{-13} = (1.82 \times 10^{-8})[OH^-]^2$; $[OH^-]^2 = 8.79 \times 10^{-6}$; $[OH^-] = 2.96 \times 10^{-3} = 3 \times 10^{-3}\ M$

pOH = 2.53; pH = 14 - 2.53 = 11.47 = 11.5

17.55 *Analyze/Plan.* We are asked which ion will precipitate first from a solution containing Pb^{2+}(aq) and Ag^+(aq) when I^-(aq) is added. Follow the logic in Sample Exercise 17.16. Calculate $[I^-]$ needed to initiate precipitation of each ion. The cation that requires lower $[I^-]$ will precipitate first. *Solve:*

Ag^+: $K_{sp} = [Ag^+][I^-]$; $8.3 \times 10^{-17} = (2.0 \times 10^{-4})[I^-]$; $[I^-] = \dfrac{8.3 \times 10^{-17}}{2.0 \times 10^{-4}} = 4.2 \times 10^{-13}\ M\ I^-$

Pb^{2+}: $K_{sp} = [Pb^{2+}][I^-]^2$; $7.9 \times 10^{-9} = (1.5 \times 10^{-3})[I^-]^2$; $[I^-] = \left(\dfrac{7.9 \times 10^{-9}}{1.5 \times 10^{-3}}\right)^{1/2} = 2.3 \times 10^{-3}\ M\ I^-$

AgI will precipitate first, at $[I^-] = 4.2 \times 10^{-13}\ M$.

17.57 *Analyze/Plan.* Use Figure 17.22 and the description of the five qualitative analysis "groups" in Section 17.7 to analyze the given data. *Solve:*

The first two experiments eliminate Group 1 and 2 ions (Figure 17.22). The fact that no insoluble phosphates form in the filtrate from the third experiment rules out Group 4 ions. The ions which might be in the sample are those of Group 3, that is, Al^{3+}, Fe^{2+}, Zn^{2+}, Cr^{3+}, Ni^{2+}, Co^{2+}, or Mn^{2+}, and those of Group 5, NH_4^+, Na^+ or K^+.

17.59 *Analyze/Plan.* We are asked to devise a procedure to separate various pairs of ions in aqueous solutions. In each case, refer to Figure 17.22 to find a set of conditions where the solubility of the two ions differs. Construct a procedure to generate these conditions. *Solve:*

(a) Cd^{2+} is in Gp. 2, but Zn^{2+} is not. Make the solution acidic using 0.5 M HCl; saturate with H_2S. CdS will precipitate, ZnS will not.

(b) $Cr(OH)_3$ is amphoteric but $Fe(OH)_3$ is not. Add excess base; $Fe(OH)_3$(s) precipitates, but Cr^{3+} forms the soluble complex $Cr(OH)_4^-$.

(c) Mg^{2+} is a member of Gp. 4, but K^+ is not. Add $(NH_4)_2HPO_4$; Mg^{2+} precipitates as $MgNH_4PO_4$, K^+ remains in solution.

(d) Ag^+ is a member of Gp. 1, but Mn^{2+} is not. Add 6 M HCl, precipitate Ag^+ as AgCl(s).

17.61 (a)   Because phosphoric acid is a weak acid, the concentration of free PO_4^{3-}(aq) in an aqueous phosphate solution is low except in strongly basic media. In less basic media, the solubility product of the phosphates that one wishes to precipitate is not exceeded.

      (b) K_{sp} for those cations in Group 3 is much larger. Thus, to exceed K_{sp} a higher $[S^{2-}]$ is required. This is achieved by making the solution more basic.

      (c)   They should all redissolve in strongly acidic solution, e.g., in 12 M HCl (all the chlorides of Group 3 metals are soluble).

Additional Exercises

17.63 The equilibrium of interest is

$$HC_5H_3O_3(aq) \rightleftharpoons H^+(aq) + C_5H_3O_3^-(aq); \quad K_a = 6.76 \times 10^{-4} = \frac{[H^+][C_5H_3O_3^-]}{[HC_5H_3O_3]}$$

Begin by calculating $[HC_5H_3O_3]$ and $[C_5H_3O_3^-]$ for each case.

(a) $\dfrac{35.0 \text{ g } HC_5H_3O_3}{0.250 \text{ L soln}} \times \dfrac{1 \text{ mol } HC_5H_3O_3}{112.1 \text{ g } HC_5H_3O_3} = 1.249 = 1.25 \ M \ HC_5H_3O_3$

         $\dfrac{30.0 \text{ g } NaC_5H_3O_3}{0.250 \text{ L soln}} \times \dfrac{1 \text{ mol } NaC_5H_3O_3}{134.1 \text{ g } NaC_5H_3O_3} = 0.8949 = 0.895 \ M \ C_5H_3O_3^-$

         $[H^+] = \dfrac{K_a[HC_5H_3O_3]}{[C_5H_3O_3^-]} = \dfrac{6.76 \times 10^{-4}(1.249 - x)}{(0.8949 + x)} \approx \dfrac{6.76 \times 10^{-4}(1.249)}{(0.8949)}$

         $[H^+] = 9.43 \times 10^{-4} \ M, \ pH = 3.025$

(b)   For dilution, $M_1V_1 = M_2V_2$

         $[HC_5H_3O_3] = \dfrac{0.250 \ M \times 30.0 \text{ mL}}{125 \text{ mL}} = 0.0600 \ M$

         $[C_5H_3O_3^-] = \dfrac{0.220 \ M \times 20.0 \text{ mL}}{125 \text{ mL}} = 0.0352 \ M$

         $[H^+] \approx \dfrac{6.76 \times 10^{-4}(0.0600)}{0.0352} = 1.15 \times 10^{-3} \ M, \ pH = 2.938$

         (yes, $[H^+]$ is < 5% of 0.0352 M)

(c)   0.0850 M × 0.500 L = 0.0425 mol $HC_5H_3O_3$

         1.65 M × 0.0500 L = 0.0825 mol NaOH

$$HC_5H_3O_3(aq) + NaOH(aq) \rightarrow NaC_5H_3O_3(aq) + H_2O(l)$$

initial	0.0425 mol	0.0825 mol	
reaction	-0.0425 mol	-0.0425mol	+0.0425 mol
after	0 mol	0.0400 mol	0.0425 mol

The strong base NaOH dominates the pH; the contribution of $C_5H_3O_3^-$ is negligible. This combination would be "after the equivalence point" of a titration. The total volume is 0.550 L.

$$[OH^-] = \frac{0.0400 \text{ mol}}{0.550 \text{ L}} = 0.0727 \, M; \quad pOH = 1.138, \quad pH = 12.862$$

17.65 $K_a = \dfrac{[H^+][In^-]}{[HIn]}$; at pH = 4.68, [HIn] = [In⁻]; $[H^+] = K_a$; pH = pKₐ = 4.68

17.68   The pH of a buffer is centered around pK_a for its conjugate acid.   From Table D.1, hypobromous acid, hypochlorous acid or phenol have pK_a values near 8.6. For the bases in Table D.2, pK_a for the conjugate acids = 14 - pK_b. 14 - pK_b = 8.6; pK_b = 5.4, $K_b = 10^{-5.4}$ = 4 × 10⁻⁶. Select two bases with K_b values near 4 × 10⁻⁶. Ammonia and hydrazine have K_b values closest to 4 × 10⁻⁶, and hydroxylamine would probably also work. We will select the two acid-base pairs with pK_a values close to 8.6, HBrO/BrO⁻ and $H_2NNH_3^+/H_2NNH_2$. In both cases, consider the dissociation of equilibrium for the conjugate acid.   For the HOBr/OBr⁻ buffer:

$$HA(aq) \rightleftharpoons H^+(aq) + A^-(aq); \quad HOBr(aq) \rightleftharpoons H^+(aq) + A^-(aq)$$

$$K_a = \frac{[H^+][A^-]}{[HA]}; \quad [H^+] = \frac{K_a[HA]}{[A^-]}; \quad \frac{[HA]}{[A^-]} = \frac{[H^+]}{K_a}; \quad \frac{[HOBr]}{[OBr^-]} = \frac{[H^+]}{K_a}$$

$[H^+] = 10^{-8.6} = 2.512 \times 10^{-9}$; $K_a = 2.5 \times 10^{-9}$

$\dfrac{[HOBr]}{[OBr^-]} = \dfrac{2.512 \times 10^{-9}}{2.5 \times 10^{-9}} = 1.005 = 1.005 = 1$. Because K_a for HOBr is very close to $[H^+]$ for the buffer, the [HA/A⁻] ratio is essentially 1. The acid and its conjugate base should be present in the same concentrations. This condition can be easily reached by starting with x moles of the acid and adding x/2 moles OH⁻(aq) to neutralize half of the acid. The absolute number of moles of HOBr and OBr⁻ aren't important, just their ratio.

For the hydrazine buffer, $H_2NNH_3^+/H_2NNH_2$, $BH^+(aq) \rightleftharpoons B(aq) + H^+(aq)$;

$$H_2NNH_3^+(aq) \rightleftharpoons H_2NNH_2(aq) + H^+(aq)$$

$$K_a = \frac{[B][H^+]}{[BH^+]}; \quad \frac{[BH^+]}{[B]} = \frac{[H^+]}{K_a}; \quad [H^+] = 2.512 \times 10^{-9} = 3 \times 10^{-9}$$

For $H_2NNH_3^+$, $K_a = K_w/K_b$ (H_2NNH_2) = 1.0×10^{-14} /1.3×10^{-6} = 7.692 × 10⁻⁹ = 7.7 × 10⁻⁹

$$\frac{[H_2NNH_3^+]}{[H_2NNH_2]} = \frac{2.512 \times 10^{-9}}{7.692 \times 10^{-9}} = 0.3265 \approx 0.3$$

The ratio of $[H_2NNH_3^+]$ to $[H_2NNH_2]$ is 0.3 to 1 or 1 to 3.1. The concentration of base in the buffer is roughly three times the concentration of the conjugate acid. To prepare this buffer, begin with x moles of H_2NNH_2 and add x/4 moles $H^+(aq)$ to neutralize one-fourth of the base. The ratio $[BH^+]/[B]$ is then 0.25/0.75x or 1 to 3.

17.70 (a)   For a monoprotic acid (one H^+ per mole of acid), at the equivalence point
moles OH^- added = moles H^+ originally present

$$M_B \times V_B = \text{g acid/molar mass}$$

$$\mathcal{M} = \frac{\text{g acid}}{M_B \times V_B} = \frac{0.2140\text{ g}}{0.0950\,M \times 0.0274\text{ L}} = 82.21 = 82.2\text{ g/mol}$$

(b)   initial mol HA $= \dfrac{0.2140\text{ g}}{82.21\text{ g/mol}} = 2.603 \times 10^{-3} = 2.60 \times 10^{-3}$ mol HA

mol OH^- added to pH 6.50 $= 0.0950\,M \times 0.0150\text{ L} = 1.425 \times 10^{-3} = 1.43 \times 10^{-3}$ mol OH^-

	HA(aq)	+	NaOH(aq)	→	$NaA(aq) + H_2O$
before rx	2.603×10^{-3} mol		1.425×10^{-3} mol		0
change	-1.425×10^{-3} mol		-1.425×10^{-3} mol		$+1.425 \times 10^{-3}$ mol
after rx	1.178×10^{-3} mol		0		1.425×10^{-3} mol

$$[HA] = \frac{1.178 \times 10^{-3}\text{ mol}}{0.0400\text{ L}} = 0.02945 = 0.0295\ M$$

$$[A^-] = \frac{1.425 \times 10^{-3}\text{ mol}}{0.0400\text{ L}} = 0.03563 = 0.0356\ M; \quad [H^+] = 10^{-6.50} = 3.162 \times 10^{-7}$$
$$= 3.2 \times 10^{-7}\ M$$

The mixture after reaction (a buffer) can be described by the acid dissociation equilibrium

	HA(aq)	⇌	$H^+(aq)$	+	$A^-(aq)$
initial	0.0295 M		0		0.0356 M
equil	$(0.0295 - 3.2 \times 10^{-7}\ M)$		$3.2 \times 10^{-7}\ M$		$(0.0356 + 3.2 \times 10^{-7})\ M$

$$K_a = \frac{[H^+][A^-]}{[HA]} \approx \frac{(3.162 \times 10^{-7})(0.03563)}{(0.02945)} = 3.8 \times 10^{-7}$$

(Although we have carried 3 figures through the calculation to avoid rounding errors, the data dictate an answer with 2 significant figures.)

17.72 (a) $\dfrac{0.4885\text{ g KHP}}{0.100\text{ L}} \times \dfrac{1\text{ mol KHP}}{204.2\text{ g KHP}} = 0.02392 = 0.0239\ M\ P^{2-}$ at the equivalence point

The pH at the equivalence point is determined by the hydrolysis of P^{2-}.

$$P^{2-}(aq) + H_2O(l) \rightleftharpoons HP^-(aq) + OH^-(aq)$$

$$K_b = \frac{[HP^-][OH^-]}{[P^{2-}]} = \frac{K_w}{K_a \text{ for } HP^-} = \frac{1.0 \times 10^{-14}}{3.1 \times 10^{-6}} = 3.23 \times 10^{-9} = 3.2 \times 10^{-9}$$

$$3.23 \times 10^{-9} = \frac{x^2}{(0.02392 - x)} \approx \frac{x^2}{0.02392}; \quad X = [OH^-] = 8.8 \times 10^{-6} \, M$$

pH = 14 - 5.06 = 8.94. From Figure 16.7, either phenolphthalein (pH 8.2 - 10.0) or thymol blue (pH 8.0 - 9.6) could be used to detect the equivalence point.

Phenolphthalein is usually the indicator of choice because the colorless to pink change is easier to see.

(b) $\quad 0.4885 \text{ g KHP} \times \dfrac{1 \text{ mol KHP}}{204.2 \text{ g KHP}} \times \dfrac{1 \text{ mol NaOH}}{1 \text{ mol KHP}} \times \dfrac{1}{0.03855 \text{ L NaOH}}$

$$= 0.06206 \, M \text{ NaOH}$$

17.75 Assume that H_3PO_4 will react with NaOH in a stepwise fashion. (This is not unreasonable, since the three K_a values for H_3PO_4 are significantly different.)

$$H_3PO_4(aq) + NaOH(aq) \rightarrow H_2PO_4^-(aq) + Na^+(aq) + H_2O(l)$$

before	0.20 mol	0.30 mol	0 mol
after	0 mol	0.10 mol	0.20 mol

$$H_2PO_4^-(aq) + NaOH(aq) \rightarrow HPO_4^-(aq) + Na^+(aq) + H_2O(l)$$

before	0.20 mol	0.10 mol	0.25 mol
after	0.10 mol	0	0.35 mol

Thus, after all NaOH has reacted, the resulting 1.00 L solution is a buffer containing 0.10 mol $H_2PO_4^-$ and 0.35 mol HPO_4^{2-}. $\quad H_2PO_4^-(aq) \rightleftharpoons H^+(aq) + HPO_4^{2-}(aq)$

$$K_a = 6.2 \times 10^{-8} = \frac{[HPO_4^{2-}][H^+]}{[H_2PO_4^-]}; \quad [H^+] = \frac{6.2 \times 10^{-8}(0.10 \, M)}{0.35 \, M} = 1.77 \times 10^{-8} = 1.8 \times 10^{-8} \, M;$$

$$pH = 7.75$$

17.78 $C_3H_5O_3^-$ will be formed by reaction of $HC_3H_5O_3$ with NaOH.

$0.1000 \, M \times 0.02500 \text{ L} = 2.500 \times 10^{-3} \text{ mol } HC_3H_5O_3; \quad b = \text{mol NaOH needed}$

$$HC_3H_5O_3 \quad + \quad NaOH \quad \rightarrow \quad C_3H_5O_3^- + H_2O + Na^+$$

initial	2.500×10^{-3}	b mol	
rx	-b mol	-b mol	+b mol
after rx	2.500×10^{-3} - b mol	0	b mol

$$K_a = \frac{[H^+][C_3H_5O_3^-]}{[HC_3H_5O_3]}; \quad K_a = 1.4 \times 10^{-4}; \quad [H^+] = 10^{-pH} = 10^{-3.75} = 1.778 \times 10^{-4} = 1.8 \times 10^{-4} \, M$$

Since solution volume is the same for $HC_3H_5O_3$ and $C_3H_5O_3^-$, we can use moles in the equation for $[H^+]$.

$K_a = 1.4 \times 10^{-4} = \dfrac{1.778 \times 10^{-4} \text{ (b)}}{(2.500 \times 10^{-3} - b)}$; $0.7874 \, (2.500 \times 10^{-3} - b) = b$, $1.969 \times 10^{-3} = 1.7874 \, b$,

$b = 1.10 \times 10^{-3} = 1.1 \times 10^{-3} \text{ mol OH}^-$

(The precision of K_a dictates that the result has 2 sig figs.)

Substituting this result into the K_a expression gives $[H^+] = 1.8 \times 10^{-4}$. This checks and confirms our result.

Calculate volume NaOH required from $M = $ mol/L.

$1.10 \times 10^{-3} \text{ mol OH}^- \times \dfrac{1 \text{ L}}{1.000 \text{ mol}} \times \dfrac{1 \text{ µL}}{1 \times 10^{-6} \text{ L}} = 1.1 \times 10^3 \text{ µL (1.1 mL)}$

17.81 After precipitation, the solution in contact with $CaF_2(s)$ is saturated. The $[Ca^{2+}]$ calculated from the K_{sp} expression gives an upper limit of $[Ca^{2+}]$ remaining in solution.

$K_{sp} = [Ca^{2+}][F^-]^2 = 3.9 \times 10^{-11}$; $[F^-] = 0.20 \, M$

$3.9 \times 10^{-11} = [Ca^{2+}](0.20)^2$; $[Ca^{2+}] = 9.75 \times 10^{-10} = 9.8 \times 10^{-10} \, M$

17.84 $PbSO_4(s) \rightleftharpoons Pb^{2+}(aq) + SO_4^{2-}(aq)$; $K_{sp} = 6.3 \times 10^{-7} = [Pb^{2+}][SO_4^{2-}]$

$SrSO_4(s) \rightleftharpoons Sr^{2+}(aq) + SO_4^{2-}(aq)$; $K_{sp} = 3.2 \times 10^{-7} = [Sr^{2+}][SO_4^{2-}]$

Let $x = [Pb^{2+}]$, $y = [Sr^{2+}]$, $x + y = [SO_4^{2-}]$

$\dfrac{x(x+y)}{y(x+y)} = \dfrac{6.3 \times 10^{-7}}{3.2 \times 10^{-7}}$; $\dfrac{x}{y} = 1.9688 = 2.0$; $x = 1.969 \, y = 2.0 \, y$

$y(1.969 \, y + y) = 3.2 \times 10^{-7}$; $2.969 \, y^2 = 3.2 \times 10^{-7}$; $y = 3.283 \times 10^{-4} = 3.3 \times 10^{-4}$

$x = 1.969 \, y$; $x = 1.969(3.283 \times 10^{-4}) = 6.464 \times 10^{-4} = 6.5 \times 10^{-4}$

$[Pb^{2+}] = 6.5 \times 10^{-4} \, M$, $[Sr^{2+}] = 3.3 \times 10^{-4} \, M$, $[SO_4^{2-}] = (3.283 + 6.464) \times 10^{-4} = 9.7 \times 10^{-4} \, M$

17.87
$$Zn(OH)_2(s) \rightleftharpoons Zn^{2+}(aq) + 2OH^-(aq) \qquad K_{sp} = 3.0 \times 10^{-16}$$

$$Zn^{2+}(aq) + 4OH^-(aq) \rightleftharpoons Zn(OH)_4^{2-}(aq) \qquad K_f = 4.6 \times 10^{17}$$

$$Zn(OH)_2(s) + 2OH^-(aq) \rightleftharpoons Zn(OH)_4^{2-}(aq) \qquad K = K_{sp} \times K_f = 138 = 1.4 \times 10^2$$

$K = 138 = 1.4 \times 10^2 = \dfrac{[Zn(OH)_4^{2-}]}{[OH^-]^2}$

If 0.015 mol $Zn(OH)_2$ dissolves, 0.015 mol $Zn(OH)_4^{2-}$ should be present at equilibrium.

$[OH^-]^2 = \dfrac{(0.015)}{138}$; $[OH^-] = 1.043 \times 10^{-2} \, M$ $[OH^-] \geq 1.0 \times 10^{-2} \, M$ or pH ≥ 12.02

Integrative Exercises

17.88 (a) Complete ionic:

$H^+(aq) + Cl^-(aq) + Na^+(aq) + CHO_2^-(aq) \rightarrow HCHO_2(aq) + Na^+(aq) + Cl^-(aq)$

Na^+ and Cl^- are spectator ions.

Net ionic: $H^+(aq) + CHO_2^-(aq) \rightleftharpoons HCHO_2(aq)$

(b) The net ionic equation in part (a) is the reverse of the dissociation of $HCHO_2$.

$$K = \frac{1}{K_a} = \frac{1}{1.8 \times 10^{-4}} = 5.55 \times 10^3 = 5.6 \times 10^3$$

(c) For Na^+ and Cl^-, this is just a dilution problem.

$M_1V_1 = M_2V_2$; V_2 is 50.0 mL + 50.0 mL = 100.0 mL

Cl^-: $\dfrac{0.15\,M \times 50.0\,mL}{100.0\,mL} = 0.075\,M$; Na^+: $\dfrac{0.15\,M \times 50.0\,mL}{100.0\,mL} = 0.075\,M$

H^+ and CHO_2^- react to form $HCHO_2$. Since K >> 1, the reaction essentially goes to completion.

$0.15\,M \times 0.0500\,mL = 7.5 \times 10^{-3}$ mol H^+

$0.15\,M \times 0.0500\,mL = 7.5 \times 10^{-3}$ mol CHO_2^-

$= 7.5 \times 10^{-3}$ mol $HCHO_2$

Solve the weak acid problem to determine $[H^+]$, $[CHO_2^-]$ and $[HCHO_2]$ at equilibrium.

$K_a = \dfrac{[H^+][CHO_2^-]}{[HCHO_2]}$; $[H^+] = [CHO_2^-] = x\,M$; $[HCHO_2] = \dfrac{(7.5 \times 10^{-3} - x)\,mol}{0.100\,L}$

$= (0.075 - x)\,M$

$1.8 \times 10^{-4} = \dfrac{x^2}{(0.075-x)} \approx \dfrac{x^2}{0.075}$; $x = 3.7 \times 10^{-3}\,M$ H^+ and $HCHO_2^-$

$[HCHO_2] = (0.075 - 0.0037) = 0.071\,M$

$\dfrac{[H^+]}{[HNO_2]} \times 100 = \dfrac{3.7 \times 10^{-3}}{0.075} \times 100 = 4.9\%$ dissociation

In summary:

$[Na^+] = [Cl^-] = 0.075\,M$, $[HCHO_2] = 0.071\,M$, $[H^+] = [CHO_2^-] = 0.0037\,M$

17.90 $n = \dfrac{PV}{RT} = 735\,torr \times \dfrac{1\,atm}{760\,torr} \times \dfrac{7.5\,L}{295\,K} \times \dfrac{K \cdot mol}{0.08206\,L \cdot atm} = 0.300 = 0.30$ mol NH_3

$0.40\,M \times 0.50\,L = 0.20$ mol HCl

	HCl(aq)	+	NH$_3$(g)	→	NH$_4^+$(aq)	+	Cl$^-$(aq)
before	0.20 mol		0.30 mol				
after	0		0.10 mol		0.20 mol		0.20 mol

The solution will be a buffer because of the substantial concentrations of NH_3 and NH_4^+ present. Use K_a for NH_4^+ to describe the equilibrium.

$$NH_4^+(aq) \rightleftharpoons NH_3(aq) + H^+(aq)$$

equil. 0.20 - x   0.10 + x x

$$K_a = \frac{1.0 \times 10^{-14}}{1.8 \times 10^{-5}} = 5.56 \times 10^{-10} = 5.6 \times 10^{-10} \; ; \quad K_a = \frac{[NH_3][H^+]}{[NH_4^+]}; \quad [H^+] = \frac{K_a[NH_4^+]}{[NH_3]}$$

Since this expression contains a ratio of concentrations, volume will cancel and we can substitute moles directly. Assume x is small compared to 0.10 and 0.20.

$$[H^+] = \frac{5.56 \times 10^{-10} \, (0.20)}{(0.10)} = 1.111 \times 10^{-9} = 1.1 \times 10^{-9} \, M, \; pH = 8.95$$

17.93 $\pi = MRT, \; M = \dfrac{\pi}{RT} = \dfrac{21 \, torr}{298 \, K} \times \dfrac{1 \, atm}{760 \, torr} \times \dfrac{K \cdot mol}{0.08206 \, L \cdot atm} = 1.13 \times 10^{-3} = 1.1 \, M$

$$SrSO_4(s) \rightleftharpoons Sr^{2+}(aq) + SO_4^{2-}(aq); \; K_{sp} = [Sr^{2+}][SO_4^{2-}]$$

The total particle concentration is 1.13×10^{-3} M. Each mole of $SrSO_4$ that dissolves produces 2 mol of ions, so $[Sr^{2+}] = [SO_4^{2-}] = 1.13 \times 10^{-3} \, M / 2 = 5.65 \times 10^{-4} = 5.7 \times 10^{-4}$ M.

$$K_{sp} = (5.65 \times 10^{-4})^2 = 3.2 \times 10^{-7}$$

18 Chemistry of the Environment

Earth's Atmosphere

18.1 (a) The temperature profile of the atmosphere (Figure 18.1) is the basis of its division into regions. The center of each peak or trough in the temperature profile corresponds to a new region.

(b) Troposphere, 0-12 km; stratosphere, 12-50 km; mesosphere, 50-85 km; thermosphere, 85-110 km.

18.3 *Analyze/Plan.* Given O_3 concentration in ppm, calculate partial pressure. Use the definition of ppm to get mol fraction O_3. For gases mole fraction = pressure fraction; $P_{O_3} = \chi_{O_3} \cdot P_{atm}$.

$$0.37 \text{ ppm } O_3 = \frac{0.37 \text{ mol } O_3}{1 \times 10^6 \text{ mol air}} = 3.7 \times 10^{-7} = \chi_{O_3}$$

Solve: $P_{O_3} = \chi_{O_3} \cdot P_{atm} = 3.7 \times 10^{-7} (650 \text{ torr}) = 2.4 \times 10^{-4}$ torr

18.5 *Analyze/Plan.* Given CO concentration in ppm, calculate number of CO molecules in 1.0 L air at given conditions. ppm CO $\rightarrow \chi_{O_3} \rightarrow$ atm CO $\rightarrow$ mol CO $\rightarrow$ molecules CO Use the ideal gas law to change atm CO to mol CO, then Avogadro's number to get molecules. *Solve:*

$$6.0 \text{ ppm CO} = \frac{6.0 \text{ mol CO}}{1 \times 10^6 \text{ mol air}} = 6.0 \times 10^{-6} = \chi_{CO}$$

$$P_{CO} = \chi_{CO} \cdot P_{atm} = 6.0 \times 10^{-6} \times 745 \text{ torr} \times \frac{1 \text{ atm}}{760 \text{ torr}} = 5.88 \times 10^{-6} = 5.9 \times 10^{-6} \text{ atm}$$

$$n_{CO} = \frac{P_{CO}V}{RT} = \frac{5.88 \times 10^{-6} \text{ atm} \times 1.0 \text{ L}}{290 \text{ K}} \times \frac{K \cdot mol}{0.08206 \text{ L} \cdot atm} = 2.4715 \times 10^{-7} = 2.5 \times 10^{-7} \text{ mol CO}$$

$$2.4715 \times 10^{-7} \text{ mol CO} \times \frac{6.022 \times 10^{23} \text{ molecules}}{mol} = 1.488 \times 10^{17} = 1.5 \times 10^{17} \text{ molecules CO}$$

The Upper Atmosphere; Ozone

18.7 *Analyze/Plan.* Given bond dissociation energy in kJ/mol, calculate the wavelength of a single photon that will rupture a C--Br bond. kJ/mol $\rightarrow$ J/molecule. $\lambda = hc/E$. ($\lambda = hc/E$ describes the energy/wavelength relationship of a single photon.) *Solve:*

$$\frac{210 \times 10^3 \text{ J}}{1 \text{ mol}} \times \frac{1 \text{ mol}}{6.022 \times 10^{23} \text{ molecules}} = 3.487 \times 10^{-19} = 3.49 \times 10^{-19} \text{ J/molecule}$$

$\lambda = c/\nu$ We also have that $E = h\nu$, so $\nu = E/h$.   Thus,

$$\lambda = \frac{hc}{E} = \frac{(6.626 \times 10^{-34} \text{ J} \cdot \text{sec})(3.00 \times 10^8 \text{ m/sec})}{3.487 \times 10^{-19} \text{ J}} = 5.70 \times 10^{-7} \text{ m} = 570 \text{ nm}$$

18.9   Photoionization of O_2 requires 1205 kJ/mol. Photodissociation requires only 495 kJ/mol. At lower elevations, solar radiation with wavelengths corresponding to 1205 kJ/mol or shorter has already been absorbed, while the longer wavelength radiation has passed through relatively well. Below 90 km, the increased concentration of O_2 and the availability of longer wavelength radiation cause the photodissociation process to dominate.

18.11   (a)   The highest rate of ozone, O_3, formation occurs at about 50 km, near the stratopause. The formation of ozone is an exothermic process as M* carries excess energy away from the O_3 molecule. The heat energy from the formation of O_3 causes the temperature to be higher near the stratopause than the lower altitude tropopause.

       (b)   The first step in the formation of O_3 is the photodissociation of O_2 to form two O atoms. Then, an O atom and an O_2 molecule collide to form O_3^*, a species with excess energy. If no other collisions occur, O_3^* spontaneously decomposes. If a carrier molecule such as N_2 or O_2 collides with O_3^* and removes the excess energy, O_3 is formed. It is the energy carried by M* that contributes to the temperature maximum at 50 km altitude.

18.13   A *hydrofluorocarbon* is a compound that contains hydrogen, fluorine and carbon; it contains hydrogen in place of chlorine. HFCs are potentially less harmful than CFCs because photodissociation does not produce Cl atoms, which catalyze the destruction of ozone.

18.15   (a)   In order to catalyze ozone depletion, the halogen must be present as single halogen atoms. These halogen atoms are produced in the stratosphere by photodissociation of a carbon-halogen bond. According to Table 8.4, the average C–F average bond dissociation energy is 485 kJ/mol, while that of C-Cl is 328 kJ/mol. The C–F bond requires more energy for dissociation and is not readily cleaved by the available wavelengths of UV light.

       (b)   Chlorine is present as chlorine atoms and chlorine oxide molecules, Cl and ClO.

Chemistry of the Troposphere

18.17   (a)   CO binds with hemoglobin in the blood to block O_2 transport to the cells; people with CO poisoning suffocate from lack of O_2.

(b) SO_2 is corrosive to lung tissue and contributes to higher levels of respiratory disease and shorter life expectancy, especially for people with other respiratory problems such as asthma. It also is a major source of acid rain, which damages forests and wildlife in natural waters.

(c) O_3 is extremely reactive and toxic because of its ability to form free radicals upon reaction with organic molecules in the body. It is particularly dangerous for asthma suffers, exercisers and the elderly. O_3 can also react with organic compounds in polluted air to form peroxyacylnitrates, which cause eye irritation and breathing difficulties.

18.19   (a)   Methane, CH_4, arises from decomposition of organic matter by certain microorganisms; it also escapes from underground gas deposits.

(b) SO_2 is released in volcanic gases, and also is produced by bacterial action on decomposing vegetable and animal matter.

(c)   Nitric oxide, NO, results from oxidation of decomposing organic matter, and is formed in lightning flashes.

(d)   CO is a possible product of some vegetable matter decay.

18.21   (a)   Acid rain is primarily $H_2SO_4(aq)$.

$H_2SO_4(aq) + CaCO_3(s) \rightarrow CaSO_4(s) + H_2O(l) + CO_2(g)$

(b)   The $CaSO_4(s)$ would be much less reactive with acidic solution, since it would require a strongly acidic solution to shift the relevant equilibrium to the right.

$CaSO_4(s) + 2H^+(aq) \rightleftharpoons Ca^{2+}(aq) + 2HSO_4^-(aq)$

Note, however, that $CaSO_4(s)$ is brittle and easily dislodged; it provides none of the structural strength of limestone.

18.23   *Analyze/Plan.* Given wavelength of a photon, place it in the electromagnetic spectrum, calculate its energy in kJ/mol, and compare it to an average bond dissociation energy. Use Figure 6.4; $E(\text{J/photon}) = hc/\lambda$. J/photon $\rightarrow$ kJ/mol. *Solve:*

(a)   Ultraviolet (Figure 6.4)

(b) $E_{photon} = hc/\lambda = \dfrac{6.626 \times 10^{-34}\ \text{J}\cdot\text{s} \times 3.00 \times 10^8\ \text{m/s}}{335 \times 10^{-9}\ \text{m}} = 5.934 \times 10^{-19}$

$= 5.93 \times 10^{-19}$ J/photon

$\dfrac{5.934 \times 10^{-19}\ \text{J}}{1\ \text{photon}} \times \dfrac{6.022 \times 10^{23}\ \text{photons}}{1\ \text{mol}} \times \dfrac{1\ \text{kJ}}{1000\ \text{J}} = 357$ kJ/mol

(c)   The average C–H bond energy from Table 8.4 is 413 kJ/mol. The energy calculated in part (b), 357 kJ/mol, is the energy required to break 1 mol of C–H bonds in formaldehyde, CH_2O. The C–H bond energy in CH_2O must be less than the "average" C–H bond energy.

18.25 Most of the energy entering the atmosphere from the sun is in the form of visible radiation, while most of the energy leaving the earth is in the form of infrared radiation. CO_2 is transparent to the incoming visible radiation, but absorbs the outgoing infrared radiation.

The World Ocean

18.27 *Analyze/Plan.* Given salinity and density, calculate molarity. A salinity of 5.3 denotes that there are 5.3 g of dry salt per kg of water. *Solve:*

$$\frac{5.3 \text{ g NaCl}}{1 \text{ kg soln}} \times \frac{1.03 \text{ kg soln}}{1 \text{ L soln}} \times \frac{1 \text{ mol NaCl}}{58.44 \text{ g NaCl}} \times \frac{1 \text{ mol Na}^+}{1 \text{ mol NaCl}} = 0.0934 = 0.093 \ M \text{ Na}^+$$

18.29 *Analyze/Plan.* g $Mg(OH)_2$ → mol $Mg(OH)_2$ → mol ratio → mol CaO → g CaO. *Solve:*

$$5.0 \times 10^6 \text{ g Mg(OH)}_2 \times \frac{1 \text{ mol Mg(OH)}_2}{58.3 \text{ g Mg(OH)}_2} \times \frac{1 \text{ mol CaO}}{1 \text{ mol Mg(OH)}_2} \times \frac{56.1 \text{ g CaO}}{1 \text{ mol CaO}} = 4.8 \times 10^6 \text{ g CaO}$$

18.31 *Analyze/Plan.* Given the concentration difference between the two solutions ($\Delta M = 0.22 - 0.01 = 0.21 \ M$) and temperature, calculate the minimum pressure for reverse osmosis. Use the relationship $\pi = MRT$ from Section 13.5. This is the pressure required to halt osmosis from the more dilute (0.01 M) to the more concentrated (0.22 M) solution. Slightly more pressure will initiate reverse osmosis. *Solve:*

$$\pi = \Delta MRT = \frac{0.21 \text{ mol}}{L} \times \frac{0.08206 \text{ L} \cdot \text{atm}}{\text{mol} \cdot K} \times 298 \ K = 5.135 = 5.1 \text{ atm}$$

The minimum pressure required to initiate reverse osmosis is greater than 5.1 atm.

Freshwater

18.33 *Analyze/Plan.* Under aerobic conditions, excess oxyen is present and decomposition leads to oxidized products, the element in its maximum oxidation state combined with oxygen. Under anaerobic conditions, little or no oxygen is present so decomposition leads to reduced products, the element in its minimum oxidation state combined with hydrogen. *Solve:*

(a) CO_2, HCO_3^-, H_2O, SO_4^{2-}, NO_3^-, HPO_4^{2-}, $H_2PO_4^-$.

(b) $CH_4(g)$, $H_2S(g)$, $NH_3(g)$, $PH_3(g)$

18.35 *Analyze/Plan.* Given the balanced equation, calculate the amount of one reactant required to react exactly with a certain amount of the other reactants. Solve the stoichiometry problem. g $C_{18}H_{29}O_3S^-$ → mol → mol ratio → mol O_2 → g O_2. *Solve:*

$$1.0 \text{ g C}_{18}\text{H}_{29}\text{O}_3\text{S}^- \times \frac{1 \text{ mol C}_{18}\text{H}_{29}\text{O}_3\text{S}^-}{325 \text{ g C}_{18}\text{H}_{29}\text{O}_3\text{S}^-} \times \frac{51 \text{ mol O}_2}{2 \text{ mol C}_{18}\text{H}_{29}\text{O}_3\text{S}^-} \times \frac{32.0 \text{ g O}_2}{1 \text{ mol O}_2} = 2.5 \text{ g O}_2$$

Notice that the mass of O_2 required is 2.5 times greater than the mass of biodegradable material.

18.37   *Analyze/Plan.* Slaked lime is $Ca(OH)_2(s)$. The reaction is metathesis. *Solve:*

$$Mg^{2+}(aq) + Ca(OH)_2(s) \rightarrow Mg(OH)_2(s) + Ca^{2+}(aq)$$

The excess $Ca^{2+}(aq)$ is removed as $CaCO_3$ by naturally occurring bicarbonate or added Na_2CO_3.

18.39   *Analyze/Plan.* Given $[Ca^{2+}]$ and $[HCO_3^-]$ calculate mole $Ca(OH)_2$ and Na_2CO_3 needed to remove the Ca^{2+} and HCO_3^-. Consider the chemical equations and reaction stoichiometry in the stepwise process. *Solve:*

$Ca(OH)_2$ is added to remove Ca^{2+} as $CaCO_3(s)$, and Na_2CO_3 removes the remaining Ca^{2+}.
$Ca^{2+}(aq) + 2HCO_3^-(aq) + [Ca^{2+}(aq) + 2OH^-(aq)] \rightarrow 2CaCO_3(s) + 2H_2O(l)$.   One mole $Ca(OH)_2$ is needed for each 2 moles of $HCO_3^-(aq)$ present. If there are 7.0×10^{-4} mol $HCO_3^-(aq)$ per liter, we must add 3.5×10^{-4} mol $Ca(OH)_2$ per liter, or a total of 0.35 mol $Ca(OH)_2$ for 10^3 L. This reaction removes 3.5×10^{-4} mol of the original Ca^{2+} from each liter of solution, leaving 1.5×10^{-4} M $Ca^{2+}(aq)$. To remove this $Ca^{2+}(aq)$, we add 1.5×10^{-4} mol Na_2CO_3 per liter, or a total of 0.15 mol Na_2CO_3, forming $CaCO_3(s)$.

18.41   A slightly basic solution contains a small excess of $OH^-(aq)$. $Al_2(SO_4)_3$ reacts with OH^- to form $Al(OH)_3(s)$, a gelatinous precipitate that occludes fine particles and bacteria present in the water. The $Al(OH)_3(s)$ settles slowly, removing the undesirable particulate matter.

$$Al_2(SO_4)_3(s) + 6OH^-(aq) \rightarrow 2Al(OH)_3(s) + 3SO_4^{2-}(aq)$$

Green Chemistry

18.43   Production of any form of energy requires a fuel and generates waste products. A more energy-efficient device or process uses less energy, which requires less fuel and generates fewer waste-products. Automobile fuel efficiency is a clear example. The better the gas mileage of a vehicle, the less gasoline per mile is burned and the fewer waste products (unburned by hydrocarbons, CO, NO_x, etc.) are generated. Electrical appliances are a less obvious but equally pertinent example. Electricity is generated at a power plant, which uses coal, oil or nuclear fuel. The less electricity required by an appliance, the less waste per appliance use that is generated at the power plant.

18.45   One use of phosgene, $Cl\!-\!\overset{\displaystyle O}{\underset{\displaystyle \|}{C}}\!-\!Cl$, is as the source of the $-\!\overset{\displaystyle O}{\underset{\displaystyle \|}{C}}\!-$ carbonyl group in a condensation polymerization. The small-molecule that is 'condensed' is HCl, a corrosive strong acid and source of Cl^- that definitely requires treatment.   Use of dimethylcarbonate in place of phosgene as a carbonyl source condenses methanol, CH_3OH, rather than HCl. Methanol is much less toxic than HCl, and it has the potential to be a second useful product, rather than waste.

Additional Exercises

18.48 $\mathcal{M}_{avg}$ at the surface = 40.0(0.17) + 16.0(0.38) + 32.0(0.45) = 27.28 = 27 g/mol.

Next, calculate the percentage composition at 200 km. The fractions can be "normalized" by saying that the 0.45 fraction of O_2 is converted into **two** 0.45 fractions of O atoms, then dividing by the total fractions, 0.17 + 0.38 + 0.45 + 0.45 = 1.45:

$$\mathcal{M}_{avg} = \frac{40.0(0.17) + 16.0(0.38) + 16.0(0.90)}{1.45} = 18.81 = 19 \text{ g/mol}$$

18.50
$$2[Cl(g) + O_3(g) \rightarrow ClO(g) + O_2(g)] \qquad [18.7]$$
$$2Cl(g) + 2O_3(g) \rightarrow 2ClO(g) + 2O_2(g)$$
$$2ClO(g) \rightarrow O_2(g) + 2Cl(g) \qquad [18.9]$$

$$2Cl(g) + 2O_3(g) + 2ClO(g) \rightarrow 2ClO(g) + 3O_2(g) + 2Cl(g)$$
$$2O_3(g) \xrightarrow{Cl} 3O_2(g) \qquad [18.10]$$

Note that Cl(g) fits the definition of a catalyst in this reaction.

18.53 From section 18.4:

$$N_2(g) + O_2(g) \rightleftharpoons 2NO(g) \qquad \Delta H = +180.8 \text{ kJ} \qquad (1)$$
$$2\,NO(g) + O_2(g) \rightleftharpoons 2NO_2(g) \qquad \Delta H = -113.1 \text{ kJ} \qquad (2)$$

In an endothermic reaction, heat is a reactant. As the temperature of the reaction increases, the addition of heat favors formation of products and the value of K increases. The reverse is true for exothermic reactions; as temperature increases, the value of K decreases. Thus, K for reaction (1), which is endothermic, increases with increasing temperature and K for reaction (2), which is exothermic, decreases with increasing temperature.

18.56 (a) According to Section 13.3, the solubility of gases in water decreases with increasing temperature. Thus, the solubility of $CO_2(g)$ in the ocean would decrease if the temperature of the ocean increased.

(b) If the solubility of $CO_2(g)$ in the ocean decreased because of global warming, more $CO_2(g)$ would be released into the atmosphere, perpetuating a cycle of increasing temperature and concomitant release of $CO_2(g)$ from the ocean.

18.59 (a) CO_3^{2-} is a relatively strong Brønsted base and produces OH^- in aqueous solution according to the hydrolysis reaction:

$$CO_3^{2-}(aq) + H_2O(l) \rightleftharpoons HCO_3^-(aq) + OH^-(aq), \quad K_b = 1.8 \times 10^{-4}$$

If $[OH^-(aq)]$ is sufficient to exceed K_{sp} for $Mg(OH)_2$, the solid will precipitate.

(b) $\dfrac{125 \text{ mg Mg}^{2+}}{1 \text{ kg soln}} \times \dfrac{1 \text{ g Mg}^{2+}}{1000 \text{ mg Mg}^{2+}} \times \dfrac{1.00 \text{ kg soln}}{1.00 \text{ L soln}} \times \dfrac{1 \text{ mol Mg}^{2+}}{24.305 \text{ g Mg}^{2+}} = 5.143 \times 10^{-3}$

$$= 5.14 \times 10^{-3} \ M \text{ Mg}^{2+}$$

$$\dfrac{4.0 \text{ g Na}_2\text{CO}_3}{1.0 \text{ L soln}} \times \dfrac{1 \text{ mol CO}_3^{2-}}{106.0 \text{ g Na}_2\text{CO}_3} = 0.03774 = 0.038 \ M \text{ CO}_3^{2-}$$

$$K_b = 1.8 \times 10^{-4} = \dfrac{[\text{HCO}_3^-][\text{OH}^-]}{[\text{CO}_3^{2-}]} \approx \dfrac{x^2}{0.03774}; \ x = [\text{OH}^-] = 2.606 \times 10^{-3}$$

$$= 2.6 \times 10^{-3} \ M$$

(This represents 6.9% hydrolysis, but the result will not be significantly different using the quadratic formula.)

$$Q = [\text{Mg}^{2+}][\text{OH}^-]^2 = (5.143 \times 10^{-3})(2.606 \times 10^{-3})^2 = 3.5 \times 10^{-8}$$

K_{sp} for $\text{Mg(OH)}_2 = 1.6 \times 10^{-12};$ $Q > K_{sp},$ so Mg(OH)_2 will precipitate.

Integrative Exercises

18.63   (a) $0.021 \text{ ppm NO}_2 = \dfrac{0.021 \text{ mol NO}_2}{1 \times 10^6 \text{ mol air}} = 2.1 \times 10^{-8} = \chi_{\text{NO}_2}$

$$P_{\text{NO}_2} = \chi_{\text{NO}_2} \bullet P_{atm} = 2.1 \times 10^{-8} (745 \text{ torr}) = 1.565 \times 10^{-5} = 1.6 \times 10^{-5} \text{ torr}$$

(b) $n = \dfrac{PV}{RT};$ molecules $= n \times \dfrac{6.022 \times 10^{23} \text{ molecules}}{\text{mol}} = \dfrac{PV}{RT} \times \dfrac{6.022 \times 10^{23} \text{ molecules}}{\text{mol}}$

$$V = 15 \text{ ft} \times 14 \text{ ft} \times 8 \text{ ft} \times \dfrac{12^3 \text{ in}^3}{\text{ft}^3} \times \dfrac{2.54^3 \text{ cm}^3}{\text{in}^3} \times \dfrac{1 \text{ L}}{1000 \text{ cm}^3} = 4.757 \times 10^4 = 5 \times 10^4$$

$$1.565 \times 10^{-5} \text{ torr} \times \dfrac{1 \text{ atm}}{760 \text{ torr}} \times \dfrac{4.757 \times 10^4 \text{ L}}{293 \text{ K}} \times \dfrac{\text{K} \bullet \text{mol}}{0.08206 \text{ L} \bullet \text{atm}}$$

$$\times \dfrac{6.022 \times 10^{23} \text{ molecules}}{\text{mol}} = 2.453 \times 10^{19} = 2 \times 10^{19} \text{ molecules}$$

18.66   (a) $\Delta H = 2D(\text{O–H}) - D(\text{O–H}) = D(\text{O–H}) = 463 \text{ kJ/mol}$

$$\dfrac{463 \text{ kJ}}{\text{mol H}_2\text{O}} \times \dfrac{1 \text{ mol H}_2\text{O}}{6.022 \times 10^{23} \text{ molecules}} \times \dfrac{1000 \text{ J}}{\text{kJ}} = 7.688 \times 10^{-19}$$

$$= 7.69 \times 10^{-19} \text{ J/H}_2\text{O molecule}$$

$$\lambda = \dfrac{hc}{\Delta E} = \dfrac{6.626 \times 10^{-34} \text{ J} \bullet \text{sec} \times 2.998 \times 10^8 \text{ m/s}}{7.688 \times 10^{-19} \text{ J}} = 2.58 \times 10^{-7} \text{ m} = 258 \text{ nm}$$

This wavelength is in the UV region of the spectrum, close to the visible.

(b)
$$OH(g) + O_3(g) \rightarrow HO_2(g) + O_2(g)$$
$$HO_2(g) + O(g) \rightarrow OH(g) + O_2(g)$$

$$\overline{OH(g) + O_3(g) + HO_2(g) + O(g) \rightarrow HO_2(g) + 2O_2(g) + OH(g)}$$

$$O_3(g) + O(g) \rightarrow 2O_2(g)$$

$OH(g)$ is the catalyst in this overall reaction, another pathway for the destruction of ozone.

18.70   From the composition of air at sea-level (Table 18.1) calculate the partial pressures of $N_2(g)$ and $O_2(g)$ in the original sample.

$P_x = \chi_x \cdot P_T$; $P_{N_2} = 0.78084 \,(1.0 \text{ atm}) = 0.78 \text{ atm}$; $P_{O_2} = 0.20948 \,(1.0 \text{ atm}) = 0.21 \text{ atm}$

	$N_2(g)$	$+$	$O_2(g)$	$\rightleftharpoons$	$2NO(g)$
initial	0.78 atm		0.21 atm		0
charge	-x		-x		+2x
equil	(0.78-x) atm		(0.21-x) atm		2x atm

$$K_p = \frac{P_{NO}^2}{P_{N_2} \times P_{O_2}} = \frac{(2x)^2}{(0.78-x)(0.21-x)} = \frac{4x^2}{0.164 - 0.99x + x^2} = \frac{4x^2}{0.164 - 0.99x + x^2} = 0.05$$

$0.05\,(0.164 - 0.99x + x^2) = 4x^2$; $0 = 3.95x^2 + 0.05x - 0.0082$

Using the quadratic formula, $x = \dfrac{-b \pm \sqrt{b^2 - 4ac}}{2a} = \dfrac{-0.05 \pm \sqrt{(0.05)^2 - 4(3.95)(-0.0082)}}{2(3.95)}$

$x = \dfrac{-0.05 \pm \sqrt{0.0025 + 0.1296}}{7.90} = \dfrac{-0.05 \pm 0.363}{7.90}$

The negative result is meaningless; $x = 0.04$ atm; $P_{NO} = 2x = 0.08$ atm

Assuming that the total pressure of the gaseous mixture at equilibrium is still 1.0 atm,

$\chi_{NO} = P_{NO} / P_T = 0.08 \text{ atm}/1.0 \text{ atm} = 0.08$

ppm for gases $= \chi \times 10^6$ (see Section 18.1)

$\text{ppm}_{CO} = 0.08 \times 10^6 = 8 \times 10^4$ ppm

18.73   (a)   According to Table 18.1, the mole fraction of CO_2 in air is 0.000355.

$P_{CO_2} = \chi_{CO_2} \cdot P_{atm} = 0.000355\,(1.00 \text{ atm}) = 3.55 \times 10^{-4}$ atm

$C_{CO_2} = kP_{CO_2} = 3.1 \times 10^{-2} \, M/\text{atm} \times 3.55 \times 10^{-4} \text{ atm} = 1.10 \times 10^{-5} = 1.1 \times 10^{-5} \, M$

(b) H_2CO_3 is a weak acid, so the $[H^+]$ is regulated by the equilibria:

$H_2CO_3(aq) \rightleftharpoons H^+(aq) + HCO_3^-(aq) \quad K_{a1} = 4.3 \times 10^{-7}$

$HCO_3^-(aq) \rightleftharpoons H^+(aq) + CO_3^{2-}(aq) \quad K_{a2} = 5.6 \times 10^{-11}$

Since the value of K_{a2} is small compared to K_{a1}, we will assume that most of the $H^+(aq)$ is produced by the first dissociation.

$$K_{a1} = 4.3 \times 10^{-7} = \frac{[H^+][HCO_3^-]}{[H_2CO_3]}; \quad [H^+] = [HCO_3^-] = x, \; [H_2CO_3] = 1.1 \times 10^{-5} - x$$

Since K_{a1} and $[H_2CO_3]$ have similar values, we cannot assume x is small compared to 1.1×10^{-5}.

$$4.3 \times 10^{-7} = \frac{x^2}{(1.1 \times 10^{-5} - x)}; \quad 4.73 \times 10^{-12} - 4.3 \times 10^{-7} x = x^2$$

$$0 = x^2 + 4.3 \times 10^{-7} - 4.73 \times 10^{-12}$$

$$x = \frac{-4.3 \times 10^{-7} \pm \sqrt{(4.3 \times 10^{-7})^2 - 4(1)(-4.73 \times 10^{-12})}}{2(1)}$$

$$x = \frac{-4.3 \times 10^{-7} \pm \sqrt{1.85 \times 10^{-13} + 1.89 \times 10^{-11}}}{2} = \frac{-4.3 \times 10^{-7} \pm 4.37 \times 10^{-6}}{2}$$

The negative result is meaningless; $x = 1.97 \times 10^{-6} = 2.0 \times 10^{-6}$ M H^+; pH = 5.71
Since this $[H^+]$ is quite small, the $[H^+]$ from the autoionization of water might be significant. Calculation shows that for $[H^+] = 2.0 \times 10^{-6}$ M from H_2CO_3, $[H^+]$ from H_2O = 5.2×10^{-9} M, which we can ignore.

19 Chemical Thermodynamics

Spontaneous Processes

19.1 *Analyze/Plan.* Follow the logic in Sample Exercise 19.1. *Solve*:

   (a) Nonspontaneous; -5°C is below the melting point of ice, so melting does not happen without continuous intervention.

   (b) Spontaneous; sugar is soluble in water, and even more soluble in hot coffee.

   (c) Spontaneous; N_2 molecules are stable relative to isolated N atoms.

   (d) Spontaneous; the filings organize in a magnetic field without intervention.

   (e) Nonspontaneous; CO_2 and H_2O are in contact continuously at atmospheric conditions in nature and do not form CH_4 and O_2.

19.3 (a) $NH_4NO_3(s)$ dissolves in water, as in a chemical cold pack. Naphthalene (moth balls) sublimes at room temperature.

   (b) Melting of a solid is spontaneous above its melting point but nonspontaneous below its melting point.

19.5 *Analyze/Plan.* Define the system and surroundings. Use the appropriate definition to answer the specific questions. *Solve*:

   (a) Water is the system. Heat must be added to the system to evaporate the water. The process is endothermic.

   (b) At 1 atm, the reaction is spontaneous at temperatures above 100°C.

   (c) At 1 atm, the reaction is nonspontaneous at temperatures below 100°C.

   (d) The two phases are in equilibrium at 100°C.

19.7 *Analyze/Plan.* Define the system and surroundings. Use the appropriate definition to answer the specific questions. *Solve*:

   (a) For a *reversible* process, the forward and reverse changes occur by the same path. There is only one reversible pathway for a specified set of conditions. Work can only be realized from a reversible process.

   (b) If a system is returned to its original state via a reversible path, the surroundings are also returned to their original state. That is, there is no net change in the surroundings.

(c)   The vaporization of water to steam is reversible if it occurs at the boiling temperature of water for a specified external (atmospheric) pressure. This is the temperature and pressure at which the two phases are in equilibrium.

19.9   No. ΔE is a state function. $\Delta E = q + w$; q and w are not state functions. Their values do depend on path, but their sum, ΔE, does not.

19.11   *Analyze/Plan*. Define the system and surroundings. Use the appropriate definition to answer the specific questions. *Solve*:

We know that melting is a process that increases the energy of the system, even though there is no change in temperature. ΔE is not zero for the process.

Entropy and the Second Law of Thermodynamics

19.13   *Analyze/Plan*. Review the definitions of isothermal and spontaneous. $w = -P_{ext}\Delta V$. *Solve*:

(a)   Yes, the process is spontaneous.

(b) $w = -P_{ext}\Delta V$. Since the gas expands into a vacuum, $P_{ext} = 0$ and $w = 0$.

(c)   The driving force for this expansion is the increase in the possible arrangements of the molecules, the increase in disorder of the system.

19.15   *Analyze/Plan*. Consider the discussion in Section 19.2 and Figures 19.5 and 19.6. *Solve*:

(a)   Each of the 4 molecules can be in either the left or the right bulb. Thus, there are $(2)^4 = 16$ total arrangements.

(b)   Only one arrangement has all 4 molecules in the right-hand flask.

(c)   The gas will spontaneously adopt the state with maximum disorder, the state with the most possible arrangements for the molecules.

19.17   (a)   Entropy is the order or randomness of a system.

(b) ΔS is negative if order increases.

(c)   No. ΔS is a state function, so it is independent of path.

19.19   *Analyze/Plan*. Consider the conditions that lead to an increase in entropy: more mol gas in products than reactants, increase in volume of sample and, therefore, number of possible arrangements, more motional freedom of molecules, etc. *Solve*:

(a)   More gaseous particles means more possible arrangements and greater disorder; ΔS is positive.

(b) ΔS is positive for Exercise 19.2 (a) and (c). Both processes represent an increase in volume and possible arrangements for the sample. (In (e), even though HCl(aq) is a mixture, there are fewer moles of gas in the product, so ΔS is not positive.)

19.21   *Analyze/Plan.* Consider the conditions that lead to an increase in entropy: more mol gas in products than reactants, increase in volume of sample and, therefore, number of possible arrangements, more motional freedom of molecules, etc. *Solve*:

S increases in (a), (b) and (c); S decreases in (d).

19.23   (a) $CH_3OH(l) \rightarrow CH_3OH(g)$, entropy increases, more mol gas in products, greater motional freedom.

   (b) $\Delta S = \dfrac{\Delta H}{T} = \dfrac{71.8\,kJ}{mol\,CH_3OH(l)} \times 1.00\,mol\,CH_3OH(l) \times \dfrac{1}{(273.15+64.7)K} \times \dfrac{1000\,J}{1\,kJ}$

$$= 213\,J/K$$

19.25   (a)   For a spontaneous process, the entropy of the universe increases; for a reversible process, the entropy of the universe does not change.

   (b)   In a reversible process, $\Delta S_{system} + \Delta S_{surroundings} = 0$. If ΔS_{system} is positive, $\Delta S_{surroundings}$ must be negative.

   (c)   Since $\Delta S_{universe}$ must be positive for a spontaneous process, $\Delta S_{surroundings}$ must be greater than –42 J/K.

Molecular Interpretation of Entropy

19.27   (a)   The entropy of a pure crystalline substance at absolute zero is zero.

   (b)   In *translational* motion, the entire molecule moves in a single direction; in *rotational* motion, the molecule rotates or spins around a fixed axis. *Vibrational* motion is reciprocating motion. The bonds within a molecule stretch and bend, but the average position of the atoms does not change.

   (c)

19.29   *Analyze/Plan.* Consider the factors that lead to higher entropy: more mol gas in products than reactants, increase in volume of sample and, therefore, number of possible arrangements, more motional freedom of molecules, etc. *Solve*:

   (a)   Ar(g) (gases have higher entropy due primarily to much larger volume)

   (b)   He(g) at 1.5 atm (larger volume and more motional freedom)

(c)   1 mol of Ne(g) in 15.0 L (larger volume provides more motional freedom)

(d) $CO_2(g)$ (more motional freedom)

19.31   *Analyze/Plan.* Consider the markers of an increase in entropy for a chemical reaction: liquids or solutions formed from solids, gases formed from either solids or liquids, increase in moles gas during reaction. *Solve*:

(a) ΔS negative (moles of gas decrease)

(b) ΔS positive (gas produced, increased disorder)

(c) ΔS negative (moles of gas decrease)

(d) ΔS positive (moles of gas increase)

19.33   *Analyze/Plan.* Consider the conditions that lead to an increase in entropy: more mol gas in products than reactants, increase in volume of sample and, therefore, number of possible arrangements, more motional freedom of molecules, etc. *Solve*:

(a)   Sc(s), 34.6 J/mol•K; Sc(g), 174.7 J/mol•K. In general, the gas phase of a substance has a larger S° than the solid phase because of the greater volume and motional freedom of the molecules.

(b) $NH_3(g)$, 192.5 J/mol•K; $NH_3(aq)$, 111.3 J/mol•K. Molecules in the gas phase have more motional freedom than molecules in solution.

(c)   1 mol of $P_4(g)$, 280 J/K; 2 mol of $P_2(g)$, 2(218.1) = 436.2 J/K. More particles have a greater number of arrangements.

(d)   C(diamond), 2.43 J/mol•K ; C(graphite) 5.69 J/mol•K. Diamond is a network covalent solid with each C atom tetrahedrally bound to four other C atoms. Graphite consists of sheets of fused planar 6-membered rings with each C atom bound in a trigonal planar arrangement to three other C atoms. The internal entropy in graphite is greater because there is translational freedom among the planar sheets of C atoms while there is very little vibrational freedom within the network covalent diamond lattice.

19.35   *Analyze/Plan.* Consider the molecular interpretation of entropy. *Solve*:

Hydrocarbon	S° (J/mol•K)
$CH_4(g)$	186.3
$C_2H_6(g)$	229.5
$C_3H_8(g)$	269.9
$C_4H_{10}(g)$	310.0

As the number of C atoms increases, the S° of the hydrocarbon increases. The increased structural complexity means more motional degrees of freedom for each molecule.

19.37   *Analyze/Plan.* Follow the logic in Sample Exercise 19.7.   *Solve:*

(a) $\Delta S° = S° \ C_2H_6(g) - S° \ C_2H_4(g) - S° \ H_2(g)$

$= 229.5 - 219.4 - 130.58 = -120.5$ J/K

$\Delta S°$ is negative because there are fewer moles of gas in the products.

(b) $\Delta S° = 2S° \ NO_2(g) - \Delta S° \ N_2O_4(g) = 2(240.45) - 304.3 = +176.6$ J/K

$\Delta S°$ is positive because there are more moles of gas in the products.

(c) $\Delta S° = \Delta S° \ BeO(s) + \Delta S° \ H_2O(g) - \Delta S° \ Be(OH)_2(s)$

$= 13.77 + 188.83 - 50.21 = +152.39$ J/K

$\Delta S°$ is positive because the product contains more total particles and more moles of gas.

(d) $\Delta S° = 2S° \ CO_2(g) + 4S° \ H_2O(g) - 2S° \ CH_3OH(g) - 3S° \ O_2(g)$

$= 2(213.6) + 4(188.83) - 2(237.6) - 3(205.0) = +92.3$ J/K

$\Delta S°$ is positive because the product contains more total particles and more moles of gas.

Gibbs Free Energy

19.39   (a) $\Delta G = \Delta H - T\Delta S$

(b)   If ΔG is positive, the process is nonspontaneous, but the reverse process is spontaneous.

(c)   There is no relationship between ΔG and rate of reaction. A spontaneous reaction, one with a $-\Delta G$, may occur at a very slow rate. For example: $2H_2(g) + O_2(g) \rightarrow 2H_2O(g)$, $\Delta G = -457$ kJ is very slow if not initiated by a spark.

19.41   *Analyze/Plan.* Consider the definitions of ΔH, $\Delta S°$ and $\Delta G°$, along with sign conventions.

$\Delta G° = \Delta H° - T\Delta S°$ *Solve:*

(a) $\Delta H°$ is negative; the reaction is exothermic.

(b) $\Delta S°$ is negative; the reaction leads to decrease in disorder (increase in order) of the system.

(c) $\Delta G° = \Delta H° - T\Delta S° = -35.4$ kJ $- 298$ K $(-0.0855$ kJ/K$) = -9.921 = -9.9$ kJ

(d)   At 298 K, $\Delta G°$ is negative. If all reactants and products are present in their standard states, the reaction is spontaneous at this temperature.

19.43   *Analyze/Plan.* Calculate $\Delta H°$ according to Equation 5.31, $\Delta S°$ by Equation 19.8 and $\Delta G°$ by Equation 19.13. Then use $\Delta H°$ and $\Delta S°$ to calculate $\Delta G°$ using Equation 19.20, $\Delta G° = \Delta H° - T\Delta S°$.   *Solve:*

(a) $\Delta H° = 2(-268.61) - [0 + 0] = -537.22$ kJ

$\Delta S° = 2(173.51) - [130.58 + 202.7] = 13.74 = 13.7$ J/K

$\Delta G° = 2(-270.70) - [0 + 0] = -541.40$ kJ

$\Delta G° = -537.22$ kJ $- 298(0.01374)$ kJ $= -541.31$ kJ

(b) $\Delta H° = -106.7 - [0 + 2(0)] = -106.7$ kJ

$\Delta S° = 309.4 - [5.69 + 2(222.96)] = -142.21 = -142.2$ J/K

$\Delta G° = -64.0 - [0 + 2(0)] = -64.0$ kJ

$\Delta G° = -106.7$ kJ $- 298(-0.14221)$ kJ $= -64.3$ kJ

(c) $\Delta H° = 2(-542.2) - [2(-288.07) + 0] = -508.26 = -508.3$ kJ

$\Delta S° = 2(325) - [2(311.7) + 205.0] = -178.4 = -178$ J/K

$\Delta G° = 2(-502.5) - [2(-269.6) + 0] = -465.8$ kJ

$\Delta G° = -508.26$ kJ $- 298(-0.1784)$ kJ $= -455.097 = -455.1$ kJ

(The discrepancy in $\Delta G°$ values is due to experimental uncertainties in the tabulated thermodynamic data.)

(d) $\Delta H° = -84.68 + 2(-241.82) - [2(-201.2) + 0] = -165.92 = -165.9$ kJ

$\Delta S° = 229.5 + 2(188.83) - [2(237.6) + 130.58] = 1.38 = 1.4$ J/K

$\Delta G° = -32.89 + 2(-228.57) - [2(-161.9) + 0] = -166.23 = -166.2$ kJ

$\Delta G° = -165.92$ kJ $- 298(0.00138)$ kJ $= -166.33 = -166.3$ kJ

19.45 *Analyze/Plan.* Follow the logic in Sample Exercise 19.8. *Solve:*

(a) $\Delta G° = 2\Delta G° \ SO_3(g) - [2\Delta G° \ SO_2(g) + \Delta G° \ O_2(g)]$

$= 2(-370.4) - [2(-300.4) + 0] = -140.0$ kJ, spontaneous

(b) $\Delta G° = 3\Delta G° \ NO(g) - [\Delta G° \ NO_2(g) + \Delta G° \ N_2O(g)]$

$= 3(86.71) - [51.84 + 103.59] = +104.70$ kJ, nonspontaneous

(c) $\Delta G° = 4\Delta G° \ FeCl_3(s) + 3\Delta G° \ O_2(g) - [6\Delta G° \ Cl_2(g) + 2\Delta G° \ Fe_2O_3(s)]$

$= 4(-334) + 3(0) - [6(0) + 2(-740.98)] = +146$ kJ, nonspontaneous

(d) $\Delta G° = \Delta G° \ S(s) + 2\Delta G° \ H_2O(g) - [\Delta G° \ SO_2(g) + 2\Delta G° \ H_2(g)]$

$= 0 + 2(-228.57) - [(-300.4) + 2(0)] = -156.7$ kJ, spontaneous

19.47 *Analyze/Plan.* Follow the logic in Sample Exercise 19.9(a). *Solve:*

(a) $C_6H_{12}(l) + 9O_2(g) \rightarrow 6CO_2(g) + 6H_2O(l)$

(b) Because there are fewer moles of gas in the products, $\Delta S°$ is negative, which makes $-T\Delta S$ positive. $\Delta G°$ is less negative (more positive) than $\Delta H°$.

19.49 *Analyze/Plan.* Based on the signs of ΔH and ΔS for a particular reaction, assign a category from Table 19.4 to each reaction. *Solve:*

(a) ΔG is negative at low temperatures, positive at high temperatures. That is, the reaction proceeds in the forward direction spontaneously at lower temperatures but spontaneously reverses at higher temperatures.

(b) ΔG is positive at all temperatures. The reaction is nonspontaneous in the forward direction at all temperatures.

(c) ΔG is positive at low temperatures, negative at high temperatures. That is, the reaction will proceed spontaneously in the forward direction at high temperature.

19.51   *Analyze/Plan.* We are told that the reaction is spontaneous and endothermic, and asked to estimate the sign and magnitude of ΔS. If a reaction is spontaneous, $\Delta G < 0$. Use this information with Equation 19.20 to solve the problem. *Solve:*

At 450 K, $\Delta G < 0$; $\Delta G = \Delta H - T\Delta S < 0$

34.5 kJ - 450 K (ΔS) < 0; 34.5 kJ < 450 K (ΔS); ΔS > 34.5 kJ/450 K

ΔS > 0.0767 kJ/K or ΔS > +76.7 J/K

19.53   *Analyze/Plan.* Follow the logic in Sample Exercise 19.11. Use Equation 19.20 to calculate T when $\Delta G = 0$. Use Table 19.4 to determine whether the reaction is spontaneous or non-spontaneous above this temperature. *Solve:*

(a) $\Delta G = \Delta H - T\Delta S$; 0 = -32 kJ - T(-98 J/K); 32 × 10^3 J = T(98 J/K)

         T = 32 × 10^3 J/(98 J/K) = 326.5 = 330 K

(b)   Nonspontaneous. The sign of ΔS is negative, so as T increases, ΔG becomes more positive.

19.55   *Analyze/Plan.* Given a chemical equation and thermodynamic data (values of ΔH_f°, ΔG_f° and S°) for reactants and products, predict the variation of $\Delta G°$ with temperature and calculate $\Delta G°$ at 800 K and 1000 K. Use Equations 5.31 and 19.8 to calculate $\Delta H°$ and $\Delta S°$, respectively; use these values to calculate $\Delta G°$ at various temperatures, using Equation 19.20. The signs of $\Delta H°$ and $\Delta S°$ determine the variation of $\Delta G°$ with temperature. *Solve:*

(a)   Calculate $\Delta H°$ and $\Delta S°$ to determine the sign of $T\Delta S°$.

         $\Delta H° = 3\Delta H° NO(g) - \Delta H° NO_2(g) - \Delta H° N_2O(g)$
            = 3(90.37) - 33.84 - 81.6 = 155.7 kJ
         $\Delta S° = 3S° NO(g) - S° NO_2(g) - S° N_2O(g)$
            = 3(210.62) - 240.45 - 220.0 = 171.4 J/K
         $\Delta G° = \Delta H° - T\Delta S°$. Since $\Delta S°$ is positive, $-T\Delta S°$ becomes more negative as T increases and $\Delta G°$ becomes more negative.

(b) $\Delta G° = \Delta H° - T\Delta S° = 155.7$kJ - (800 K)(0.1714 kJ/K)
         $\Delta G° = 155.7$ kJ - 137 kJ = 19 kJ
         Since $\Delta G°$ is positive at 800 K, the reaction is not spontaneous at this temperature.

(c) $\Delta G° = 155.7$ kJ - $(1000$ K$)(0.1714$ kJ/K$) = 155.7$ kJ - 171.4 kJ = -15.7 kJ

$\Delta G°$ is negative at 1000 K and the reaction is spontaneous at this temperature.

19.57 *Analyze/Plan.* Follow the logic in Sample Exercise 19.11. *Solve:*

(a) $\Delta S°_{vap} = \Delta H°_{vap}/T_b$; $T_b = \Delta H°_{vap}/\Delta S°_{vap}$

$\Delta H°_{vap} = \Delta H°$ $C_6H_6(g) - \Delta H°$ $C_6H_6(l) = 82.9 - 49.0 = 33.9$ kJ

$\Delta S°_{vap} = S°$ $C_6H_6(g) - S°$ $C_6H_6(l) = 269.2 - 172.8 = 96.4$ J/K

$T_b = 33.9 \times 10^3$ J$/96.4$ J/K $= 351.66 = 352$ K $= 79°C$

(b)   From the *Handbook of Chemistry and Physics*, 74th Edition, $T_b = 80.1°C$. The values are remarkably close; the small difference is due to deviation from ideal behavior by $C_6H_6(g)$ and experimental uncertainty in the boiling point measurement and the thermodynamic data.

19.59 *Analyze/Plan.* We are asked to write a balanced equation for the combustion of acetylene, calculate $\Delta H°$ for this reaction and calculate maximum useful work possible by the system. Combustion is combination with O_2 to produce CO_2 and H_2O. Calculate $\Delta H°$ using data from Appendix C and Equation 5.31. The maximum obtainable work is ΔG (Equation 19.19), which can be calculated from data in Appendix C and Equation 19.13. *Solve:*

(a) $C_2H_2(g) + 5/2$ $O_2(g)$ → $2CO_2(g) + H_2O(l)$

(b) $\Delta H° = 2\Delta H°$ $CO_2(g) + \Delta H°$ $H_2O(l) - \Delta H°$ $C_2H_2(g) - 5/2\Delta H°$ $O_2(g)$

$= 2(-393.5) - 285.83 - 226.7 - 5/2(0) = -1299.5$ kJ produced/mol C_2H_2 burned

(c) $w_{max} = \Delta G° = 2\Delta G°$ $CO_2(g) + \Delta G°$ $H_2O(l) - \Delta G°$ $C_2H_2(g) - 5/2$ $\Delta G°$ $O_2(g)$

$= 2(-394.4) - 237.13 - 209.2 - 5/2(0) = -1235.1$ kJ

The negative sign indicates that the system does work on the surroundings; the system can accomplish a maximum of 1235.1 kJ of work on its surroundings.

Free Energy and Equilibrium

19.61 *Analyze/Plan.* We are given a chemical reaction and asked to predict the effect of the partial pressure of $O_2(g)$ on the value of ΔG for the system. Consider the relationship $\Delta G = \Delta G° + RT \ln Q$ where Q is the reaction quotient. *Solve:*

(a) $O_2(g)$ appears in the denominator of Q for this reaction. An increase in pressure of O_2 decreases Q and ΔG becomes smaller or more negative. Increasing the concentration of a reactant increases the tendency for a reaction to occur.

(b) $O_2(g)$ appears in the numerator of Q for this reaction. Increasing the pressure of O_2 increases Q and ΔG becomes more positive. Increasing the concentration of a product decreases the tendency for the reaction to occur.

(c) $O_2(g)$ appears in the numerator of Q for this reaction. An increase in pressure of O_2 increases Q and ΔG becomes more positive. Since pressure of O_2 is raised to the third power in Q, an increase in pressure of O_2 will have the largest effect on ΔG for this reaction.

19.63 *Analyze/Plan.* Given a chemical reaction, we are asked to calculate $\Delta G°$ from Appendix C data, and ΔG for a given set of initial conditions. Use Equation 19.13 to calculate $\Delta G°$, and Equation 19.21 to calculate ΔG. Follow the logic in Sample Exercise 19.12 when calculating ΔG. *Solve:*

(a) $\Delta G° = \Delta G°\ N_2O_4(g) - 2\Delta G°\ NO_2(g) = 98.28 - 2(51.84) = -5.40$ kJ

(b) $\Delta G = \Delta G° + RT\ \ln\ P_{N_2O_4} / P_{NO_2}^2$

   $= -5.40$ kJ $+ \dfrac{8.314 \times 10^{-3}\ kJ}{K \cdot mol} \times 298\ K \times \ln[1.60/(0.40)^2] = 0.3048 = 0.30$ kJ

19.65 *Analyze/Plan.* Given a chemical reaction, we are asked to calculate K_{eq} using $\Delta G_f°$ data from Appendix C. Follow the logic in Sample Exercise 19.13. $\Delta G° = -RT\ \ln\ K_{eq}$, Equation 19.22; $\ln\ K_{eq} = -\Delta G°/RT$ *Solve:*

(a) $\Delta G° = 2\Delta G°\ HI(g) - \Delta G°\ H_2(g) - \Delta G°\ I_2(g)$
     $= 2(1.30) - 0 - 19.37 = -16.77$ kJ

   $\ln\ K_{eq} = \dfrac{-(-16.77\ kJ) \times 10^3\ J/kJ}{8.314\ J/K \times 298\ K} = 6.76876 = 6.769;\ \ K_{eq} = 870$

(b) $\Delta G° = \Delta G°\ C_2H_4(g) + \Delta G°\ H_2O(g) - \Delta G°\ C_2H_5OH(g)$

     $= 68.11 - 228.57 - (-168.5) = 8.04 = 8.0$ kJ

   $\ln\ K_{eq} = \dfrac{-8.04\ kJ \times 10^3\ J/kJ}{8.314\ J/K \times 298\ K} = -3.24511 = -3.2;\ K_{eq} = 0.04$

(c) $\Delta G° = \Delta G°\ C_6H_6(g) - 3\Delta G°\ C_2H_2(g) = 129.7 - 3(209.2) = -497.9$ kJ

   $\ln\ K_{eq} = \dfrac{-\Delta G°}{RT} = \dfrac{-(-497.9\ kJ) \times 10^3\ J/kJ}{8.314\ J/K \times 298\ K} = 200.963 = 201.0;\ \ K_{eq} = 2 \times 10^{87}$

19.67 *Analyze/Plan.* Given a chemical reaction and thermodynamic data in Appendix C, calculate the equilibrium pressure of $CO_2(g)$ at two temperatures. $K_{eq} = P_{CO_2}$. Calculate $\Delta G°$ at the two temperatures using $\Delta G° = \Delta H° - T\Delta S°$ and then calculate K_{eq} and P_{CO_2}. *Solve:*

$\Delta H° = \Delta H°\ BaO(s) + \Delta H°\ CO_2(g) - \Delta H°\ BaCO_3(s)$
   $= -553.5 + -393.5 - (-1216.3) = +269.3$ kJ

$\Delta S° = S°\ BaO(s) + S°\ CO_2(g) - S°\ BaCO_3(s)$
   $= 70.42 + 213.6 - 112.1 = 171.92$ J/K $= 0.1719$ kJ/K

(a) ΔG at 298 K $= 269.3$ kJ $- 298$ K $(0.17192$ kJ/K$) = 218.07 = 218.1$ kJ

   $\ln\ K_{eq} = \dfrac{-\Delta G°}{RT} = \dfrac{-218.07 \times 10^3\ J}{8.314\ J/K \times 298\ K} = -88.017 = -88.02$

   $K_{eq} = 6.0 \times 10^{-39};\ \ \ P_{CO_2} = 6.0 \times 10^{-39}$ atm

(b)　　　ΔG at 1100 K = 269.3 kJ - 1100 K (0.17192 kJ) = 80.19 = +80.2 kJ

$$\ln K_{eq} = \frac{-\Delta G^\circ}{RT} = \frac{-80.19 \times 10^3 \text{ J}}{8.314 \text{ J/K} \times 1100 \text{ K}} = -8.768 = -8.77$$

$K_{eq} = 1.6 \times 10^{-4}$; $P_{CO_2} = 1.6 \times 10^{-4}$ atm

19.69　*Analyze/Plan.* Given an acid dissociation equilibrium and the corresponding K_a value, calculate ΔG° and ΔG for a given set of concentrations. Use Equation 19.22 to calculate ΔG° and Equation 19.21 to calculate ΔG. *Solve*:

(a)　　　$HNO_2(aq) \rightleftharpoons H^+(aq) + NO_2^-(aq)$

(b)　　　$\Delta G^\circ = -RT \ln K_a = -(8.314 \times 10^{-3})(298) \ln (4.5 \times 10^{-4}) = 19.0928 = 19.1$ kJ

(c)　　　$\Delta G = 0$ at equilibrium

(d)　　　$\Delta G = \Delta G^\circ + RT \ln Q$

$$= 19.09 \text{ kJ} + (8.314 \times 10^{-3})(298) \ln \frac{(5.0 \times 10^{-2})(6.0 \times 10^{-4})}{0.20} = -2.72 \text{ kJ}$$

Additional Exercises

19.73

Process	ΔH	ΔS
(a)	+	+
(b)	-	-
(c)	+	+
(d)	+	+
(e)	-	+

19.77　Propylene will have a higher S° at 25°C. At this temperature, both are gases, so there are no lattice effects (see Solution 19.78). Since they have the same molecular formula, only the details of their structures are different. In propylene, there is free rotation around the C–C single bond, while in cyclopropane the 3-membered ring severely limits rotation. The greater motional freedom of the propylene molecule leads to a higher absolute entropy.

19.81　$\Delta G = \Delta G^\circ + RT \ln Q$

(a)　　　$Q = \dfrac{P_{NH_3}^2}{P_{N_2} \times P_{H_2}^3} = \dfrac{(1.2)^2}{(2.6)(5.9)^3} = 2.697 \times 10^{-3} = 2.7 \times 10^{-3}$

$\Delta G^\circ = 2\Delta G^\circ\ NH_3(g) - \Delta G^\circ\ N_2(g) - 3\Delta G^\circ\ H_2(g)$

$= 2(-16.66) - 0 - 3(0) = -33.32$ kJ

$\Delta G = -33.32 \text{ kJ} + \dfrac{8.314 \times 10^{-3} \text{ kJ}}{K \cdot mol} \times 298 \text{ K} \times \ln(2.69 \times 10^{-3})$

$\Delta G = -33.32 - 14.66 = -47.98$ kJ

(b) $Q = \dfrac{P_{N_2}^3 \times P_{H_2O}^4}{P_{N_2H_4}^2 \times P_{NO_2}^2} = \dfrac{(0.5)^3(0.3)^4}{(5.0 \times 10^{-2})^2(5.0 \times 10^{-2})^2} = 162 = 2 \times 10^2$

$\Delta G° = 3\Delta G° \, N_2(g) + 4\Delta G° \, H_2O(g) - 2\Delta G° \, N_2H_4(g) - 2\Delta G° \, NO_2(g)$

$= 3(0) + 4(-228.57) - 2(159.4) - 2(51.84) = -1336.8 \text{ kJ}$

$\Delta G = -1336.8 \text{ kJ} + 2.478 \ln 162 = -1324.2 \text{ kJ}$

(c) $Q = \dfrac{P_{N_2} \times P_{H_2}^2}{P_{N_2H_4}} = \dfrac{(1.5)(2.5)^2}{0.5} = 18.75 = 2 \times 10^1$

$\Delta G° = \Delta G° \, N_2(g) + 2\Delta G° \, H_2(g) - \Delta G° \, N_2H_4(g)$

$= 0 + 2(0) - 159.4 = -159.4 \text{ kJ}$

$\Delta G = -159.4 \text{ kJ} + 2.478 \ln 18.75 = -152.1 \text{ kJ}$

19.83   (a) $K_{eq} = \dfrac{\chi_{CH_3COOH}}{\chi_{CH_3OH} \, P_{CO}}$

$\Delta G° = -RT \ln K_{eq}; \quad \ln K_{eq} = -\Delta G/RT$

$\Delta G° = \Delta G° \, CH_3COOH(l) - \Delta G° \, CH_3OH(l) - \Delta G° \, CO(g)$

$= -392.4 - (-166.23) - (-137.2) = -89.0 \text{ kJ}$

$\ln K_{eq} = \dfrac{-(-89.0 \text{ kJ})}{(8.314 \times 10^{-3} \text{ kJ/K})(298 \text{ K})} = 35.922 = 35.9; \quad K_{eq} = 4 \times 10^{15}$

(b) $\Delta H° = \Delta H° \, CH_3COOH(l) - \Delta H° \, CH_3OH(l) - \Delta H° \, CO(g)$

$= -487.0 - (-238.6) - (-110.5) = -137.9 \text{ kJ}$

The reaction is exothermic, so the value of K_{eq} will decrease with increasing temperature, and the mole fraction of CH_3COOH will also decrease. Elevated temperatures must be used to increase the speed of the reaction. Thermodynamics cannot predict the rate at which a reaction reaches equilibrium.

(c) $\Delta G° = -RT \ln K_{eq}; \quad K_{eq} = 1, \ln K_{eq} = 0, \Delta G° = 0$

$\Delta G° = \Delta H° - T\Delta S°; \quad \text{when } \Delta G° = 0, \Delta H° = T\Delta S°$

$\Delta S° = S° \, CH_3COOH(l) - S° \, CH_3OH(l) - S° \, CO(g)$

$= 159.8 - 126.8 - 197.9 = -164.9 \text{ J/K} = -0.1649 \text{ kJ/K}$

$-137.9 \text{ kJ} = T(-0.1649 \text{ kJ/K}), \quad T = 836.3 \text{ K}$

The equilibrium favors products up to 836 K or 563 °C, so the elevated temperatures to increase the rate of reaction can be safely employed.

19.86 $\Delta G°$ for the metabolism of glucose is:

$6\Delta G° \; CO_2(g) + 6\Delta G° \; H_2O(l) - \Delta G° \; C_6H_{12}O_6(s) - 6\Delta G° \; O_2(g)$

$\Delta G° = 6(-394.4) + 6(-237.13) - (-910.4) + 6(0) = -2878.8 \text{ kJ}$

moles ATP = $-2878.8 \text{ kJ} \times 1 \text{ mol ATP} / (-30.5 \text{ kJ}) = 94.4 \text{ mol ATP} /$ mol glucose

19.89   (a)   Both equations describe the entropy change of the system when a gas expands at constant temperature.

$\Delta S = nR \ln(V_2/V_1); \quad \Delta S = q_{rev}/T \text{ (Equation 19.1)}$
$q_{rev}/T = nR \ln(V_2/V_1); \; q_{rev} = nRT \ln(V_2/V_1)$

(b) $n = 0.50 \text{ mol}, V_1 = 10.0 \text{ L}, V_2 = 75.0 \text{ L}$
$\Delta S = 0.50 \text{ mol} (8.314 \text{ J/mol•K}) \ln (75.0 \text{ L}/10.0 \text{ L}) = 8.376 \; = 8.4 \text{ J/K}$

(c)   When a gas expands, there are more possible arrangements for the particles, and entropy increases. The positive sign for ΔS in part (b) is consistent with this prediction.

(d) $n = 8.5; V_2 = 1/8 \; V_1; V_2/V_1 = 1/8$
$\Delta S = 8.5 \text{ mol} (8.314 \text{ J/mol•K}) \ln (1/8) = -146.95 = -1.5 \times 10^2 \text{ J/K}$

Integrative Exercises

19.93   (a)   Polymerization is the process of joining many small molecules (monomers) into a few very large molecules (polymers). Polyethylene in particular can have extremely high molecular weights. In general, reducing the number of particles in a system reduces entropy, so ΔS_{poly} is expected to be negative.

(b) $\Delta G_{poly} = \Delta H_{poly} - T\Delta S_{poly}$. If the polymerization of ethylene is spontaneous, ΔG_{poly} is negative. If ΔS_{poly} is negative, $-T\Delta S_{poly}$ is positive, so ΔH_{poly} must be negative for ΔG_{poly} to be negative. The enthalpy of polymerization must be exothermic.

(c)   According to Equation 12.1, polymerization of ethylene requires breaking one C=C and forming 2C–C per monomer (1C–C between the C-atoms of the monomer and 2 × 1/2 C–C to two other monomers).

$\Delta H = D(C=C) - 2D(C-C) = 614 - 2(348) = -82 \text{ kJ/mol } C_2H_4$

$$\frac{-82 \text{ kJ}}{\text{mol } C_2H_4} \times \frac{1 \text{ mol}}{6.022 \times 10^{23} \text{ molecules}} \times \frac{1000 \text{ J}}{1 \text{ kJ}} = 1.36 \times 10^{-19} \text{ J/}C_2H_4 \text{ monomer}$$

(d)   The products of a condensation polymerization are the polymer and a small molecule, typically H_2O; there is usually one small molecule formed per monomer unit. Unlike addition polymerization, the total number of particles is not reduced. A condensation polymer does impose more order on the monomer or monomers than an addition polymer. If there is a single monomer, it has different functional groups at the two ends and only one end can react to join the polymer, so orientation is required. If there are two different monomers, as in nylon, the monomers alternate in the polymer, so only the correct monomer can react to join the polymer. In terms of structure, the condensation polymer imposes more order on the monomer(s) than an addition polymer. But, condensation polymerization does not lead to a reduction in the number of particles in the system, so ΔS_{poly} will be less negative than for addition polymerization.

19.96 (a) 16 e⁻, 8 e⁻ pairs. The C-S bond order is approximately 2.

(b) 2 e⁻ domains around C, linear e⁻ domain geometry, linear molecular structure

(c) $CS_2(l) + 3O_2(g) \rightarrow CO_2(g) + 2SO_2(g)$

(d) $\Delta H° = \Delta H° \; CO_2(g) + 2\Delta H° \; SO_2(g) - \Delta H° \; CS_2(l) - 3 \Delta H \Delta H° \; O_2(g)$

$= -393.5 + 2(-296.9) - (89.7) - 3(0) = -1077.0 \text{ kJ}$

$\Delta G° = \Delta G° \; CO_2(g) + 2\Delta G° \; SO_2(g) - \Delta G° \; CS_2(l) - 3 \Delta G° \; O_2(g)$

$= -394.4 + 2(-300.4) - (65.3) - 3(0) = -1060.5 \text{ kJ}$

The reaction is exothermic ($-\Delta H°$) and spontaneous ($-\Delta G°$) at 298 K.

(e) vaporization: $CS_2(l) \rightarrow CS_2(g)$

$\Delta G°_{vap} = \Delta H°_{vap} - T\Delta S°_{vap}; \quad \Delta S°_{vap} = (\Delta H°_{vap} - \Delta G°_{vap})/T$

$\Delta G°_{vap} = \Delta G° \; CS_2(g) - \Delta G° \; CS_2(l) = 67.2 - 65.3 = 1.9 \text{ kJ}$

$\Delta H°_{vap} = \Delta H° \; CS_2(g) - \Delta H° \; CS_2(l) = 117.4 - 89.7 = 27.7 \text{ kJ}$

$\Delta S°_{vap} = (27.7 - 1.9) \text{ kJ}/298 \text{ K} = 0.086577 = 0.0866 \text{ kJ/K} = 86.6 \text{ J/K}$

ΔS_{vap} is always positive, because the gas phase occupies a greater volume, has more motional freedom and a larger absolute entropy than the liquid.

(f) At the boiling point, $\Delta G = 0$ and $\Delta H_{vap} = T_b \Delta S_{vap}$.

$T_b = \Delta H_{vap}/\Delta S_{vap} = 27.7 \text{ kJ}/0.086577 \text{ kJ/K} = 319.9 = 320 \text{ K}$

$T_b = 320 \text{ K} = 47°\text{C}$. CS_2 is a liquid at 298 K, 1 atm

19.99 (a) $\Delta G° = 3\Delta G°_f \; S(s) + 2\Delta G°_f \; H_2O(g) - \Delta G°_f \; SO_2(g) - 2\Delta G°_f \; H_2S(g)$

$= 3(0) + 2(-228.57) - (-300.4) - 2(-33.01) = -90.72 = -90.7 \text{ kJ}$

$\ln K_{eq} = \dfrac{-\Delta G°}{RT} = \dfrac{-(-90.72 \text{ kJ})}{(8.314 \times 10^{-3} \text{ kJ/K})(298 \text{ K})} = 36.6165 = 36.6; \quad K_{eq} = 7.99 \times 10^{15}$

$= 8 \times 10^{15}$

(b) The reaction is highly spontaneous at 298 K and feasible in principle. However, use of $H_2S(g)$ produces a severe safety hazard for workers and the surrounding community.

(c) $P_{H_2O} = \dfrac{25 \text{ torr}}{760 \text{ torr/atm}} = 0.033 \text{ atm}$

$K_{eq} = \dfrac{P_{H_2O}^2}{P_{SO_2} \times P_{H_2S}^2}$; $P_{SO_2} = P_{H_2S} = x$ atm

$K_{eq} = 7.99 \times 10^{15} = \dfrac{(0.033)^2}{x\,(x)^2}$; $x^3 = \dfrac{(0.033)^2}{7.99 \times 10^{15}}$

$x = 5 \times 10^{-7}$ atm

(d) $\Delta H° = 3\Delta H_f°\ S(s) + 2\Delta H_f°\ H_2O(g) - \Delta H_f°\ SO_2(g) - 2\Delta H_f°\ H_2S(g)$

$= 3(0) + 2(-241.82) - (-296.9) - 2(-20.17) = -146.4$ kJ

$\Delta S° = 3S°\ S(s) + 2S°\ H_2O(g) - S°\ SO_2(g) - 2S°\ H_2S(g)$

$= 3(31.88) + 2(188.83) - 248.5 - 2(205.6) = -186.4$ J/K

The reaction is exothermic ($-\Delta H$), so the value of K_{eq} will decrease with increasing temperature. The negative $\Delta S°$ value means that the reaction will become nonspontaneous at some higher temperature. The process will be less effective at elevated temperatures.

20 Electrochemistry

Oxidation-Reduction Reactions

20.1 (a) *Oxidation* is the loss of electrons.

   (b) The electrons appear on the products side (right side) of an oxidation half-reaction.

   (c) The *oxidant* is the reactant that is reduced; it gains the electrons that are lost by the substance being oxidized.

20.3 *Analyze/Plan.* Given a chemical equation, we are asked to indicate which elements undergo a change in oxidation number and the magnitude of the change. Assign oxidation numbers according to the rules given in Section 4.4. Note the changes and report the magnitudes. *Solve*:

   (a) I is reduced from +5 to 0; C is oxidized from +2 to +4.

   (b) Hg is reduced from +2 to 0; N is oxidized from -2 to 0.

   (c) N is reduced from +5 to +2; S is oxidized from -2 to 0.

   (d) Cl is reduced from +4 to +3; O is oxidized from -1 to 0.

20.5 *Analyze/Plan.* Write the balanced chemical equation and assign oxidation numbers. The substance oxidized is the reductant and the substance reduced is the oxidant. *Solve*:

   (a) $TiCl_4(g) + 2Mg(l) \rightarrow Ti(s) + 2MgCl_2(l)$

   (b) $Mg(l)$ is the reductant; $TiCl_4(g)$ is the oxidant.

20.7 *Analyze/Plan.* Follow the logic in Sample Exercises 20.2 and 20.3. If the half-reaction occurs in basic solution, balance as in acid, then add OH^- to each side. *Solve*:

   (a) $Sn^{2+}(aq) \rightarrow Sn^{4+}(aq) + 2e^-$, oxidation

   (b) $TiO_2(s) + 4H^+(aq) + 2e^- \rightarrow Ti^{2+}(aq) + 2H_2O(l)$, reduction

   (c) $ClO_3^-(aq) + 6H^+(aq) + 6e^- \rightarrow Cl^-(aq) + 3H_2O(l)$, reduction

   (d) $4OH^-(aq) \rightarrow O_2(g) + 2H_2O(l) + 4e^-$, oxidation

   (e) $SO_3^{2-}(aq) + 2OH^-(aq) \rightarrow SO_4^{2-}(aq) + H_2O(l) + 2e^-$, oxidation

20.9 *Analyze/Plan.* Follow the logic in Sample Exercises 20.2 and 20.3 to balance the given equations. Use the method in Sample Exercise 20.1 to identify oxidizing and reducing agents. *Solve*:

   (a) $Cr_2O_7^{2-}(aq) + I^-(aq) + 8H^+ \rightarrow 2Cr^{3+}(aq) + IO_3^-(aq) + 4H_2O(l)$

   oxidizing agent, $Cr_2O_7^{2-}$; reducing agent, I^-

(b)   The half-reactions are:

$$4[MnO_4^-(aq) + 8H^+(aq) + 5e^- \rightarrow Mn^{2+}(aq) + 4H_2O(l)]$$

$$5[CH_3OH(aq) + H_2O(l) \rightarrow HCO_2H(aq) + 4H^+(aq) + 4e^-]$$

$$4MnO_4^-(aq) + 5CH_3OH(aq) + 12H^+(aq) \rightarrow 4Mn^{2+}(aq) + 5HCO_2H(aq) + 11H_2O(l)$$

oxidizing agent, MnO_4^-; reducing agent, CH_3OH

(c) $$I_2(s) + 6H_2O(l) \rightarrow 2IO_3^-(aq) + 12H^+(aq) + 10e^-$$

$$5[OCl^-(aq) + 2H^+(aq) + 2e^- \rightarrow Cl^-(aq) + H_2O(l)]$$

$$I_2(s) + 5OCl^-(aq) + H_2O(l) \rightarrow 2IO_3^-(aq) + 5Cl^- + 2H^+(aq)]$$

oxidizing agent, OCl^-; reducing agent, I_2

(d) $$As_2O_3(s) + 5H_2O(l) \rightarrow 2H_3AsO_4(aq) + 4H^+(aq) + 4e^-$$

$$2NO_3^-(aq) + 6H^+(aq) + 4e^- \rightarrow N_2O_3(aq) + 3H_2O(l)$$

$$As_2O_3(s) + 2NO_3^-(aq) + 2H_2O(l) + 2H^+(aq) \rightarrow 2H_3AsO_4(aq) + N_2O_3(aq)$$

oxidizing agent, NO_3^-; reducing agent, As_2O_3

(e) $$2[MnO_4^-(aq) + 2H_2O(l) + 3e^- \rightarrow MnO_2(s) + 4OH^-]$$

$$Br^-(aq) + 6OH^-(aq) \rightarrow BrO_3^-(aq) + 3H_2O(l) + 6e^-$$

$$2MnO_4^-(aq) + Br^-(aq) + H_2O(l) \rightarrow 2MnO_2(s) + BrO_3^-(aq) + 2OH^-(aq)$$

oxidizing agent, MnO_4^-; reducing agent, Br^-

(f) $$Pb(OH)_4^{2-}(aq) + ClO^-(aq) \rightarrow PbO_2(s) + Cl^-(aq) + 2OH^-(aq) + H_2O(l)$$

oxidizing agent, ClO^-; reducting agent, $Pb(OH)_4^{2-}$

Voltaic Cells; Cell Potential

20.11 (a)   The reaction $Cu^{2+}(aq) + Zn(s) \rightarrow Cu(s) + Zn^{2+}(aq)$ is occurring in both Figures. In Figure 20.3, the reactants are in contact, and the concentrations of the ions in solution aren't specified. In Figure 20.4, the oxidation half-reaction and reduction half-reaction are occurring in separate compartments, joined by a porous connector. The concentrations of the two solutions are initially 1.0 *M*. In Figure 20.4, electrical current is isolated and flows through the voltmeter. In Figure 20.3, the flow of electrons cannot be isolated or utilized.

(b)   In the cathode compartment of the voltaic cell in Figure 20.5, Cu^{2+} cations are reduced to Cu atoms, decreasing the number of positively charged particles in the compartment. Na^+ cations are drawn into the compartment to maintain charge balance as Cu^{2+} ions are removed.

20.13   *Analyze/Plan.* Follow the logic in Sample Exercise 20.4. *Solve*:

(a) $Ag^+(aq) + 1e^- \rightarrow Ag(s)$; $Fe(s) \rightarrow Fe^{2+}(aq) + 2e^-$

(b) $Fe(s)$ is the anode, $Ag(s)$ is the cathode.

(c) $Fe(s)$ is negative; $Ag(s)$ is positive.

(d)   Electrons flow from the $Fe(-)$ electrode toward the $Ag(+)$ electrode.

(e)   Cations migrate toward the $Ag(s)$ cathode; anions migrate toward the $Fe(s)$ anode.

20.15   (a)   *Electromotive force*, emf, is the driving force that causes electrons to flow through the external circuit of a voltaic cell. It is the potential energy difference between an electron at the anode and an electron at the cathode.

(b)   One *volt* is the potential energy difference required to impart 1 J of energy to a charge of 1 coulomb. $1 V = 1 J/C$.

(c)   *Cell potential*, E_{cell}, is the emf of an electrochemical cell.

20.17   (a) $2H^+(aq) + 2e^- \rightarrow H_2(g)$

(b)   A *standard* hydrogen electrode is a hydrogen electrode where the components are at standard conditions, $1\,M\,H^+(aq)$ and $H_2(g)$ at 1 atm.

(c)   The platinum foil in an SHE serves as an inert electron carrier and a solid reaction surface.

20.19   (a)   A *standard reduction potential* is the relative potential of a reduction half-reaction measured at standard conditions, 1 M aqueous solutions and 1 atm gas pressure.

(b) $E^{\circ}_{red} = 0 V$ for a standard hydrogen electrode.

(c)   The reduction of $Ag^+(aq)$ to $Ag(s)$ is much more energetically favorable, because it has a substantially more positive E°_{red} (0.799 V) than the reduction of $Sn^{2+}(aq)$ to $Sn(s)$ (-0.136 V).

20.21   *Analyze/Plan.* Follow the logic in Sample Exercise 20.5. *Solve*:

(a)   The two half-reactions are:

$$Tl^{3+}(aq) + 2e^- \rightarrow Tl^+(aq) \qquad \text{cathode } E^{\circ}_{red} = ?$$
$$2[Cr^{2+}(aq) \rightarrow Cr^{3+}(aq) + e^-] \quad \text{anode} \quad E^{\circ}_{red} = -0.41$$

(b) $E^{\circ}_{cell} = E^{\circ}_{red}$ (cathode) $- E^{\circ}_{red}$ (anode); $1.19 V = E^{\circ}_{red} - (-0.41 V)$;

$E^{\circ}_{red} = 1.19 V - 0.41 V = 0.78 V$

(c)

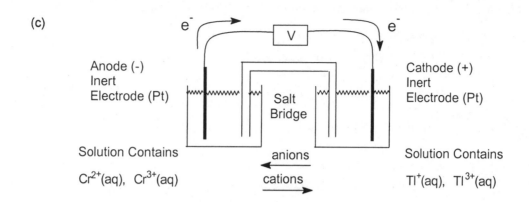

Note that because $Cr^{2+}(aq)$ is readily oxidized, it would be necessary to keep oxygen out of the left-hand cell compartment.

20.23   *Analyze/Plan.* Follow the logic in Sample Exercise 20.6. *Solve*:

a) $Cl_2(g) \rightarrow 2Cl^-(aq) + 2e^-$ $E^{\circ}_{red} = 1.359$ V

$I_2(s) + 2e^- \rightarrow 2I^-(aq)$ $E^{\circ}_{red} = 0.536$ V

$E^{\circ} = 1.359$ V $- 0.536$ V $= 0.823$ V

(b) $Ni(s) \rightarrow Ni^{2+}(aq) + 2e^-$ $E^{\circ}_{red} = -0.28$ V

$2[Ce^{4+}(aq) + 1e^- \rightarrow Ce^{3+}(aq)]$ $E^{\circ}_{red} = 1.61$ V

$E^{\circ} = 1.61$ V $- (-0.28$ V$) = 1.89$ V

(c) $Fe(s) \rightarrow Fe^{2+}(aq) + 2e^-$ $E^{\circ}_{red} = -0.440$ V

$2[Fe^{3+}(aq) + 1e^- \rightarrow Fe^{2+}(aq)]$ $E^{\circ}_{red} = +0.771$ V

$E^{\circ} = 0.771$ V $- (-0.440$ V$) = 1.211$ V

(d) $3[Ca(s) \rightarrow Ca^{2+}(aq) + 2e^-]$ $E^{\circ}_{red} = -2.87$ V

$2[Al^{3+}(aq) + 3e^- \rightarrow Al(s)]$ $E^{\circ}_{red} = -1.66$ V

$E^{\circ} = -1.66$ V $- (-2.87$ V$)] = 1.21$ V

20.25   *Analyze/Plan.* Given four half-reactions, find E°_{red} from Appendix E and combine them to obtain a desired E_{cell}. (a) The largest E_{cell} will combine the half-reaction with the most positive E°_{red} as the cathode reaction and the one with the most negative E°_{red} as the anode reaction. (b) The smallest positive E_{cell} will combine two half-reactions whose E°_{red} values are closest in magnitude **and** sign.   *Solve*:

(a) $3[Ag^+(aq) + 1e^- \rightarrow Ag(s)]$ $E^{\circ}_{red} = 0.799$

$Cr(s) \rightarrow Cr^{3+}(aq) + 3e^-$ $E^{\circ}_{red} = -0.74$

$\overline{}$

$3Ag^+(aq) + Cr(s) \rightarrow 3Ag(s) + Cr^{3+}(aq)$ $E^{\circ} = 0.799 - (-0.74) = 1.54$ V

(b)   Two of the combinations have essentially equal E° values.

$$2[Ag^+(aq) + 1e^- \rightarrow Ag(s)] \qquad E^\circ_{red} = 0.799 \text{ V}$$

$$Cu(s) \rightarrow Cu^{2+}(aq) + 2e^- \qquad E^\circ_{red} = 0.337 \text{ V}$$

$$2Ag^+(aq) + Cu(s) \rightarrow 2Ag(s) + Cu^{2+}(aq) \qquad E^\circ = 0.799 \text{ V} - 0.337 \text{ V} = 0.462 \text{ V}$$

$$3[Ni^{2+}(aq) + 2e^- \rightarrow Ni(s)] \qquad E^\circ_{red} = -0.28 \text{ V}$$

$$2[Cr(s) \rightarrow Cr^{3+}(aq) + 3e^-] \qquad E^\circ_{red} = -0.74 \text{ V}$$

$$3Ni^{2+}(aq) + 2Cr(s) \rightarrow 3Ni(s) + 2Cr^{3+}(aq) \qquad E^\circ = -0.28 \text{ V} - (-0.74 \text{ V}) = 0.46 \text{ V}$$

20.27 *Analyze/Plan.* follow the logic in Sample Exercise 20.7. *Solve:*

(a) $MnO_4^-(aq) + 8H^+(aq) + 5e^- \rightarrow Mn^{2+}(aq) + 4H_2O(l)$ $E^\circ_{red} = 1.51 \text{ V}$

(b)   Because the half-reaction in part (a) is the more favorable reduction, it is the cathode reaction.

(c) $Sn^{2+}(aq) \rightarrow Sn^{4+}(aq) + 2e^-$ $\qquad\qquad\qquad\qquad E^\circ_{red} = 0.154 \text{ V}$

(d)   Balance electrons by multiplying the cathode reaction by 2 and the anode reaction by 5. $5Sn^{2+}(aq) + 2MnO_4^-(aq) + 16H^+(aq) \rightarrow 5Sn^{4+}(aq) + 2Mn^{2+}(aq) + 8H_2O(l)$

(e) $E^\circ = 1.51 \text{ V} - 0.154 \text{ V} = 1.356 = 1.36 \text{ V}$

20.29 *Analyze/Plan.* Given the description of a voltaic cell, answer questions about this cell. Combine ideas in Sample Exercises 20.4 and 20.7. The reduction half-reactions are:

$$Cu^{2+}(aq) + 2e^- \rightarrow Cu(s) \qquad E^\circ = 0.337 \text{ V}$$

$$Sn^{2+}(aq) + 2e^- \rightarrow Sn(s) \qquad E^\circ = -0.136 \text{ V}$$

Solve:

(a)   It is evident that Cu^{2+} is more readily reduced. Therefore, Cu serves as the cathode, Sn as the anode.

(b)   The copper electrode gains mass as Cu is plated out, the Sn electrode loses mass as Sn is oxidized.

(c)   The overall cell reaction is $Cu^{2+}(aq) + Sn(s) \rightarrow Cu(s) + Sn^{2+}(aq)$

(d) $E^\circ = 0.337 \text{ V} - (-0.136 \text{ V}) = 0.473 \text{ V}$

Oxidizing and Reducing Agents; Spontaneity

20.31 *Analyze/Plan.* Use the definitions of oxidizing agent, reducing agent and the convention for writing reduction half-reactions to answer the stated questions. *Solve:*

(a)   Negative. A strong reductant is likely to be oxidized, thus having a negative reduction potential.

(b)   Right. Reducing agents are likely to be oxidized, and thus to be in a low oxidation state; the products of reduction half-reactions are in lower oxidation states than reactants.

20.33   *Analyze/Plan.* Follow the logic in Sample Exercise 20.8. In each case, choose the half-reaction with the more positive reduction potential and with the given substance on the left. *Solve:*

(a) $Cl_2(g)$ (1.359 V vs. 1.065 V)   (b) $Ni^{2+}(aq)$ (-0.28V vs. -0.403 V)

(c) $BrO_3^-(aq)$ (1.52 V vs. 1.195 V)   (d) $O_3(g)$ (2.07 V vs. 1.776 V)

20.35   *Analyze/Plan.* If the substance is on the left of a reduction half-reaction, it will be an oxidant; if it is on the right, it will be a reductant. The sign and magnitude of the E°_{red} determines whether it is strong or weak. *Solve:*

(a) $Cl_2(aq)$: strong oxidant (on the left, E°_{red} = 1.359 V)

(b) MnO_4^- (aq, acidic): strong oxidant (on the left, E°_{red} = 1.51 V)

(c)   Ba(s): strong reductant (on the right, E°_{red} = -2.90 V)

(d)   Zn(s): reductant (on the right, E°_{red} = -0.763 V)

20.37   *Analyze/Plan.* Follow the logic in Sample Exercise 20.8. *Solve:*

(a)   Arranged in order of increasing strength as oxidizing agents (and increasing reduction potential):

$$Cu^{2+}(aq) < O_2(g) < Cr_2O_7^{2-}(aq) < Cl_2(g) < H_2O_2(aq)$$

(b)   Arranged in order of increasing strength as reducing agents (and decreasing reduction potential):

$$H_2O_2(aq) < I^-(aq) < Sn^{2+}(aq) < Zn(s) < Al(s)$$

20.39   *Analyze/Plan.* In order to reduce Eu^{3+} to Eu^{2+}, we need an oxidizing agent, one of the reduced species from Table 20.1 or Appendix E. It must have a greater tendency to be oxidized than Eu^{3+} has to be reduced. That is, E°_{red} must be more negative than -0.43 V. *Solve:*

Any of the **reduced** species in Table 20.1 or Appendix E from a half-reaction with a reduction potential more negative than -0.43 V will reduce Eu^{3+} to Eu^{2+}. From the list of possible reductants in the Exercise, Al and $H_2C_2O_4$ will reduce Eu^{3+} to Eu^{2+}.

20.41   *Analyze/Plan.* Follow the logic in Sample Exercises 20.9 and 20.10. *Solve:*

(a)   The more positive the emf of a reaction the more spontaneous the reaction.

(b)   Reactions (a), (b), (c) and (d) in Exercise 20.23 have positive E° values and are spontaneous.

(c) $\Delta G° = -nFE°$; $F = 96,500$ J/V•mol $e^- = 96.5$ kJ/V•mol e^-

20.23 (a) $\Delta G° = $ -2 mol $e^- \times \dfrac{96.5\,kJ}{V•mol\ e^-} \times 0.823$ V $= -158.839 = -159$ kJ

20.23 (b) $\Delta G° = -2(96.5)(1.89) = -364.77 = -365$ kJ

20.23 (c) $\Delta G° = -2(96.5)(1.211) = -233.72 = -234$ kJ

20.23 (d) $\Delta G° = -6(96.5)(1.21) = -700.59 = -701$ kJ

20.43   *Analyze/Plan.* In each reaction, $Fe^{2+} \rightarrow Fe^{3+}$ will be the oxidation half-reaction and one of the other given half-reactions will be the reduction half-reaction. Follow the logic in Sample Exercise 20.10 to calculate E° and $\Delta G°$ for each reaction. *Solve*:

(a) $2Fe^{2+}(aq) + S_2O_6{}^{2-}(aq) + 4H^+(aq) \rightarrow 2Fe^{3+}(aq) + 2H_2SO_3(aq)$

   $E° = 0.60$ V - 0.77 V $= -0.17$ V

   $2Fe^{2+}(aq) + N_2O(aq) + 2H^+(aq) \rightarrow 2Fe^{3+}(aq) + N_2(g) + H_2O(l)$

   $E° = -1.77$ V - 0.77 V $= -2.54$ V

   $Fe^{2+}(aq) + VO_2{}^+(aq) + 2H^+(aq) \rightarrow Fe^{3+}(aq) + VO^{2+}(aq) + H_2O(l)$

   $E° = 1.00$ V - 0.77 V $= +0.23$ V

(b) $\Delta G° = -nFE°$ For the first reaction,

   $\Delta G° = $ -2 mol $\times \dfrac{96,500\,J}{1\ V•mol} \times (-0.17\,V) = 3.3 \times 10^5$ J or 33 kJ

   For the second reaction, $\Delta G° = -2(96,500)(-2.54) = 4.90 \times 10^2$ kJ

   For the third reaction, $\Delta G° = -1(96,500)(0.23) = -22$ kJ

EMF and Concentration

20.45 (a)   The *Nernst equation* is applicable when the components of an electrochemical cell are at nonstandard conditions.

(b)   Q = 1 if all reactants and products are at standard conditions.

(c)   If concentration of reactants increases, Q decreases, and E increases.

20.47   *Analyze/Plan.* Given a circumstance, determine its effect on cell emf. Each circumstance changes the value of Q. An increase in Q reduces emf; a decrease in Q increases emf. *Solve*:

   $Zn(s) + 2H^+(aq) \rightarrow Zn^{2+}(aq) + H_2(g)$; $E = E° - \dfrac{0.0592}{n} \log Q$; $Q = \dfrac{[Zn^{2+}]\,P_{H_2}}{[H^+]^2}$

(a) P_{H_2} increases, Q increases, E decreases

(b) $[Zn^{2+}]$ increases, Q increases, E decreases

(c) $[H^+]$ decreases, Q increases, E decreases

(d)   No effect; does not appear in the Nernst equation

20.49 *Analyze/Plan.* Follow the logic in Sample Exercise 20.11. *Solve:*

(a)
$$Ni^{2+}(aq) + 2e^- \rightarrow Ni(s) \qquad\qquad E^{\circ}_{red} = -0.28\ V$$
$$Zn(s) \rightarrow Zn^{2+}(aq) + 2e^- \qquad\qquad E^{\circ}_{red} = -0.763\ V$$

$$Ni^{2+}(aq) + Zn(s) \rightarrow Ni(s) + Zn^{2+}(aq) \qquad E^{\circ} = -0.28 - (-0.763) = 0.483 = 0.48\ V$$

(b)
$$E = E^{\circ} - \frac{0.0592}{n} \log \frac{[Zn^{2+}]}{[Ni^{2+}]}; \ n = 2$$

$$E = 0.483 - \frac{0.0592}{2} \log \frac{(0.100)}{(3.00)} = 0.483 - \frac{0.0592}{2} \log (0.0333)$$

$$E = 0.483 - \frac{0.0592\,(-1.477)}{2} = 0.483 + 0.0437 = 0.527 = 0.53\ V$$

(c)
$$E = 0.483 - \frac{0.0592}{2} \log \frac{(0.900)}{(0.200)} = 0.483 - 0.0193 = 0.464 = 0.46\ V$$

20.51 *Analyze/Plan.* Follow the logic in Sample Exercise 20.11. *Solve:*

(a)
$$4[Fe^{2+}(aq) \rightarrow Fe^{3+}(aq) + 1e^-] \qquad E^{\circ}_{red} = 0.771\ V$$
$$O_2(g) + 4H^+(aq) + 4e^- \rightarrow 2H_2O(l) \qquad E^{\circ}_{red} = 1.23\ V$$

$$4Fe^{2+}(aq) + O_2(g) + 4H^+(aq) \rightarrow 4Fe^{3+}(aq) + 2H_2O(l) \quad E^{\circ} = 1.23 - 0.771 = 0.459 = 0.46$$

(b)
$$E = E^{\circ} - \frac{0.0592}{n} \log \frac{[Fe^{3+}]^4}{[Fe^{2+}]^4 [H^+]^4 P_{O_2}}; \ n = 4, [H^+] = 1.00 \times 10^{-3}\ M$$

$$E = 0.459\ V - \frac{0.0592}{4} \log \frac{(0.010)^4}{(3.0)^4 (1.0 \times 10^{-3})^4 (0.50)} = 0.459 - \frac{0.0592}{4} \log (246.9)$$

$$E = 0.459 - \frac{0.0592}{4} (2.393) = 0.459 - 0.0354 = 0.4236 = 0.42\ V$$

20.53 *Analyze/Plan.* We are given a concentration cell with Zn electrodes. Use the definition of a concentration cell in Section 20.6 to answer the stated questions. Use Equation 20.16 to calculate the cell emf. For a concentration cell, Q = [dilute]/[concentrated]. *Solve:*

(a) The compartment with the more dilute solution will be the anode. That is, the compartment with $[Zn^{2+}] = 1.00 \times 10^{-2}\ M$ is the anode.

(b) Since the oxidation half-reaction is the opposite of the reduction half-reaction, E° is zero.

(c)
$$E = E^{\circ} - \frac{0.0592}{n} \log Q; \quad Q = [Zn^{2+}, dilute]\,/\,[Zn^{2+}, conc.]$$

$$E = 0 - \frac{0.0592}{2} \log \frac{(1.00 \times 10^{-2})}{(5.00)} = 0.0799\ V$$

(d)   In the anode compartment, $Zn(s) \rightarrow Zn^{2+}(aq)$, so $[Zn^{2+}]$ increases from 1.00×10^{-2} M. In the cathode compartment, $Zn^{2+}(aq) \rightarrow Zn(s)$, so $[Zn^{2+}]$ decreases from 5.00 M.

20.55   *Analyze/Plan.* Follow the logic in Sample Exercise 20.12. *Solve*:

$$E = E° - \frac{0.0592}{2} \log \frac{[P_{H_2}][Zn^{2+}]}{[H^+]^2}; \quad E° = 0.0 \text{ V} - (-0.763 \text{ V}) = 0.763 \text{ V}$$

$$0.684 = 0.763 - \frac{0.0592}{2} \times (\log[P_{H_2}][Zn^{2+}] - 2\log[H^+]) = 0.763 - \frac{0.0592}{2} \times (-0.5686 - 2\log[H^+])$$

$$0.684 = 0.763 + 0.0168 + 0.0592 \log[H^+]; \quad \log[H^+] = \frac{0.684 - 0.0168 - 0.763}{0.0592}$$

$$\log[H^+] = -1.6188 = -1.6; \quad [H^+] = 0.0241 = 0.02 \; M; \quad pH = 1.6$$

20.57   *Analyze/Plan.* Follow the logic in Sample Exercise 20.14. $E° = \dfrac{0.0592 \text{ V}}{n} \log K_{eq}$;

$\log K_{eq} = \dfrac{nE°}{0.0592 \text{ V}}$.   *Solve*:

(a) $E° = -0.28 - (-0.440) = 0.16$ V, $n = 2$ ($Ni^{2+} + 2e^- \rightarrow Ni$)

$$\log K_{eq} = \frac{2(0.16)}{0.0592} = 5.4054 = 5.4; \quad K_{eq} = 2.54 \times 10^5 = 3 \times 10^5$$

(b) $E° = 0 - (-0.277) = 0.277$ V; $n = 2$ ($2H^+ + 2e^- \rightarrow H_2$)

$$\log K_{eq} = \frac{2(0.277)}{0.0592} = 9.358 = 9.36; \quad K_{eq} = 2.3 \times 10^9$$

(c) $E° = 1.51 - 1.065 = 0.445 = 0.45$ V; $n = 10$ ($2MnO_4^- + 10e^- \rightarrow 2Mn^{+2}$)

$$\log K_{eq} = \frac{10(0.445)}{0.0592} = 75.169 \approx 75; \quad K_{eq} = 1.5 \times 10^{75} = 10^{75}$$

20.59   *Analyze/Plan.* Follow the logic in Sample Exercise 20.14. $E° = \dfrac{0.0592 \text{ V}}{n} \log K_{eq}$;

$\log K_{eq} = \dfrac{nE°}{0.0592 \text{ V}}$.   *Solve*:

(a) $\log K_{eq} = \dfrac{1(0.177 \text{ V})}{0.0592 \text{ V}} = 2.9899 = 2.99; \quad K_{eq} = 9.8 \times 10^2$

(b) $\log K_{eq} = \dfrac{2(0.177 \text{ V})}{0.0592 \text{ V}} = 5.9797 = 5.98; \quad K_{eq} = 9.5 \times 10^5$

(c) $\log K_{eq} = \dfrac{3(0.177 \text{ V})}{0.0592 \text{ V}} = 8.9696 = 8.97; \quad K_{eq} = 9.32 \times 10^8 = 9.3 \times 10^8$

Batteries; Corrosion

20.61 (a) A *battery* is a portable, self-contained electrochemical power source composed of one or more voltaic cells.

(b) A *primary* battery is not rechargeable, while a *secondary* battery can be recharged.

(c) No. No single voltaic cell is capable of producing 7.5 V. If a single voltaic cell could be designed to produce 2.5 V, three of these cells connected in series would produce the desired voltage.

20.63 *Analyze/Plan.* Given mass of a reactant (Pb), calculate mass of product (PbO_2). This is a stoichiometry problem; we need the balanced equation for the chemical reaction that occurs in the lead-acid battery. Then, g Pb $\rightarrow$ mol Pb $\rightarrow$ mol PbO_2 $\rightarrow$ g PbO_2. *Solve:*

The overall cell reaction (Equation [20.19]) is:

$$Pb(s) + PbO_2(s) + 2H^+(aq) + 2HSO_4^-(aq) \rightarrow 2PbSO_4(s) + 2H_2O(l)$$

$$382 \text{ g Pb} \times \frac{1 \text{ mol Pb}}{207.2 \text{ g Pb}} \times \frac{1 \text{ mol PbO}_2}{1 \text{ mol Pb}} \times \frac{239.2 \text{ g PbO}_2}{1 \text{ mol PbO}_2} = 441 \text{ g PbO}_2$$

20.65 *Analyze/Plan.* We are given a redox reaction and asked to write half-reactions, calculate E°, and indicate whether Li(s) is the anode or cathode. Determine which reactant is oxidized and which is reduced. Separate into half-reactions, find E°_{red} for the half-reactions from Appendix E and calculate E°. *Solve:*

(a) Li(s) is oxidized at the anode.

(b)
$$Ag_2CrO_4(s) + 2e^- \rightarrow 2Ag(s) + CrO_4^{2-}(aq) \qquad E^{\circ}_{red} = 0.446 \text{ V}$$
$$2[Li(s) \rightarrow Li^+(aq) + 1e^-] \qquad\qquad E^{\circ}_{red} = -3.05 \text{ V}$$

$$Ag_2CrO_4(s) + 2Li(s) \rightarrow 2Ag(s) + CrO_4^-(aq) + 2Li^+(aq)$$

$$E° = 0.446 \text{ V} - (-3.05 \text{ V}) = 3.496 = 3.50 \text{ V}$$

(c) The emf of the battery, 3.5 V, is exactly the cell potential calculated in part (b).

20.67 *Analyze/Plan.* (a) Consider the function of Zn in an alkaline battery. What effect would it have on the redox reaction and cell emf if Cd replaces Zn? (b) Both batteries contain Ni. What is the difference in environmental impact between Cd and the metal hydride? *Solve:*

(a) E°_{red} for Cd (-0.40 V) is less negative than E°_{red} for Zn (-0.76 V), so E_{cell} will have a smaller (less positive) value.

(b) NiMH batteries use an alloy such as $ZrNi_2$ as the anode material. This eliminates the use and concomitant disposal problems associated with Cd, a toxic heavy metal.

20.69   *Analyze/Plan.* (a) Decide which reactant is oxidized and which is reduced. Write the balanced half-reactions and assign the appropriate one as anode and cathode. (b) Write the balanced half-reaction for $Fe^{2+}(aq) \rightarrow Fe_2O_3 \cdot 3H_2O$. Use the reduction half-reaction from part (a) to obtain the overall reaction. *Solve:*

    (a)   anode: $Fe(s) \rightarrow Fe^{2+}(aq) + 2e^-$
                  cathode: $O_2(g) + 4H^+(aq) + 4e^- \rightarrow 2H_2O(l)$

    (b) $2Fe^{2+}(aq) + 6H_2O(l) \rightarrow Fe_2O_3 \cdot 3H_2O(s) + 6H^+(aq) + 2e^-$

         $O_2(g) + 4H^+(aq) + 4e^- \rightarrow 2H_2O(l)$

         (Multiply the oxidation half-reaction by two to balance electrons and obtain the overall balanced reaction.)

20.71   *Analyze/Plan.* Follow the logic in Sample exercise 20.15. *Solve:*

    (a) Zn^{2+} has a more negative reduction potential than Fe^{2+}, so $Zn(s)$ is more readily oxidized. If Zn and Fe are both available for oxidation by O_2 (corrosion), Zn will be oxidized and Fe will not; Zn acts as a sacrificial anode.

    (b)   During the corrosion of galvanized iron, Zn acts as the anode and Fe acts as the inert cathode at which O_2 is reduced. Zn protects Fe by making it the cathode in the electrochemical process; this is called *cathodic protection*.

Electrolysis; Electrical Work

20.73   (a)   *Electrolysis* is an electrochemical process driven by an outside energy source.

    (b)   Electrolysis reactions are, by definition, nonspontaneous.

    (c) $2Cl^-(l) \rightarrow Cl_2(g) + 2e^-$

20.75   *Analyze/Plan.* (a) If the products in the two environments are different, one or both of the half-reactions must be different. Consider available reactants other than $MgCl_2$. (b) Write balanced equations for the two redox reactions. (c) Follow the logic in Sample Exercise 20.16. Solve:

    (a)   The products are different because in aqueous electrolysis water is reduced in preference to Mg^{2+}.

    (b) $MgCl_2(l) \rightarrow Mg(l) + Cl_2(g)$

         $2Cl^-(aq) + 2H_2O(l) \rightarrow Cl_2(g) + H_2(g) + 2OH^-(aq)$

         The aqueous solution electrolysis is entirely analogous to that for NaCl(aq), Section 20.9.

(c) $Mg^{2+}(aq) + 2e^- \rightarrow Mg(s)$ $E^{\circ}_{red} = -2.37$ V

           $2Cl^-(aq) \rightarrow Cl_2(g) + 2e^-$ $E^{\circ}_{red} = 1.359$ V

           $MgCl_2(aq) \rightarrow Mg(s) + Cl_2(g)$ $E^{\circ} = -2.37 - 1.359 = -3.73$ V

           $H_2O(l) + 2e^- \rightarrow H_2(g) + 2OH^-(aq)$ $E^{\circ}_{red} = -0.83$ V
           $2Cl^-(aq) \rightarrow Cl_2(g) + 2e^-$ $E^{\circ}_{red} = 1.359$ V

           $2Cl^-(aq) + 2H_2O(l) \rightarrow Cl_2(g) + H_2(g) + 2OH^-(aq)$ $E^{\circ} = -0.83 - 1.359 = -2.19$ V

           The minus signs mean that voltage must be applied in order for the reaction to occur.

20.77 *Analyze/Plan.* Write the balanced half-reactions for the electrolysis of $CuCl_2(aq)$. Assign the oxidation process to the anode and reduction process to the cathode. Indicate the direction of electron flow and ion flow. *Solve:*

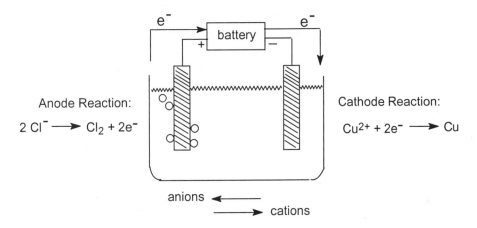

Anode Reaction:
$2\ Cl^- \longrightarrow Cl_2 + 2e^-$

Cathode Reaction:
$Cu^{2+} + 2e^- \longrightarrow Cu$

anions ⟵
⟶ cations

           Cl^- is oxidized in preference to water because production of Cl_2 is kinetically favored.

20.79 *Analyze/Plan.* Follow the logic in Sample Exercise 20.17, paying close attention to units. Coulombs = amps•s; since this is a $3e^-$ reduction, each mole of $Cr(s)$ requires 3 Faradays. *Solve:*

(a) $7.75\ A \times 1.50\ d \times \dfrac{24\ hr}{1\ d} \times \dfrac{60\ min}{1\ hr} \times \dfrac{60\ s}{1\ min} \times \dfrac{1\ C}{1\ amp \cdot s} \times \dfrac{1\ F}{96,500\ C}$

        $\times\ \dfrac{1\ mol\ Cr}{3\ F} \times \dfrac{52.00\ g\ Cr}{1\ mol\ Cr} = 180\ g\ Cr(s)$

(b) $0.250\ mol\ Cr \times \dfrac{3\ F}{1\ mol\ Cr} \times \dfrac{96,500\ C}{F} \times \dfrac{1\ amp \cdot s}{1\ C} \times \dfrac{1}{8.00\ hr} \times \dfrac{1\ hr}{60\ min} \times \dfrac{1\ min}{60\ s}$

                                                                                            $= 2.51$ A

20.81 *Analyze/Plan.* Follow the logic in Sample Exercise 20.17, paying close attention to units. Coulombs = amps • s; since $2Cl^- \rightarrow Cl_2$ is a $2e^-$ oxidation, each mole of Cl_2 requires 2 Faradays. *Solve:*

(a) $16.8 \text{ A} \times 90.0 \text{ min} \times \dfrac{60 \text{ s}}{1 \text{ min}} \times \dfrac{1 \text{ C}}{1 \text{ amp} \cdot \text{s}} \times \dfrac{1 \text{ F}}{96{,}500 \text{ C}} \times \dfrac{1 \text{ mol Cl}_2}{2 \text{ F}}$

$\times \dfrac{22.400 \text{ L Cl}_2}{1 \text{ mol Cl}_2} = 10.5 \text{ L Cl}_2$

(b)   From the balanced equation (Section 20.9), we see that 2 mol NaOH are formed per mol Cl_2. Proceeding as in (a), but replacing the last factor by (2 mol NaOH/1 mol Cl_2), we obtain 0.940 mol NaOH.

20.83   *Analyze/Plan.* Given a spontaneous chemical reaction, calculate the maximum possible work for a given amount of reactant at standard conditions. Separate the equation into half-reactions and calculate cell emf. Use Equation 20.21, w_{max} = -nFE, to calculate maximum work. At standard conditions, E = E°.   Solve:

$I_2(s) + 2e^- \rightarrow 2I^-(aq)$ E°_{red} = 0.536 V

$Sn(s) \rightarrow Sn^{2+}(aq) + 2e^-$ E°_{red} = -0.136 V

$I_2(s) + Sn(s) \rightarrow 2I^-(aq) + Sn^{2+}(aq)$ E° = 0.536 - (-0.136) = 0.672 V

w_{max} = -2(96.5)(0.672) = -129.7 = -130 kJ/mol Sn

$\dfrac{-129.7 \text{ kJ}}{\text{mol Sn(s)}} \times 0.850 \text{ mol Sn} = -110 \text{ kJ}$

20.85   *Analyze/Plan.* Follow the logic in Sample Exercise 20.18, paying close attention to units. *Solve*:

(a) $7.5 \times 10^4 \text{ A} \times 24 \text{ hr} \times \dfrac{3600 \text{ s}}{1 \text{ hr}} \times \dfrac{1 \text{ C}}{1 \text{ amp} \cdot \text{s}} \times \dfrac{1 \text{ F}}{96{,}500 \text{ C}} \times \dfrac{1 \text{ mol Li}}{1 \text{ F}}$

$\times \dfrac{6.94 \text{ g Li}}{1 \text{ mol Li}} \times 0.85 = 3.961 \times 10^5 = 4.0 \times 10^5 \text{ g Li}$

(b)   If the cell is 85% efficient, $\dfrac{96{,}500 \text{ C}}{\text{F}} \times \dfrac{1 \text{ F}}{0.85 \text{ mol}} = 1.135 \times 10^5$

$= 1.1 \times 10^5$ C/mol Li required

Energy = $7.5 \text{ V} \times \dfrac{1.135 \times 10^5 \text{ C}}{\text{mol Li}} \times \dfrac{1 \text{ J}}{1 \text{ C} \cdot \text{V}} \times \dfrac{1 \text{ kWh}}{3.6 \times 10^6 \text{ J}} = 0.24 \text{ kWh/mol Li}$

Additional Exercises

20.87   (a) $MnO_4{}^{2-}(aq) + 4H^+(aq) + 2e^- \rightarrow MnO_2(s) + 2H_2O(l)$

$2[MnO_4{}^{2-}(aq) \rightarrow MnO_4{}^-(aq) + 1e^-]$

$3MnO_4{}^{2-}(aq) + 4H^+(aq) \rightarrow 2MnO_4{}^-(aq) + MnO_2(s) + 2H_2O(l)$

(b) $H_2SO_3(aq) + 4H^+(aq) + 4e^- \rightarrow S(s) + 3H_2O(l)$

  $2[H_2SO_3(aq) + H_2O(l) \rightarrow HSO_4^-(aq) + 3H^+(aq) + 2e^-]$
  _____

  $3H_2SO_3(aq) \rightarrow S(s) + 2HSO_4^-(aq) + 2H^+(aq) + H_2O(l)$

(c) $Cl_2(aq) + 2H_2O(l) \rightarrow 2ClO^-(aq) + 4H^+(aq) + 2e$
  $\quad\quad 4OH^-(aq) \quad\quad\quad + 4OH^-(aq)$
  _____

  $Cl_2(aq) + 4OH^-(aq) \rightarrow 2ClO^-(aq) + 2H_2O(l) + 2e^-$

  $Cl_2(aq) + 2e^- \rightarrow 2Cl^-(aq)$
  _____

  $1/2[2Cl_2(aq) + 4OH^-(aq) \rightarrow 2Cl^-(aq) + 2ClO^-(aq) + 2H_2O(l)]$

  $Cl_2(aq) + 2OH^-(aq) \rightarrow Cl^-(aq) + ClO^-(aq) + H_2O(l)$

20.90 $2[Rh^{3+}(aq) + 3e^- \rightarrow Rh(s)]$ $E^{\circ}_{red} = ?$

  $3[Cd(s) \rightarrow Cd^{2+}(aq) + 2e^-]$ $E^{\circ}_{red} = -0.403\ V$
  _____

  $2Rh^{3+}(aq) + 3Cd(s) \rightarrow 2Rh(s) + 3Cd^{2+}(aq)$ $E^{\circ} = 1.20\ V$

(b)   Cd(s) is the anode, and Rh(s) is the cathode.

(c)   The cell is at standard conditions. $E^{\circ}_{cell} = E^{\circ}_{red}$ (cathode) - E°_{red} (anode)

  $E^{\circ}_{red} = E^{\circ}_{cell} + E^{\circ}_{red}$ (anode) = 1.20 V - 0.403 V = 0.80 V

(d) $\Delta G^{\circ} = -nFE^{\circ} = -6(96.5)(1.20) = -695\ kJ$

20.93   (a) $2[Ag^+(aq) + 1e^- \rightarrow Ag(s)]$ $E^{\circ}_{red} = 0.80\ V$

  $Ni(s) \rightarrow Ni^{2+}(aq) + 2e^-$ $E^{\circ}_{red} = -0.28\ V$
  _____

  $2Ag^+(aq) + Ni(s) \rightarrow 2Ag(s) + Ni^{2+}(aq)$ $E^{\circ} = 0.80 - (-0.28) = 1.08\ V$

(b)   As the reaction proceeds, $Ni^{2+}(aq)$ is produced, so $[Ni^{2+}]$ increases as the cell operates.

(c) $E = E^{\circ} - \dfrac{0.0592}{n} \log K_{eq};\ \ 1.12 = 1.08 - \dfrac{0.0592}{2} \log \dfrac{[Ni^{2+}]}{[Ag^+]^2}$

  $- \dfrac{0.04(2)}{0.0592} = \log(0.0100) - \log[Ag^+]^2;\ \ \log[Ag^+]^2 = \log(0.0100) + \dfrac{0.04(2)}{0.0592}$

  $\log[Ag^+]^2 = -2.000 + 1.351 = -0.649;\ \ [Ag^+]^2 = 0.255\ M;\ \ [Ag^+] = 0.474 = 0.5\ M$

  (Strictly speaking, [E - E°] having only one sig fig leads (after several steps) to the answer having only one sig fig. This is not a very precise or useful result.)

20.95
$$Cu^+(aq) \rightarrow Cu^{2+}(aq) + 1e^- \qquad E^\circ_{red} = +0.153 \text{ V}$$
$$1e^- + Cu^+(aq) \rightarrow Cu^\circ(s) \qquad E^\circ_{red} = +0.521 \text{ V}$$

$$2Cu^+(aq) \rightarrow Cu^\circ(s) + Cu^{2+}(aq) \qquad E^\circ = +0.521 - 0.153 = 0.368 \text{ V}$$

$$E^\circ = \frac{0.0592}{n} \log K_{eq}; \quad \log K_{eq} = \frac{nE^\circ}{0.0592} = \frac{1(0.368)}{0.0592} = 6.216 = 6.22$$

$$K_{eq} = 10^{6.216} = 1.6 \times 10^6$$

20.97 (a) In discharge: $Cd(s) + 2NiO(OH)(s) + 2H_2O(l) \rightarrow Cd(OH)_2(s) + 2Ni(OH)_2(s)$
In charging, the reverse reaction occurs.

(b) $E^\circ = 0.49 \text{ V} - (-0.76 \text{ V}) = 1.25 \text{ V}$

(c) The 1.25 V calculated in part (b) is the standard cell potential, E°. The concentrations of reactants and products inside the battery are adjusted so that the cell output is greater than E°. Note that most of the reactants and products are pure solids or liquids, which do not appear in the Q expression. It must be [OH⁻] that is other than 1.0 M, producing an emf of 1.30 rather than 1.25.

20.100 It is well established that corrosion occurs most readily when the metal surface is in contact with water. Thus, moisture is a requirement for corrosion. Corrosion also occurs more readily in acid solution, because O_2 has a more positive reduction potential in the presence of $H^+(aq)$. SO_2 and its oxidation products dissolve in water to produce acidic solutions, which encourage corrosion. The anodic and cathodic reactions for the corrosion of Ni are:

$$Ni(s) \rightarrow Ni^{2+}(aq) + 2e^- \qquad E^\circ_{red} = -0.28 \text{ V}$$
$$O_2(g) + 4H^+(aq) + 4e^- \rightarrow 2H_2O(l) \qquad E^\circ_{red} = 1.23 \text{ V}$$

Nickel(II) oxide, NiO(s), can form by the dry air oxidation of Ni. This NiO coating serves to protect against further corrosion. However, NiO dissolves in acidic solutions such as those produced by SO_2 or SO_3, according to the reaction: $NiO(s) + 2H^+(aq) \rightarrow Ni^{2+}(aq) + H_2O(l)$ This exposes Ni(s) to further wet corrosion.

20.103 $3.20 \text{ amp} \times 40 \text{ min} \times \dfrac{60 \text{ s}}{1 \text{ min}} \times \dfrac{1 \text{ C}}{1 \text{ amp}\cdot\text{s}} \times \dfrac{1 \text{ F}}{96,500 \text{ C}} \times \dfrac{1 \text{ mol e}^-}{1 \text{ F}} = 0.0796 = 0.080 \text{ mol e}^-$

$\dfrac{4.57\text{g In}}{0.0796 \text{ mol e}^-} \times \dfrac{1 \text{ mol In}}{114.8 \text{ g In}} = 0.50 \text{ mol In}/1 \text{ mol e}^-$

This result tells us that In must be in the +2 oxidation state in the molten halide.

Integrative Exercises

20.107 *Analyze/Plan*. We are given a reaction that is spontaneous at standard conditions and asked if it will be spontaneous at a different set of conditions. A reaction is spontaneous if the sign the cell emf is positive. $E = E^\circ - \dfrac{0.0592}{n} \log Q$ [Equation 20.16]. Calculate E° from data in

Appendix E. Write the Q expression, which will contain a term for [H$^+$]. Calculate [H$^+$] for the buffer listed. Finally, calculate the value of ΔG and evaluate the sign. *Solve*:

The half-reactions are:

$$O_2(g) + 4H^+(aq) + 4e^- \rightarrow 2H_2O(l) \qquad E^{\circ}_{red} = 1.23\ V$$
$$2[2Br^-(aq) \rightarrow Br_2(l) + 2e^-] \qquad E^{\circ}_{red} = 1.065\ V$$
$$\overline{\hspace{6cm}}$$
$$E^{\circ} = 1.23 - 1.065 = 0.165 = 0.17\ V$$

Calculate [H$^+$]. K$_a$ for benzoic acid is 6.3 × 10^{-5}. pK$_a$ = 4.20

pH = pK$_a$ + log[base]/[acid] = 4.20 + log(0.12/0.10) = 4.28.   [H$^+$] = 10$^{-4.28}$ = 5.25 × 10^{-5} *M*

Calculate E. Q = 1/P$_{O_2}$ × [H$^+$]^4 × [Br$^-$]^4. At standard conditions, P$_{O_2}$ = 1 atm and [Br$^-$] = 1 *M*; only [H$^+$] has been adjusted.

$$E = E^{\circ} - \frac{0.0592}{n}\log Q = 0.165 - \frac{0.0592}{4}\log(1/1 \times [H^+]^4 \times 1)$$

$$E = 0.165 - \frac{0.0592}{4}\log[1/(5.25 \times 10^{-5})^4] = 0.165 - \frac{0.0592}{4}(17.120)$$

$$E = 0.165 - 0.2534 = -0.0884 = -0.088\ V$$

The sign of E is negative, so the reaction is not spontaneous in this buffer.

Comment: The same result can be obtained by calculating ΔG$^{\circ}$ from the data in Appendix C and using the ΔG = ΔG$^{\circ}$ - RT lnQ [Equation 19.21]. The sign of ΔG must be positive for a reaction to be spontaneous. The two methods are related by Equation 20.12, ΔG$^{\circ}$ = -nFE$^{\circ}$.

20.110 (a)

$$Ag^+(aq) + e^- \rightarrow Ag(s) \qquad\qquad E^{\circ}_{red} = 0.799\ V$$
$$Fe^{2+}(aq) \rightarrow Fe^{3+}(aq) + 1e^- \qquad E^{\circ}_{red} = 0.771\ V$$
$$\overline{\hspace{6cm}}$$
$$Ag^+(aq) + Fe^{2+}(aq) \rightarrow Ag(s) + Fe^{3+}(aq) \qquad E^{\circ} = 0.799\ V - 0.771\ V = 0.028\ V$$

(b) Ag$^+$(aq) is reduced at the cathode and Fe^{2+}(aq) is oxidized at the anode.

(c) ΔG$^{\circ}$ = -nFE$^{\circ}$ = -(1)(96.5)(0.028) = -2.7 kJ

ΔS$^{\circ}$ = S$^{\circ}$ Ag(s) + S$^{\circ}$ Fe^{3+}(aq) - S$^{\circ}$Ag$^+$(aq) - S$^{\circ}$ Fe^{2+}(aq)

= 42.55 J + 293.3 J - 73.93 J - 113.4 J = 148.5 J

ΔG$^{\circ}$= ΔH$^{\circ}$ - TΔS$^{\circ}$ Since ΔS$^{\circ}$ is positive, ΔG$^{\circ}$ will become more negative and E$^{\circ}$ will become more positive as temperature is increased.

20.113

$$AgSCN(s) + e^- \rightarrow Ag(s) + SCN^-(aq) \qquad E^{\circ}_{red} = 0.0895\ V$$
$$Ag(s) \rightarrow Ag^+(aq) + e^- \qquad\qquad E^{\circ}_{red} = 0.799\ V$$
$$\overline{\hspace{7cm}}$$
$$AgSCN(s) \rightarrow Ag^+(aq) + SCN^-(aq) \qquad E^{\circ} = 0.0895 - 0.799 = -0.710\ V$$

$$E^{\circ} = \frac{0.0592}{n}\log K_{sp}; \quad \log K_{sp} = \frac{(-0.710)(1)}{0.0592} = -11.993 = -12.0$$

$$K_{sp} = 10^{-11.993} = 1.02 \times 10^{-12} = 1 \times 10^{-12}$$

20.116 The cell reaction is presumed to be:

$$Sn^{2+}(aq) + H_2O(l) \rightarrow Sn(s) + 1/2\ O_2(g) + 2H^+(aq)$$

Calculate mol Sn^{2+} reduced:

$$4.50\ amp \times 25.00\ min \times \frac{60\ s}{1\ min} \times \frac{1\ C}{1\ amp \cdot s} \times \frac{1\ F}{96,500\ C} \times \frac{1\ mol\ Sn^{2+}}{2\ F} = 0.03497$$

$$= 0.0350\ mol\ Sn^{2+}$$

Initially there were $\frac{0.600\ mol}{L} \times (0.500\ L) = 0.300\ mol$. Thus, following electrolysis, there are $0.300 - 0.0350 = 0.265\ mol\ Sn^{2+}$.

$$[Sn^{2+}] = \frac{0.265\ mol}{0.500\ L} = 0.530\ M$$

Electrolysis also produces $2(0.0350) = 0.0700\ mol\ H^+(aq)$.

Thus $[H^+] = \frac{0.0700\ mol}{0.500\ L} = 0.140\ M$. The concentration of SO_4^{2-} remains unchanged.

21 Nuclear Chemistry

Radioactivity

21.1 *Analyze/Plan.* Given various nuclide descriptions, determine the number of protons and neutrons in each nuclide. The left superscript is the mass number, protons plus neutrons. If there is a left subscript, it is the atomic number, the number of protons. Protons can always be determined from chemical symbol; all isotopes of the same element have the same number of protons. A number following the element name, as in part (c) is the mass number. *Solve:*

p = protons, n = neutrons, e = electrons; number of protons = atomic number;
number of neutrons = mass number - atomic number

(a) $^{55}_{25}$Mn: 25p, 30n   (b) ^{201}Hg: 80p, 121n   (c) ^{39}K: 19p, 20n

21.3 *Analyze/Plan.* See definitions in Section 21.1. In each case, the left superscript is mass number, the left subscript is related to atomic number. *Solve:*

(a) $^1_1$p or $^1_1$H   (b) $^0_1$e   (c) $^{\ \ 0}_{-1}$β or $^{\ \ 0}_{-1}$e

21.5 *Analyze/Plan.* Follow the logic in Sample Exercises 21.1 and 21.2. Pay attention to definitions of decay particles and conservation of mass and charge. *Solve:*

(a) $^{214}_{83}$Bi → $^{214}_{84}$Po + $^{\ \ 0}_{-1}$e   (b) $^{195}_{79}$Au + $^{\ \ 0}_{-1}$e (orbital electron) → $^{195}_{78}$Pt

(c) $^{38}_{19}$K → $^{38}_{18}$Ar + $^0_1$e   (d) $^{242}_{94}$Pu → $^{238}_{92}$U + $^4_2$He

21.7 *Analyze/Plan.* Using definitions of the decay processes and conservation of mass number and atomic number, work backwards to the reactants in the nuclear reactions. *Solve:*

(a) $^{211}_{82}$Pb → $^{211}_{83}$Bi + $^{\ \ 0}_{-1}$β   (b) $^{50}_{25}$Mn → $^{50}_{24}$Cr + $^0_1$e

(c) $^{179}_{74}$W + $^{\ \ 0}_{-1}$e → $^{179}_{73}$Ta   (d) $^{230}_{90}$Th → $^{226}_{88}$Ra + $^4_2$He

21.9 *Analyze/Plan.* Given the starting and ending nuclides in a nuclear decay sequence, we are asked to determine the number of alpha and beta emissions. Use the total change in A and Z, along with definitions of alpha and beta decay, to answer the question. *Solve:*

The total mass number change is (235-207) = 28. Since each α particle emission decreases the mass number by four, whereas emission of a β particle does not correspond to a mass change, there are 7 α particle emissions. The change in atomic number in the series is 10. Each α particle results in an atomic number lower by two. The 7 α particle emissions alone would cause a decrease of 14 in atomic number. Each β particle emission raises the atomic number by one. To obtain the observed lowering of 10 in the series, there must be 4 β emissions.

Nuclear Stability

21.11 *Analyze/Plan.* Follow the logic in sample Exercise 21.3, paying attention to the guidelines for neutron-to-proton ratio. *Solve:*

(a) $^{8}_{5}B$ - low neutron/proton ratio, positron emission (for low atomic numbers, positron emission is more common than orbital electron capture)

(b) $^{68}_{29}Cu$ - high neutron/proton ratio, beta emission

(c) $^{241}_{93}Np$ - high neutron/proton ratio, beta emission

(Even though ^{241}Np has an atomic number ≥ 84, the most common decay pathway for nuclides with neutron/proton ratios higher than the isotope listed on the periodic chart is beta decay.)

(d) $^{39}_{17}Cl$ - high neutron/proton ratio, beta emission

21.13 *Analyze/Plan.* For each nuclide, determine the number of protons and neutrons and find the location on Figure 21.2. If the nuclide does not lie in the belt of stability, refer to the guidelines for neutron-to-proton ratio to determine likely decay modes. *Solve:*

(a) No - high neutron/proton ratio; should be a beta emitter.

(b),(c) No - low neutron/proton ratio; should be a positron emitter, or possibly undergo orbital electron capture.

(d) No - high atomic number; it should be an alpha emitter.

21.15 *Analyze/Plan.* Use the criteria listed in Table 21.3. *Solve:*

(a) Stable: $^{39}_{19}K$ odd proton, even neutron more abundant than odd proton, odd neutron; 20 neutrons is a magic number.

(b) Stable: $^{209}_{83}Bi$ odd proton, even neutron more abundant than odd proton, odd neutron; 126 neutrons is a magic number.

(c) Stable: $^{25}_{12}Mg$ even though $^{24}_{10}Ne$ is an even proton, even neutron nuclide, it has a very high neutron/proton ratio and lies outside the band of stability.

21.17   *Analyze/Plan.* For each nuclide, determine the number of protons and neutrons and decide if they are magic numbers. *Solve*:

        (a) $^{4}_{2}He$ (c) $^{40}_{20}Ca$ (e) $^{208}_{82}Pb$

        (d) $^{58}_{28}Ni$ has a magic number of protons, but not neutrons.

21.19   *Analyze/Plan.* For each nuclide, determine the number of protons and neutrons and find the location on Figure 21.2. Rationalize the location based on magic numbers, neutron-to-proton ratio and Z value. Predict radioactivity (nonstability of nucleus). *Solve*:

        Radioactive: $^{14}_{8}O$, $^{115}_{52}Te$ – low neutron/proton ratio; $^{208}_{84}Po$ – atomic number ≥ 84

        Stable: $^{32}_{16}S$, $^{78}_{34}Se$ – even proton, even neutron, stable neutron/proton ratio

Nuclear Transmutations

21.21   Protons and alpha particles are positively charged and must be moving very fast to overcome electrostatic forces which would repel them from the target nucleus. Neutrons are electrically neutral and not repelled by the nucleus.

21.23   *Analyze/Plan.* Determine A and Z for the missing particle by conservation principles. Find the appropriate symbol for the particle. *Solve*:

        (a) $^{32}_{16}S + {}^{1}_{0}n \rightarrow {}^{1}_{1}p + {}^{32}_{15}P$ (b) $^{7}_{4}Be + {}^{0}_{-1}e$ (orbital electron) $\rightarrow {}^{7}_{3}Li$

        (c) $^{187}_{75}Re \rightarrow {}^{187}_{76}Os + {}^{0}_{-1}e$ (d) $^{98}_{42}Mo + {}^{2}_{1}H \rightarrow {}^{1}_{0}n + {}^{99}_{43}Tc$

        (e) $^{235}_{92}U + {}^{1}_{0}n \rightarrow {}^{135}_{54}Xe + {}^{99}_{38}Sr + 2\,{}^{1}_{0}n$

21.25   *Analyze/Plan.* Follow the logic in Sample Exercise 21.5, paying attention to conservation of A and Z. *Solve*:

        (a) $^{238}_{92}U + {}^{1}_{0}n \rightarrow {}^{239}_{92}U + {}^{0}_{0}\gamma$ (b) $^{14}_{7}N + {}^{1}_{1}H \rightarrow {}^{11}_{6}C + {}^{4}_{2}He$

        (c) $^{18}_{8}O + {}^{1}_{0}n \rightarrow {}^{19}_{9}F + {}^{0}_{-1}e$

Rates of Radioactive Decay

21.27   Chemical reactions do not affect the character of atomic nuclei. The energy changes involved in chemical reactions are much too small to allow us to alter nuclear properties via chemical processes. Therefore, the nuclei that are formed in a nuclear reaction will continue to emit radioactivity regardless of any chemical changes we bring to bear. However, we can hope to use chemical means to separate radioactive substances, or remove them from foods or a portion of the environment.

21.29 *Analyze/Plan.* Follow the logic in Sample Exercise 21.6. *Solve:*

After 12.3 yr, one half-life, there are (1/2)48.0 = 24.0 mg. 49.2 yr is exactly four half-lives. There are then $(48.0)(1/2)^4$ = 3.0 mg tritium remaining.

21.31 *Analyze/Plan.* Given decay time (t), N_o and N_t, calculate the half-life of curium-243. Use the given information with Equation 21.19 to calculate the rate constant, k. Then use Equation 21.20 to calculate half-life. *Solve:*

Using Equation 21.19, $k = \dfrac{-1}{t} \ln \dfrac{N_t}{N_o} = \dfrac{-1}{1.00 \text{ yr}} \times \ln \dfrac{2921}{3012} = 0.03068 = 0.0307 \text{ yr}^{-1}$

Using Equation 21.20, $t_{1/2}$ = 0.693/k = 0.693/(0.03068 yr^{-1}) = 22.6 yr

21.33 *Analyze/Plan.* Follow the logic in Sample Exercise 21.7. In this case, we are given initial sample mass as well as mass at time t, so we can proceed directly to calculate k [Equation 21.20] and then t [Equation 21.19]. *Solve:*

k = 0.693 / $t_{1/2}$ = 0.693/27.8 d = 0.02493 = 0.0249 d^{-1}

$t = \dfrac{-1}{k} \ln \dfrac{N_t}{N_o} = \dfrac{-1}{0.02493 \text{ d}^{-1}} \ln \dfrac{1.50}{5.75}$ = 53.9 d

21.35 (a) *Analyze/Plan.* $^{226}_{88}\text{Ra} \rightarrow {}^{222}_{86}\text{Rn} + {}^{4}_{2}\text{He}$

1 α particle is produced for each ^{226}Ra that decays. Calculate the mass of ^{226}Ra remaining after 1.0 min, calculate by subtraction the mass that has decayed, and use Avogadro's number to get the number of $^{4}_{2}$He particles. *Solve:*

Calculate k in min^{-1}. 1600 yr $\times \dfrac{365 \text{ d}}{1 \text{ yr}} \times \dfrac{24 \text{ hr}}{1 \text{ d}} \times \dfrac{60 \text{ min}}{1 \text{ hr}} = 8.410 \times 10^8$ min

$k = \dfrac{0.693}{t_{1/2}} = \dfrac{0.693}{8.410 \times 10^8 \text{ min}} = 8.241 \times 10^{-10} \text{ min}^{-1}$

$\ln \dfrac{N_t}{N_o} = -kt = (-8.241 \times 10^{-10} \text{ min}^{-1})(1.0 \text{ min}) = -8.241 \times 10^{-10}$

$\dfrac{N_t}{N_o} = e^{-8.241 \times 10^{-10}} = (1.000 - 8.241 \times 10^{-10})$; (don't round here!)

$N_t = 5.0 \times 10^{-3}$ g $(1.00 - 8.241 \times 10^{-10})$ The amount that decays is $N_o - N_t$:

5.0×10^{-3} g $- [5.0 \times 10^{-3} (1.00 - 8.241 \times 10^{-10})] = 5.0 \times 10^{-3}$ g (8.241×10^{-10})

$= 4.120 \times 10^{-12} = 4.1 \times 10^{-12}$ g Ra

$[N_o - N_t] = 4.120 \times 10^{-12}$ g Ra $\times \dfrac{1 \text{ mol Ra}}{226.0 \text{ g Ra}} \times \dfrac{6.022 \times 10^{23} \text{ Ra atoms}}{1 \text{ mol Ra}} \times \dfrac{1 \, {}^{4}_{2}\text{He}}{1 \text{ Ra atom}}$

$= 1.098 \times 10^{10} = 1.1 \times 10^{10}$ α particles emitted in 1 min

(b)   Plan. The result from (a) is disintegrations/min. Change this to dis/s and apply the definition 1 Ci = 2.7 × 10^{10} dis/s.

$$1.098 \times 10^{10} \frac{dis}{min} \times \frac{1\ min}{60\ s} \times \frac{1\ Ci}{3.7 \times 10^{10}\ dis/s} \times \frac{1000\ mCi}{Ci} = 4.945 = 4.9\ mCi$$

21.37   *Analyze/Plan.* Follow the logic in Sample Exercise 21.7. *Solve:*

$$t = \frac{-1}{k} \ln \frac{N_t}{N_o};\ k = 0.693/5715\ yr = 1.213 \times 10^{-4} = 1.21 \times 10^{-4}\ yr^{-1}$$

$$t = \frac{-1}{1.213 \times 10^{-4}\ yr^{-1}} \ln \frac{24.9}{32.5} = 2.20 \times 10^{3}\ yr$$

21.39   *Analyze/Plan.* Follow the procedure outlined in Sample Exercise 21.7. The original quantity of ^{238}U is 50.0 mg plus the amount that gave rise to 14.0 mg of ^{206}Pb. This amount is 14.0(238/206) = 16.2 mg. *Solve:*

$$k = 0.693/4.5 \times 10^{9}\ yr = 1.54 \times 10^{-10} = 1.5 \times 10^{-10}\ yr^{-1}$$

$$t = \frac{-1}{k} \ln \frac{N_t}{N_o} = \frac{-1}{1.54 \times 10^{-10}\ yr^{-1}} \ln \frac{50.0}{66.2} = 1.8 \times 10^{9}\ yr$$

Energy Changes

21.41   *Analyze/Plan.* Given an energy change, find the corresponding change in mass. Use Equation 21.22, E = mc^2. *Solve:*

$$\Delta E = c^2 \Delta m;\ \Delta m = \Delta E/c^2;\ 1\ J = kg \cdot m^2/s^2$$

$$\Delta m = \frac{393.5 \times 10^{3}\ kg \cdot m^2/s^2}{(2.9979 \times 10^{8}\ m/s)^2} \times \frac{1000\ g}{1\ kg} = 4.378 \times 10^{-9}\ g$$

21.43   *Analyze/Plan.* Given the mass of a ^{23}Na nucleus, find the energy required to separate the nucleus into protons and neutrons. This corresponds to the binding energy of the nucleus. Calculate the total mass of the separate particles and subtract the mass of the nucleus. Convert the difference to energy using Equation 21.22. Use Avogadro's number to calculate energy per mole of nuclei. *Solve:*

Δm = mass of individual protons and neutrons - mass of nucleus

Δm = 11(1.0072765 amu) + 12(1.0086649 amu) - 22.983733 amu = 0.2002873
$$= 0.200287\ amu$$

$$\Delta E = (2.9979246 \times 10^{8}\ m/s)^2 \times 0.2002873\ amu \times \frac{1\ g}{6.0221421 \times 10^{23}\ amu} \times \frac{1\ kg}{1 \times 10^{3}\ g}$$

$$= 2.989123 \times 10^{-11} = 2.98912 \times 10^{-11}\ J\ /\ ^{23}Na\ nucleus\ required$$

$$2.989123 \times 10^{-11} \frac{J}{nucleus} \times \frac{6.0221421 \times 10^{23}\ atoms}{mol} = 1.80009 \times 10^{13}\ J/mol\ ^{23}Na$$

21.45 *Analyze/Plan.* In each case, calculate the mass defect (Δm), total nuclear binding energy and then binding energy per nucleon. *Solve:*

(a) $\Delta m = 6(1.0072765) + 6(1.0086649) - 11.996708 = 0.0989404 = 0.098940$ amu

$$\Delta E = 0.0989404 \text{ amu} \times \frac{1 \text{ g}}{6.0221421 \times 10^{23} \text{ amu}} \times \frac{1 \text{ kg}}{1000 \text{ g}} \times \frac{8.987551 \times 10^{16} \text{ m}^2}{\text{s}^2}$$

$$= 1.476604 \times 10^{-11} = 1.4766 \times 10^{-11} \text{ J}$$

binding energy/nucleon = 1.476604×10^{-11} J $/12 = 1.2305 \times 10^{-12}$ J/nucleon

(b) $\Delta m = 17(1.0072765) + 20(1.0086649) - 36.956576 = 0.3404225 = 0.340423$ amu

$$\Delta E = 0.3404225 \text{ amu} \times \frac{1 \text{ g}}{6.0221421 \times 10^{23} \text{ amu}} \times \frac{1 \text{ kg}}{1000 \text{ g}} \times \frac{8.987551 \times 10^{16} \text{ m}^2}{\text{s}^2}$$

$$= 5.080525 \times 10^{-11} = 5.08053 \times 10^{-11} \text{ J}$$

binding energy/ nucleon = 5.080525×10^{-11} J $/ 37 = 1.37312 \times 10^{-12}$ J/nucleon

(c)   Calculate the nuclear mass by subtracting the electron mass from the atomic mass.

136.905812 amu - 56(5.485799 $\times 10^{-4}$ amu) = 136.875092 amu

$\Delta m = 56(1.0072765) + 81(1.0086649) - 136.875092 = 1.2342489 = 1.234249$ amu

$$\Delta E = 1.2342489 \text{ amu} \times \frac{1 \text{ g}}{6.0221421 \times 10^{23} \text{ amu}} \times \frac{1 \text{ kg}}{1000 \text{ g}} \times \frac{8.987551 \times 10^{16} \text{ m}^2}{\text{s}^2}$$

$$= 1.842014 \times 10^{-10} \text{ J}$$

binding energy/nucleon = 1.842014×10^{-10} J $/ 137 = 1.344536 \times 10^{-12}$ J/nucleon

21.47 *Analyze/Plan.* Use Equation 21.22 to calculate the mass equivalence of the solar radiation. *Solve:*

(a) $\dfrac{1.07 \times 10^{16} \text{ kJ}}{1 \text{ min}} \times \dfrac{60 \text{ min}}{1 \text{ hr}} \times \dfrac{24 \text{ hr}}{1 \text{ day}} = 1.541 \times 10^{19} \dfrac{\text{kJ}}{\text{day}} = 1.54 \times 10^{22}$ J/day

$$\Delta m = \frac{1.541 \times 10^{22} \text{ kg} \cdot \text{m}^2/\text{s}^2/\text{d}}{(2.998 \times 10^8 \text{ m/s})^2} = 1.714 \times 10^5 = 1.71 \times 10^5 \text{ kg/d}$$

(b)   *Analyze/Plan.* Calculate the mass change in the given nuclear reaction, then a conversion factor for g ^{235}U to mass equivalent. *Solve:*

$\Delta m = 140.8833 + 91.9021 + 2(1.0086649) - 234.9935 = -0.19077 = -0.1908$ amu

Converting from atoms to moles and amu to grams, it requires 1.000 mol or 235.0 g ^{235}U to produce energy equivalent to a change in mass of 0.1908 g.

0.10% of 1.714×10^5 kg is 1.714×10^2 kg = 1.714×10^5 g

$$1.714 \times 10^5 \text{ g} \times \frac{235.0 \text{ g } ^{235}\text{U}}{0.1908 \text{ g}} = 2.111 \times 10^8 = 2.1 \times 10^8 \text{ g } ^{235}\text{U}$$

(This is about 230 tons of ^{235}U **per day**.)

21.49 We can use Figure 21.13 to see that the binding energy per nucleon (which gives rise to the mass defect) is greatest for nuclei of mass numbers around 50. Thus (a) $^{59}_{27}\text{Co}$ should possess the greatest mass defect per nucleon.

Effects and Uses of Radioisotopes

21.51 The ^{59}Fe would be incorporated into the diet component, which in turn is fed to the rabbits. After a time blood samples could be removed from the animals, the red blood cells separated, and the radioactivity of the sample measured. If the iron in the dietary compound has been incorporated into blood hemoglobin, the blood cell sample should show beta emission. Samples could be taken at various times to determine the rate of iron uptake, rate of loss of the iron from the blood, and so forth.

21.53 (a)   *Control rods* control neutron flux so that there are enough neutrons to sustain the chain reaction but not so many that the core overheats.

   (b)   A *moderator* slows neutrons so that they are more easily captured by fissioning nuclei.

21.55 *Analyze/Plan.* Use conservation of A and Z to complete the equations, keeping in mind the symbols and definitions of various decay products. *Solve*:

   (a) $^{235}_{92}\text{U} + {}^{1}_{0}\text{n} \rightarrow {}^{160}_{62}\text{Sm} + {}^{72}_{30}\text{Zn} + 4\,{}^{1}_{0}\text{n}$ (b) $^{239}_{94}\text{Pu} + {}^{1}_{0}\text{n} \rightarrow {}^{144}_{58}\text{Ce} + {}^{94}_{36}\text{Kr} + 2\,{}^{1}_{0}\text{n}$

21.57 The extremely high temperature is required to overcome the electrostatic charge repulsions between the nuclei so that they come together to react.

21.59 •OH is a free radical; it contains an unpaired (free) electron, which makes it an extremely reactive species. (As an odd electron molecule, it violates the octet rule.) It can react with almost any particle (atom, molecule, ion) to acquire an electron and become OH^-. This often starts a disruptive chain of reactions, each producing a different free radical.
Hydroxide ion, OH^-, on the other hand, will be attracted to cations or the positive end of a polar molecule. Its most common reaction is ubiquitous and innocuous: $\text{H}^+ + \text{OH}^- \rightarrow \text{H}_2\text{O}$. The acid-base reactions of OH^- are usually much less disruptive to the organism than the chain of redox reactions initiated by •OH radical.

21.61 *Analyze/Plan.* Use definitions of the various radiation units and conversion factors to calculate the specified quantities. Pay particular attention to units. *Solve*:

   (a) $1\text{ Ci} = 3.7 \times 10^{10}$ disintegrations(dis)/s; $1\text{ Bq} = 1\text{ dis/s}$

   $8.7\text{ mCi} \times \dfrac{1\text{ Ci}}{1000\text{ mCi}} \times \dfrac{3.7 \times 10^{10}\text{ dis/s}}{\text{Ci}} = 3.22 \times 10^8 = 3.2 \times 10^8\text{ dis/s} = 3.2 \times 10^8\text{ Bq}$

   (b) $1\text{ rad} = 1 \times 10^{-2}$ J/kg; $1\text{ Gy} = 1$ J/kg $= 100$ rad. From part (a), the activity of the source is 3.2×10^8 dis/s.

$$3.22 \times 10^8 \text{ dis/s} \times 2.0 \text{ s} \times 0.65 \times \frac{9.12 \times 10^{-13} \text{ J}}{\text{dis}} \times \frac{1}{0.250 \text{ kg}} = 1.53 \times 10^{-3}$$

$$= 1.5 \times 10^{-3} \text{ J/kg}$$

$$1.5 \times 10^{-3} \text{ J/kg} \times \frac{1 \text{ rad}}{1 \times 10^{-2} \text{ J/kg}} \times \frac{1000 \text{ mrad}}{\text{rad}} = 1.5 \times 10^2 \text{ mrad}$$

$$1.5 \times 10^{-3} \text{ J/kg} \times \frac{1 \text{ Gy}}{1 \text{ J/kg}} = 1.5 \times 10^{-3} \text{ Gy}$$

(c) rem = rad (RBE); Sv = Gy (RBE) = 100 rem

mrem = 1.53×10^2 mrad (9.5) = 1.45×10^3 = 1.5×10^3 mrem (or 1.5 rem)

Sv = 1.53×10^{-3} Gy (9.5) = 1.45×10^{-2} = 1.5×10^{-2} Sv

Additional Exercises

21.63 $^{222}_{86}\text{Rn} \rightarrow \text{X} + 3\,^4_2\text{He} + 2\,^0_{-1}\beta$

This corresponds to a reduction in mass number of (3 × 4 =) 12 and a reduction in atomic number of (3 × 2 - 2) = 4. The stable nucleus is $^{210}_{82}\text{Pb}$. [This is part of the sequence in Figure 21.4.]

21.65 The most massive radionuclides will have the highest neutron/proton ratios. Thus, they are most likely to decay by a process that lowers this ratio, beta emission. The least massive nuclides, on the other hand, will decay by a process that increases the neutron/proton ratio, positron emission or orbital electron capture.

21.68 This is similar to Solutions 21.35 and 21.36.

$$^{212}_{86}\text{Rn} \rightarrow \,^{208}_{84}\text{Po} + \,^4_2\text{He}$$

Each ^{212}Rn nucleus that decays is 1 disintegration. Calculate the mass of ^{212}Rn remaining after 1.0 s, calculate by subtraction the mass that has decayed, and use Avogadro's number to get the number of nuclei that have decayed.

Calculate k in s^{-1}. 25 min × $\dfrac{60 \text{ s}}{1 \text{ min}}$ = 1.5×10^3 s

k = 0.693 / $t_{1/2}$ = 0.693/1.5×10^3 s = 4.62×10^{-4} = 4.6×10^{-4} s^{-1}

$\ln(N_t / N_o)$ - kt = -(4.62×10^{-4} s^{-1})(1.0 s) = -4.62×10^{-4} = -4.6×10^{-4}

N_t / N_o = $e^{-4.62 \times 10^{-4}}$ = $(1.00 - 4.62 \times 10^{-4})$; N_t = 1.0×10^{-12} g $(1.000 - 4.62 \times 10^{-4})$

The amount that decays is $N_o - N_t$:

1.0×10^{-12} g $- [1.0 \times 10^{-12}$ g $(1.000 - 4.62 \times 10^{-4})] = 1.0 \times 10^{-12}$ g (4.62×10^{-4})

$$= 4.62 \times 10^{-16} = 4.6 \times 10^{-16} \text{ g } ^{212}\text{Rn}$$

$N_o - N_t = 4.62 \times 10^{-16}$ g Rn $\times \dfrac{1 \text{ mol Rn}}{212 \text{ g Rn}} \times \dfrac{6.022 \times 10^{23} \text{ Rn atoms}}{1 \text{ mol Rn}} = 1.31 \times 10^6 = 1.3 \times 10^6$ dis

This is 1.3×10^6 disintegrations in 1.0 s, or approximately 1.3×10^6 α particles/s

1.31×10^6 dis/s $\times \dfrac{1 \text{ Ci}}{3.7 \times 10^{10} \text{ dis/s}} = 3.547 \times 10^{-5} = 3.5 \times 10^{-5}$ Ci

21.70 1×10^{-6} curie $\times \dfrac{3.7 \times 10^{10} \text{ dis/s}}{\text{curie}} = 3.7 \times 10^4$ dis/s

rate $= 3.7 \times 10^4$ nuclei/s $= kN$

$k = \dfrac{0.693}{t_{1/2}} = \dfrac{0.693}{28.8 \text{ yr}} \times \dfrac{1 \text{ yr}}{365 \times 24 \times 3600 \text{ sec}} = 7.630 \times 10^{-10} = 7.63 \times 10^{-10}$ s^{-1}

3.7×10^4 nuclei/s $= (7.63 \times 10^{-10}/\text{s})$ N; $N = 4.849 \times 10^{13} = 4.8 \times 10^{13}$ nuclei

mass ^{90}Sr $= 4.849 \times 10^{13}$ nuclei $\times \dfrac{90 \text{ g Sr}}{6.022 \times 10^{23} \text{ nuclei}} = 7.2 \times 10^{-9}$ g Sr

21.73 Assume that no depletion of iodide from the water due to plant uptake has occurred. Then the activity after 32 days would be:

$k = 0.693/t_{1/2} = 0.693/8.04$ d $= 0.0862 = 0.086$ d^{-1}

$\ln \dfrac{N_t}{N_o} = -(0.0862 \text{ d}^{-1})(32 \text{ d}) = -2.758 = -2.8$; $\dfrac{N_t}{N_o} = 0.0634 = 0.06$

We thus expect $N_t = 0.0634(175) = 11.1$ counts/min. We can assume that the plants did not absorb iodide, because absorption would have resulted in an observed level of remaining activity that was **lower** than the theoretical value of 11.1 counts/min.

21.75 Because of the relationship $\Delta E = \Delta mc^2$, the mass defect (Δm) is directly related to the binding energy (ΔE) of the nucleus.

^{7}Be: 4p, 3n; $4(1.0072765) + 3(1.0086649) = 7.05510$ amu

Total mass defect $= 7.0551 - 7.0147 = 0.0404$ amu

0.0404 amu/7 nucleons $= 5.77 \times 10^{-3}$ amu/nucleon

$\Delta E = \Delta m \times c^2 = \dfrac{5.77 \times 10^{-3} \text{ amu}}{\text{nucleon}} \times \dfrac{1 \text{ g}}{6.022 \times 10^{23} \text{ amu}} \times \dfrac{1 \text{ kg}}{1 \times 10^3 \text{ g}} \times \dfrac{8.988 \times 10^{16} \text{ m}^2}{\text{sec}^2}$

$= \dfrac{5.77 \times 10^{-3} \text{ amu}}{\text{nucleon}} \times \dfrac{1.4925 \times 10^{-10} \text{ J}}{1 \text{ amu}} = 8.612 \times 10^{-13} = 8.61 \times 10^{-13}$ J/nucleon

^{9}Be: 4p, 5n; 4(1.0072765) + 5(1.0086649) = 9.07243 amu

Total mass defect = 9.0724 - 9.0100 = 0.06243 = 0.0624 amu

0.0624 amu/9 nucleons = 6.937 × 10^{-3} = 6.94 × 10^{-3} amu/nucleon

6.937 × 10^{-3} amu/nucleon × 1.4925 × 10^{-10} J/amu = 1.035 × 10^{-12} = 1.04 × 10^{-12} J/nucleon

^{10}Be: 4p, 6n; 4(1.0072765) + 6(1.0086649) = 10.0811 amu

Total mass defect = 10.0811 - 10.0113 = 0.0698 amu

0.0698 amu/10 nucleons = 6.98 × 10^{-3} amu/nucleon

6.98 × 10^{-3} amu/nucleon × 1.4925 × 10^{-10} J/amu = 1.042 × 10^{-12} = 1.04 × 10^{-12} J/nucleon

The binding energies/nucleon for ^{9}Be and ^{10}Be are very similar; that for ^{10}Be is slightly higher.

21.77 $1000 \text{ Mwatts} \times \dfrac{1 \times 10^6 \text{ watts}}{1 \text{ Mwatt}} \times \dfrac{1 \text{ J}}{1 \text{ watt} \cdot \text{s}} \times \dfrac{1\ ^{235}\text{U atom}}{3 \times 10^{-11} \text{ J}} \times \dfrac{1 \text{ mol U}}{6.02 \times 10^{23} \text{ atoms}}$

$\times \dfrac{235 \text{ g U}}{1 \text{ mol}} \times \dfrac{3600 \text{ s}}{1 \text{ hr}} \times \dfrac{24 \text{ hr}}{1 \text{ d}} \times \dfrac{365 \text{ d}}{1 \text{ yr}} \times \dfrac{40}{100} \text{ (efficiency)} = 1.64 \times 10^5$

$= 2 \times 10^5$ g U/ yr = 200 kg U/yr

Integrative Exercises

21.79 Calculate the molar mass of $NaClO_4$ that contains 31% ^{36}Cl. Atomic mass of the enhanced Cl is 0.31(36) + 0.69(35.453) = 35.62. The molar mass of $NaClO_4$ is then (22.99 + 35.62 + 64.00) = 122.61.   Calculate N, the number of ^{36}Cl nuclei, the value of k in s^{-1}, and the activity in dis/s.

$49.5 \text{ mg NaClO}_4 \times \dfrac{1 \text{ g}}{1000 \text{ mg}} \times \dfrac{1 \text{ mol NaClO}_4}{122.61 \text{ g NaClO}_4} \times \dfrac{1 \text{ mol Cl}}{1 \text{ mol NaClO}_4} \times \dfrac{6.022 \times 10^{23} \text{ Cl atoms}}{\text{mol Cl}}$

$\times \dfrac{31\ ^{36}\text{Cl atoms}}{100 \text{ Cl atoms}} = 7.537 \times 10^{19} = 7.54 \times 10^{19}\ ^{36}\text{Cl atoms}$

$k = 0.693/t_{1/2} = \dfrac{0.693}{3.0 \times 10^5 \text{ yr}} \times \dfrac{1 \text{ yr}}{365 \times 24 \times 3600 \text{ s}} = 7.32 \times 10^{-14} = 7.3 \times 10^{-14} \text{ s}^{-1}$

rate = kN = (7.32 × 10^{-14} s^{-1})(7.547 × 10^{19} nuclei) = 5.52 × 10^6 = 5.5 × 10^6 dis/s

21.81 (a) $0.18 \text{ Ci} \times \dfrac{3.7 \times 10^{10} \text{ dis/s}}{\text{Ci}} \times \dfrac{3600 \text{ s}}{\text{hr}} \times \dfrac{24 \text{ hr}}{\text{d}} \times 235 \text{ d} = 1.35 \times 10^{17}$

$= 1.4 \times 10^{17}$ α particles

(b) $P = nRT/ V = 1.35 \times 10^{17} \text{ He atoms} \times \dfrac{1 \text{ mol He}}{6.022 \times 10^{23} \text{ atoms}} \times \dfrac{295 \text{ K}}{0.0150 \text{ L}} \times \dfrac{0.08206 \text{ L} \cdot \text{atn}}{\text{K} \cdot \text{mol}}$

$= 3.62 \times 10^{-4} = 3.6 \times 10^{-4}$ atm = 0.28 torr

22 Chemistry of the Nonmetals

Periodic Trends and Chemical Reactions

22.1 *Analyze/Plan.* Use the color coded periodic chart on the front-inside cover of the text to classify the given elements. *Solve:*

Metals: (b) Sr, (c) Ce, (e) Rh;   nonmetals: (d) Se, (f) Kr;   metalloid: (a) Sb

22.3 *Analyze/Plan.* Follow the logic in Sample Exercise 22.1. *Solve:*

   (a)   Cl   (b) K

   (c)   K in the gas phase (lowest ionization energy), Li in aqueous solution (most positive E° value)

   (d)   Ne; Ne and Ar are difficult to compare because they do not form compounds and their radii are not measured in the same way as other elements. However, Ne is several rows to the right of C and surely has a smaller atomic radius. The next smallest is C.

   (e)   C

22.5 *Analyze/Plan.* Use the position of the specified elements on the periodic chart, periodic trends and the arguments in Sample Exercise 22.1 to explain the observations. *Solve:*

   (a)   Nitrogen is too small to accommodate five fluorine atoms about it. The P and As atoms are larger. Furthermore, P and As have available 3d and 4d orbitals, respectively, to form hybrid orbitals that can accommodate more than an octet of electrons about the central atom.

   (b)   Si does not readily form π bonds, which would be necessary to satisfy the octet rule for both atoms in SiO.

   (c)   A reducing agent is a substance that readily loses electrons. As has a lower electronegativity than N; that is, it more readily gives up electrons to an acceptor and is more easily oxidized.

22.7 *Analyze/Plan.* Follow the logic in Sample Exercise 22.2. *Solve:*

   (a) $LiN_3(s) + H_2O(l) \rightleftharpoons HN_3(aq) + LiOH(aq)$

   (b) $2C_3H_7OH(l) + 9O_2(g) \rightarrow 6CO_2(g) + 8H_2O(l)$

   (c) $NiO(s) + C(s) \rightarrow CO(g) + Ni(s)$ or $2NiO(s) + C(s) \rightarrow CO_2(g) + 2Ni(s)$

(d) $AlP(s) + 3H_2O(l) \rightarrow PH_3(g) + Al(OH)_3(s)$

(e) $Na_2S(s) + 2HCl(aq) \rightarrow H_2S(g) + 2NaCl(aq)$

Hydrogen, the Noble Gases, and the Halogens

22.9   *Analyze/Plan.* Use information on the isotopes of hydrogen in Section 22.2 to list their symbols, names and relative abundances. *Solve*:

a) $_1^1H$ - protium; $_1^2H$ - deuterium; $_1^3H$ - tritium

b)   The order of abundance is proteum > deuterium > tritium.

22.11   *Analyze/Plan.* Consider the electron configuration and electronegativity of hydrogen and the halogens. *Solve*:

Like other elements in group 1A, hydrogen has only one valence electron. Like other elements in group 7A, hydrogen needs only one electron to complete its valence shell. The most common oxidation number of H is +1, like the group 1A elements; H can also exist in the -1 oxidation state, a state common to the group 7A elements.

22.13   *Analyze/Plan.* Use information on the descriptive chemistry of hydrogen in Section 22.2 to formulate the required equations. Steam is $H_2O(g)$. *Solve*:

(a) $Mg(s) + 2H^+(aq) \rightarrow Mg^{2+}(aq) + H_2(g)$

(b) $C(s) + H_2O(g) \xrightarrow{1000\,^{\circ}C} CO(g) + H_2(g)$

(c) $CH_4(g) + H_2O(g) \xrightarrow{1100\,^{\circ}C} CO(g) + 3H_2(g)$

22.15   *Analyze/Plan.* Use information on the descriptive chemistry of hydrogen given in Section 22.2 to complete and balance the equations. *Solve*:

(a) $NaH(s) + H_2O(l) \rightarrow NaOH(aq) + H_2(g)$

(b) $Fe(s) + H_2SO_4(aq) \rightarrow Fe^{2+}(aq) + H_2(g) + SO_4^{2-}(aq)$

(c) $H_2(g) + Br_2(g) \rightarrow 2HBr(g)$

(d) $2Na(l) + H_2(g) \rightarrow 2NaH(s)$

(e) $PbO(s) + H_2(g) \xrightarrow{\Delta} Pb(s) + H_2O(g)$

22.17   *Analyze/Plan.* If the element bound to H is a nonmetal, the hydride is molecular. If H is bound to a metal with integer stoichiometry, the hydride is ionic; with noninteger stoichiometry, the hydride is metallic. *Solve*:

(a)   Molecular   (b) ionic   (c) metallic

22.19 *Analyze/Plan.* Consider the periodic properties of Xe and Ar. *Solve*:

Xenon is larger, and can more readily accommodate an expanded octet. More important is the lower ionization energy of xenon; because the valence electrons are a greater average distance from the nucleus, they are more readily promoted to a state in which the Xe atom can form bonds with fluorine.

22.21 *Analyze/Plan.* Follow the rules for assigning oxidation numbers in Section 4.4 and the logic in Sample Exercise 4.8. *Solve*:

(a) BrO_3^-, +5 (b) HI, -1 (c) BrF_3; Br, +3; F, -1

(d) NaOCl, +1 (e) $HClO_4$, +7 (f) XeF_4, +4; F, -1

22.23 *Analyze/Plan.* Review the nomenclature rules and ion names in Section 2.8. *Solve*:

(a) potassium chlorate (b) calcium iodate (c) aluminum chloride

(d) bromic acid (e) paraperiodic acid (f) xenon tetrafluoride

22.25 *Analyze/Plan.* Consider intermolecular forces and periodic properties, including oxidizing power, of the listed substances. *Solve*:

(a) Van der Waals intermolecular attractive forces increase with increasing numbers of electrons in the atoms.

(b) F_2 reacts with water: $F_2(g) + H_2O(l) \rightarrow 2HF(aq) + 1/2\ O_2(g)$. That is, fluorine is too strong an oxidizing agent to exist in water.

(c) HF has extensive hydrogen bonding.

(d) Oxidizing power is related to electronegativity. Electronegativity decreases in the order given.

22.27 *Analyze/Plan.* Use information on the descriptive chemistry of the halogens given in Section 22.4 to complete and balance the equations. *Solve*:

(a) $Br_2(l) + 2OH^-(aq) \rightarrow BrO^-(aq) + Br^-(aq) + H_2O(l)$

(b) $Cl_2(g) + 2I^-(aq) \rightarrow I_2(l) + 2Cl^-(aq)$

22.29 *Analyze/Plan.* For each substance, count valence electrons, draw the correct Lewis structure, and apply the rules of VSEPR to decide electron domain geometry and geometric structure. *Solve*:

(a) square-planar (b) trigonal pyramidal (c) octahedral about the central iodine

(d) linear

Oxygen and the Group 6A Elements

22.31 *Analyze/Plan.* Consider the industrial uses of oxygen and ozone given in Section 22.5. *Solve:*

(a) As an oxidizing agent in steel-making; to bleach pulp and paper; in oxyacetylene torches; in medicine to assist in breathing

(b) Synthesis of pharmaceuticals, lubricants and other organic compounds where C=C bonds are cleaved; in water treatment

22.33 *Analyze/Plan.* Use information on the descriptive chemistry of oxygen given in Section 22.5 to complete and balance the equations. *Solve:*

(a) $CaO(s) + H_2O(l) \rightarrow Ca^{2+}(aq) + 2OH^-(aq)$

(b) $Al_2O_3(s) + 6H^+(aq) \rightarrow 2Al^{3+}(aq) + 3H_2O(l)$

(c) $Na_2O_2(s) + 2H_2O(l) \rightarrow 2Na^+(aq) + 2OH^-(aq) + H_2O_2(aq)$

(d) $N_2O_3(g) + H_2O(l) \rightarrow 2HNO_2(aq)$

(e) $2KO_2(s) + 2H_2O(l) \rightarrow 2K^+(aq) + 2OH^-(aq) + O_2(g) + H_2O_2(aq)$

(f) $NO(g) + O_3(g) \rightarrow NO_2(g) + O_2(g)$

22.35 *Analyze/Plan.* Oxides of metals are bases, oxides of nonmetals are acids, oxides that act as both acids and bases are amphoteric and oxides that act as neither acids nor bases are neutral. *Solve:*

(a) Neutral   (b) acidic (oxide of a nonmetal)

(c) basic (oxide of a metal)   (d) amphoteric

22.37 *Analyze/Plan.* Follow the rules for assigning oxidation numbers in Section 4.4 and the logic in Sample Exercise 4.8. *Solve:*

(a) SeO_3, +6   (b) $Na_2S_2O_3$, +2   (c) SF_4, +4   (d) H_2S, -2   (e) H_2SO_3, +4
Oxygen (a group 6A element) is in the -2 oxidation state in compounds (a), (b) and (e).

22.39 *Analyze/Plan.* The half-reaction for oxidation in all these cases is:
$H_2S(aq) \rightarrow S(s) + 2H^+ + 2e^-$ (The product could be written as $S_8(s)$, but this is not necessary. In fact it is not necessarily the case that S_8 would be formed, rather than some other allotropic form of the element.) Combine this half-reaction with the given reductions to write complete equations. The reduction in (c) happens only in acid solution. The reactants in (d) are acids, so the medium is acidic. *Solve:*

(a) $2Fe^{3+}(aq) + H_2S(aq) \rightarrow 2Fe^{2+}(aq) + S(s) + 2H^+(aq)$

(b) $Br_2(l) + H_2S(aq) \rightarrow 2Br^-(aq) + S(s) + 2H^+(aq)$

(c) $2MnO_4^-(aq) + 6H^+(aq) + 5H_2S(aq) \rightarrow 2Mn^{2+}(aq) + 5S(s) + 8H_2O(l)$

(d) $2NO_3^-(aq) + H_2S(aq) + 2H^+(aq) \rightarrow 2NO_2(aq) + S(s) + 2H_2O(l)$

22.41 *Analyze/Plan.* For each substance, count valence electrons, draw the correct Lewis structure, and apply the rules of VSEPR to decide electron domain geometry and geometric structure. *Solve:*

(a) $\left[\begin{array}{c} :\ddot{O}-Se-\ddot{O}: \\ | \\ :\ddot{O}: \end{array}\right]^{2-}$

trigonal pyramidal

(b) $:\ddot{C}l\overset{\ddot{S}-\ddot{S}}{\diagup\diagdown}\ddot{C}l:$

bent (free rotation around S-S bond)

(c) $:\ddot{O}-\overset{:\ddot{O}:}{\underset{|}{S}}-\ddot{C}l:$
$\quad\quad\underset{\ddot{O}-H}{}$

tetrahedral

22.43 *Analyze/Plan.* Use information on the descriptive chemistry of sulfur given in Section 22.6 to complete and balance the equations. *Solve:*

(a) $SO_2(s) + H_2O(l) \rightarrow H_2SO_3(aq) \rightleftharpoons H^+(aq) + HSO_3^-(aq)$

(b) $ZnS(s) + 2HCl(aq) \rightarrow ZnCl_2(aq) + H_2S(g)$

(c) $8SO_3^{2-}(aq) + S_8(s) \rightarrow 8S_2O_3^{2-}(aq)$

(d) $SO_3(aq) + H_2SO_4(l) \rightarrow H_2S_2O_7(l)$

Nitrogen and the Group 5A Elements

22.45 *Analyze/Plan.* Follow the rules for assigning oxidation numbers in Section 4.4 and the logic in Sample Exercise 4.8. *Solve:*

(a) $NaNO_2$, +3 (b) NH_3, -3   (c) N_2O, +1   (d) $NaCN$, -3

(e) HNO_3, +5   (f) NO_2, +4

22.47 *Analyze/Plan.* For each substance, count valence electrons, draw the correct Lewis structure, and apply the rules of VSEPR to decide electron domain geometry and geometric structure. *Solve:*

(a) $\left[\begin{array}{c} H \\ | \\ H-N-H \\ | \\ H \end{array}\right]^{+}$

tetrahedral

(b) $:\ddot{O}-\overset{:\ddot{O}:}{N}-\ddot{O}-H \longleftrightarrow \overset{:\ddot{O}:}{\underset{\|}{O}}=N-\ddot{O}-H \longleftrightarrow :\ddot{O}-N\overset{:\ddot{O}:}{=}O-$

The geometry around nitrogen is trigonal planar, but the hydrogen atom is not required to lie in this plane. The third resonance form makes a much smaller contribution to the structure than the first two.

(c) $:\ddot{N}=N=\ddot{O}: \longleftrightarrow :N\equiv N-\ddot{\ddot{O}}: \longleftrightarrow :\ddot{N}-N\equiv O:$

The molecule is linear. Again, the third resonance form makes less contribution to the structure because of the high formal charges involved.

(d)

$$\ddot{O}=\ddot{N}-\ddot{\underset{..}{O}}: \quad \longleftrightarrow \quad :\ddot{\underset{..}{O}}-\ddot{N}=\ddot{O}:$$

The molecule is bent (nonlinear).

22.49   *Analyze/Plan.* Use information on the descriptive chemistry of nitrogen given in Section 22.7 to complete and balance the equations. *Solve:*

(a) $Mg_3N_2(s) + 6H_2O(l) \rightarrow 3Mg(OH)_2(s) + 2NH_3(aq)$

(b) $2NO(g) + O_2(g) \rightarrow 2NO_2(g)$

(c) $N_2O_5(g) + H_2O(l) \rightarrow 2H^+(aq) + 2NO_3^-(aq)$

(d) $NH_3(aq) + H^+(aq) \rightarrow NH_4^+(aq)$

(e) $N_2H_4(l) + O_2(g) \rightarrow N_2(g) + 2H_2O(g)$

22.51   *Analyze/Plan.* Follow the method for writing balanced half-reactions given in Section 20.1 and Sample Exercises 20.2 and 20.3. Find standard reduction potentials in figure 22.30. *Solve:*

(a) $2NO_3^-(aq) + 12H^+(aq) + 10e^- \rightarrow N_2(g) + 6H_2O(l)$ $E^{\circ}_{red} = +1.25$ V

(b) $2NH_4^+(aq) \rightarrow N_2(g) + 8H^+(aq) + 6e^-$ $E^{\circ}_{red} = 0.27$ V

22.53   *Analyze/Plan.* Follow the rules for assigning oxidation numbers in Section 4.4 and the logic in Sample Exercise 4.8. *Solve:*

(a) H_3PO_4, +5   (b) H_3AsO_3, +3   (c) **Sb_2S_3**, +3   (d) $Ca(H_2PO_4)_2$, +5   (e) K_3P, -3

22.55   *Analyze/Plan.* Consider the structures of the componds of interest when explaining the observations. *Solve:*

(a)   Phosphorus is a larger atom and can more easily accommodate five surrounding atoms and an expanded octet of electrons than nitrogen can. Also, P has energetically "available" 3d orbitals which participate in the bonding, but nitrogen does not.

(b)   Only one of the three hydrogens in H_3PO_2 is bonded to oxygen. The other two are bonded directly to phosphorus and are not easily ionized because the P–H bond is not very polar.

(c) PH_3 is a weaker base than H_2O (PH_4^+ is a stronger acid than H_3O^+). Any attempt to add H^+ to PH_3 in the presence of H_2O merely causes protonation of H_2O.

(d)   White phosphorus consists of P_4 molecules, with P–P–P bond angles of 60°. Each P atom has four VSEPR pairs of electrons, so the predicted electron pair geometry is tetrahedral and the preferred bond angle is 109°. Because of the severely strained bond angles in P_4 molecules, white phosphorus is highly reactive.

22.57 *Analyze/Plan.* Use information on the descriptive chemistry of phosphorus given in Section 22.8 to complete and balance the equations. *Solve:*

(a) $2Ca_3(PO_4)_2(s) + 6SiO_2(s) + 10C(s) \xrightarrow{\Delta} P_4(g) + 6CaSiO_3(l) + 10CO(g)$

(b) $3H_2O(l) + PCl_3(l) \rightarrow H_3PO_3(aq) + 3H^+(aq) + 3Cl^-(aq)$

(c) $6Cl_2(g) + P_4(s) \rightarrow 4PCl_3(l)$

Carbon, the Other Group 4A Elements, and Boron

22.59 *Analyze/Plan.* Review the nomenclature rules and ion names in Section 2.8. *Solve:*

(a)   HCN   (b) SiC   (c) $CaCO_3$ (d) CaC_2

22.61 *Analyze/Plan.* Use the correct number of valence electrons and satisfy the octet rule for all atoms. *Solve:*

(a) $\left[:C\equiv N:\right]^-$ (b) $:C\equiv O:$ (c) $\left[:C\equiv C:\right]^{2-}$

(d) $\ddot{S}=C=\ddot{S}$ (e) $\ddot{O}=C=\ddot{O}$ (f) $\left[\begin{array}{c} :\ddot{O}: \\ C \\ :\ddot{O} \quad \ddot{O}: \end{array}\right]^{2-}$

one of three equivalent
resonance structures

22.63 *Analyze/Plan.* Use information on the descriptive chemistry of carbon given in Section 22.9 to complete and balance the equations. *Solve:*

(a) $ZnCO_3(s) \xrightarrow{\Delta} ZnO(s) + CO_2(g)$

(b) $BaC_2(s) + 2H_2O(l) \rightarrow Ba^{2+}(aq) + 2OH^-(aq) + C_2H_2(g)$

(c) $C_2H_4(g) + 3O_2(g) \rightarrow 2CO_2(g) + 2H_2O(g)$

(d) $2CH_3OH(l) + 3O_2(g) \rightarrow 2CO_2(g) + 4H_2O(g)$

(e) $NaCN(s) + H^+(aq) \rightarrow Na^+(aq) + HCN(g)$

22.65 *Analyze/Plan.* Use information on the descriptive chemistry of carbon given in Section 22.9 to complete and balance the equations. *Solve:*

(a) $2CH_4(g) + 2NH_3(g) + 3O_2(g) \xrightarrow[\text{cat}]{800^\circ C} 2HCN(g) + 6H_2O(g)$

(b) $NaHCO_3(s) + H^+(aq) \rightarrow CO_2(g) + H_2O(l) + Na^+(aq)$

(c) $2BaCO_3(s) + O_2(g) + 2SO_2(g) \rightarrow 2BaSO_4(s) + 2CO_2(g)$

22.67 *Analyze/Plan.* Follow the rules for assinging oxidation numbers in Section 4.4 and the logic in Sample Exercise 4.8. *Solve:*

(a) H_3BO_3, +3   (b) $SiBr_4$, +4   (c) $PbCl_2$, +2 or $PbCl_4$, + 4

(d) $Na_2B_4O_7 \cdot 10H_2O$, +3   (e) B_2O_3, +3

22.69 *Analyze/Plan.* Consider periodic trends within a family, particularly metallic character. *Solve:*

(a)   Carbon   (b) lead   (c) silicon

22.71 *Analyze/Plan.* Consider the structural chemistry of silicates discussed in Section 22.10 and shown in Figures 22.51-22.53. *Solve:*

(a) SiO_4^{4-} (b) SiO_3^{2-} (c) SiO_3^{2-}

22.73 (a)   Diborane (Figure 22.55 and below) has bridging H atoms linking the two B atoms. The structure of ethane shown below has the C atoms bound directly, with no bridging atoms.

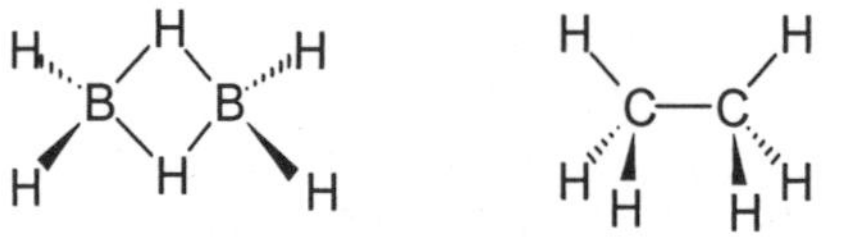

(b) B_2H_6 is an electron deficient molecule. It has 12 valence electrons, while C_2H_6 has 14 valence electrons. The 6 valence electron pairs in B_2H_6 are all involved in B–H sigma bonding, so the only way to satisfy the octet rule at B is to have the bridging H atoms shown in Figure 22.55.

(c)   A hydride ion, H^-, has two electrons while an H atom has one. The term *hydridic* indicates that the H atoms in B_2H_6 have more than the usual amount of electron density for a covalently bound H atom.

Additional Exercises

22.76 (a) $10.0 \text{ lb FeTi} \times \dfrac{453.6 \text{ g}}{1 \text{ lb}} \times \dfrac{1 \text{ mol FeTi}}{103.7 \text{ g FeTi}} \times \dfrac{1 \text{ mol H}_2}{1 \text{ mol FeTi}} \times \dfrac{2.016 \text{ g H}}{1 \text{ mol H}_2} = 88.18$

$= 88.2 \text{ g H}$

(b) $V = \dfrac{88.18 \text{ g H}_2}{2.016 \text{ g/mol H}_2} \times \dfrac{0.08206 \text{ L} \cdot \text{atm}}{\text{mol} \cdot \text{K}} \times \dfrac{273 \text{ K}}{1 \text{ atm}} = 979.9 = 980 \text{ L}$

22.79 Substances that will burn in O_2: SiH_4, CO, Mg.

The others, SiO_2, CO_2 and CaO, have Si, C and Ca in maximum oxidation states, so O_2 cannot act as an oxidizing agent.

22.81   (a) $H_2SO_4 - H_2O \rightarrow SO_3$ (b) $2HClO_3 - H_2O \rightarrow Cl_2O_5$

         (c) $2HNO_2 - H_2O \rightarrow N_2O_3$ (d) $H_2CO_3 - H_2O \rightarrow CO_2$

         (e) $2H_3PO_4 - 3H_2O \rightarrow P_2O_5$

22.84   (a) PO_4^{3-}, + 5; NO_3^-, + 5

         (b)   The Lewis structure for NO_4^{3-} would be:

The formal charge on N is +1 and on each O atom is -1. The four electronegative oxygen atoms withdraw electron density, leaving the nitrogen deficient. Since N can form a maximum of four bonds, it cannot form a π bond with one or more of the O atoms to regain electron density, as the P atom in PO_4^{3-} does. Also, the short N–O distance would lead to a tight tetrahedron of O atoms subject to steric repulsion.

22.87 $GeO_2(s) + C(s) \xrightarrow{\Delta} Ge(l) + CO_2(g)$

        $Ge(l) + 2Cl_2(g) \rightarrow GeCl_4(l)$

        $GeCl_4(l) + 2H_2O(l) \rightarrow GeO_2(s) + 4HCl(g)$

        $GeO_2(s) + 2H_2(g) \rightarrow Ge(s) + 2H_2O(l)$

Integrative Exercises

22.91 $2XeO_3(s) \rightarrow 2Xe(g) + 3O_2(g)$

$$0.500 \text{ g } XeO_3 \times \frac{1 \text{ mol } XeO_3}{179.1 \text{ g } XeO_3} \times \frac{5 \text{ mol gas}}{2 \text{ mol } XeO_3} = 6.979 \times 10^{-3} = 6.98 \times 10^{-3} \text{ mol gas}$$

$$P = \frac{(6.979 \times 10^{-3} \text{ mol})(0.08206 \text{ L} \cdot \text{atm/mol} \cdot \text{K})(303 \text{ K})}{1.00 \text{ L}} = 0.17354 = 0.174 \text{ atm}$$

22.93   (a) $H_2(g) + 1/2 \, O_2(g) \rightarrow H_2O(l)$; $\Delta H = -285.83$ kJ

         $CH_4(g) + 2O_2(g) \rightarrow CO_2(g) + 2H_2O(l)$

         $\Delta H = 2(-285.83) - 393.5 - (-74.8) = -890.4$ kJ

         (b)   for H_2: $\dfrac{-285.83 \text{ kJ}}{1 \text{ mol } H_2} \times \dfrac{1 \text{ mol } H_2}{2.0159 \text{ g } H_2} = -141.79$ kJ/g H_2

               for CH_4: $\dfrac{-890.4 \text{ kJ}}{1 \text{ mol } CH_4} \times \dfrac{1 \text{ mol } CH_4}{16.043 \text{ g } CH_4} = -55.50$ kJ/g CH_4

         (c)   Find the number of moles of gas that occupy 1 m^3 at STP:

$$n = \frac{1 \text{ atm} \times 1 \text{ m}^3}{273 \text{ K}} \times \frac{1 \text{ K} \cdot \text{mol}}{0.08206 \text{ L} \cdot \text{atm}} \times \left[\frac{100 \text{ cm}}{1 \text{ m}} \right]^3 \times \frac{1 \text{ L}}{10^3 \text{ cm}^3} = 44.64 \text{ mol}$$

for H_2: $\dfrac{-285.83\ kJ}{1\ mol\ H_2} \times \dfrac{44.64\ mol\ H_2}{1\ m^3\ H_2} = 1.276 \times 10^4\ kJ/m^3\ H_2$

for CH_4: $\dfrac{-890.4\ kJ}{1\ mol\ CH_4} \times \dfrac{44.64\ mol\ CH_4}{1\ m^3\ CH_4} = 3.975 \times 10^4\ kJ/m^3\ CH_4$

22.96 (a) $SO_2(g) + 2H_2S(s) \rightarrow 3S(s) + 2H_2O(g)$ or, if we assume S_8 is the product,

$8SO_2(g) + 16H_2S(g) \rightarrow 3S_8(s) + 16H_2O(g)$.

(b) $2000\ lb\ coal \times \dfrac{0.035\ lb\ S}{1\ lb\ coal} \times \dfrac{453.6\ g\ S}{1\ lb\ S} \times \dfrac{1\ mol\ S}{32.07\ g\ S} \times \dfrac{1\ mol\ SO_2}{1\ mol\ S} \times \dfrac{2\ mol\ H_2S}{1\ mol\ SO_2}$

$= 1.98 \times 10^3 = 2.0 \times 10^3\ mol\ H_2S$

$V = \dfrac{1.98 \times 10^3\ mol\ (0.08206\ L \cdot atm/mol \cdot K)(300\ K)}{(740/760)\ atm} = 5.01 \times 10^4 = 5.0 \times 10^4\ L$

(c) $1.98 \times 10^3\ mol\ H_2S \times \dfrac{3\ mol\ S}{2\ mol\ H_2S} \times \dfrac{32.07\ g\ S}{1\ mol\ S} = 9.5 \times 10^4\ g\ S$

This is about 210 lb S per ton of coal combusted. (However, two-thirds of this comes from the H_2S, which was presumably also obtained from coal.)

22.98 The reactions can be written as follows:

$H_2(g) + X(std\ state) \rightarrow H_2X(g)$ ΔH_f°

$2H(g) \rightarrow H_2(g)$ $\Delta H_f^{\circ}(H{-}H)$

$X(g) \rightarrow X(std\ state)$ ΔH_3

Add: $2H(g) + X(g) \rightarrow H_2X(g)$ $\Delta H = \Delta H_f^{\circ} + \Delta H_f^{\circ}(H{-}H) + \Delta H_3$

These are all the necessary ΔH values. Thus,

Compound	ΔH	D H–X
H_2O	ΔH = -242 kJ - 436 kJ - 248 kJ = -926 kJ	463 kJ
H_2S	ΔH = -20 kJ - 436 kJ - 277 kJ = -733 kJ	367 kJ
H_2Se	ΔH = +30 kJ - 436 kJ - 227 kJ = -633 kJ	316 kJ
H_2Te	ΔH = +100 kJ - 436 kJ - 197 kJ = -533 kJ	266 kJ

The average H–X bond energy in each case is just half of ΔH. The H–X bond energy decreases steadily in the series. The origin of this effect is probably the increasing size of the orbital from X with which the hydrogen 1s orbital must overlap.

22.101 $(CH_3)_2N_2H_2(g) + 2N_2O_4(g) \rightarrow 2CO_2(g) + 3N_2(g) + 4H_2O(g)$

$4.0\ tons\ (CH_3)_2N_2H_2 \times \dfrac{2000\ lb}{1\ ton} \times \dfrac{453.6\ g}{1\ lb} \times \dfrac{1\ mol\ (CH_3)_2N_2H_2}{60.10\ g\ (CH_3)_2N_2H_2}$

$\times \dfrac{2\ mol\ N_2O_4}{1\ mol\ (CH_3)_2N_2H_2} \times \dfrac{92.02\ g\ N_2O_4}{1\ mol\ N_2O_4} \times \dfrac{1\ lb}{453.6\ g} \times \dfrac{1\ ton}{2000\ lb} = 12\ tons\ N_2O_4$

23 Metals and Metallurgy

Metallurgy

23.1 *Analyze/Plan.* Use Table 23.1 and other information in Section 23.1 to find important natural sources of Al and Fe. Use the rules for assigning oxidation numbers in Section 4.4 to determine the oxidation state of the metal in each natural source. *Solve:*

The important sources of iron are **hematite** (Fe_2O_3) and **magnetite** (Fe_3O_4). The major source of aluminum is **bauxite** ($Al_2O_3 \cdot xH_2O$). In ores, iron is present as the +3 ion, or in both the +2 and +3 states, as in magnetite. Aluminum is always present in the +3 oxidation state.

23.3 An ore consists of a little bit of the stuff we want, (chalcopyrite, $CuFeS_2$) and lots of other junk (gangue).

23.5 *Analyze/Plan.* Use principles of writing and balancing chemical equations from Chapter 3 to complete and balance the given reactions. The Δ above each arrow indicates that the reactions take place at elevated temperature. Information in Section 23.2 on *pyrometallurgy* will probably be useful. *Solve:*

(a) $2PbS(s) + 3O_2(s) \xrightarrow{\Delta} 2PbO(s) + 2SO_2(g)$

(b) $PbCO_3(s) \xrightarrow{\Delta} PbO(s) + CO_2(g)$

(c) $WO_3(s) + 3H_2(g) \xrightarrow{\Delta} W(s) + 3H_2O(g)$

(d) $ZnO(s) + CO(g) \xrightarrow{\Delta} Zn(l) + CO_2(g)$

23.7 *Analyze/Plan.* Use information on *pyrometallurgy* in Section 23.2, along with principles of writing and balancing equations to provide the requested information. *Solve:*

(a) $SO_3(g)$

(b) $CO(g)$ provides a reducing environment for the transformation of Pb^{2+} to Pb.

(c) $PbSO_4(s) \rightarrow PbO(s) + SO_3(g)$

$PbO(s) + CO(g) \rightarrow Pb(s) + CO_2(g)$

23.9 *Analyze/Plan.* Use information on *pyrometallurgy* in Section 23.2, along with principles of writing and balancing equations to provide the requested information. *Solve:*

$FeO(s) + H_2(g) \rightarrow Fe(s) + H_2O(g)$

$FeO(s) + CO(g) \rightarrow Fe(s) + CO_2(g)$

$Fe_2O_3(s) + 3H_2(g) \rightarrow 2Fe(s) + 3H_2O(g)$

$Fe_2O_3(s) + 3CO(g) \rightarrow 2Fe(s) + 3CO_2(g)$

23.11   *Analyze/Plan.* Use information on *pyrometallurgy* in Section 23.2, along with principles of writing and balancing equations to provide the requested information. *Solve:*

(a)   Air serves primarily to oxidize coke (C) to CO, the main reducing agent in the blast furnace. This exothermic reaction also provides heat for the furnace.

$2C(s) + O_2(g) \rightarrow 2CO(g)$ $\Delta H = -221$ kJ

(b)   Limestone, $CaCO_3$, is the source of basic oxide for slag formation.

$CaCO_3(s) \xrightarrow{\Delta} CaO(s) + CO_2(g)$; $CaO(l) + SiO_2(l) \rightarrow CaSiO_3(l)$

(c)   Coke is the fuel for the blast furnace, and the source of CO, the major reducing agent in the furnace.

$2C(s) + O_2(g) \rightarrow 2CO(g)$; $4CO(g) + Fe_3O_4(s) \rightarrow 4CO_2(g) + 3Fe(l)$

(d)   Water acts as a source of hydrogen, and as a means of controlling temperature. (see Equation [23.8]). $C(s) + H_2O(g) \rightarrow CO(g) + H_2(g)$ $\Delta H = +131$ kJ

23.13   *Analyze/Plan.* Consider the information on hydrometallurgy in Section 23.3 to provide the requested information on the Bayer process. *Solve:*

(a)   The Bayer process is necessary to separate the unwanted iron-containing solids from bauxite before electroreduction.

(b)   The Bayer process takes advantage of the fact that Al^{3+} is amphoteric, but Fe^{3+} is not. Because it is amphoteric, Al^{3+} reacts with excess OH^- to form the soluble complex ion $Al(OH)_4^-$ while the Fe^{3+} solids cannot. This allows separation of the iron-containing solids by filtration.

23.15   *Analyze/Plan.* Use information on the *electrometallurgy* of Cu as a model for describing how electrometallurgy can be employed to purify pure Co. Compare the ease of oxidation and reduction of cobalt with that of water. *Solve:*

Cobalt could be purified by constructing an electrolysis cell in which the crude metal was the anode and a thin sheet of pure cobalt was the cathode. The electrolysis solution is aqueous with a soluble cobalt salt such as $CoSO_4 \cdot 7H_2O$ serving as the electrolyte. (Other soluble salts with anions that do not participate in the cell reactions could be used.) Anode reaction: $Co(s) \rightarrow Co^{2+}(aq) + 2e^-$; cathode reaction: $Co^{2+}(aq) + 2e^- \rightarrow Co(s)$. Although $E°$ for reduction of $Co^{2+}(aq)$ is slightly negative (-0.277 V), it is less than the standard reduction potential for $H_2O(l)$, -0.83 V.

Metals and Alloys

23.17 *Analyze/Plan.* Compare the bonding characteristics of metallic sodium and ionic sodium chloride and use them to explain the difference in malleability. *Solve:*

Sodium is metallic; each atom is bonded to many nearest neighbor atoms by metallic bonding involving just one electron per atom, and delocalized over the entire three-dimensional structure. When sodium metal is distorted, each atom continues to have bonding interactions with many nearest neighbors. In NaCl the ionic forces are strong, and the arrangement of ions in the solid is very regular. When subjected to physical stress, the three-dimensional lattice tends to cleave along the very regular lattice planes, rather than undergo the large distortions characteristic of metals.

23.19 *Analyze/Plan.* Apply the description of the electron-sea model of metallic bonding given in Section 23.5 to the conductivity of silver. *Solve:*

In the electron-sea model for metallic bonding, the valence electrons of the silver atoms move about the three-dimensional metallic lattice, while the silver atoms maintain regular lattice positions. Under the influence of an applied potential the electrons can move throughout the structure, giving rise to high electrical conductivity. The mobility of the electrons facilitates the transfer of kinetic energy and leads to high thermal conductivity.

23.21 *Analyze/Plan.* Consider trends in atomic mass and volume of the elements listed to explain the variation in density. *Solve:*

The variation in densities reflects shorter metal-metal bond distances. These shorter distances suggest that the extent of metal-metal bonding increases in the series. Thus, it would appear that all the valence electrons in these elements (1, 2, 3 and 4, respectively) are involved in metallic bonding.

23.23 *Analyze/Plan.* Consider the definitions of insulators, conductors and semiconductors given in 'A Closer Look' in Section 23.5. *Solve:*

According to band theory, an *insulator* has a completely filled valence band and a large energy gap between the valence band and the nearest empty band; electrons are localized within the lattice. A *conductor* must have a partially filled energy band; a small excitation will promote electrons to previously empty levels within the band and allow them to move freely throughout the lattice, giving rise to the property of conduction. A *semiconductor* has a filled valence band, but the gap between the filled and empty bands is small enough to jump to the empty conduction band. The presence of an impurity may also place an electron in an otherwise empty band (producing an n-type semiconductor), or create a vacancy in an otherwise full band (producing a p-type semiconductor), providing a mechanism for conduction.

23.25 *Analyze/Plan.* Recall the diamond and closest-packed structures described in Sections 11.7 and 11.8. Use these structures to draw conclusions about Sn–Sn distance and electrical conductivity in the two allotropes. *Solve:*

White tin, with a characteristic metallic structure, is expected to be more metallic in character. The electrical conductivity of the white allotropic form is higher because the valence electrons are shared with 12 nearest neighbors rather than being localized in four bonds to nearest neighbors as in gray tin. The Sn–Sn distance should be longer in white tin; there are only four valence electrons from each atom, and 12 nearest neighbors. The **average** tin–tin bond order can, therefore, be only about 1/3, whereas in gray tin the bond order is one. (In gray tin the Sn–Sn distance is 2.81 Å in white tin it is 3.02 Å.)

23.27   *Analyze/Plan.* Use information in Section 23.6 to define *alloy*, and compare the various types of alloys. Solve:

An *alloy* contains atoms of more than one element and has the properties of a metal. *Solution alloys* are homogeneous mixtures with different kinds of atoms dispersed randomly and uniformly. In *heterogeneous alloys* the components (elements or compounds) are not evenly dispersed and their properties depend not only on composition but methods of preparation. In an *intermetallic compound* the component elements have interacted to form a compound substance, for example, Cu_3As. As with more familiar compounds, these are homogeneous and have definite composition and properties.

Transition Metals

23.29   *Analyze/Plan.* Consider the definitions of the properties listed (Chapter 7 and Chapter 23) and whether they refer to single, isolated atoms or bulk material. *Solve:*

Of the properties listed, (b) the first ionization energy, (c) atomic radius and (f) electron affinity are characteristic of isolated atoms. Electrical conductivity (a), melting point (d) and heat of vaporization (e) are properties of the bulk metal.

23.31   *Analyze/Plan.* Define lanthanide contraction (Section 23.7). Based on the definition, list properties related to atomic radius. *Solve:*

The *lanthanide contraction* is the name given to the decrease in atomic size due to the build-up in effective nuclear charge as we move through the lanthanides (elements 58-71) and beyond them. This effect offsets the expected increase in atomic size going from the second to the third transition series. The lanthanide contraction affects size-related properties such as ionization energy, electron affinity and density.

23.33   *Analyze/Plan.* Use Figure 23.24 to determine the highest oxidation state of each metal. Write formulas of the metal fluorides, given that fluoride ion is F^-. *Solve:*

(a) ScF_3 (b) CoF_3 (c) ZnF_2

23.35   *Analyze/Plan.* Consider the electron configurations of Cr and Al to rationalize observed oxidation states. *Solve:*

Chromium, $[Ar]4s^1 3d^5$, has six valence-shell electrons, some or all of which can be involved in bonding, leading to multiple stable oxidation states. By contrast, aluminum, $[Ne]3s^2 3p^1$, has only three valence electrons which are all lost or shared during bonding, producing the +3 state exclusively.

23.37   *Analyze/Plan.* Write electron configurations for the neutral elements and their positive ions recalling that valence electrons are last in order of descending *n*-value. *Solve:*

(a) Cr^{3+}: $[Ar]3d^3$ (b) Au^{3+}: $[Xe]4f^{14}5d^8$ (c) Ru^{2+}: $[Kr]4d^6$

(d) Cu^+: $[Ar]3d^{10}$ (e) Mn^{4+}: $[Ar]3d^3$ (f) Ir^{3+}: $[Xe]4f^{14}5d^6$

23.39   *Analyze/Plan.* Oxidation is loss of electrons. Which periodic trend determines how tightly a valence electron is held in a particular atom or ion? *Solve:*

Ease of oxidation decreases from left to right across a period (owing to increasing effective nuclear charge); Ti^{2+} should be more easily oxidized than Ni^{2+}.

23.41   *Analyze/Plan.* Consider Equation 23.26 regarding the oxidation states of iron. *Solve:*

Fe^{2+} is a reducing agent that is readily oxidized to Fe^{3+} in the presence of O_2 from air.

23.43   *Analyze/Plan.* Consider information on the descriptive chemistry of iron in Section 23.8. *Solve:*

(a) $Fe(s) + 2HCl(aq) \rightarrow FeCl_2(aq) + H_2(g)$

(b) $Fe(s) + 4HNO_3(aq) \rightarrow Fe(NO_3)_3(aq) + NO(g) + 2H_2O(l)$
         (See net ionic equation, Equation 23.28) In concentrated nitric acid, the reaction can produce $NO_2(g)$ according to the reaction:
         $Fe(s) + 6HNO_3(aq) \rightarrow Fe(NO_3)_3(aq) + 3NO_2(g) + 3H_2O(l)$

23.45   *Analyze/Plan.* Consider the definitions of *paramagnetic* and *diamagnetic.* Solve:

The unpaired electrons in a *paramagnetic* material cause it to be weakly attracted into a magnetic field. A *diamagnetic* material, where all electrons are paired, is very weakly repelled by a magnetic field.

Additional Exercises

23.47 $PbS(s) + O_2(g) \rightarrow Pb(l) + SO_2(g)$

Regardless of the metal of interest, $SO_2(g)$ is a product of roasting sulfide ores. In an oxygen rich environment, $SO_2(g)$ is oxidized to $SO_3(g)$, which dissolves in $H_2O(l)$ to form sulfuric acid, $H_2SO_4(aq)$. Because of its corrosive nature, $SO_2(g)$ is a dangerous environmental pollutant (Section 18.4) and cannot be freely released into the atmosphere. A sulfuric acid plant near a roasting plant would provide a means for disposing of $SO_2(g)$ that would also generate a profit.

23.49   CO(g): Pb(s); H_2(g): Fe(s); Zn(s): Au(s)

23.52   Because selenium and tellurium are both nonmetals, we expect them to be difficult to oxidize. Thus, both Se and Te are likely to accumulate as the free elements in the so-called anode slime, along with noble metals that are not oxidized.

23.55   (a)   Substitutional alloys and intermetallic compounds are both homogeneous solution alloys. Intermetallic compounds have a definite stoichiometry and properties, while substitutional alloys have a range of compositions.

        (b)   A paramagnetic substance has unpaired electrons and is attracted into a magnetic field. A diamagnetic substance has only paired electrons and is weakly repelled by a magnetic field.

        (c)   Insulators have a filled valence band with a large energy gap between the valence and the conduction band, making delocalization difficult. Semiconductors have a filled valence band but a smaller band gap, so that some electrons can move to the conduction band.

        (d)   In metallic conduction, metal atoms are stationary while a few valence electrons are mobile and available to carry charge throughout the substance. In electrolytic conduction, mobile ions carry charge throughout the liquid.

23.57   The equilibrium of interest is $[ZnL_4] \rightleftharpoons Zn^{2+}$(aq) + 4L   K = 1/$K_f$
        Since $Zn(H_2O)_4^{2+}$ is Zn^{2+}(aq), its reduction potential is -0.763 V. As the stability (K_f) of the complexes increases, K decreases. Since E° is directly proportional to log K_{eq} (Equation 20.18), E° values for the complexes will become more negative as K_f increases.

23.60   In a ferromagnetic solid, the magnetic centers are coupled such that the spins of all unpaired electrons are parallel. As the temperature of the solid increases, the average kinetic energy of the atoms increases until the energy of motion overcomes the force aligning the electron spins. The substance becomes paramagnetic; it still has unpaired electrons, but their spins are no longer aligned.

23.63   (a) $2NiS(s) + 3O_2(g) \rightarrow 2NiO(s) + 2SO_2(g)$

        (b) $2C(s) + O_2(g) \rightarrow 2CO(g)$; $C(s) + H_2O(g) \rightarrow CO(g) + H_2(g)$

              $NiO(s) + CO(g) \rightarrow Ni(s) + CO_2(g)$; $NiO(s) + H_2(g) \rightarrow Ni(s) + H_2O(g)$

        (c) $Ni(s) + 2HCl(aq) \rightarrow NiCl_2(aq) + H_2(g)$

        (d) $NiCl_2(aq) + 2NaOH(aq) \rightarrow Ni(OH)_2(s) + 2NaCl(aq)$

        (e) $Ni(OH)_2(s) \xrightarrow{\Delta} NiO(s) + H_2O(g)$

Integrative Exercises

23.65 *Analyze/Plan.* Given the mass of Fe produced, calculate the mass of C required. Write the balanced equations for the reaction of Fe_2O_3 with CO, and for the formation of CO. Solve the stoichiometry problem, using mole ratios from the balanced equations and paying attention to units. *Solve*:

$$Fe_2O_3(s) + 3CO(g) \rightarrow 2Fe(s) + 3CO_2(g)$$

$$2C(s) + O_2(g) \rightarrow 2CO(g)$$

$$9.00 \times 10^3 \, \text{tan Fe} \times \frac{2000 \, \text{lb}}{1 \, \text{ton}} \times \frac{453.6 \, \text{g}}{1 \, \text{lb}} \times \frac{1 \, \text{mol Fe}}{55.845 \, \text{g Fe}} \times \frac{3 \, \text{mol CO}}{3 \, \text{mol Fe}} \times \frac{2 \, \text{mol C}}{2 \, \text{mol CO}} \times \frac{12.011 \, \text{g C}}{1 \, \text{mol C}}$$

$$= 2.634 \times 10^9 = 2.63 \times 10^9 \, \text{g}$$

This amount can also be expressed as 2.63×10^6 kg or 2.90×10^3 ton.

23.68 The first equation indicates that one mole Ni^{2+} is formed from passage of two moles of electrons, and the second equation indicates the same thing. Thus, the simple ratio (1 mol Ni^{2+}/2F).

$$67 \, \text{A} \times 11.0 \, \text{hr} \times \frac{3600 \, \text{s}}{1 \, \text{hr}} \times \frac{1 \, \text{C}}{1 \, \text{A} \cdot \text{s}} \times \frac{1 \, \text{F}}{96,500 \, \text{C}} \times \frac{1 \, \text{mol Ni}^{2+}}{2 \, \text{F}} \times \frac{58.7 \, \text{g Ni}^{2+}}{1 \, \text{mol Ni}^{2+}}$$

$$\times \frac{0.90 \, \text{g Ni actual}}{1.00 \, \text{g Ni theoretical}} = 7.3 \times 10^2 \, \text{g Ni}^{2+}(aq)$$

23.70 (a) According to Section 20.8, the reduction of O_2 during oxidation of Fe(s) to Fe_2O_3 requires H^+. Above pH 9, iron does not corrode. At the high temperature of the converter, it is unlikely to find H_2O or H^+ in contact with the molten Fe. Also, the basic slag (CaO(l)) that is present to remove phosphorus will keep the environment basic rather than acidic. Thus, the H^+ necessary for oxidation of Fe in air is not present in the converter.

(b) $C + O_2(g) \rightarrow CO_2(g)$
$S + O_2(g) \rightarrow SO_2(g)$
$P + O_2(g) \rightarrow P_2O_5(l)$; $P_2O_5(l) + 3CaO(l) \rightarrow Ca_3(PO_4)(l)$
$Si + O_2(g) \rightarrow SiO_2$
$M + O_2(g) \rightarrow M_xO_y(l)$; $M_xO_y + SiO_2 \rightarrow$ silicates

CO_2 and SO_2 escape as gases. P_2O_5 reacts with CaO(l) to form $Ca_3(PO_4)_2(l)$, which is removed with the basic slag layer. SiO_2 and metal oxides can combine to form other silicates; SiO_2, M_xO_y and complex silicates are all removed with the basic slag layer.

23.73   (a)   The standard reduction potential for $H_2O(l)$ is much greater than that of $Mg^{2+}(aq)(-0.83$ V vs. -2.37 V). In aqueous solution, $H_2O(l)$ would be preferentially reduced and no $Mg(s)$ would be obtained.

        (b) $97,000 \text{ A} \times 24 \text{ hr} \times \dfrac{3600 \text{ s}}{1 \text{ hr}} \times \dfrac{1 \text{ C}}{1 \text{ A} \cdot \text{s}} \times \dfrac{1 \text{ F}}{96,500 \text{ C}} \times \dfrac{1 \text{ mol Mg}}{2 \text{ F}} \times \dfrac{24.31 \text{ g Mg}}{1 \text{ mol Mg}} \times 0.96$

$$= 1.0 \times 10^6 \text{ g Mg} = 1.0 \times 10^3 \text{ kg Mg}$$

23.76   (a)   (See Solution 17.49)

$$Ag_2S(s) \rightleftharpoons 2Ag^+(aq) + S^{2-}(aq) \qquad\qquad K_{sp}$$

$$\underline{2[Ag^+(aq) + 2CN^-(aq) \rightleftharpoons Ag(CN)_2^-] \qquad\qquad K_f^2}$$

$$Ag_2S(s) + 4CN^-(aq) \rightleftharpoons 2Ag(CN)_2^-(aq) + S^{2-}(aq)$$

$$K = K_{sp} \times K_f^2 = [Ag^+]^2[S^{2-}] \times \frac{[Ag(CN)_2^-]^2}{[Ag^+]^2[CN^-]^4} = (6 \times 10^{-51})(1 \times 10^{21})^2 = 6 \times 10^{-9}$$

        (b)   The equilibrium constant for the cyanidation of Ag_2S, 6×10^{-9}, is much less than one and favors the presence of reactants rather than products. The process is not practical.

        (c)

$$AgCl(s) \rightleftharpoons Ag^+(aq) + Cl^-(aq) \qquad\qquad K_{sp}$$

$$\underline{Ag^+(aq) + 2CN^-(aq) \rightleftharpoons Ag(CN)_2^-(aq) \qquad\qquad K_f}$$

$$AgCl(s) + 2CN^-(aq) \rightleftharpoons Ag(CN)_2^-(aq) + Cl^-(aq)$$

$$K = K_{sp} \times K_f = [Ag^+][Cl^-] \times \frac{[Ag(CN)_2^-]}{[Ag^+][CN^-]^2} = (1.8 \times 10^{-10})(1 \times 10^{21}) = 2 \times 10^{11}$$

Since $K \gg 1$ for this process, it is potentially useful for recovering silver from horn silver. However the magnitude of K says nothing about the rate of reaction. The reaction could be slow and require heat, a catalyst or both to be practical.

24 Chemistry of Coordination Compounds

Introduction to Metal Complexes

24.1   (a)   A *metal complex* consists of a central metal ion bonded to a number of surrounding molecules or ions. The number of bonds formed by the central metal ion is the *coordination number*. The surrounding molecules or ions are the *ligands*.

      (b)   A Lewis acid is an electron pair acceptor and a Lewis base is an electron pair donor. All ligands have at least one unshared pair of valence electrons. Metal ions have empty valence orbitals (d, s or p) that can accommodate donated electron pairs. Ligands act as electron pair donors, or Lewis bases, and metal ions act as electron pair acceptors, or Lewis acids, via their empty valence orbitals.

24.3   *Analyze/Plan.* Follow the logic in Sample Exercises 24.1 and 24.2. *Solve*:

      (a)   This compound is electrically neutral, and the NH_3 ligands carry no charge, so the charge on Ni must balance the -2 charge of the 2 Br^- ions. The charge and oxidation state of Ni is +2.

      (b)   Since there are 6 NH_3 molecules in the complex, the likely coordination number is 6. In some cases Br^- acts as a ligand, so the coordination number could be other than 6.

      (c)   Assuming that the 6 NH_3 molecules are the ligands, 2 Br^- ions are not coordinated to the Ni^{2+}, so 2 mol AgBr(s) will precipitate. (If one or both of the Br^- act as a ligand, the mol AgBr(s) would be different.)

24.5   (a)   Coordination number = 4, oxidation number = +2

      (b)   5, +4   (c) 6, +3   (d) 5, +2   (e) 6, +3   (f) 4, +2

24.7   *Analyze/Plan.* Given the formula of a coordination compound, determine the number and kinds of donor atoms. The ligands are enclosed in the square brackets. Decide which atom in the ligand has an unshared electron pair it is likely to donate. *Solve*:

      (a)   4 Cl^- (b) 4 Cl^-, 1 O^{2-} (c) 4 N, 2 Cl^-

      (d)   5 C. In CN^-, both C and N have an unshared electron pair. C is less electronegative and more likely to donate its unshared pair.

(e)   6 O. $C_2O_4^{2-}$ is a bidentate ligand; each ion is bound through 2 O atoms for a total of 6 O donor atoms.

(f)   4 N. en is a bidentate ligand bound through 2 N atoms.

Polydendate ligands; Nomenclature

24.9   (a)   A monodendate ligand binds to a metal in through one atom, a bidendate ligand binds through two atoms.

        (b)   If a bidentate ligand occupies two coordination sites, three bidentate ligands fill the coordination sphere of a six-coordinate complex.

        (c)   A tridentate ligand has at least three atoms with unshared electron pairs in the correct orientation to simultanously bind one or more metal ions.

24.11   *Analyze/Plan*. Given the formula of a coordination compound, determine the number of coordination sites occupied by the polydentate ligand. The coordination number of the complexes is either 4 or 6. Note the number of monodentate ligands and determine the number of coordination sites occupied by the polydentate ligands. *Solve*:

        (a) *ortho*-phenanthroline, *o*-phen, is bidentate

        (b) oxalate, $C_2O_4^{2-}$, is bidentate

        (c) ethylenediaminetetraacetate, EDTA, is pentadentate

        (d) ethylenediamine, en, is bidentate

24.13   (a)   The term *chelate effect* means there is a special stability associated with formation of a metal complex containing a polydentate (chelate) ligand relative to a complex containing only monodentate ligands.

        (b)   When a single chelating ligand replaces two or more monodendate ligands, the number of free molecules in the system increases and the entropy of the system increases. Chemical reactions with $+\Delta S$ tend to be spontaneous, have negative ΔG, and large positive values of K_{eq}.

        (c)   Polydentate ligands can be used to bind metal ions and prevent them from undergoing unwanted chemical reactions without removing them from solution. The polydentate ligand thus hides or *sequesters* the metal ion.

24.15   *Analyze/Plan*. Given the name of a coordination compound, write the chemical formula. Refer to Table 24.2 to find ligand formulas. Place the metal complex (metal ion + ligands) inside square brackets and the counter ion (if there is one) outside the brackets. *Solve*:

        (a) $[Cr(NH_3)_6](NO_3)_3$ (b) $[Co(NH_3)_4CO_3]_2SO_4$ (c) $[Pt(en)_2Cl_2]Br_2$

        (d) $K[V(H_2O)_2Br_4]$ (e) $[Zn(en)_2][HgI_4]$

24.17 Analyze/Plan. Follow the logic in Sample Exercise 24.4, paying attention to naming rules in Section 24.3. *Solve*:

(a)   tetraamminedichlororhodium(III) chloride

(b)   potassium hexachlorotitanate(IV)

(c)   tetrachlorooxomolybdenum(VI)

(d)   tetraaqua(oxalato)platinum(IV) bromide

Isomerism

24.19 *Analyze/Plan.* Consider the definitions of the various types of isomerism, and which of the complexes could exhibit isomerism of the specified type. *Solve*:

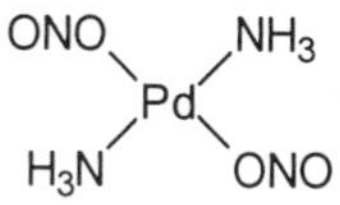

(a)

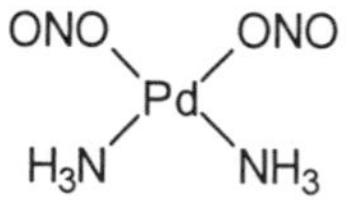

(b) $[Pd(NH_3)_2(ONO)_2]$, $[Pd(NH_3)_2(NO_2)_2]$

(c)

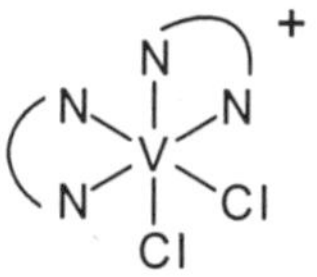

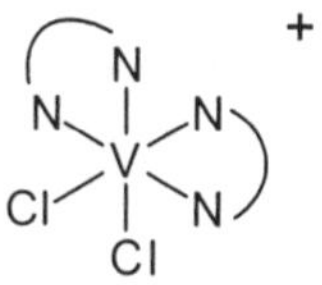

(d) $[Co(NH_3)_4Br_2]Cl$, $[Co(NH_3)_4BrCl]Br$

24.21 Yes. A tetrahedral complex of the form MA_2B_2 would have neither structural nor stereoisomers. For a tetrahedral complex, no differences in connectivity are possible for a single central atom, so the terms *cis* and *trans* do not apply. No optical isomers with tetrahedral geometry are possible because M is not bound to four different groups. The complex must be square planar with *cis* and *trans* geometric isomers.

24.23 *Analyze/Plan.* Follow the logic in Sample Exercises 24.5 and 24.6. *Solve*:

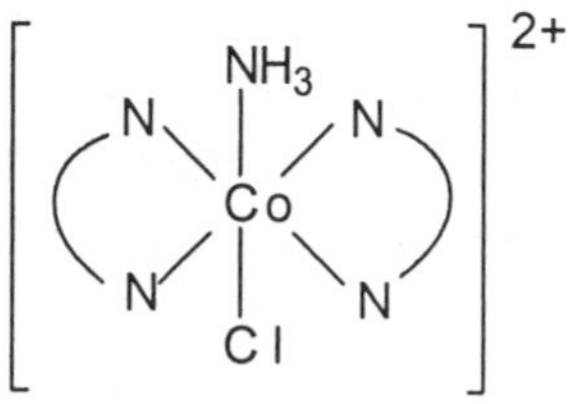

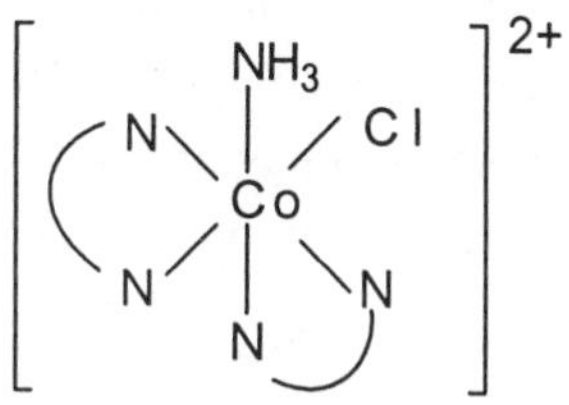

The *cis* isomer is chiral.

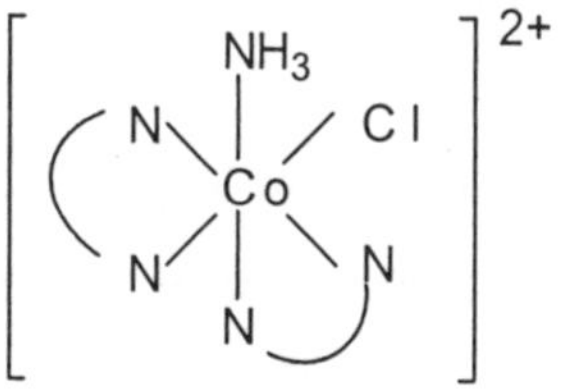

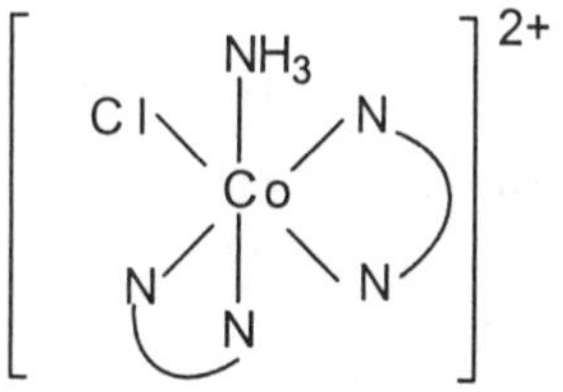

24.25 *Analyze/Plan.* Follow the logic in Sample Exercise 24.5 and 24.6. *Solve:*

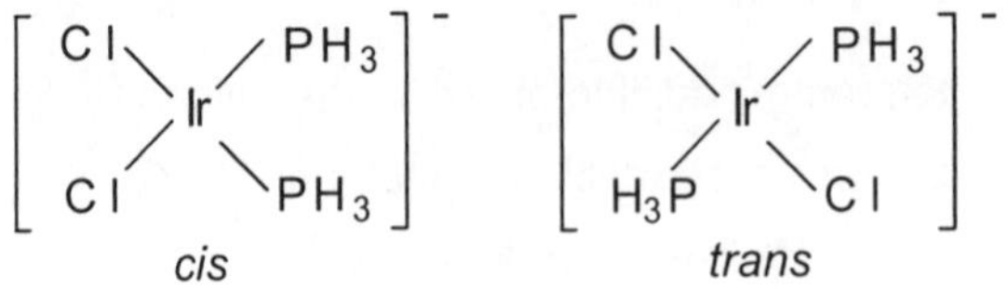

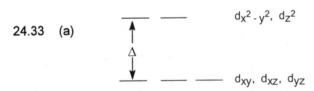

cis   *trans*

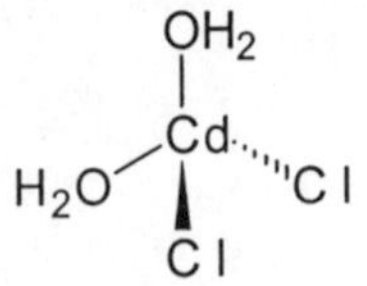

(c)

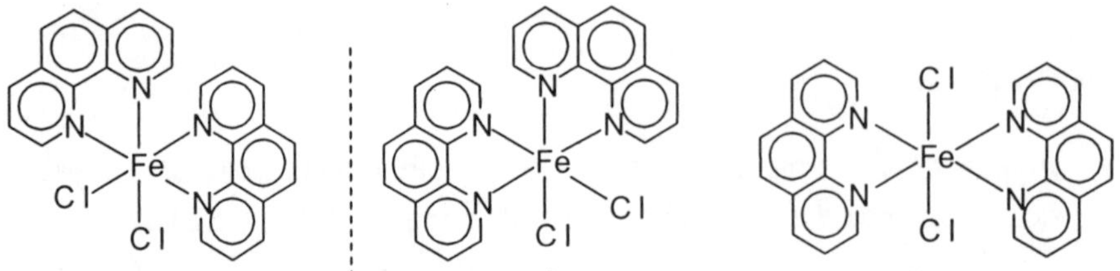

cis   *cis*   *trans*

optical isomers

(The three isomeric complex ions in part (c) each have a 1+ charge.)

Color, Magnetism; Crystal-Field Theory

24.27 (a)   Visible light has wavelengths between 400 and 700 nm.

(b)   *Complementary* colors are opposite each other on a color wheel such as Figure 24.25.

(c)   A colored metal complex absorbs visible light of its complementary color. For example, a red complex absorbs green light.

24.29 *Analyze/Plan.* A compound that absorbs visible light of one color appears as the complementary color. *Solve:*

Blue to blue-violet (Figure 24.25)

24.31 Most of the electrostatic interaction between a metal ion and a ligand is the attractive interaction between a positively charged metal cation and the full negative charge of an anionic ligand or the partial negative charge of a polar covalent ligand. Whether the interaction is ion-ion or ion-dipole, the ligand is strongly attracted to the metal center and can be modeled as a point negative charge.

24.33 (a)

$$d_{x^2-y^2},\ d_{z^2}$$

Δ

$$d_{xy},\ d_{xz},\ d_{yz}$$

(b)   The magnitude of Δ and the energy of the d-d transition for a d^1 complex are equal.

(c)   The spectrochemical series is an ordering of ligands according to their ability to increase the energy gap Δ.

24.35 *Analyze/Plan.* Consider the relationship between the color of a complex, the wavelength of absorbed light and the position of a ligand in the spectrochemical series. *Solve:*

Cyanide is a strong field ligand. The d-d electronic transitions occur at relatively high energy, because Δ is large. A yellow color corresponds to absorption of a photon in the violet region of the visible spectrum, between 430 and 400 nm. H_2O is a weaker field ligand than CN^-. The blue or green colors of aqua complexes correspond to absorptions in the region of 620 nm. Clearly, this is a region of lower energy photons than those with characteristic wavelengths in the 430 to 400 nm region. These are very general and imprecise comparisons. Other factors are involved, including whether the complex is high spin or low spin.

24.37 *Analyze/Plan.* Determine the charge on the metal ion, subtract it from the row number (3-12) of the transition metal, and the remainder is the number of d-electrons. *Solve:*

(a) Ru^{3+}, d^5 (b) Cu^{2+}, d^9 (c) Co^{3+}, d^6 (d) Mo^{5+}, d^1 (e) Re^{3+}, d^4

24.39 *Analyze/Plan.* Follow the logic in Sample Exercise 24.9. *Solve:*

(a)   Mn: $[Ar]4s^2 3d^5$ (b) Ru: $[Kr]5s^1 4d^7$ (c) Rh: $[Kr]5s^1 4d^8$
       Mn^{3+}: $[Ar]3d^4$ Ru^{3+}: $[Kr]4d^5$ Rh^{3+}: $[Kr]4d^6$

2 unpaired electrons   1 unpaired electron   0 unpaired electrons

24.41 *Analyze/Plan.* All complexes in this exercise are six-coordinate octahedral. Use the definitions of high-spin and low-spin along with the orbital diagram from Sample Exercise 24.9 to place electrons for the various complexes. *Solve:*

(a) d^4, high spin   (b) d^5, high spin   (c) d^6, low spin

(d) d^5, low spin   (e) d^3 (f) d^8

24.43 *Analyze/Plan.* Follow the ideas but reverse the logic in Sample Exercise 24.9. *Solve:*

high spin

Additional Exercises

24.45 (a) $[Ni(en)_2Cl_2]$; $[Ni(en)_2(H_2O)_2]Cl_2$

(b) $K_2[Ni(CN)_4]$; $[Zn(H_2O)_4](NO_3)_2$; $[Cu(NH_3)_4]SO_4$

(c) $[CoF_6]^{3-}$, high spin; $[Co(NH_3)_6]^{3+}$ or $[Co(CN)_6]^{3-}$, low spin

(d) thiocyanate, SCN^- or NCS^-; nitrite, NO_2^- or ONO^-

(e) $[Co(en)_2Cl_2]Cl$; see Exercise 24.25(c) for another example.

(f) $[Co(en)_3]Cl_3$, $K_3[Fe(ox)_3]$

24.48 (a)

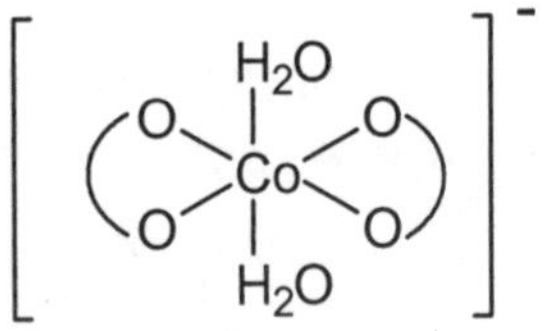

octahedral

(b)

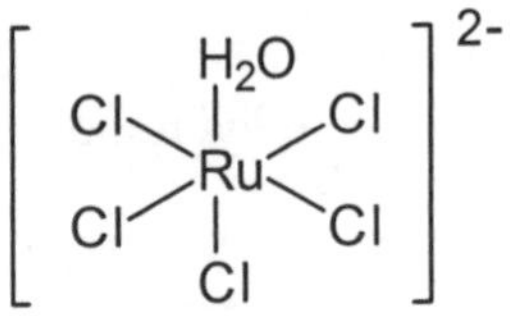

octahedral

(c)

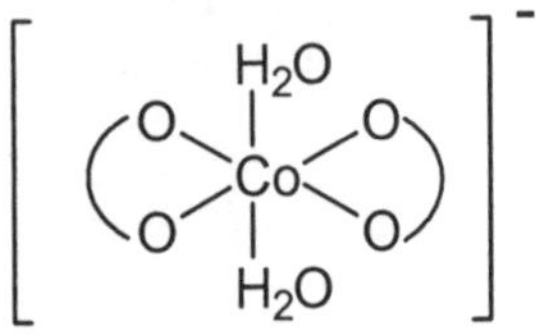

octahedral

(d)

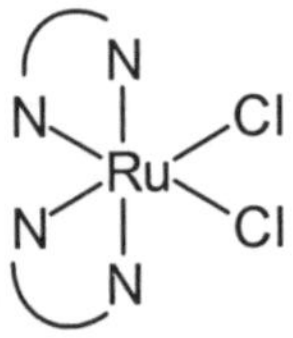

octahdedral

24.51 (a) In a square planar complex such as $[Pt(en)Cl_2]$, if one pair of ligands is *trans*, the remaining two coordination sites are also *trans* to each other. Ethylenediamine is a relatively short bidentate ligand that cannot occupy *trans* coordination sites, so the *trans* isomer is unknown.

(b) A polydentate ligand such as EDTA necessarily occupies *trans* positions in an octahedral complex. The minimum steric requirement for a bidentate ligand is a medium-length chain between the two coordinating atoms that will occupy the *trans* positions. In terms of reaction rate theory, it is unlikely that a flexible bidentate ligand will be in exactly the right orientation to coordinate *trans*. The polydentate ligand has a much better chance of occupying *trans* positions, because it locks the metal ion in place with multiple coordination sites (and shields the metal ion from competing ligands present in the solution).

24.54 (a) $AgCl(s) + 2NH_3(aq) \rightarrow [Ag(NH_3)_2]^+(aq) + Cl^-(aq)$

(b) $[Cr(en)_2Cl_2]Cl(aq) + 2H_2O(l) \rightarrow [Cr(en_2)(H_2O)_2]^{3+}(aq) + 3Cl^-(aq)$

　　green　　　　　　　　　　　　brown-orange

$3Ag^+(aq) + 3Cl^-(aq) \rightarrow 3AgCl(s)$

$[Cr(en)_2(H_2O)_2]^{3+}$ and $3NO_3^-$ are spectator ions in the second reaction.

(c) $Zn(NO_3)_2(aq) + 2NaOH(aq) \rightarrow Zn(OH)_2(s) + 2NaNO_3(aq)$

         $Zn(OH)_2(s) + 2NaOH(aq) \rightarrow [Zn(OH_3)_4]^{2-}(aq) + 2Na^+(aq)$

(d) $Co^{2+}(aq) + 4Cl^-(aq) \rightarrow [CoCl_4]^{2-}(aq)$

24.57   (a) left shoe   (c) wood screw   (e) a typical golf club

24.60   According to the spectrochemical series, the order of increasing Δ for the ligands is $Cl^- < H_2O$ < NH_3. (The tetrahedral Cl^- complex will have an even smaller Δ than an octahedral one.) The smaller the value of Δ, the longer the wavelength of visible light absorbed. The color of light absorbed is the complement of the observed color. A blue complex absorbs orange light (580-650 nm), a pink complex absorbs green light (490-560 nm) and a yellow complex absorbs violet light (400-430 nm). Since $[CoCl_4]^{2-}$ absorbs the longest wavelength, it appears blue. $[Co(H_2O)_6]^{2+}$ absorbs green and appears pink, and $[Co(NH_3)_6]^{3+}$ absorbs violet and appears yellow.

24.63   (a) $[FeF_6]^{4-}$. Both complexes contain the same metal ion, Fe^{2+}; F^- is a weak-field ligand that imposes a smaller Δ and longer λ for the complex ion.

         (b) $[V(H_2O)_6]^{2+}$. Both complexes contain the same ligand, H_2O. V^{2+} has a lower charge, so the interaction with the ligand will produce a weaker field, a smaller Δ and a longer absorbed wavelength.

         (c) $[CoCl_4]^{2-}$. Both complexes contain the same metal ion, Co^{2+}; Cl^- is a weak-field ligand that imposes a smaller Δ and a longer λ for the complex ion.

24.66   (a)

         (b)   sodium dicarbonyltetracyanoferrate(II)

         (c)   +2, 6 d electrons

         (d)   We expect the complex to be low spin. Cyanide (and carbonyl) are high on the spectrochemical series, which means the complex will have a large Δ splitting characteristic of low spin complexes.

Integrative Exercises

24.71   (a)   Both compounds have the same general formulation, so Co is in the same (+3) oxidation state in both complexes.

(b)   Cobalt(III) complexes are generally inert; that is, they do not rapidly exchange ligands inside the coordination sphere. Therefore, the ions that form precipitates in these two cases are probably outside the coordination sphere. The dark violet compound A forms a precipitate with $BaCl_2(aq)$ but not $AgNO_3(aq)$, so it has SO_4^{2-} outside the coordination sphere and coordinated Br^-, $[Co(NH_3)_5Br]SO_4$. The red-violet compound B forms a precipitate with $AgNO_3(aq)$ but not $BaCl_2(aq)$ so it has Br^- outside the coordination sphere and coordinated SO_4^{2-}, $[Co(NH_3)_5SO_4]Br$.

Compound A, dark violet   Compound B, red-violet

(c)   Compounds A and B have the same formula but different properties (color, chemical reactivity), so they are isomers. They vary by which ion is inside the coordination sphere, so they are *coordination sphere isomers*.

(d)   Compound A is an ionic sulfate and compound B is an ionic bromide, so both are strong electrolytes. According to the solubility rules in Table 4.1, both should be water-soluble.

24.74   Determine the empirical formula of the complex, assuming the remaining mass is due to oxygen, and a 100 g sample.

$$10.0 \text{ g Mn} \times \frac{1 \text{ mol Mn}}{54.94 \text{ g Mn}} = 0.1820 \text{ mol Mn}; \ 0.182 / 0.182 = 1$$

$$28.6 \text{ g K} \times \frac{1 \text{ mol K}}{39.10 \text{ g K}} = 0.7315 \text{ mol K}; \ 0.732 / 0.182 = 4$$

$$8.8 \text{ g C} \times \frac{1 \text{ mol C}}{12.0 \text{ g C}} = 0.7327 \text{ mol C}; \ 0.733 / 0.182 = 4$$

$$29.2 \text{ g Br} \times \frac{1 \text{ mol Br}}{79.904 \text{ g Br}} = 0.3654 \text{ mol Br}; \ 0.365 / 0.182 = 2$$

$$23.4 \text{ g O} \times \frac{1 \text{ mol O}}{16.00 \text{ g O}} = 1.463 \text{ mol O}; \ 1.46 / 0.182 = 8$$

There are 2 C and 4 O per oxalate ion, for a total of two oxalate ligands in the complex. To match the conductivity of $K_4[Fe(CN)_6]$, the oxalate and bromide ions must be in the coordination sphere of the complex anion. Thus, the compound is $K_4[Mn(ox)_2Br_2]$.

24.76 Calculate the concentration of Mg^{2+} alone, and then the concentration of Ca^{2+} by difference.

M × L = mol

$$\frac{0.0104 \text{ mol EDTA}}{1 \text{ L}} \times 0.0187 \text{L} \times \frac{1 \text{ mol Mg}^{2+}}{1 \text{ mol EDTA}} \times \frac{24.31 \text{ g Mg}^{2+}}{1 \text{ mol Mg}^{2+}} \times \frac{1000 \text{ mg}}{\text{g}}$$

$$\times \frac{1}{0.100 \text{ L H}_2\text{O}} = 47.28 = 47.3 \text{ mg Mg}^{2+}/\text{L}$$

$0.0104 \, M$ EDTA × 0.0315 L = mol ($Ca^{2+} + Mg^{2+}$)

$0.0104 \, M$ EDTA × 0.0187 L = mol Mg^{2+}

$0.0104 \, M$ EDTA × 0.0128 L = mol Ca^{2+}

$$0.0104 \, M \text{ EDTA} \times 0.0128 \text{ L} \times \frac{1 \text{ mol Ca}^{2+}}{1 \text{ mol EDTA}} \times \frac{40.08 \text{ g Ca}^{2+}}{1 \text{ mol Ca}^{2+}} \times \frac{1000 \text{ mg}}{\text{g}} \times \frac{1}{0.100 \text{ L H}_2\text{O}}$$

$$= 53.35 = 53.4 \text{ mg Ca}^{2+}/\text{L}$$

25 The Chemistry of Life: Organic and Biological Chemistry

Introduction to Organic Compounds; Hydrocarbons

25.1 *Analyze/Plan.* Given a condensed structural formula, determine the bond angles and hybridization about each carbon atom in the molecule. Visualize the number of electron domains about each carbon. State the bond angle and hybridization based on electron domain geometry.

Solve:

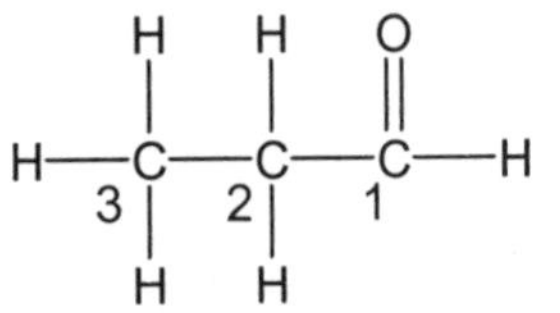

C2 and C3 both have tetrahedral electron domain geometry, $109°$ bond angles and sp^3 hybridization. C1 has trigonal planar electron domain geometry, $120°$ bond angles and sp^2 hybridization.

25.3 Carbon (of course), hydrogen, oxygen, nitrogen, sulfur, phosphorus, chlorine (and other halogens). According to periodic trends and Figure 8.6, oxygen, nitrogen and chlorine are more electronegative than carbon. Sulfur has the same electronegativity as carbon.

25.5 (a) A *straight-chain hydrocarbon* has all carbon atoms connected in a continuous chain; no carbon atom is bound to more than two other carbon atoms. A *branched-chain hydrocarbon* has a branch; at least one carbon atom is bound to three or more carbon atoms.

(b) An *alkane* is a complete molecule composed of carbon and hydrogen in which all bonds are single (sigma) bonds. An *alkyl group* is a substituent formed by removing a hydrogen atom from an alkane.

(c) Alkanes are said to be *saturated* because they contain only single bonds. Multiple bonds that enable addition of H_2 or other substances are absent. The bonding capacity of each carbon atom is fulfilled with single bonds to C or H.

25.7 *Analyze/Plan.* Consider the definition of the stated classification and apply it to a compound containing 5 C atoms. *Solve:*

(a) $CH_3CH_2CH_2CH_2CH_3$, C_5H_{12} (b)

C_5H_{10}

(c) $CH_2=CHCH_2CH_2CH_3$, C_5H_{10} (d) $HC\equiv CCH_2CH_2CH_3$, C_5H_8

saturated: (a), (b);   unsaturated: (c), (d)

25.9   *Analyze/Plan.* The general formula of an alkane is C_nH_{2n+2}. For an alkene, with 2 fewer H atoms, the general formula is C_nH_{2n}. *Solve:*

A dialkene has one more C=C and thus two fewer H atoms than an alkene. The general formula is C_nH_{2n-2} .

25.11   *Analyze/Plan.* Follow the logic in Sample Exercise 25.3. *Solve:*

CH_3—CH_2—CH_2—CH=CH_2
pentene

CH_3—CH_2—CH=CH—CH_3
2-pentene

CH_2=CH—$\overset{\overset{\displaystyle CH_3}{|}}{CH}$—$CH_3$
3-methyl-1-butene

CH_2=$\overset{\overset{\displaystyle CH_3}{|}}{C}$—$CH_2$—$CH_3$
2-methyl-1-butene

CH_3—$\overset{\overset{\displaystyle CH_3}{|}}{C}$=$CH$—$CH_3$
2-methyl-2-butene

25.13   *Analyze/Plan.* Follow the logic in Sample Exercise 25.1 to name each compound. Decide which structures are the same compound. *Solve:*

(a) 2,2,4-trimethylpentane   (b) 3-ethyl-2-methylpentane

(c) 2,3,4-trimethylpentane   (d) 2,3,4-trimethylpentane

(c) and (d) are the same molecule

25.15   (a) 109°   (b) 120°   (c) 180°

25.17   *Analyze/Plan.* Follow the rules for naming alkanes given in Section 25.3 and illustrated in Sample Exercise 25.1. *Solve:*

(a)   2-methylhexane   (b) 4-ethyl-2,4-dimethyldecane

(c) 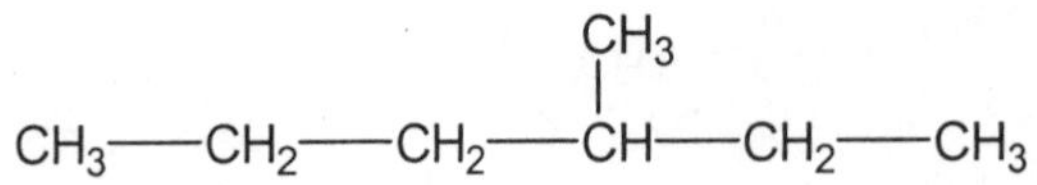 CH_3—CH_2—CH_2—$\overset{\overset{\textstyle CH_3}{|}}{CH}$—$CH_2$—$CH_3$

(d) 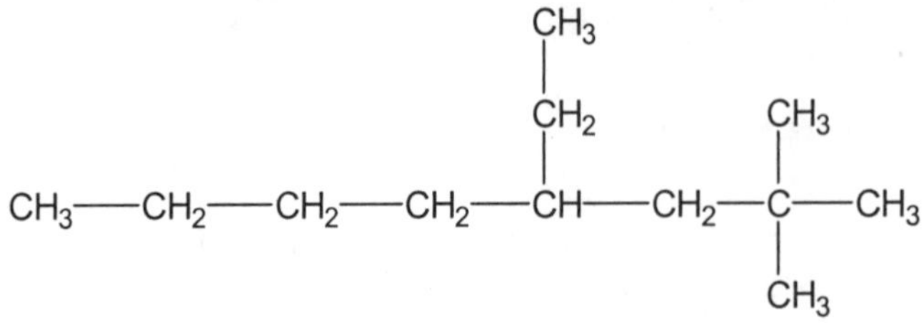 CH_3—CH_2—CH_2—CH_2—$\overset{\overset{\textstyle CH_2}{|}\overset{\textstyle CH_3}{|}}{CH}$—$CH_2$—$\overset{\overset{\textstyle CH_3}{|}}{\underset{\underset{\textstyle CH_3}{|}}{C}}$—$CH_3$

(e)

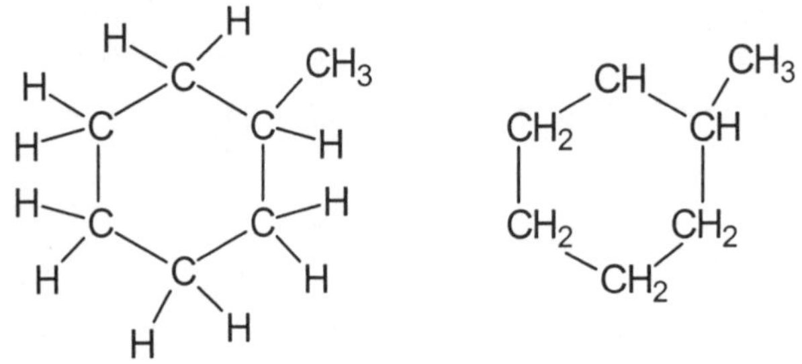

25.19 *Analyze/Plan.* Follow the logic in Sample Exercises 25.1 and 25.4. *Solve:*

(a) 2,3-dimethylheptane   (b) *cis*-6-methyl-3-octene   (c) *para*-dibromobenzene

(d) 4,4-dimethyl-1-hexyne   (e) methylcyclobutane

25.21 Each doubly bound carbon atom in an alkene has two unique sites for substitution. These sites cannot be interconverted because rotation about the double bond is restricted; geometric isomerism results. In an alkane, carbon forms only single bonds, so the three remaining sites are interchangeable by rotation about the single bond. Although there is also restricted rotation around the triple bond of an alkyne, there is only one additional bonding site on a triply bound carbon, so no isomerism results.

25.23 *Analyze/Plan.* In order for geometrical isomerism to be possible, the molecule must be an alkene with two different groups bound to each of the alkene C atoms.

(a) 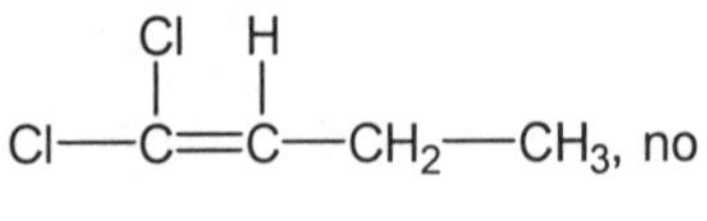 Cl—$\overset{\overset{\textstyle Cl}{|}}{C}$=$\overset{\overset{\textstyle H}{|}}{C}$—$CH_2$—$CH_3$, no

(b)

(c)   no, not an alkene

(d)   no, not an alkene

25.25   Assuming that each component retains its effective octane number in the mixture (and this isn't always the case), we obtain: octane number = 0.35(0) + 0.65(100) = 65.

Reactions of Hydrocarbons

25.27   (a)   An addition reaction is the addition of some reagent to the two atoms that form a multiple bond. In a substitution reaction, one atom or group of atoms replaces (substitutes for) another atom or group of atoms. In an addition reaction, two atoms and a multiple bond on the target molecule are altered; in a substitution reaction, the environment of one atom in the target molecule changes. Alkenes typically undergo addition, while aromatic hydrocarbons usually undergo substitution.

(b)   *Plan.* consider the general form of addition across a double bond. The π bond is broken and one new substituent (in this case two Br atoms) adds to each of the C atoms involved in the π bond.   *Solve:*

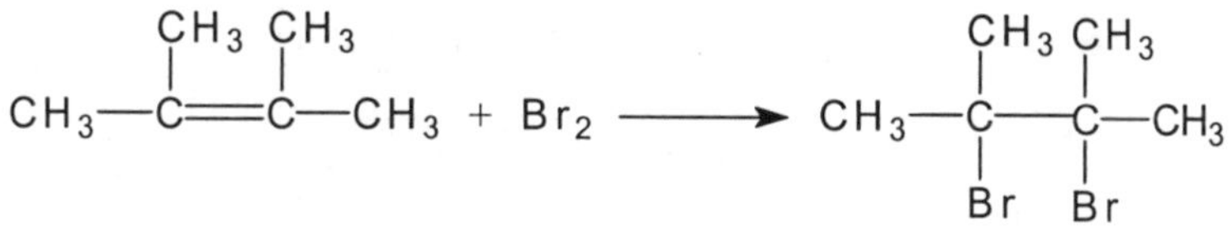

(c)   *Plan.* Consider the general form of a substitution reaction. A Cl atom will replace one of the H atoms on the benzene ring. In the target molecule, all H atoms are equivalent, so no choice of position is required.   *Solve:*

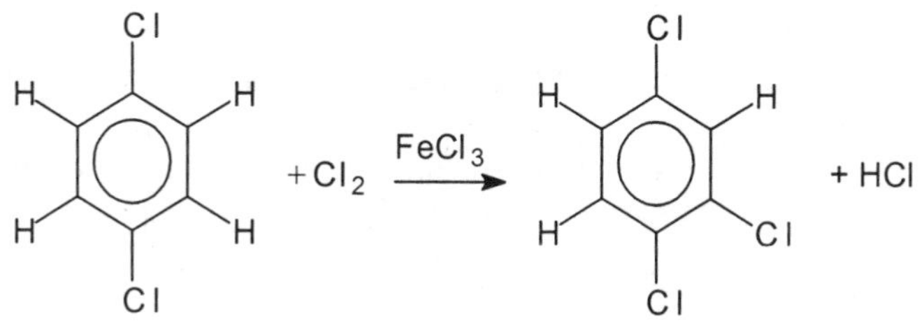

25.29   (a)   *Plan.* Consider the structures of cyclopropane, cyclopentane and cyclohexane. *Solve:*

The small 60° C-C-C angles in the cyclopropane ring cause strain that provides a driving force for reactions that result in ring-opening. There is no comparable strain in the five- or six-membered rings.

(b)   *Plan.* First form an alkyl halide: $C_2H_4(g) + HBr(g) \rightarrow CH_3CH_2Br(l)$; then carry out a Friedel-Crafts reaction. *Solve:*

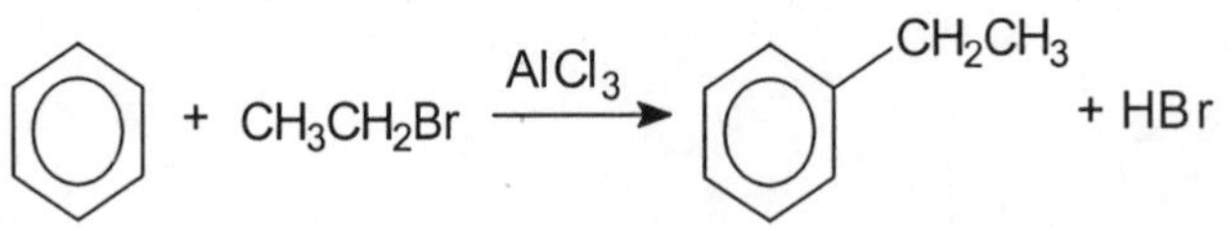

25.31 The partially positive end of the hydrogen halide, $\overset{\delta^+}{H}\!-\!\overset{\delta^-}{X}$, is attached to the π electron cloud of the alkene, cyclohexene. The electrons that formed the π bond in cyclohexene form a sigma bond to the H atom of HX, leaving a halide ion, X^-. The intermediate is a carbocation; one of the C atoms formerly involved in the π bond is now bound to a second H atom. The other C atom formerly involved in the π bond carries a full positive charge and forms only three sigma bonds, two to adjacent C atoms and one to H.

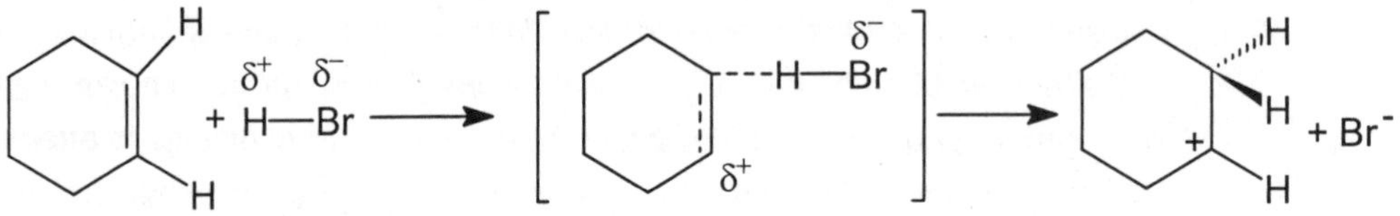

25.33 *Analyze/Plan.* Both combustion reactions produce CO_2 and H_2O:

$C_3H_6(g) + 9/2\ O_2(g) \rightarrow 3CO_2(g) + 3H_2O(l)$

$C_5H_{10}(g) + 15/2\ O_2(g) \rightarrow 5CO_2(g) + 5H_2O(l)$

Thus, we can calculate the ΔH_{comb} / CH_2 group for each compound. *Solve:*

$$\frac{\Delta H_{comb}}{CH_2\ \text{group}} = \frac{2089\ \text{kJ/mol}\ C_3H_6}{3\ CH_2\ \text{groups}} = \frac{696.3\ \text{kJ}}{\text{mol}\ CH_2}; \quad \frac{3317\ \text{kJ/mol}\ C_5H_{10}}{5\ CH_2\ \text{groups}} = 663.4\ \text{kJ/mol}\ CH_2$$

$\Delta H_{comb}/CH_2$ group for cyclopropane is greater because C_3H_6 contains a strained ring. When combustion occurs, the strain is relieved and the stored energy is released during the reaction.

Functional Groups and Chirality

25.35 (a) ketone   (b) carboxylic acid   (c) alcohol   (d) ester   (e) amide   (f) amine

25.37 *Analyze/Plan.* Given the name of a molecule, write the structural formula of an isomer that contains a specified functional group. Consider the definition of isomer, write the molecular formula of the given molecule, draw the structural formula of a molecule with the same formula that contains the specified functional group. *Solve:*

(a)   The formula of acetone is C_3H_6O. An aldehyde contains the group $-\overset{\displaystyle O}{\underset{}{C}}\!\diagup^{\!\!O}_{\!\!H}$

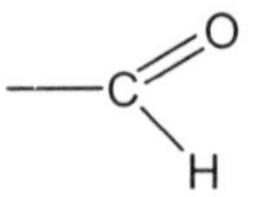

An aldehyde that is an isomer of acetone is propionaldehyde (or propanal),

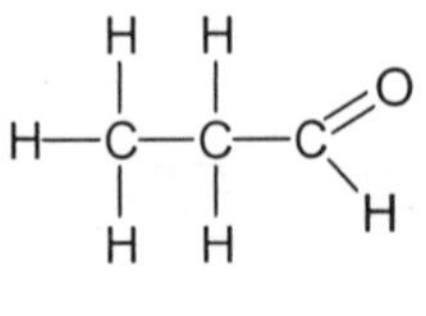

(b)   The formula of 1-propanol is C_3H_8O. An ether contains the group –O–. An ether that is an isomer of 1-propanol is:

ethylmethyl ether,

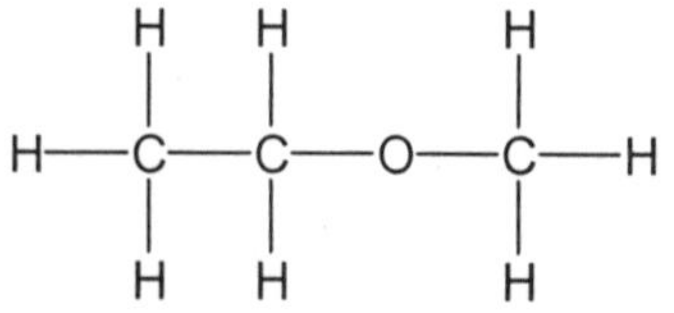

$$H-\overset{\overset{\displaystyle H}{|}}{\underset{\underset{\displaystyle H}{|}}{C}}-\overset{\overset{\displaystyle H}{|}}{\underset{\underset{\displaystyle H}{|}}{C}}-O-\overset{\overset{\displaystyle H}{|}}{\underset{\underset{\displaystyle H}{|}}{C}}-H$$

25.39 *Analyze/Plan.* Count the number of C atoms in each chain, including the carboxyl C atom. Name the chain and the acid. *Solve*:

(a)   methanoic acid   (b) butanoic acid   (c) 3-methylpentanoic acid

25.41 *Analyze/Plan.* In a condensation reaction between an alcohol and a carboxylic acid, the alcohol loses its –OH hydrogen atom and the acid loses its –OH group. The alkyl group from the acid is attached to the carbonyl group and the alkyl group from alcohol is attached to the ether oxygen of the ester. The name of the ester is the alkyl group from the alcohol plus the alkyl group from the acid plus the suffix *-oate*. *Solve*:

(a) $CH_3CH_2O-\overset{\overset{\displaystyle O}{\|}}{C}-$ (benzene ring)

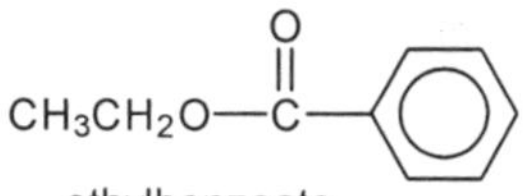

ethylbenzoate

(b) $CH_3\overset{\overset{\displaystyle H}{|}}{N}-\overset{\overset{\displaystyle O}{\|}}{C}CH_3$

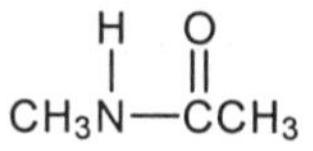

N-methylethanamide
or N-methylacetamide

(c) (benzene ring)$-O-\overset{\overset{\displaystyle O}{\|}}{C}CH_3$

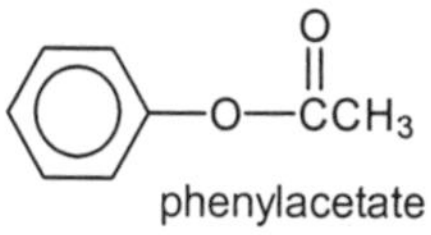

phenylacetate

25.43 *Analyze/Plan.* Follow the logic in Sample Exercise 25.6. *Solve*:

(a) $CH_3CH_2\overset{\overset{\displaystyle O}{\|}}{C}-O-CH_3 + NaOH \longrightarrow \left[CH_3CH_2C\!\!\begin{smallmatrix} O \\ \\ O \end{smallmatrix} \right]^- + Na^+ + CH_3OH$

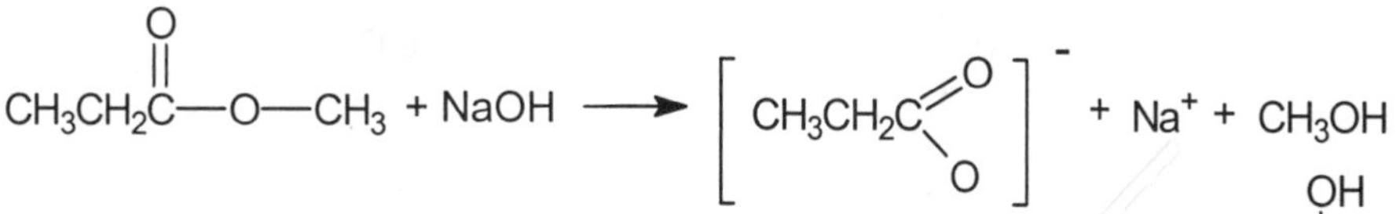

(b) $CH_3\overset{\overset{\displaystyle O}{\|}}{C}-O-$(benzene ring)$ + NaOH \longrightarrow \left[CH_3C\!\!\begin{smallmatrix} O \\ \\ O \end{smallmatrix} \right]^- + Na^+ +$ (benzene ring)$-OH$

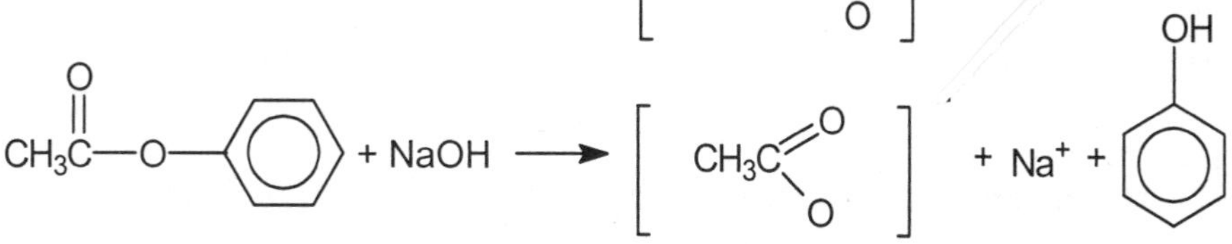

25.45 *Analyze/Plan.* Follow the logic in Sample Exercise 25.2, incorporating functional group information from Table 25.4. *Solve*:

(a) $CH_3CH_2\overset{\overset{\displaystyle OH}{|}}{C}HCH_3$ (b) $HOCH_2CH_2OH$ (c) $H-\overset{\overset{\displaystyle O}{\|}}{C}-OCH_3$

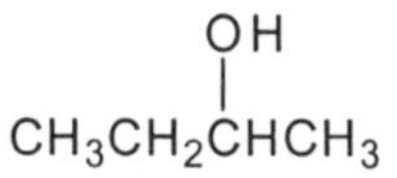

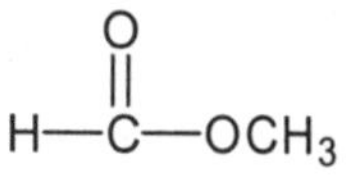

(d) $CH_3CH_2\overset{\overset{\displaystyle O}{\|}}{C}CH_2CH_3$ (e) $CH_3CH_2OCH_2CH_3$

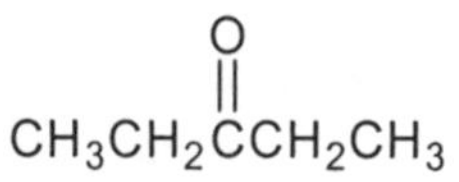

25.47   *Analyze/Plan.* Reverse the rules for naming alkanes and haloalkanes; draw the structures. That is, draw the carbon chain indicated by the root name, place substituents, fill remaining positions with H atoms. Each C atom attached to four different groups is chiral. *Solve*:

(a)

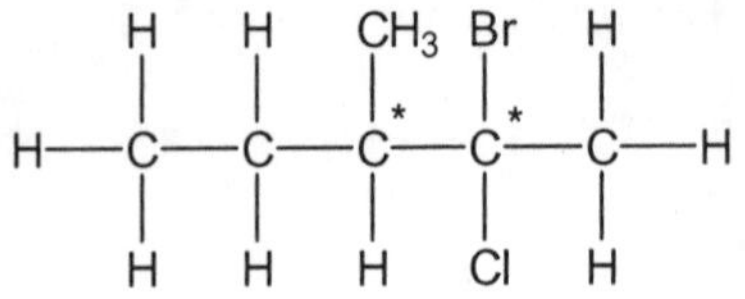

* chiral C atoms

C2 is obviously attached to four different groups. C3 is chiral because the substituents on C2 render the C1-C2 group different than the C4-C5 group.

(b)

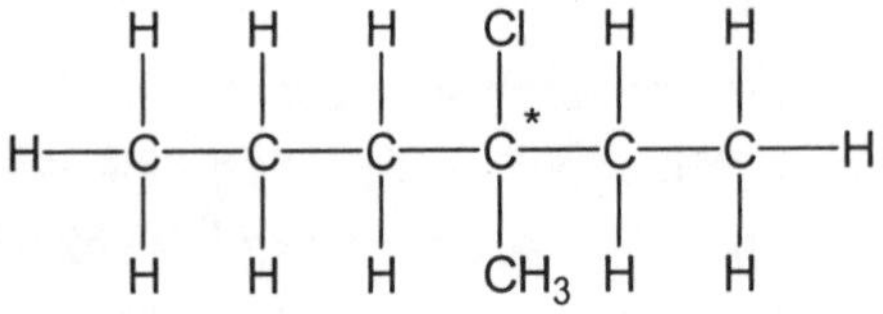

Yes, the molecule has optical isomers. The chiral carbon atom is attached to chloro, methyl, ethyl and propyl groups. [If the root was a 5-carbon chain, the molecule would not have optical isomers because two of the groups would be ethyl groups.]

Proteins

25.49   (a)   An α-amino acid contains an NH_2 group attached to the carbon that is bound to the carbon of the carboxylic acid function.

(b)   In forming a protein, amino acids undergo a condensation reaction between the amino group and carboxylic acid:

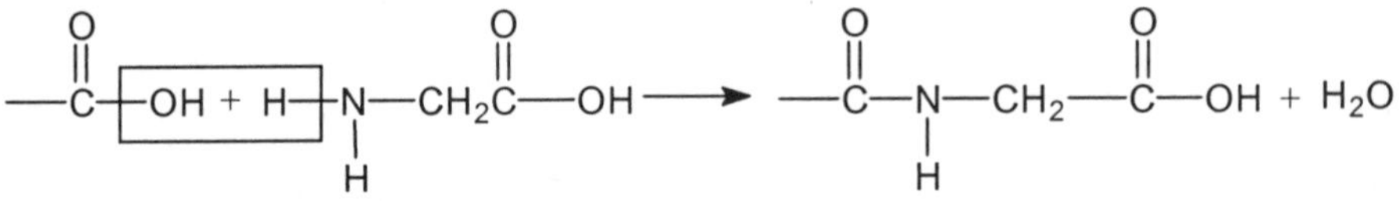

25.51   *Analyze/Plan.* Either peptide can have the terminal carboxyl group or the terminal amino group. *Solve*:

Two dipeptides are possible:

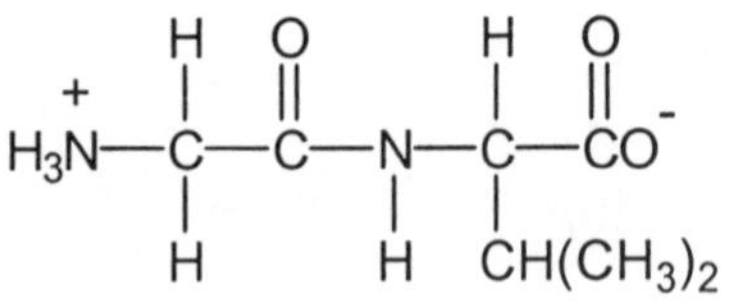

and

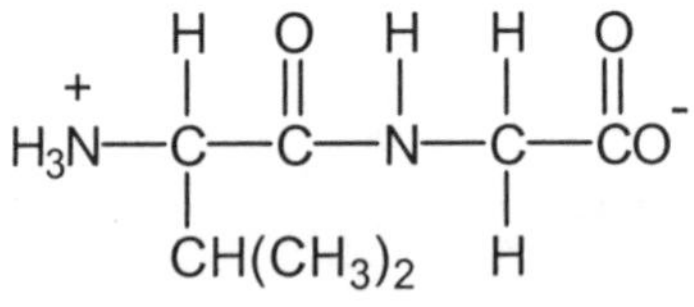

glycylvaline   valylglycine

25.53 *Analyze/Plan.* Follow the logic in Sample Exercise 25.7. *Solve:*

(a)

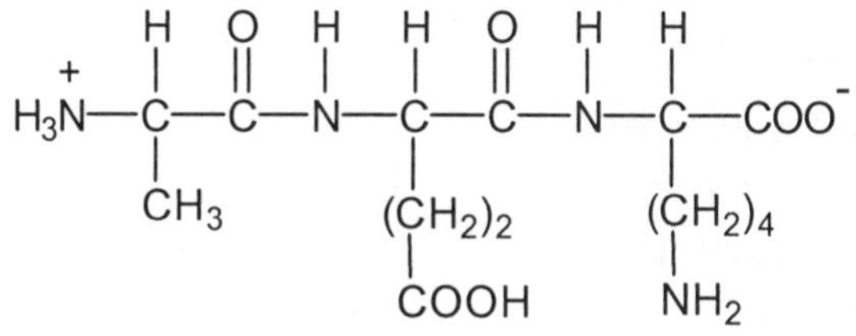

(b) Eight: Ser-Ser-Ser; Ser-Ser-Phe; Ser-Phe-Ser; Phe-Ser-Ser; Ser-Phe-Phe;
Phe-Ser-Phe; Phe-Phe-Ser; Phe-Phe-Phe

25.55 The *primary structure* of a protein refers to the sequence of amino acids in the chain. Along any particular section of the protein chain the configuration may be helical, or it may be an open chain, or arranged in some other way. This is called the *secondary structure*. The overall shape of the protein molecule is determined by the way the segments of the protein chain fold together, or pack. The interactions which determine the overall shape are referred to as the *tertiary structure*.

Carbohydrates

25.57 (a) Carbohydrates, or sugars, are composed of carbon, hydrogen and oxygen. From a chemical viewpoint, they are polyhydroxyaldehydes or ketones. Carbohydrates are primarily derived from plants and are a major food source for animals.

(b) A monosaccharide is a simple sugar molecule that cannot be decomposed into smaller sugar molecules by (acid) hydrolysis.

(c) A disaccharide is a carbohydrate composed of two simple sugar units. Hydrolysis breaks the disaccharides into two monosaccharides.

25.59 (a) In the linear form of galactose, the aldehydic carbon is C1. Carbon atoms 2, 3, 4 and 5 are chiral because they each carry four different groups. Carbon 6 is not chiral because it contains two H atoms.

(b) The structure is best deduced by comparing galactose with glucose, and inverting the configurations at the appropriate carbon atoms. Recall from Solution 25.58 that both the β-form (shown here) and the α-form (OH on carbon 1 on the opposite side of ring as the CH_2OH on carbon 5) are possible.

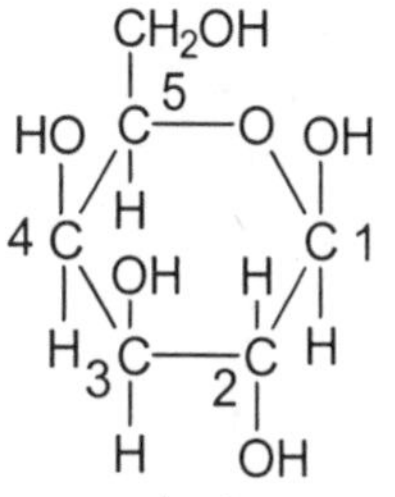

galactose

25.61 The empirical formula of glycogen is $C_6H_{10}O_5$. The six-membered ring form of glucose is the unit that forms the basis of glycogen. The monomeric glucose units are joined by α linkages.

Nucleic Acids

25.63 A *nucleotide* consists of a nitrogen-containing aromatic compound, a sugar in the furanose (5-membered) ring form, and a phosphoric acid group. The structure of deoxycytidine monophosphate is shown at right.

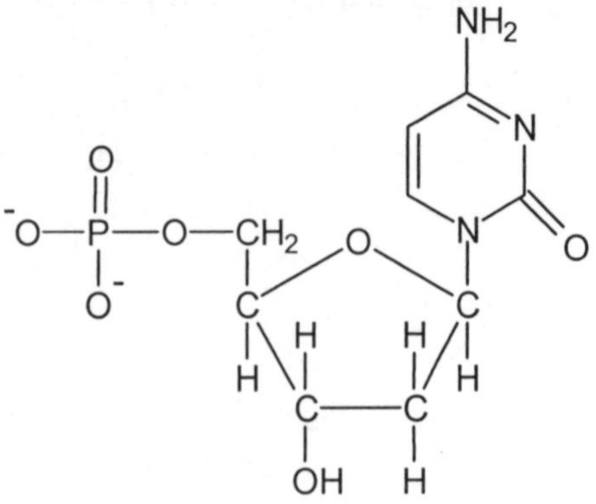

25.65 $C_4H_7O_3CH_2OH + HPO_4^{2-} \rightarrow C_4H_7O_3CH_2\text{-}O\text{-}PO_3^{2-} + H_2O$

25.67 In the helical structure for DNA, the strands of the polynucleotides are held together by hydrogen-bonding interactions between particular pairs of bases. It happens that adenine and thymine form an especially effective base pair, and that guanine and cytosine are similarly related. Thus, each adenine has a thymine as its opposite number in the other strand, and each guanine has a cytosine as its opposite number. In the overall analysis of the double strand, total adenine must then equal total thymine, and total guanine equals total cytosine.

Additional Exercises

25.69

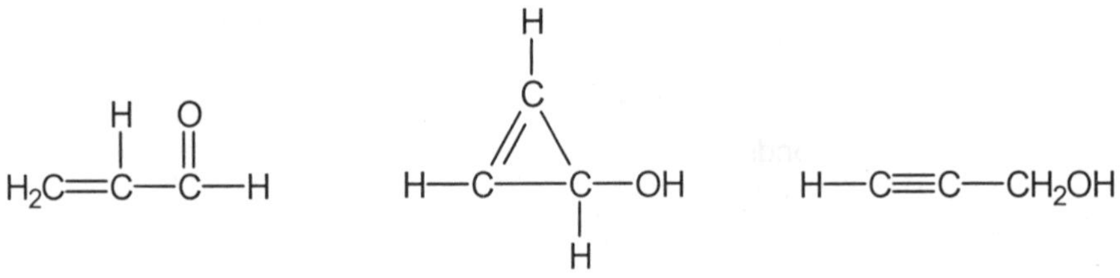

25.72

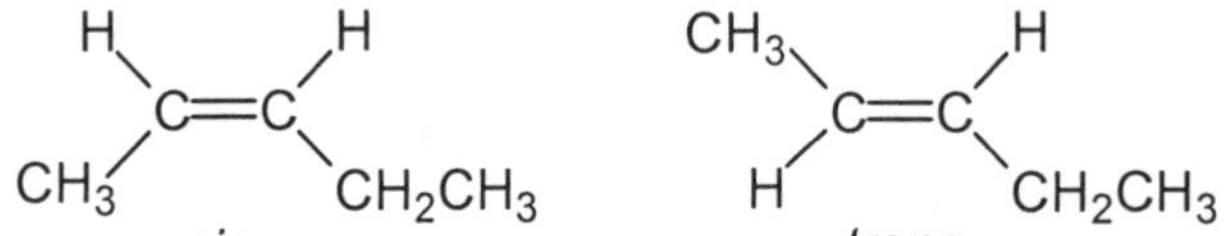

Cyclopentene does not show *cis-trans* isomerism because the existence of the ring demands that the C-C bonds be *cis* to one another.

25.75 $H_2C\text{=}CH\text{—}CH_2OH$

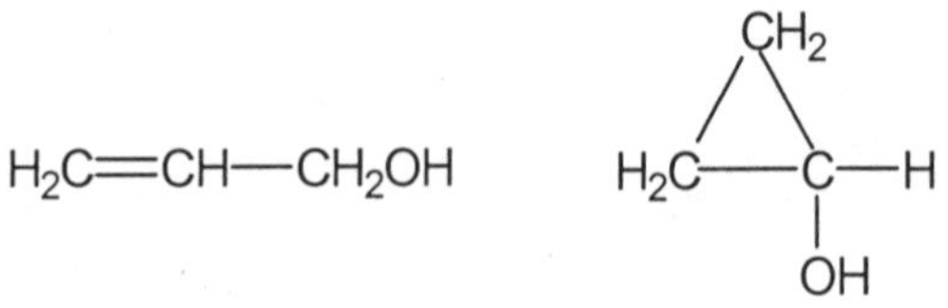

(The –OH group cannot be attached to an alkene carbon atom; these molecules are called "vinyl alcohols" and are unstable.)

25.80   The difference between an alcoholic hydrogen and a carboxylic acid hydrogen lies in the carbon to which the –OH is attached. In a carboxylic acid, the electronegative carbonyl oxygen withdraws electron density from the O–H bond, rendering the bond more polar and the H more ionizable. In an alcohol no electronegative atoms are bound to the carbon that holds the –OH group, and the H is tightly bound to the O.

25.83   (a)   None

       (b)   The carbon bearing the secondary –OH has four different groups attached, and is thus chiral.

       (c)   The carbon bearing the $-NH_2$ group and the carbon bearing the CH_3 group are both chiral.

25.85   Glu-Cys-Gly is the only possible structure.

25.87   Both glucose and fructose contain six C atoms, so both are hexoses. Glucose contains an aldehyde group at C1, so it is an aldohexose. Fructose has a ketone at C2, so it is a ketohexose.

Integrative Exercises

25.89 CH_3CH_2OH CH_3-O-CH_3
         ethanol   dimethyl ether

Ethanol contains –O–H bonds which form strong intermolecular hydrogen bonds, while dimethyl ether experiences only weak dipole-dipole and dispersion forces.

difluoromethane   tetrafluoromethane

CH_2F_2 is a polar molecule, while CF_4 is nonpolar. CH_2F_2 experiences dipole-dipole and dispersion forces, while CF_4 experiences only dispersion forces.

In both cases, stronger intermolecular forces lead to the higher boiling point.

25.91   Determine the empirical formula, molar mass and thus molecular formula of the compound. Confirm with physical data.

$$66.7 \text{ g C} \times \frac{1 \text{ mol C}}{12.01 \text{ g C}} = 5.554 \text{ mol C}; \quad 5.554 / 1.388 = 4$$

$$11.2 \text{ g H} \times \frac{1 \text{ mol H}}{1.008 \text{ g H}} = 11.11 \text{ mol H}; \quad 11.11 / 1.388 = 8$$

$$22.2 \text{ g O} \times \frac{1 \text{ mol O}}{16.00 \text{ g O}} = 1.388 \text{ mol O}; \quad 1.388 / 1.388 = 1$$

The empirical formula is C_4H_8O. Using Equation 10.11 ($\mathcal{M}$ = molar mass):

$$\mathcal{M} = \frac{(2.28 \text{ g/L})(0.08206 \text{ L} \cdot \text{atm} / \text{mol} \cdot \text{K})(373 \text{ K})}{0.970 \text{ atm}} = 71.9$$

The formula weight of C_4H_8O is 72, so the molecular formula is also C_4H_8O. Since the compound has a carbonyl group and cannot be oxidized to an acid, the only possibility is 2-butanone.

$$\overset{\overset{\textstyle O}{\|}}{CH_3}CCH_2CH_3$$

The boiling point of 2-butanone is 79.6°C, confirming the identification.

25.93   The reaction is: $2NH_2CH_2COOH(aq) \rightarrow NH_2CH_2CONHCH_2COOH(aq) + H_2O(l)$

$\Delta G° = (-488) + (-285.83) - 2(-369) = -35.8 = -36 \text{ kJ}$

25.97 $AMPOH^-(aq) \rightleftharpoons AMPO^{2-}(aq) + H^+(aq)$

$pK_a = 7.21$; $K_a = 10^{-pK_a} = 6.17 \times 10^{-8} = 6.2 \times 10^{-8}$

$K_a = \dfrac{[AMPO^{2-}][H^+]}{[AMPOH^-]} = 6.2 \times 10^{-8}$. When pH = 7.40, $[H^+] = 3.98 \times 10^{-8} = 4.0 \times 10^{-8}$.

Then $\dfrac{[AMPOH^-]}{[AMPO^{2-}]} = 3.98 \times 10^{-8} / 6.17 \times 10^{-8} = 0.65$